Pharmaceutical Process Validation

Second Edition, Revised and Expanded

DRUGS AND THE PHARMACEUTICAL SCIENCES

A Series of Textbooks and Monographs

edited by

James Swarbrick
School of Pharmacy
University of North Carolina
Chapel Hill, North Carolina

- Lyphollized or Injecteables Product
- Patches

Pharmaceutical Process Validation

Second Edition, Revised and Expanded

edited by
Ira R. Berry
Banner Pharmacaps
Elizabeth, New Jersey

Robert A. Nash
College of Pharmacy and Allied Health Professions
St. John's University
Jamaica, New York

Marcel Dekker, Inc.   New York • Basel • Hong Kong

Library of Congress Cataloging-in-Publication Data

Pharmaceutical process validation / edited by Ira R. Berry, Robert A.
Nash. -- 2nd ed., rev. & expanded.
p.   cm. -- (Drugs and the pharmaceutical sciences ; v. 57)
Includes bibliographical references and index.
ISBN 0-8247-8777-3 (alk. paper)
1. Pharmaceutical industry--Quality control. 2. Drugs--Standards-
-United States. I. Berry, Ira R. II. Nash, Robert A.
III. Series.
[DNLM: 1. Drug Evaluation--standards--United States. 2. Drug
Industry--standards--United States. 3. Quality Control. W1 DR893B
v.57]
RS189.P46 1993
615.1'068'5--dc20
DNLM/DLC
for Library of Congress   92-49060
                                                                      CIP

This book is printed on acid-free paper.

MARCEL DEKKER, INC.
270 Madison Avenue, New York, New York 10016

Current printing (last digit):
10 9 8 7 6 5 4 3

PRINTED IN THE UNITED STATES OF AMERICA

Dedicated to Theodore E. Byers and Bernard T. Loftus (both formerly of the U.S. Food and Drug Administration), the proud parents of process validation in the pharmaceutical industry.

And to an old friend, Reginald F. Johnson, for contributing greatly to our understanding of the process validation concept.

Preface

It has been eight years since the publication of the first edition of *Pharmaceutical Process Validation*, and a great deal has happened in the interim. For one, the publication of *Validation of Aseptic Pharmaceutical Processes* (Marcel Dekker, 1986); for another, the FDA issued its *Guidelines on General Principles of Process Validation* in 1987 and, more recently, its preapproval inspection requirements for NDA/ANDAs.

Currently, we are in a proactive regulatory period with respect to Current Good Manufacturing Practices (CGMP) regulations, and, naturally, there is a great deal of emphasis on the need for adequate process validation documentation. The publication of the second edition could not come at a better time.

The number of chapters has nearly doubled to reflect growing interest in topics not covered in the first edition, such as "Validation of Water Systems" by Johnson, "Cleaning Validation" by McCormick and Cullen, "Computer Systems Validation" by Krueger and Krueger, and "Equipment Validation" by Ferenc et al. Several special topics have also been added. These include "Validation of Lyophilized Products" by Trappler, "Validation of Inhalation Aerosols" by Bozzone, and "Recent Trends in Process Validation" by Lee.

A number of important chapters from the first edition have been retained and, in some cases, revised. These include "The Regulatory Basis for Process Validation" by Loftus, "Organizing for Validation" by Jeater et al., "Validation of Solid Dosage Forms" by Rudolph, "Prospective Process Validation" by Chao et al., "Retrospective Process Validation" by Trubinski, "Process Validation of

Raw Materials" by Berry, "Analytical Methods Validation" by Pasteelnick, and "Validation Terminology" by Chapman.

"Validation of Sterile Products" by Akers and Anderson has been expanded by adding a companion chapter on recent developments by Hofmann. A chapter on analysis of multivariate data by Horhota has been added to complement the chapter "Analysis of Retrospective Production Data Using Quality Control Charts" by Cheng and Dutt. An introduction to process validation has been added at the beginning of the book.

Some reviewers criticized the first edition for placing too much emphasis on the growing importance of the process validation principle. We believe, however, that time has proven our judgment correct.

Ira R. Berry
Robert A. Nash

Contents

Contributors

Michael J. Akers, Ph.D.   Manager, Quality Assurance, Eli Lilly and Company, Indianapolis, Indiana

Neil R. Anderson, Ph.D.   Department Head, Pharmacy Research, Marion Merrell Dow, Inc., Kansas City, Missouri

Ira R. Berry   Corporate Vice President-Technical Affairs, Banner Pharmacaps, Elizabeth, New Jersey

Scott Bozzone, Ph.D.   Research Associate, Process Development, Parke-Davis Pharmaceutical Research Division, Warner-Lambert Company, Morris Plains, New Jersey

*Allen Y. Chao, Ph.D.**   G. D. Searle & Co., Inc., Skokie, Illinois

Kenneth G. Chapman   Pfizer, Inc., Groton, Connecticut

Peter H. Cheng   New York State Research Foundation for Mental Hygiene, New York, New York

Leo F. Cullen, Ph.D.   Director, Pharmaceutical Development, Wyeth-Ayerst Research Laboratories, Radnor, Pennsylvania

John E. Dutt   EM Industries, Inc., Hawthorne, New York

Bohdan M. Ferenc   Associate Director, Equipment and Systems Validation, Sandoz Pharmaceuticals Corporation, Inc., East Hanover, New Jersey

Current affiliation:
*President, Watson Laboratories, Inc., Corona, California

F. St. John Forbes, Ph.D.* G. D. Searle & Co., Inc., Skokie, Illinois

Karl L. Hofmann, Jr. Director, Pharmaceutical Group, Technical Operations, Bristol-Myers Squibb Company, Syracuse, New York

Stephen T. Horhota, Ph.D. Senior Principal Scientist, Pharmaceutics, Boehringer Ingelheim Parmaceuticals, Inc., Ridgefield, Connecticut

J. Patrick Jeater Wyeth-Ayerst Research Laboratories, Radnor, Pennsylvania

Reginald F. Johnson⁺ G. D. Searle & Co., Inc., Skokie, Illinois

Ward M. Johnson, M.S.M. Assistant Director, Regulatory Compliance, Pharmaceuticals Division, CIBA-GEIGY Corporation, Summit, New Jersey

Luanne Kot Equipment and Systems Validation, Sandoz Pharmaceuticals Corporation, Inc., East Hanover, New Jersey

James E. Krueger, Ph.D. Krueger Associates, New City, New York

Jonathan Krueger Ingres, an ASK company, Alameda, California

John Y. Lee Executive Director, Pharmaceutical Compliance Associates, North Massapequa, New York

Bernard T. Loftus Director, Bernard T. Loftus, Consultant, Fairfax, Virginia

Paul Y. McCormick Director, Technical Services, Sterile Products Division, Wyeth-Ayerst Research Laboratories, West Chester, Pennsylvania

Robert A. Nash, Ph.D. College of Pharmacy and Allied Health Professions, St. John's University, Jamaica, New York

G. J. Papariello, Ph.D. Vice President, Development, Wyeth-Ayerst Research Laboratories, Radnor, Pennsylvania

Louis A. Pasteelnick Warner-Lambert Company, Morris Plains, New Jersey

Carl B. Rifino, Ph.D. ICI Pharmaceuticals Group, Newark, Delaware

Jeffrey S. Rudolph, Ph.D. ICI Pharmaceuticals Group, Wilmington, Delaware

Rodney Thomas Equipment and Systems Validation, Sandoz Pharmaceuticals Corporation, Inc., East Hanover, New Jersey

---

Current affiliations:

***Manager, New Product Development, American Cyanamid, Pearl River, New York**

⁺ **Quality Systems and Technology, Naperville, Illinois**

Edward H. Trappler   President, Lyophilization Technology, Langhorne, Pennsylvania

Chester J. Trubinski, M.B.A.   Vice President, Quality Control, Carter-Wallace, Inc., Cranbury, New Jersey

Paul von Doehren   Director, Preclinical Statistics, G. D. Searle & Co., Inc., Skokie, Illinois

Introduction

Robert A. Nash   *St. John's University, Jamaica, New York*

I. FDA GUIDELINES

The U.S. Food and Drug Administration (FDA) in its most recently proposed guidelines has offered the following definition for process validation [1]:

> Process validation is establishing documented evidence which provides a high degree of assurance that a specific process (such as the manufacture of pharmaceutical dosage forms) will consistently produce a product meeting its predetermined specifications and quality characteristics.

According to the FDA, assurance of product quality is derived from careful (and systemic) attention to a number of (important) factors, including: selection of quality (components) and materials, adequate product and process design, and (statistical) control of the process through in-process and end-product testing.

Thus it is through careful design (qualification) and validation of both the process and its control systems that a high degree of confidence can be established that all individual manufactured units of a given batch or succession of batches that meet specifications will be acceptable.

According to the FDA's Current Good Manufacturing Practices (CGMPs) (21CFR 211.110)

> Control procedures shall be established to *monitor* output and to *validate* performance of the manufacturing processes that may be responsible for causing variability in the characteristics of in-process material and the drug product. Such control procedures shall include, but are not limited to the following, where appropriate [2]:

1. Tablet or capsule weight variation
2. Disintegration time
3. Adequacy of mixing to assure uniformity and homogeneity
4. Dissolution time and rate
5. Clarity, completeness, or pH of solutions

The first four items listed above are directly related to the manufacture and validation of solid dosage forms. Items 1 and 3 are normally associated with variability in the manufacturing process, while items 2 and 4 are usually influenced by the selection of the ingredients in the product formulation. With respect to content uniformity and unit potency control (item 3), adequacy of mixing to assure uniformity and homogeneity is considered a high-priority concern.

Conventional quality control procedures for finished product testing encompass three basic steps:

1. Establishment of specifications and performance characteristics
2. Selection of appropriate methodology, equipment, and instrumentation to ensure that testing of the product meets specifications
3. Testing of the final product, using validated analytical and testing methods to ensure that finished product meets specifications.

With the emergence of the pharmaceutical process validation concept, the following four additional steps have been added:

4. Qualification and validation of the processing facility and its equipment
5. Qualification and validation of the manufacturing process through appropriate means
6. Auditing, monitoring, sampling, or challenging the key steps in the process for conformance to in-process and final product specifications
7. Requalification and revalidation when there is a significant change in either the product or its manufacturing process [3].

II. TOTAL APPROACH TO PHARMACEUTICAL PROCESS VALIDATION

It has been said that there is no specific basis for requiring a separate set of process validation guidelines since the essentials of process validation are embodied within the purpose and scope of the present CGMP regulations [2]. With this in mind, the entire CGMP document, from subpart B through subpart M, may be viewed as being a set of principles applicable to the *overall process* of manufacturing, i.e., medical devices as well as drug products, and thus may be subjected, subpart by subpart, to the application of the principles of qualification, validation, control, in addition to requalification and revalidation, where applicable. Although not a specific requirement of current regulations, such a comprehensive validation

Table 1 Checklist of Validation and Control Documentation

Subpart	Section of CGMP	Validation and control documentation
A	Introduction	
B	Organization and personnel	Establishment and facility installation and qualification [4,5]
C	Buildings and facilities	Plant and facility installation and qualification [4,5]
		Maintenance and sanitation [6]
		Microbial and pest control [7]
D	Equipment	Installation and qualification cleaning methods [8]
E	Control of raw materials, in-process material, product	Incoming components [9]
		Manufacturing nonsterile products [10]
F	Production and process controls	Process control systems [11] (instrumentation and computers)
G	Packaging and labeling controls	Depyrogenation, sterile packaging, filling, and closing [12,13]
H	Holding and distribution	Facilities [14]
I	Laboratory controls	Analytical methods [15]
J	Records and reports	Computer systems [16]
K	Returned and salvaged drug product	Batch reprocessing [17]
L	Air and water quality	Water treatment and steam systems air, heat, and vacuum handling [18–20]
M	Sterilization	LVPs [21,22]
		Autoclaves and process
		Parametrics [23–25]
		Aseptic facilities [26]
		Devices [27]
		Sterilizing filters [28,29]

approach with respect to each subpart of the CGMP document has been adopted by many drug firms.

A checklist of validation and control documentation with respect to CGMPs is provided in Table 1. A number of these topics are discussed separately in other chapters of this book.

III. WHY ENFORCE PROCESS VALIDATION?

The FDA, under the authority of existing CGMP regulations, guidelines [1] and directives [30], considers process validation necessary and because it makes good

Table 2   Data Taken from FDA Enforcement Actions

Fiscal year	Number of recalls	Fiscal year	Number of recalls
1978	1116	1984	1408
1979	1290	1985	2085
1980	864	1986	3068
1981	658	1987	2398
1982	709	1988	1526
1983	915	1989	2183

engineering sense. The basic concept, according to Mead [31], has long been applied in other industries, often without formal recognition that such a concept was being used. For example, the terms *reliability engineering* and *qualification* have been used in the past by the automotive and aerospace industries to represent the process validation idea.

Process validation should result in fewer product recalls and troubleshooting assignments in manufacturing operations. In the first edition of *Pharmaceutical Process Validation* we suggested that the number of recalls reported by the FDA could be used to assess the effectiveness of industry-wide validation programs. At that time (early 1980s) the trend showed a favorable downward turn in recalls but, unfortunately, headed up after the publication of our book (see Table 2).

We now know that the overall recall numbers can be misleading [32]. For example, the recent problems associated with the generic industry and tryptophan toxicity would be recorded as hundreds of recalls in FDA records; yet, in most cases, they have nothing to do with validation concerns.

Process validation should result in more technically and economically sound products and their manufacturing processes. In the old days R&D "gurus" would literally hand down the "go" sometimes overformulated product and accompanying obtuse manufacturing procedure, usually with little or no justification or rationale provided. Today, under the recently installed FDA preapproval inspection program [30], such actions are no longer acceptable. The watchword now is to provide scientifically sound justifications (including qualification and validation documentation) for everything coming out of the pharmaceutical R & D function.

IV.   WHAT IS PROCESS VALIDATION?

Unfortunately, there is still much confusion as to what process validation is and what constitutes process validation documentation. At the beginning of this introductory chapter several different definitions for process validation were provided, which were taken from FDA guidelines and CGMPs. Chapman calls process validation simply "organized, documented common sense" [33].

One problem is that we use the term *validation* generically to cover the entire spectrum of CGMP concerns, most of which are essentially facility, equipment, component, procedures, and process qualification. The specific term *process validation* should be reserved for the final stages of the product and process development sequence. The essential or key steps or stages of a successfully completed product and process development program are presented in Table 3 [34].

The end of the sequence that has been assigned to process validation is derived from the fact that the specific exercise of process validation should never be designed to fail. Failure in carrying out the process validation assignment is often the result of incomplete or faulty understanding of the process's capability, in other words, what the process can and cannot do under a given set of operational circumstances. In a well-designed, well-run overall validation program, most of the budget dollars should be spent on facilities, equipment, components, methods, and process qualification. In such a program, the formalized final process validation sequence provides only the necessary process validation documentation required by the FDA, in other words, the "Good Housekeeping Seal of Approval," which shows that the manufacturing process is under a state of control.

Such a strategy is consistent with the FDA's newly instituted preapproval inspection program [30], wherein the applicant firm under either an NDA or ANDA submission must show the necessary CGMP information and process qualification data (including appropriate development reports), together with the formal protocol for the forthcoming full-scale process validation runs required prior to product launch.

Table 3 Key Stages in the Product and Process Development Sequence

Development stage	Pilot scale-up phase[a]
Product design	$1 \times$ size
Product characterization	
Product selection	
Process design	
Product optimization	$10 \times$ size
Process characterization	
Process optimization	
Process qualification	
Process qualification	$100 \times$ size
Process validation	
Product certification	

[a]Explained later in this introduction.
Source: Ref. 34.

Again, the term *validation* has both a specific meaning and a general one, depending on whether the word "process" is used. Determine during the course of your reading whether the entire concept is discussed in connection with the topic—i.e., design, characterization, optimization, qualification, validation, and/or revalidation—or whether the author has concentrated on the specifics of the validation of a given product and/or its manufacturing process. In this way the text will take on greater meaning and clarity.

V. PILOT SCALE-UP AND PROCESS VALIDATION

The following operations are normally carried out by the development function prior to the preparation of the first pilot-production batch. The development activities are listed as follows:

1. Formulation design, selection, and optimization
2. Preparation of the first pilot-laboratory batch
3. Conduct initial accelerated stability testing
4. If the formulation is deemed stable, preparation of additional pilot laboratory batches of the drug product for expanded nonclinical and/or clinical use

The pilot program is defined as the scale-up operations conducted subsequent to the product and its process leaving the development laboratory and prior to its acceptance by the full-production manufacturing unit. For the pilot program to be successful, elements of process validation (e.g., product and process qualification studies) must be included and completed during the developmental or pilot-laboratory phase of the work.

Thus product and process scale-up should proceed in graduated steps with elements of process validation (such as qualification) incorporated at each stage of the piloting program [35].

A. Laboratory Batch

The first step in the scale-up process is the selection of a suitable preliminary formula for more critical study and testing based upon certain agreed-upon initial design criteria, requirements and/or specifications. The work is performed in the development laboratory. The formula selected is designated as the $(1 \times)$ laboratory batch. The size of the $(1 \times)$ laboratory batch is usually 3–5 kg of a solid or semi-solid, 3–5 liters of a liquid, or 3000 to 5000 units of a tablet or capsule.

B. Laboratory Pilot Batch

After the $(1 \times)$ laboratory batch is determined to be both physically and chemically stable based upon accelerated, elevated temperature testing (i.e., 1 month at 45°C or 3 months at 40°C or 40°C/80% RH), the next step in the scale-up process is the preparation of the (10×) laboratory pilot batch. The (10×) laboratory pilot batch represents the first replicated scale-up of the designated formula. The size of the laboratory pilot batch is usually 30–50 kg, 30–50 liters, or 30,000 to 50,000 units.

It is usually prepared in small pilot equipment within a designated CGMP-approved area of the development laboratory. The number and actual size of the laboratory pilot batches may vary in response to one or more of the following factors:

1. Equipment availability
2. Active drug substance availability
3. Cost of raw materials
4. Inventory requirements for clinical and nonclinical studies

Process qualification or process capability studies are usually started in this important second stage of the pilot program. Such qualification or capability studies consist of process ranging, process characterization, and process optimization as a prerequisite to the more formal validation program that follows later in the piloting sequence.

C. Pilot Production

The pilot-production phase may be carried out either as a shared responsibility between the development laboratories and its appropriate manufacturing counterpart or as a process demonstration by a separate, designated pilot-plant or process-development function. The two organization piloting options are presented separately in Figure 1. The creation of a separate pilot-plant or process-development unit has been favored in recent years because it is ideally suited to carry out process qualification and/or validation assignments in a timely manner. On the other hand, the joint pilot-operation option provides direct communication between the development laboratory and pharmaceutical production.

The objective of the pilot-production batch is to scale the product and process by another order of magnitude (100×) to, for example, 300–500 kg, 300–500 liters, or 300,000–500,000 dosage-form units (tablets or capsules) in size. For most drug products this represents a full production batch in standard production equipment. If required, pharmaceutical production is capable of scaling the product and process to even larger batch sizes should the product require expanded production output. If the batch size changes significantly (say, to 500× or 1000×), additional validation studies would be required.

Usually large production batch scale-up is undertaken only after product introduction. Again, the actual size of the pilot-production (100×) batch may vary due to equipment and raw material availability. The need for additional pilot-production batches ultimately depends upon the successful completion of a first

Figure 1 Main piloting options. (Top) separate pilot plant functions—engineering concept. (Bottom) joint pilot operation.

pilot batch and its process validation program. Usually three successfully completed pilot-production batches are required for validation purposes.

In summary, process capability studies start in the development laboratories and/or during product and process development, and continue in well-defined stages until the process is validated in the pilot plant and/or pharmaceutical production.

An approximate timetable for new product development and its pilot scale-up program is suggested in Table 4.

VI. PROCESS VALIDATION: ORDER OF PRIORITY

Because of resource limitation, it is not always possible to validate an entire company's product line at once. With the obvious exception that a company's most profitable products should be given a higher priority, it is advisable to draw up a list of product categories that are to be validated.

The following order of importance or priority with respect to validation is suggested:

A. Sterile Products and Their Processes

1. Large-volume parenterals (LVPs)
2. Small-volume parenterals (SVPs)
3. Ophthalmics, other sterile products, and medical devices

Table 4 Approximate Timetable for New Product Development and Pilot Scale-Up Trials

Event	Calendar months
Formula selection and development	2–4
Assay methods development and formula optimization	2–4
Stability in standard packaging 3-month readout (1× size)	3–4
Pilot-laboratory batches (10× size)	1–3
Preparation and release of clinical supplies (10× size) and establishment of process qualification	1–4
Additional stability testing in approved packaging 6–8-month readout (1× size) 3-month readout (10× size)	3–4
Validation protocols and pilot batch request	1–3
Pilot-production batches (100× size)	1–3
Additional stability testing in approved packaging 9–12-month readout (1× size) 6–8-month readout (10× size) 3-month readout (100× size)	3–4
Interim approved technical product development report with approximately 12 months stability (1× size)	1–3
Totals	18–36

Source: Ref. 34.

B. Nonsterile Products and Their Processes

1. Low-dose/high-potency tablets and capsules
2. Drugs with stability problems
3. Other tablets and capsules
4. Oral liquids, topicals, and diagnostic aids

VII. WHO DOES PROCESS VALIDATION?

Process validation is done by those individuals with the necessary training and experience to carry out the mission.

The specifics of how a dedicated group, team, or committee is organized to conduct process validation assignments is beyond the scope of this introductory chapter. The responsibilities that must be carried out and the organizational structures best equipped to handle each assignment are outlined in Table 5.

The concept of divided validation responsibilities can be used for the pur-

Table 5 Specific Responsibilities of Each Organizational Structure within the Scope of Process Validation

Engineering	Install, qualify, and certify plant, facilities, equipment, and support systems.
Development	Design, optimize, and qualify manufacturing process within design limits, specifications, and/or requirements—in other words, the establishment of process capability information.
Manufacturing	Operate and maintain plant, facilities, equipment, support systems, and the specific manufacturing process within its design limits, specifications, and/or requirements.
Quality assurance	Establish approvable validation protocols and conduct process validation by monitoring, sampling, testing, challenging, and/or auditing the specific manufacturing process for compliance with design limits, specifications, and/or requirements.

Source: Ref. 34.

pose of constructing a validation progress time chart (Table 6). Such a chart is capable of examining the logical sequence of key events or milestones (both parallel and series) that take place during the time course of new product introduction and is similar to a Gantt chart constructed by Chapman [34].

In Table 6, facilities and equipment are the responsibility of engineering and manufacturing, while process and product are the responsibility of the product and process development function(s). The engineering and development functions in conjunction with quality assurance come together to prepare the validation protocols during the qualification stage of product and process development.

In the past, quality assurance and process development/pilot plant functions played a major role in initiating qualification and validation assignments. Today, with the advent of FDA preapproval and extensive plant inspection programs, pharmaceutical R & D has been asked to play a more active role with respect to qualification and validation concerns. In some instances, though, a completely separate corporate validation function has been established with the responsibility of interacting with and coordinating activities among the more traditional engineering, development, manufacturing, and QC/QA structures.

VIII.   PROCESS CAPABILITY DESIGN AND TESTING AND PROCESS QUALIFICATION

Process capability is defined as the carrying out of studies to determine the *critical* process parameters or operating variables that influence process output and the range of numerical data for each of the critical process parameters that result in acceptable process output.

Table 6 Validation Progress Gantt Chart

Key elements	Design stage	Qualification stage		Validation stage	
		Installation	Operational	Prospective	Concurrent
Facilities and equipment	Engineering phase ──→ (Validation protocols) ──→ Manufacturing start-up ──→ (Batch records and validation documentation)				
Process and product	Developmental phase (formula definition and stability testing) ──→ Scale-up phase (process optimization and pilot production) ──→ QA and manufacturing phase (full production)				

Time line for new product introduction →

The objectives of process capability design and testing may be listed as follows:

1. To determine the number and relative importance of the critical parameters in a process that affect the quality of process output
2. To show that the numerical data generated for each critical parameter are within at least statistical quality control limits (i.e., ± 3 standard deviations) and that there is no drift or assignable cause of variation in the process data

If the capability of a process is properly delineated, the process should consistently stay within the defined limits of its critical process parameters and product characteristics [36].

Process qualification, on the other hand, represents the actual studies or trials conducted to show that all systems, subsystems, or unit operations of a manufacturing process perform as intended; that all critical process parameters operate within their assigned control limits; and that such studies and trials, which form the basis of process capability design and testing, are verifiable and certifiable through appropriate documentation. Process qualification is often referred to as *operational* or *performance qualification*.

The manufacturing process is briefly defined as the ways and means used to convert raw materials into a finished product. The ways and means also include people, equipment, facilities, and support systems required to operate the process in a planned and effectively managed way. Therefore, let us assume that all people, equipment, facilities, and support systems required to run the process qualification trials have been themselves qualified and validated beforehand.

The steps and the sequence of events required to perform process capability design and testing are outlined in Table 7.

Using the basic process for the manufacture of a pharmaceutical dosage form, we will attempt here to highlight some of the important elements of the process capability and qualification sequence.

1. Basic information is obtained from the ($1\times$) size laboratory batch.

a. Quantitative formula is scaled to ($10\times$) size batch and rationale for inert ingredient selection provided.
b. Critical specifications, test methods, and acceptance criteria for each raw material used in the formula are provided.
c. Proposed specifications, test methods, and acceptance criteria for the finished dosage form are provided.
d. Interim stability report on ($1\times$) size laboratory batch is provided.
e. Detailed operating instructions for preparing the ($10\times$) size batch are provided.

2. Preparation of a simple flow chart or flow diagram of the process should be provided. An enhanced flow chart should show all the unit operations in a

Table 7 Protocol for Process Capability Design and Testing

Objective	Process capability design and testing
Types of process	Batch, intermittent, continuous
Typical processes	Chemical, pharmaceutical, filling, and packaging
Definition of process	Flow diagram, equipment/materials in-process, finished product
Definition of process output	Potency, yield, physical parameters
Definition of test methods	Methods, equipment, calibration, traceability, precision, accuracy
Analysis of process	Definition of process variables, influence matrix, fractional factorial analysis
Review and analysis of data	Data plot (x–y plots, histogram, control chart) time sequence, sources of variation
Pilot batch trials	Define stable/extended runs, define sample and testing, remove sources of variation
Pilot batch replication	Different shifts and days, different materials, different facilities and equipment
Need for process capability redefinition	Data analysis, modification of influence matrix, reclassification of variables
Process capability of evaluated process	Stability and variability of process output, conformance to defined specifications, economic limits of process
Final report and recommendations	Recommended SOP, limits on process adjustments, recommended specifications

logical sequence, the major pieces of equipment to be used, and the stages or operations at which the various ingredients are added. In Figure 2a the enclosed rectangular *modules* represent the various operations in the manufacturing process. The arrows represent transfers of material into and out of each unit operation. The overall material balance of the manufacturing process represents the sum of the individual material balances of all the unit operations. A list of unit operations, shown in Table 8, has been prepared to assist the reader in selecting suitable unit operations for the construction of flow charts. The sequential arrangement of unit operations should be analogous to the major sequential steps in the operating instructions of the manufacturing process.

3. Using the flow chart (Figure 2a) as a guide, a list of process or control variables are next drawn up for each unit operation or step in the process. A test parameter or response to be objectively measured is then assigned to each process variable. The control parameters represent process variables plus their test parameters. There may be as many as six unit operations or processing steps, with one or more process variables for each unit operation and one or more key test parameters for each of the processing steps. Examples of this approach to process qualification/ validation are given in chapters 5, 7, and 8.

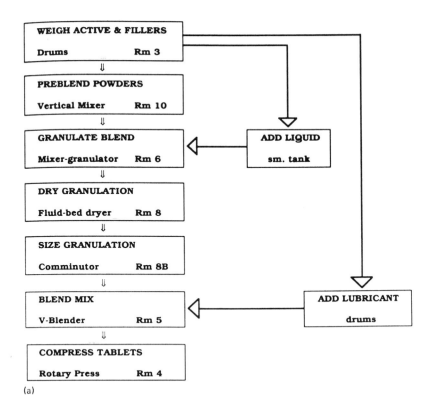

(a)

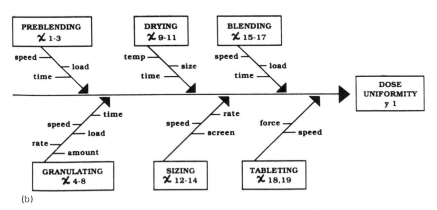

(b)

Figure 2 (a) Process flow diagram for the manufacture of a tablet dosage form by the wet granulation method. (b) A simple "fishbone" diagram of the processing steps and in process variables during tablet manufacture that may influence the quality and consistency of final product-dose uniformity.

Table 8 Unit Operations According to Categories

Heat transfer processes
Cooking, cooling, evaporating, freezing, heating, irradiating, freeze-drying, sterilizing

Change in state
Crystallizing, dispersing, dissolving, immersing, freeze-drying, neutralizing

Change in size
Agglomerating, blending, coating, compacting, crushing, crystallizing, densifying, emulsifying, extruding, flaking, flocculating, grinding, homogenizing, milling, mixing, pelletizing, pressing, pulverizing, precipitating, sieving

Moisture transfer processes
Dehydrating, desiccating, evaporating, fluidizing, humidifying, freeze-drying, washing, wetting

Separation processes
Centrifuging, clarifying, deareating, degassing, deodorizing, dialyzing, exhausting, extracting, filtering, ion exchange, pressing, sieving, sorting, washing

Transfer processes
Conveying, filling, inspecting, pumping, sampling, storing, transporting, weighing

---

Source: Ref. 38.

Often the weighing of active and inert ingredients may be eliminated from the analysis. Weighing operations are a general consideration in all manufacturing processes. Balances and measuring devices are normally qualified and validated separately on a routine basis as required by CGMP guidelines.

4. How do we determine which process variables and/or unit operations are critical with respect to the product outcomes or attributes? To determine the critical process parameters, *process characterization* and *process ranging* studies should be carried out in connection with the performance qualification trials. Process characterization represents the methods used to determine the critical processing steps and process control variables that affect the quality and consistency of the product outcomes or attributes. Process ranging represents the studies that are used to identify the critical process or test parameters and their respective control limits, which will also affect the quality and consistency of the product outcomes or attributes.

IX. PROCESS CHARACTERIZATION

The following process characterization techniques may be used to designate the critical unit operations in a manufacturing process.

A. Cause-and-Effect, or "Fishbone" Diagram

The "fishbone" diagram (Figure 2b) represents all possible relationships and interrelationships that may exist among the various process variables (possible causes of variation) and the single response or product attribute (effect). The central line of the cause-and-effect diagram is a composite of all the possible factors that may influence the quality and consistency of the final outcome. Branches off the central line represent the influence of the unit operations or process steps. The principal process variables for each process step that can cause or influence the final outcome (effect) are depicted as subbranches of each of the main unit operation branches. In the procedure, each process variable (possible cause) is varied in a measured way within operating ranges, and its influence on the final outcome is measured. If there is no effect, the input variable is then considered noncritical. In this way, only variables that influence the final outcome are considered critical.

The problem arises when there are large numbers of input variables (say, nine or more) to be tested. Additional strategies are then needed to simplify process characterization and analysis.

B. Constraint Analysis

One procedure that makes subsystem evaluations and performance qualification trials manageable is the application of constraint analysis. Boundary limits of any technology and restrictions as to what constitutes acceptable output from unit operations or process steps should in most situations constrain the number of process variables and product attributes that require analysis. The application of the constraint analysis principle should also limit and restrict the operational range of each process variable and/or the specification limits of each product attribute. Information about constraining process variables usually comes from the following sources:

1. Previous successful experience with related products and processes
2. Technical and engineering support functions of major processing equipment manufacturers and suppliers
3. Published scientific and technical literature concerning the specific technology under investigation

The Pareto Principle

A practical guide often called the Pareto principle (named after an Italian sociologist) or the 80–20 rule can be used to reinforce the usefulness of constraint analysis. The Pareto rule simply states that about 80% of the variation in the process output is caused by (or is directly related to) only about 20% of all the input process variables. The objective of process characterization and analysis is therefore to find and control these key or critical input process variables.

X. QUALIFICATION TRIAL OPTIONS

There are several ways to carry out the process capability qualification trials. The options are discussed as follows.

A. Replication of Optimal or Midrange Values

Using midrange input values the process may be run as a pilot-laboratory batch (10× size) in accordance with an agreed-upon standard operating procedure and the protocol for in-process testing. Expected outputs are then measured after each unit operation and, if the results are within in-process specifications, the process is permitted to continue to the next processing step. At the end of the procedure, representative samples of final finished product are next subjected to end product testing for potency, dose uniformity, and compliance with established physical specifications. Having completed an acceptable run, the process may be repeated several times to establish process reproducibility.

In the course of this approach, if one or more of the processing steps fails to comply with the expected in-process outcomes, additional development time will be spent to get these particular unit operations up to standard operating conditions. This option is therefore a simple *go–no go* procedure, where the process qualification proceeds upon the completion of each unit operation and each pilot batch. In this simple, straightforward qualification option, control limits are never tested and critical steps in the overall process are never fully established.

B. Fractional Factorial Design

An experimental design is a series of statistically sufficient qualification trials that are planned in a specific arrangement and include all processing variables that can possibly affect the expected outcome of the process under investigation. In the case of a full factorial design *n* equals the number of factors or process variables, each at two levels (i.e., the upper- and lower-control limits). Such a design is known as a $2n$ factorial. Using a large number of process variables (say, 12) we could, for example, have to run 2^{12}, or 4096, qualification trials to complete the full factorial design.

The fractional factorial is designed to reduce the number of qualification trials to a reasonable number, e.g., eight, while holding the number of processing variables to be evaluated to a reasonable number as well—again eight. The technique was developed as a nonparametric test for process evaluation by Box and Hunter [39] and reviewed by Hendrix [40]. The details of evaluating the fractional factorial are beyond the scope of the present chapter. However, a design for an 8 × 8 fractional factorial is given in Table 9. Each processing variable is studied at both its control limits. The positive (+) symbol is used for the upper control limit and the negative (−) symbol is used for the lower control limit. In this way a full factorial of 2^8 may be reduced from 256 experiments to only eight.

Table 9 Fractional Factorial Design (8 Variables in 8 Experiments)

Trial no.	X_1	X_2	X_3	X_4	X_5	X_6	X_7	X_8
1	−	+	+	−	−	+	+	−
2	+	−	−	−	−	+	+	+
3	−	+	−	−	+	−	+	+
4	−	+	−	+	−	+	−	+
5	+	−	+	−	+	−	+	−
6	−	+	+	+	+	−	−	−
7	+	−	+	+	−	+	−	−
8	+	−	−	+	+	−	−	+

XI. OPTIMIZATION TECHNIQUES

Optimization techniques are used to find either the best possible quantitative formula for a product or the best possible set of experimental conditions (input values) that are needed to run the process. Optimization techniques may be employed in the laboratory stage to develop the most stable, least sensitive formula, or in the qualification and validation stages of scale-up to develop the most stable, least variable process within its proven acceptable range(s) of operation, Chapman's so-called PAR principle.

Optimization techniques may be classified as parametric statistical methods and nonparametric search methods.

A. Parametric Statistical Methods

Parametric Statistical Methods, usually employed for optimization, are full-factorial designs [42], half-factorial designs [43], simplex design [44], and Lagrangian multiple-regression analysis [45]. Parametric methods are best suited for formula optimization in the early stages of product development. The application of constraint analysis, which was described previously, is used to simplify the testing protocol and the analysis of experimental results.

The steps involved in the parametric optimization procedure for pharmaceutical systems have been fully described by Schwartz [46]. The optimization technique consists of the following essential operations:

1. Selection of a suitable experimental design
2. Selection of variables (independent Xs and dependent Ys) to be tested
3. Performance of a set of statistically designed experiments (i.e., 2^3 or 3^2 factorials)

4. Measurement of responses (dependent variables)
5. Development of a predictor, polynomial equation based upon statistical and regression analysis of the generated experimental data
6. Development of a set of optimized requirements for the formula based upon mathematical and graphical analysis of the data generated.

B. Nonparametric Search Methods

Nonparametric search methods are relatively simple techniques used to fine-tune or optimize a process by varying the critical process parameters that were found during the qualification and validation stages of process development. The procedure is so constrained that no process variable is ever permitted to exceed its lower or upper control limit. In searching a given process, it is assumed that there is optimal peak (set of experimental conditions or inputs) where the process operates most efficiently. Two basic search methods are used for this purpose: *evolutionary operation* (EVOP) and *random evolutionary operation* (REVOP). The difference between the two methods is not objectivity but simplicity of the experimental design chosen.

C. Process Improvement Through EVOP

The process variables whose perturbation or slight change might lead to improvement in process performance are usually identified during the qualification trials in which the operational and control limits for the process have been developed. Next, initial perturbation steps away from the present operational inputs are selected for each of the critical process variables. These steps must be sufficiently small so that no input goes beyond the control limits of the process and no output goes out of product and process specification. In the traditional box EVOP design [47] a simple two-factor, two-level design is created about the present condition or input values.

By using a *simplex EVOP design* [48], where connecting triangles are created from two additional experimental conditions, it is possible to complete the optimization search in fewer trial runs than with box EVOP.

D. Process Improvement Through REVOP

REVOP is a comparatively little-used method for process and product optimization [49]. The technique, developed by F. E. Satterthwaite, employs a random direction of movement under constraint analysis to discover a probable pathway of ascent to peak process performance. If the linear direction chosen is not promising, the direction is reversed and the opposite pathway is chosen in an effort to improve performance. Movement continues along the new path, in the direction previously established, as long as the results are positive. Movement will then proceed at right angles when progress ceases on the previously chosen pathway. Peak performance is almost always achieved in fewer than 20 trial runs.

In summary, process capability studies and qualification trials should be undertaken during the first stage of pilot scale-up, i.e., with the preparation of the pilot-laboratory batch (10×) size. The objective of such studies is to test the proposed upper and lower control limits and to determine those critical processing steps and process variables that affect end-product performance. In this connection, nonparametric methods such as fractional factorial experimental designs and search methods such as EVOP and REVOP should prove useful in connection with process optimization and process capability testing, which should be carried out prior to the start of the more formal process validation program.

XII. WHAT ARE THE PROCESS VALIDATION OPTIONS?

The guidelines on general principles of process validation [1] mention three options. They are prospective process validation (also called premarket validation), retrospective process validation, and revalidation. In actuality there are four possible options.

A. Prospective Process Validation

In prospective process validation, an experimental plan called the *validation protocol* is executed (following completion of the qualification trials) before the process is put into commercial use. Most validation efforts require some degree of prospective experimentation to generate validation support data. This particular type of process validation is normally carried out in connection with the introduction of new drug products and their manufacturing processes. *The formalized process validation program should never be undertaken unless and until the following operations and procedures have been completed satisfactorily*:

1. The facilities and equipment in which the process validation is to be conducted meet CGMP requirements (completion of *installation qualification*)
2. The operators and supervising personnel, who will be "running" the validation batch(es), have an understanding of the process and its requirements
3. The design, selection, and optimization of the formula have been completed
4. The qualification trials using (10× size) pilot-laboratory batches have been completed, in which the critical processing steps and process variables have been identified, and the provisional operational control limits for each critical test parameter have been provided
5. Detailed technical information on the product and the manufacturing process have been provided, including documented evidence of product stability
6. Finally, at least one qualification trial of a pilot-production (100× size) batch has been made and shows, upon scale-up, that there were no significant deviations from the expected performance of the process

Table 10 Outline for Process Validation Program

Objective	Proving or demonstrating that the process works
Types of validation	Prospective, concurrent, retrospective, revalidation
Typical processes	Chemical, pharmaceutical, fabrication, packaging, sterilization
Definition of process	Flow diagram, equipment/materials, in-process, finished product
Definition of process output	Potency, yield, physical parameters
Definition of test methods	Methods, equipment, calibration, traceability, precision, and accuracy
Analysis of process	Critical modules and variables defined by process capability design and testing program
Control limits of critical variables	Defined by process capability design and testing program
Preparation of validation protocol	Facility, equipment, process, product number of validation trials and type, sampling frequency, type, size tests to be performed, method, criteria definition of successful validation
Organizing for validation trials	Responsibility, authority
Planning validation trials	Timetable and PERT chart, availability, material acquisition and disposal
Validation trials	Supervision/administration, process documentation
Validation findings	Data summary, data analysis, conclusions
Final report and recommendations	Process validated, further trials, requires more process capability design and testing

The steps and sequence of events required to carry out a process validation assignment are outlined in Table 10. The first half of the procedure is similar to that developed for process capability design and testing. The objective of prospective validation is to prove or demonstrate that the process will work in accordance with validation protocol prepared for the pilot-production ($100\times$ size) trials.

In practice, usually two or three pilot-production ($100\times$ size) batches are prepared for validation purposes. The first batch to be included in the sequence may be the already successfully concluded first qualification trial at $100\times$ size, which should be prepared under the direction of the organizational function directly responsible for pilot scale-up activities. Later, replicate batch manufacture may be performed by the pharmaceutical production function.

The strategy selected for process validation should be simple and straightforward. The following five points are presented here for the reader's consideration:

1. The use of different lots of raw materials should be included, i.e., active drug substance and major excipients.

2. Batches should be run in succession and on different days and shifts (the latter condition, if appropriate).
3. Batches should be manufactured in the equipment and facilities designated for eventual commercial production.
4. Critical process variables should be set within their *operating ranges* and should not exceed their upper and lower control limits during process operation. Output responses should be well within finished product specifications.
5. Failure to meet the requirements of the validation protocol with respect to process input and output control should be subjected to process *requalification* and subsequent *revalidation* following a thorough analysis of process data and formal discussion by the validation team.

B. Retrospective Validation

The retrospective validation option is chosen for established products whose manufacturing processes are considered stable (e.g., long-history state-of-control operation) and when, on the basis of economic considerations alone and resource limitations, prospective qualification and validation experimentation cannot be justified. Prior to undertaking retrospective validation, wherein the numerical in-process and/or end-product test data of historic production batches are subjected to statistical analysis, the equipment, facilities, and subsystems used in connection with the manufacturing process must be qualified and validated in conformance with CGMP requirements.

The concept of using accumulated final product as well as in-process numerical test data and batch records to provide documented evidence of product and/or process validation was originally advanced by Meyers [50] and Simms [51] of Eli Lilly and Company in 1980. Retrospective validation has gained wide acceptance since that time, and the topic has been covered adequately in separate articles by Agalloco [52] and Trubinski and Majeed [53]. The concept is also recognized in the FDA's *Guidelines on General Principles of Process Validation* [1].

Using either data-based computer systems [54,55] or manual methods, retrospective validation may be conducted in the following manner:

1. Gather the numerical values from the completed batch record and include assay values, end-product test results, and in-process data.
2. Organize these data in a chronological sequence, according to batch manufacturing data using a spreadsheet format.
3. Include data from at least the last 20–30 manufactured batches for analysis. If the number of manufactured batches is less than 20, then include all manufactured batches in your analysis.
4. Trim the data by eliminating test results from noncritical processing steps and delete all gratuitous numerical information.
5. Subject the resultant data to statistical analysis and evaluation.

6. Draw conclusions as to the state of control of the manufacturing process based upon the analysis of retrospective validation data.
7. Issue a report of your findings (documented evidence).

One or more of the following output values (measured responses), which have been shown to be critical in terms of the specific manufacturing process being evaluated, are usually selected for statistical analysis.

Solid Dosage Forms

1. Individual assay results from content uniformity testing
2. Individual tablet hardness values
3. Individual tablet thickness values
4. Tablet or capsule weight variation
5. Individual tablet or capsule dissolution time (usually at $t_{50\%}$) or disintegration time
6. Individual tablet or capsule moisture content

Semisolid and Liquid Dosage Forms

1. pH value (aqueous system)
2. Viscosity
3. Density
4. Color or clarity values
5. Average particle size or distribution
6. Unit weight variation and/or potency values

The statistical methods that may be employed to analyze numerical output data from the manufacturing process are listed as follows:

1. Basic statistics (mean, standard deviation, and tolerance limits) [56]
2. Analysis of variance (ANOVA and related techniques) [56]
3. Regression analysis [56]
4. Cumulative sum analysis (CUSUM) [57]
5. Cumulative difference analysis [57]
6. Control charting (averages and range) [58, 59]

Control charting, with the exception of basic statistical analysis, is probably the most useful statistical technique one might use to analyze retrospective and concurrent process data. Control charting forms the basis of modern statistical process control.

C. Concurrent Validation

In-process monitoring of critical processing steps and end-product testing of current production can provide documented evidence to show that the manufacturing process is in a state of control. Such validation documentation can be provided from the test parameter and data sources disclosed in the section on retrospective validation.

Test parameter	Data source
Average unit potency	End-product testing
Content uniformity	End-product testing
Dissolution time	End-product testing
Weight variation	End-product testing
Powder-blend uniformity	In-process testing
Moisture content	In-process testing
Particle or granule size distribution	In-process testing
Weight variation	In-process testing
Tablet hardness	In-process testing
pH value	In-process testing
Color or clarity	In-process testing
Viscosity or density	In-process testing

Not all of the in-process tests enumerated above are required to demonstrate that the process is in a state of control. Selections of test parameters should be made on the basis of the *critical* processing variables to be evaluated.

D. Revalidation

Conditions requiring revalidation study and documentation are listed as follows:

1. Change in a *critical* component (usually refers to raw materials)
2. Change or replacement in a *critical* piece of modular (capital) equipment
3. Change in a facility and/or plant (usually location or site)
4. Significant (usually order of magnitude) increase or decrease in batch size
5. Sequential batches that fail to meet product and process specifications

In some situations performance requalification studies may be required prior to undertaking specific revalidation assignments.

The FDA process validation guidelines [1] refer to a quality assurance system in place which requires revalidation whenever there are changes in packaging (assumed to be the primary container-closure system), formulation, equipment or processes (meaning not clear) which could impact on product effectiveness or product characteristics and whenever there are changes in product characteristics.

Approved packaging is normally selected after completing package performance qualification testing as well as product compatibility and stability studies. Since in most cases (exceptions: transdermal delivery systems, diagnostic tests, and medical devices) packaging is not intimately involved in the manufacturing process of the product itself, it differs from other factors, including raw materials, equipment, and formulation and facility changes, all of which may profoundly influence product quality and performance. Package changes should be handled in existing, separate product stability testing programs.

Revalidation remains an important validation option and should be considered whenever the continued state of control and reliable performance of the manufacturing process are in doubt.

XIII. DIAGNOSTIC SYSTEMS VALIDATION

The validation of diagnostic testing systems (reagent kits and instrumentation) represents an interesting challenge to the qualification/validation concept for the following reasons:

1. It is difficult to set priorities among test methods and instrumentation systems. All tests requested by the physician are of equal importance in determining the health status of the patient.
2. Instrumentation, assay methods, computer systems, and kits (reagents and consumables) must all be qualified and validated separately before being combined into an integrated diagnostic system for further overall validation.

The great advantage of diagnostic systems lies in the fact that, unlike medical devices and drug products, the end user represents a machine in some outside laboratory rather than a living patient. Thus it permits designated outside instrumentation to be integrated into a strategy for overall process validation through the use of certified calibrators and standard samples. Such a strategy is currently being used in the pharmaceutical industry to qualify and validate in vitro dissolution equipment and methods.

XIV. STATISTICAL PROCESS CONTROL AND PROCESS VALIDATION

Statistical process control (SPC) (also called statistical quality control) and process validation (PV) represent two sides of the same coin. SPC comprises the various mathematical tools (histogram, correlation chart or scatter diagram, run chart, and control chart) used to monitor a manufacturing process and to keep it within in-process and final product specification limits. W. T. Kelvin, the British mathematician and physicist (1824–1907), once said, "When you can measure what you are speaking about, and express it in numbers, you know something about it." Such a thought provides the necessary link between the two concepts. Thus SPC represents the tools to be used, while PV represents the procedural environment in which those tools are used.

There are three ways of establishing quality products and their manufacturing processes.

1. In-process and final product testing, which normally depends upon sampling size (the larger the better). In some instances, nothing short of total sampling can ensure, for example, sterility.
2. Establishment of tighter (so called "in-house") specification limits that hold the product and the manufacturing process to a more demanding standard will often reduce the need for more extensive sampling requirements.
3. The modern approach, based upon Japanese quality engineering [62], is the pursuit of "zero defects" by applying tighter control over process variability (meeting a so called 6 sigma standard). Most products and manufacturing processes in the United States today are normally designed to meet a 4 sigma limit (which would permit as many as eight defects per one thousand units). The new approach is carried out by "centering" the process (where the grand average, $\overline{X}$ in the control chart is made to coincide with either 100% label potency or the target value of a given specification) and reducing the process variability (noise) to the mean or to an achievable minimum and holding both to the new standard, batch-after-batch. By doing so, a 6 sigma limit is possible (i.e., not more than three or four defects per one million units)—the "zero defect" objective.

According to Generu Taguchi [63] the new "zero defect" standard is achievable by fine-tuning one, or at most two, identified key or critical process variables during the actual processing run. This is best accomplished by using analyzed in-process numerical output data to provide adjustments to the input control limits of the one or two key process variables. Sometimes EVOP and REVOP techniques are used during actual batch production to fine-tune the process.

Some new thinking, however, on the part of the "regulated" and the "regulators" will be required to formally recognize the use of in-house action limits and the need to adjust key controls during actual batch processing.

In the final sense, it is the in-plant operator(s) of the critical unit operations or processing steps who ultimately controls product and process quality. Such control on the part of the operator or processor is best achieved by accepting only quality input materials from the previous processing step (supplier) and supplying only quality output material(s) to the very next processing step (customer) in the manufacturing sequence. Personal responsibility on the part of the operator for performance and quality before, during, and after each critical unit operation is the best way to achieve and maintain quality output. In addition, the operator should have the ability to fine-tune the unit operation with the concurrence and approval of managerial, advisory, and technical support functions.

The reader should realize that there is no one way to establish proof or evidence of process validation (i.e., a product and process in control). If the manufacturer is certain that its products and processes are under statistical control and in compliance with CGMP regulations, it should be a relatively simple matter to establish documented evidence of process validation through the use of prospective, concurrent, or retrospective pilot and/or product quality information and data. The choice of procedures and methods to be used to establish validation documentation is left with the manufacturer.

This introduction was written to aid scientists and technicians in the pharmaceutical and allied industries in the selection of procedures and approaches that may be employed to achieve a successful outcome with respect to product performance and process validation. The authors of the following chapters explore the same topics from their own perspective and experience. It is hoped that the reader will gain much from the diversity and richness of these varied approaches.

REFERENCES

1. *Guidelines on General Principles of Process Validation*, Division of Manufacturing and Product Quality (HFN-320) Center for Drugs and Biologics (FDA), Rockville, Maryland (May 1987).
2. Current Good Manufacturing Practices in Manufacture, Processing, Packaging and Holding of Human and Veterinary Drugs, *Federal Register* 43(190), 45085 and 45086, September 1978.
3. *Pharmaceutical Process Validation*, Loftus, B. T., and Nash, R. A., Marcel Dekker, New York (1984).
4. Ralston, A. H., and Ricigliano, J. V., Planning for commissioning and validation of pharmaceutical building systems, *Pharm. Eng.* (July/August 1988).
5. Estes, G. K., and Luthell, G. H., An approach to process validation in a multiproduct pharmaceutical plan, *Pharm. Tech.* (April 1983).
6. Hess, A., An integrated approach to validation, *BioPharm.* (March 1988).
7. Cipriano, P. A., Designing clean rooms for FDA process validation, *BioPharm.* (June 1983).
8. Harder, S. W., The validation of cleaning procedures, *BioPharm.* (May 1984).
9. Berry, I. R., Process validation of raw materials, *Pharmaceutical Process Validation*, *Op. Cit.*
10. Avallone, H. L., The primary elements of validation of solid oral and topical dosage forms, *Pharm. Eng.* (January 1985).
11. Motise, P. J., What to expect when FDA audits computer-controlled processes, *Pharm. Mfg.* (July 1984).
12. Wolber, P., and Dosmar, M., Depyrogenation of pharmaceutical solutions by ultra-filtration: Aspects of validation, *Pharm. Tech.* (September 1987).
13. Stellon, R. C., Sterile packaging: Process validation and GMP requirements, *MD&DI* (October 1986).
14. Cipriano, P. A., Process validation begins with initial plant design, *Pharm. Eng.* (May/June 1982).
15. Williams, D. R., An overview of test method validation, *BioPharm.* (November 1987).
16. Kahan, J. S., Validating computer systems, *MD&DI* (March 1987).

17. Concepts for reprocessing drug products, PMA Committee Report, *Pharm. Tech.* (September 1985).
18. Protection of water treatment systems: Validation and control, PMA Committee Report, *Pharm. Tech.* (September 1984).
19. Validation and control concepts for water treatment systems, PMA Committee Report, *Pharm. Tech.* (November 1985).
20. Cattaneo, D. J., HVAC and the clean room, *Pharm. Eng.* (November/December 1984).
21. Proceedings of Third PMA Seminar on Validation of Sterile Manufacturing Processes, Lincolnshire, Illinois (February 1980).
22. *Validation of Aseptic Pharmaceutical Processes*, Carleton, F. J., and Agalloco, J. P., Marcel Dekker, New York (1986).
23. Simmons, P. L., Sterilizer validation, *Pharm. Tech.* (April 1979).
24. Vogel, D. G., Schmidt, W. C., and Sanford, B. G., A computer interface for sterilization validation, *Pharm. Tech.* (June 1984).
25. Nash, R. A., A method for calculating thermal sterilization conditions based upon process parametrics, *J. Parent. Sci. Tech. 39*:251–255 (1985).
26. Wasynczuk, J., Validation of aseptic filling processes, *Pharm. Tech.* (May 1986).
27. Cabernoch, J. L., Materials qualification and design for medical device packaging, *MD&DI* (August 1982).
28. Olson, W. P., Validation and qualification of filtration systems for bacterial removal, *Pharm. Tech.* (November 1979).
29. Goldsmith, S. H., and Grundelman, G. P., Validation of filters, *Pharm. Mfg.* (November 1985).
30. Commentary, Pre-approval inspections/investigations, FDA, *J. Parent. Sci. & Tech. 45*:56–63 (1991).
31. Mead, W. J., Process validation in cosmetic manufacture, *Drug Cosmet. Ind.* (September 1981).
32. Greenberg, E. F., The legal impact, *Packaging Digest* (November 1990).
33. Chapman, K. G., A history of validation in the United States, Part I, *Pharm. Tech.* (November 1991).
34. Nash, R. A., The essentials of pharmaceutical validation. In *Pharmaceutical Dosage Forms: Tablets*, Vol. 3, 2nd ed., Lieberman, H. A., Lachman, L., and Schwartz, J. B., eds., Marcel Dekker, New York (1990).
35. Nash, R. A., Product formulation, *CHEMTECH*, (April 1976).
36. Concept developed in process validation seminars presented by R. F. Johnson, P. E., Quality Systems & Tech., P. O. Box 29, Naperville, IL 60566.
37. Nadkarni, R. A., The quest for quality in the laboratory, *Anal. Chem. 63*:675A–681A (1991).
38. Farkas, D. F., Unit operations concepts optimize operations, *CHEMTECH* (July 1977).
39. Box, G. E., Hunter, W. G., and Hunter, J. S., *Statistics for Experimenters*, Wiley, New York (1978).
40. Hendrix, C. D., What every technologist should know about experimental design, *CHEMTECH* (March 1979).

41. Chapman, K. G., The PAR approach to process validation, *Pharm. Tech.* (December 1984).
42. Schwartz, J. B., Klamholz, J. R., and Press, R. H., Computer optimization of pharmaceutical formulations, *J. Pharm. Sci. 62*:1165–1170 (1973).
43. Cooper, L., and Steinberg, D., *Introduction to Methods of Optimization*, Saunders, Philadelphia (1970).
44. *The Design and Analysis of Industrial Experiments*, Davies, O. L., ed., Macmillan (Hafner), New York (1967).
45. Fonner, D. E., Buck, J. R., and Banker, G. S., Mathematical optimization techniques in drug product design and process analysis, *J. Pharm. Sci. 59*:1587–1596 (1970).
46. Schwartz, J. B., Optimization techniques in product formulation, *J. Soc. Cosmet. Chem. 32*:287–301 (1981).
47. Hill, R. A., Process improvement by evolutionary operation, *Amer. Perf. Cosm.* (September 1965).
48. Hahn, G. J., Process improvement through simplex EVOP, *CHEMTECH*, (May 1976).
49. Satterthwaite, F. E., Seminars on REVOP, Statistical Engineering Institute, Wellesley Hills, Massachusetts (1970).
50. Meyer, R. J., Validation of products and processes from a production, quality control viewpoint, PMA Seminar on Validation of Solid Dosage Form Process, Atlanta, Georgia (May 1980).
51. Simms, L., Validation of existing products by statistical evaluation, *Op. cit.*
52. Agalloco, J. P., Practical considerations in retrospective validation, *Pharm. Tech.* (June 1983).
53. Trubinski, C. J., and Majeed, M., Retrospective process validation. In *Pharmaceutical Process Validation*, *Op. cit.*
54. Kuzel, N. R., Fundamentals of computer system validation and documentation in the pharmaceutical industry, *Pharm. Tech.* (September 1985).
55. Fraade, D. J., The application of digital control systems in the pharmaceutical industry, *Pharm. Mfg.* (May 1984).
56. Bolton, S., *Pharmaceutical Statistics: Practical and Clinical Applications*, 2nd ed., Marcel Dekker, New York (1990).
57. Butler, J. J., Statistical quality control with CUSUM charts, *Chem. Eng.* (August 1983).
58. Deming, S. N., Quality by design, *CHEMTECH* (September 1988).
59. Contino, A. V., Improved plant performance with statistical process control, *Chem. Eng.* (July 1987).
60. Ishikawa, K., *What is Total Quality Control?: The Japanese Way*, Prentice-Hall, Englewood Cliffs, NJ (1985).
61. Deming, S. N., and Morgan, S. L., Experimental Design: A Chemometric Approach, Elsevier, Amsterdam (1987).
62. Schwartz, S., Sr. Vice Pres., IBM Corp., *New York Times* (January 13, 1991).
63. Ross, P. J., *Taguchi Techniques for Quality Engineering*, McGraw-Hill, New York (1993).

1

The Regulatory Basis for Process Validation

Bernard T. Loftus   *Fairfax, Virginia*

I. INTRODUCTION

While I was still the Director of the Division of Drug Manufacturing in the Food and Drug Administration's Bureau of Drugs, an industry colleague remarked to me that process validation had been FDA's gimmick of the 1970s. He then asked me to speculate as to what I thought the agency's gimmick would be for the 1980s. This happened in 1978, shortly after FDA had published in the Federal Register [1] its extensive revisions to its current good manufacturing practice (CGMP) regulations for drug products [2]. Later, I could understand why that scientist said what he did. Seemingly out of nowhere, in the mid-1970s, FDA's Bureau of Drugs [3] had insisted, in paper after paper presented at industry and university-sponsored meetings and symposia, that process validation was not only desirable but also mandated by law [4]. Yet, when the revised regulations appeared in the Federal Register on September 29, 1978, not only was the term *process validation* not defined, it did not appear anywhere in the text. Too, a representative of FDA's Bureau of Medical Devices [5] had gone on public record that his bureau was not going to enforce or require process validation, relying instead on enforcing the good manufacturing practice regulations themselves. It is easy to understand why industry scientists involved in making processes work might have wondered whether the Bureau of Drugs was superficial or serious and, if indeed serious, why it had not coordinated the changes in the regulations with its new process validation regulatory philosophy. My answer was that process validation had not been an FDA gimmick. It was here to stay, a necessary part of CGMP. Time has proved this to have been correct. The misunderstandings of those early years have been worked out, and the agency is today heavily committed to insisting on process validation from the regulated industries. The industry, for its part, is just as convinced of the need for, and the advantages of, process validation.

II. WHAT IS PROCESS VALIDATION?

The term *process validation* is not defined in the law [6] or in FDA's CGMP regulations [2]. Many definitions have been offered by industry spokespersons, by university representatives, and even by FDA representatives and FDA itself. In a general way, they all say the same thing, but they express it in terms peculiar to their own experience. The process will do what it purports to do. The process works. The proof is documented. An FDA compliance program entitled Drug Process Inspections, issued in June 1978 (before the publication of the revised CGMP regulations) contained the following definition [7]:

> A validated manufacturing process is one which has been proved to do what it purports or is represented to do. The proof of validation is obtained through the collection and evaluation of data, preferably, beginning from the process development phase and continuing through into the production phase. Validation necessarily includes process qualification (the qualification of materials, equipment, systems, buildings, personnel), but it also includes the control of the entire process for repeated batches or runs.

That particular definition did not appear in any of the yearly revisions of that particular compliance program [7]. But, until March 29, 1983, it was the only official FDA definition of process validation.

On March 29, 1983, FDA announced the availability of copies of a draft guideline entitled Guideline on General Principles of Process Validation, which it finalized in May 1987. The first draft, a weak document, was followed by progressively better drafts. The final document was, in my opinion, excellent, but the definition remained essentially unchanged and was finalized as follows:

> A documented program which provides a high degree of assurance that a specific process will consistently produce a product meeting its pre-determined specifications and quality attributes.

This definition, although a good one, in my opinion is not new. It had been used in frequent FDA speeches to the industry over the years. The definition is essentially the same as the definition referred to above, which was first offered by FDA in 1978.

III. THE REGULATORY BASIS FOR PROCESS VALIDATION

Once the concept had evolved, it was incumbent on the regulatory officials, who intended to use process validation as a regulatory tool, to establish that there was a legal basis for requiring such a concept. The legal authority on which FDA had to rely ultimately was Section 501(a)(2)(B) of the Federal Food, Drug and Cosmetic Act [6], the so-called CGMP section. That section stated that a drug, whether for human or animal use, was deemed to be adulterated if the methods used in, or the facilities or controls used for, its manufacture, processing, packing, or holding did not conform to or were not operated or administered in conformity with current good manufacturing practice. Assurance must be given that the drug would meet the requirements of the act as to safety and would have the identity and strength, and meet the quality and purity characteristics, which it purported or was represented to possess. One who is most familiar with the subject will find the requirement of process validation in the terms of that definition from the law. In 1978, however, it was not that easy. Instead, those who were in decision-making positions at the time chose to rely on the language of Section 211.40 of the CGMP regulations then current for support. That section stated: "Production [procedures] and control procedures shall include all reasonable precautions . . . to assure that the drugs produced have the safety, identity, strength, quality, and purity they purport to possess." That language was clearer, and it was incorporated into the Drug Process Inspections Compliance Program. Unfortunately, when a few months later the CGMP regulations were rewritten, that particular text dropped from the regulations. So, in succeeding issues of the Drug Process Inspections Compliance Program, the following was inserted:

> This requirement of process validation is implicit in the language of 21 CFR 211.100 of the Current Good Manufacturing Practice regulations which states: There shall be written procedures for production and process control designed to assure that the drug products have the identity, strength, quality, and purity they purport or are represented to possess [8].

21 CFR 211.100 in the above text is the legal way to refer to Section 211.100 of the CGMP regulations.

So, the regulatory basis for process validation is found in Section 501(a)(2)(B) of the act itself, as interpreted by FDA in Section 211.100 of the CGMP regulations for drug products. Since bulk pharmaceutical chemicals are also deemed by the act to be drugs, and since there are no existing CGMP regulations covering such articles, FDA simply relies on Section 501(a)(2)(B) of the act itself as its basis for requiring process validation.

IV. THE REGULATORY HISTORY OF PROCESS VALIDATION

In a March 20, 1981, speech at an industrial pharmaceutical association meeting, one of my former colleagues, then Chief of the Manufacturing Standards and Industry Liaison Branch, of the (then) Bureau of Drugs, speculated that all the emphasis on validation had not started on any precise date that he could recall but he stated that it evolved, he believed, over the previous 5 years. He quipped: "Surely, as we are fond of pointing out, it has always been a requirement, at least since the 1963 CGMPs became effective, although couched in different words" [9]. He was correct on both points. The requirement of process validation (per se) was no more than 5 years old, and the requirement of process validation (under different words) had been in effect since the original 1963 CGMP regulations for what was then called Finished Pharmaceuticals.

The Kefauver-Harris Drug Amendments to the Federal Food, Drug, and Cosmetic Act were approved October 10, 1962, and one of the amendments was Section 501(a)(2)(B), the CGMP requirement of the law. Prior to that time, CGMP was simply not required by the law.

Again, prior to the 1962 drug amendments, the only way under the law that the Food and Drug Administration could establish that a drug product was adulterated was by taking a sample from the suspect lot, examining that sample in the laboratory, and determining through that examination that the sample either did not conform to its specifications or was otherwise adulterated. The sample may not have conformed to the requirements of the USP or NF monograph, or it may have had some foreign matter in it. It may have been filthy, or putrid, or decomposed, in whole or in part. Moreover, it may have been prepared under unsanitary conditions so that it became contaminated by filth or rendered injurious to health. Its container may have held a poisonous substance. Something may have been mixed with it to reduce its quality or strength or been substituted wholly or in part for the drug. The burden was on the FDA to prove there was something wrong.

This situation existed for many years, and it caused regulatory difficulties; it also caused public health concerns. FDA was aware of and worried about the problem for many years, but people had to be injured, and some had to die, before FDA and the Congress understood the problem well enough to do something about it under the law. Because the agency was so hampered in its regulatory activities— what use was there in making inspections if the agency found things wrong in the plants but could not document the findings in laboratory examinations of samples from finished products—FDA tended to concentrate its regulatory activities in other areas, particularly in the food areas where it was possible to initiate court cases on the basis of factory evidence. Many pharmaceutical manufacturing establishments went uninspected for years. The in-depth types of systems inspections, so common today, were almost unheard of at that time.

What brought about the change in the law was a series of accidents that were well documented by the agency, accidents in which people were injured and some died. Most of these incidents involved cross-contamination problems, situations in which a drug product—usually tablets—became contaminated by dust from other drug materials being handled in the establishment. The contamination might have taken place during the processing operations, or it might have taken place after the finished tablets were ready for packaging. All kinds of cross-contamination problems were ongoing, but those that were the easiest to document were problems involving substances like diethylstilbestrol and penicillin. Unfortunately, it was not easy to know what to look for in the laboratory until patients had been injured and manifested symptoms that might be associated with the hormone or the antibiotic. The Congress did listen to FDA in 1962, and thereafter FDA was able to deem a drug product adulterated if the manufacturing processes being used were not acceptable. This was the additional powerful regulatory tool that FDA required.

FDA very quickly put together, and caused to be published in the Federal Register, the CGMP regulations that became effective in 1963. The substance of the 1963 regulations was gleaned largely from the text of the Pharmaceutical Manufacturing Association's Manufacturing Control Guidelines at that time.

Another new requirement of the law, brought into the act by the 1962 drug amendments, was a requirement that FDA must inspect every manufacturing establishment that produced drugs at least once in each 2-year period. At first, FDA did this with great diligence, but, after the worst CGMP manufacturing situations had been dealt with in the courts, and violations of the law became less obvious, FDA eased up its pharmaceutical plant inspection activities and turned its resources to what appeared at that time to be more serious problems.

CGMP cases that were suitable for presentation in court were difficult to develop, and many of the cases that were presented to the bureau's compliance office for referral to the courts were not approved. Often there was insufficient evidence. Sometimes the bureau believed the problem could be handled better if the FDA District Office's managers conferred with the offending firm and offered to help them correct their problems. The net result was that very few cases were referred to the courts and, as a consequence of this, the district offices tended to turn their resources to more productive projects.

There was a strong belief in the Bureau of Drugs during the late 1960s and early 1970s that establishment inspections were generally nonproductive and that the bureau and the agency should concentrate its resources on what the agency called its Drug Product Quality Assurance Program. This was a massive sampling effort in which FDA would collect samples from finished batches of particularly important drugs, in terms of both clinical significance and dollar volume, test them, take legal action against batches that fell outside specifications, and inspect the offending firms until they were proved to be in compliance. This approach was both good and bad. It was one thing to test samples for conformity to specifications if it could be assumed that every sample would represent the lot from which it came. How could this approach be effective when sterility was to be determined, or when there was some other contaminant present in the plant that the FDA chemist could not know about and, therefore, could not check for? Finished product testing of samples for sterility does not assure that the lot from which the sample was taken is sterile. It does not even assure that the sample itself is necessarily sterile. Cross-contamination with dangerous drugs and other chemicals could go undetected, and it did.

Things began to change in the late 1960s and early 1970s. Following up on complaints of clinical failures with such tablet products as digoxin, digitoxin, prednisolone, and prednisone, FDA found that most of the batches being manufactured by some companies had been poorly mixed. This resulted in a certification program initiated by FDA which produced many seizures and recalls, and it ultimately resulted in many companies improving product content uniformity, while other firms, failing, went out of business altogether. It was the manufacturing process itself that was at fault, not quality control necessarily, although there were quality-control problems in some of the firms. Two manufacturers of large-volume parenteral drug products experienced complaints involving injuries and some deaths. These firms, and their competitors as well, had massive quality-control programs in place. They had voluminous files attesting to the fact that the samples they had tested for sterility had been sterile. FDA had inspected those records many times without objection. Extensive investigations were done by both FDA and CDC (Centers for Disease Control, Atlanta, Georgia). The cause of the microbiological contamination of the products involved was never established but several probable causes were identified. Some of the solutions may have been produced at time-temperature ratios that produced too low an F value (see Chapter 3). Water used to cool the sterilized bottles was certainly proved to be nonsterile, and it was speculated that during the cool-down there might have been back-seepage into the bottles through (in the one company's case) the screw-type cap and (in the other company's case) through the conventional rubber bung. Live organisms were found inside the caps in some "sterilized" bottles. What became apparent to FDA was that there had been no real proof in the case of those firms that their products were sterile. Perhaps this was also true of competitors. Perhaps no firm that manufactured any kind of injectible drug products was without fault. FDA felt that it was "sitting on a powder keg."

What we were all learning, after all our many years of experience as drug regulatory officials and so-called experts, was that we had never really looked at the process itself—certainly not the entire process—in our regulatory activities. We were quality control rather than quality assurance oriented. All of us were familiar with validation of laboratory test methodology, but none of us thought in terms of process validation. In going back over old FDA speeches presented by myself and other FDA officials, the earliest reference I have been able to find to the term process validation was a paper entitled "A Systems Approach to Validation" [10] presented at Purdue University September 21, 1977, by an FDA field engineer. My own speeches on validation—and I suppose I made more such speeches than anyone else in FDA—dated from early 1978.

The paper that I believe was FDA's entry into process validation was one presented by Mr. Ted Byers, on October 11, 1974, entitled "Design for Quality" [11]. In this paper Byers said that FDA was giving increased attention to adequacy of processes for the production of pharmaceuticals. The word *validation* was not used at all, but the concept was clearly validation. In my paper, presented June 16, 1978, before the Parenteral Drug Association at Philadelphia and entitled Validation and Stability, I discussed the legal basis for the requirement that processes be validated [12].

One might wonder why it was, or how it came about, that FDA did not include in the revised CGMP regulations for drug products, which were published in the Federal Register on September 29, 1978, in very clear language and with a precise definition of the term validation, what was meant by process validation and exactly how it fit into CGMP. The reason is that the revisions to the CGMP regulations and the evolution of the concept of process validation were actually running on separate FDA tracks. We first talked about process validation in FDA some time between the 1974 "Design for Quality" paper and the 1977 paper "A Systems Approach to Validation." Exactly when, or by whom the term was brought into FDA, I cannot say. Some time in 1973, I was charged with putting together the revisions to the CGMP regulations which were published in the Federal Register February 13, 1976, and published as a final order September 29, 1978. In 1978, we seriously discussed amending the proposal to include a definition of the term process validation and to explain the concept in the regulations' scope statement. The problem we had was that the task had gone on for several years, and the document had been held up many times for many reasons. Had we published an amendment to the 1976 proposal, we would have faced a legal requirement that we again hold up the final order until an adequate comment period had passed and we had had an opportunity to review and act on the comments. All this came about at a time when the national administration was placing much pressure on agency administrators to forego promulgating any regulations that were not absolutely necessary. We had a commitment from the then deputy commissioner that he would sign the final order. In those circumstances, we chose to go forward with the final order, cause it to be published, and then later opt to amend it. It is my opinion that had we not made that decision when we did the September 29, 1978, CGMP revisions would not have been published at all.

It seems that FDA's May 1987 Guideline on General Principles of Process Validation has corrected the problem. Now, the entire drug, device, and veterinary medicine industries can know in no uncertain terms what it is FDA is saying about process validation, and they can be sure that the agency's bureaus are all speaking of the same concept. Process validation is here to stay. Although this chapter has not discussed medical devices at all, FDA's guideline does indeed apply to medical devices as well as human and veterinary drugs. I have much experience with FDA's dedication to process validation with regard to medical devices.

NOTES

1. Federal Register, Vol. 43, No. 190, 9/29/78, pp. 45013–45089. U.S. Government Printing Office, Washington, DC.
2. Title 21, Code of Federal Regulations, Parts 210 & 211. Cited 21 CFR 210 & 211. U.S. Government Printing Office, Washington, DC.
3. On June 22, 1982 the units of the Bureaus of Drugs and Biologics were merged into a new National Center for Drugs and Biologics, and the bureaus were abolished.
4. Federal Food, Drug, and Cosmetic Act. Title 21 U.S. Code, Section 301 et seq. Cited 21 U.S.C. 301 et seq. The particular section of the act was section 501(a)(2)(B), cited in the U.S. Code as 21 U.S.C. 351(a)(2)(B).
5. On October 8, 1982, the units of the Bureaus of Medical Devices and Radiological Health were merged into a new National Center for Devices and Radiological Health, and the Bureaus were abolished.
6. Section 510(a)(2)(B) of the Federal Food, Drug, and Cosmetic Act.
7. Food and Drug Administration Compliance Program No. 7356.002. Compliance programs are updated yearly and published in the FDA Compliance Program Guidance Manual, available from National Technical Information Service (NTIS), U.S. Dept. of Commerce, 5285 Port Royal Road, Springfield, VA.
8. Section 211.100 of the CGMP regulations. Cited as 21 CFR 211.100.
9. Clifford G. Broker, Chief (now retired), Manufacturing Standards & Industry Liaison Branch, Bureau of Drugs, Food and Drug Administration, Rockville, Md. Presented March 20, 1981 at a Parenteral Drug Association meeting. Copies available through requests to FDA under the Freedom of Information Act. Paper also published in *Journal of Parenteral Science and Technology 35*, No. 4, July/August 1981, The Parenteral Drug Association, Philadelphia, PA.
10. Paul F. Shatto (deceased), Chemical Engineer, Field Investigations Branch, Office of Executive Director of Regional Operations, Food and Drug Administration, Rockville, MD. Copies available from FDA under Freedom of Information Act requests.
11. T. E. Byers (now retired), Associate Director for Compliance, Bureau if Drugs, Food and Drug Administration, Rockville, MD. Presented October 11, 1974 at the Manufacturing Controls Seminar, The Proprietary Association, Cherry Hill, NJ. Copies available from FDA under Freedom of Information Act requests.
12. Bernard T. Loftus (now retired), Director, Division of Drug Manufacturing, Bureau of Drugs, Food and Drug Administration, Rockville, MD. Copies available from FDA under Freedom of Information Act requests.

2

Organizing for Validation

J. Patrick Jeater, Leo F. Cullen, and G. J. Papariello *Wyeth-Ayerst Research Laboratories, Radnor, Pennsylvania*

I. INTRODUCTION

From surveys of the literature and discussions with appropriate individuals, it is apparent that process validation work in the pharmaceutical industry is organized using one of the following structures: the consultant, the task force concept, or the dedicated group.

In this chapter the advantages and disadvantages of these structures and the departments that are typically in charge of the work are discussed. Additionally, comments are made about the scope of the studies and likely manpower requirements for both sterile and nonsterile products. Finally, some detail is given about protocols and documentation needed for validation.

II. STRUCTURES

A. The Consultant

Consultants are individuals or a group of persons hired by a company on a contractual basis. The advantages and disadvantages of having work performed by consultants are the same in validation as they are in other situations. Consultants can be considered individuals who are immediately able to review processes and present protocols for validation. They are in a position to apply experience gained in other companies and fields to problems that individuals within the hiring company may not have anticipated. This also has the advantage of efficiency, because the company hiring the consultant will not need to go through the

9

potentially time-consuming and arduous task of recruiting individuals with highly specialized talents. Additionally, the workers associated with the consultant are not necessarily permanent members of the hiring company. This aspect is economically advantageous, since they will work on specific projects under contractual agreements with firm costs and completion dates.

On the other hand, whereas the consultant who is hired has the necessary expertise, the training and experience of the team members associated with the consulting firm may be unacceptable. The economic advantage of employing a consultant can be offset by cost overruns. If a validation job is not completed within the time and cost bounds set within the initial contract, the company may be left with an incomplete job and extra expense. Consultants' estimates and contracts between companies and consultants must be carefully written. It can be disappointing for all concerned if consultants are hired based on a low estimate because of an inadequate understanding of the complexities of the project.

B. The Task Force

The task force concept refers to the organizational approach in which the personnel assigned to the validation effort are individuals from various divisions within the corporation. When validation work is to be performed, the personnel meet as a committee consisting of members from each of the production, engineering, quality-assurance, and research and development departments.

Thus, a broad spectrum of opinions may be gathered relative to the requirements of validation and the acceptability of the data obtained. The head of this committee is most usefully the person responsible for validation work and documentation, and this person has the task of delegating work to other committee members. The major advantages are:

1. The task force members bring experience from a range of departments to apply to a related topic. When the job is complete, they can return full time to their previous functions. In this way, the need to hire full-time professionals dedicated solely to validation work is avoided.
2. The membership of the task force can change, depending on the work to be tackled. This is important if, for example, parenterals and solid dosage form products are to be investigated by the same task force. Generally, the requirements for sterile product validation are significantly different from those for nonsterile products.

The obvious disadvantage to this concept is that the members of the task force will have dual responsibilities within the corporation. An individual will be expected to perform simultaneously the dual tasks of a validation committee member and those from the normal department. This could easily present conflicts of interest.

C. The Dedicated Group

The dedicated group describes a set of people whose principal task is that of validation. The validation department may exist as a subgroup within another larger department but it would normally be autonomous.

The advantages of this type of organization are that the employees in such a group are totally dedicated to and responsible for the validation effort. This has the effect of producing a smoother path for reviewing the manufacturing systems and developing protocols at the start of the validation effort. Interaction with production and quality-assurance scheduling is important and therefore must also be taken into consideration. The use of a dedicated group affords a better overview of the situation and eliminates a dual reporting system, which could lead to conflicts of interest.

Inherent within the dedicated group concept is the need to create new positions within the responsible department and perhaps some additional space requirement for that department. If the members of a dedicated validation group do not report to the production or quality-assurance groups, they could have only limited influence should a situation arise in which corrective action is necessary. As an example, consider the case in which work is being performed on a product that has been made successfully for many years. During the validation work, it is found that manufacturing equipment is not operating correctly or is not sufficient for the purpose. It is then the responsibility of the production department to make the necessary alterations; the validation group can only make the recommendations.

Obviously, there are positive and negative aspects in each of these methods of organization (and there are probably many types that are homologations of the three outlined here). The way that validation groups are developed and controlled will depend on local circumstances, organizational size, and structures and personalities of the people who are charged with establishing a validation function.

III. RESPONSIBLE DEPARTMENTS

Having decided which structure is best for the validation group, it is then necessary to detail which department within the company has the responsibility for directing the process-validation effort. There are four major departments that could typically have this responsibility: production, engineering, quality assurance, or research and development.

Generally, there is agreement in the industry that the group responsible for carrying out validation work will need to be able to accept or be aware of information from all of the departments listed above.

A. Production

An example of the first on the list, production, was given by Guillemoteau at Sandoz [1]. As a "matrix organization," this validation group imposes a secondary structure onto the four major groups already existing within the company, but it responds directly to the vice president of manufacturing. The benefits from this type of structure are given as uninterrupted production, ease of interdepartmental communications, confining validation responsibility to one person, and consistency of technical thought and action. Hence, it is possible to describe this matrix as a task force oriented group.

In essence, none of these reported benefits is confined to this concept simply because the group reports through the production structure. These same advantages could be achieved by coordinating the group through any of the other major departments. This reinforces the thoughts expressed earlier about the influence that circumstances and individuals have on initial organizational structures.

B. Quality Assurance

Greer [2] expounded on the quality-assurance organization that is responsible for validation at Eli Lilly. Entitled Process Control Services, this unit is divided into two parts dealing with facilities and systems and with production processes. Although this Process Control Services group responds through Production Operations in the management structure, it is considered a quality-control group. It was explained that this particular arrangement was set up because of the particular situation within the company at that time.

The major concern of the group performing validation work is the current implementation and execution of corporate quality-assurance policies. It also takes a broad view of facilities, their support systems, services (for example, air and water), and processes used to manufacture product. In this fashion, it is assured that the facilities are "qualified and controlled to deliver acceptable conditions and parameters required for the product." The products are then validated by the retrospective data concept. Meyer [3] and Simms [4] gave details on the justification and type of statistical, end-product testing performed on solid dosage forms.

C. Engineering

An example of validation under the auspices of the engineering department was developed by Primm [5] at Mead Johnson. The validation effort is organized by a committee that is chaired by a member of the Process Engineering Department. The role of the engineering department was defined and compared with definitions of validation of processes, facilities, and equipment.

The Process Engineering Department was justified as being in charge of validation work. This department in Mead Johnson assumes many responsibilities that are assigned to other departments in other companies. For example, scale-up of new products, manufacturing of product for clinical trials, maintenance of batch records, and troubleshooting are all part of the engineering department functions.

In this particular structure, three committees were operational. The first identified the products and processes that required validation (sterile products, solids, liquids, etc.) and their order of importance. The second detailed facilities and equipment to be investigated. The third performed the work under the supervision of an industrial engineering coordinator. It was believed that the systematic approach to solving problems typical of that department lent itself to validation work.

It should be noted that R&D parts of the company are marketing-oriented and have little input to the validation effort.

D.   Research and Development

In some corporations, validation work is organized through the Pilot Plant Division of the Pharmacy Research and Development Department using the dedicated group concept. Papariello [6] explained that this specific R&D group is best fitted to perform validation work because it is inextricably involved with the optimization, scale-up and validation of new products and processes. Since this was the case, validation of existing products was a logical extension of this work.

It was pointed out that the validation effort is the responsibility of individuals within the pilot plants already existing at each manufacturing site. These responsible persons must enlist the cooperation of the quality-assurance, the engineering, and the production departments on whom they are dependent to a large extent for results of analytical testing and maintenance of schedules.

IV.   SCOPE OF VALIDATION WORK

A.   General

The general scope of validation work is readily discernible from the relevant section of the Current Good Manufacturing Practices document (CGMP) [7]; however, the actual scope of investigation varies widely from company to company.

In some companies, validation work encompasses all facets of a manufacturing facility. This could include all items given in the list below:

Validation work	Tested for
Personnel	Qualifications, responsibilities
Buildings	Design, construction

Services	Water (city, deionized, distilled, water for injection), lighting, heating/cooling, cleaning, ventilation, waste disposal, sanitation
Equipment	Design, size, location, materials of construction, manufacturers' drawings, change parts, maintenance, operating parameters, cleaning
Raw material and components	Control, testing, storage, vendor audit
Procedures	Standard operating procedures, manufacturing directions, sampling, yield calculations, processing time limitations, microbial contamination, reprocessing
Packaging/labeling	Materials, issue of labels, expiry dating
Warehousing/ distribution	General procedures
Laboratory controls	Testing, release, stability testing, special tests, reserve samples (etc.)
Records and reports	Equipment cleaning and use, components, containers, closures, labels, master and batch production control, production record review, laboratory, distribution and complaint records, product returns

Although this comprehensive list should be considered, there is general agreement [8,9] that validation work is carried out to prove that manufacturing procedures "do what they purport to do." Furthermore, control procedures should be established to monitor the output and performance of those processes that may be responsible for causing variability in the characteristics of in-process material and drug products. This would seem to indicate that items such as buildings, construction, warehousing, and training are performed satisfactorily by departments not necessarily directly under validation control.

B. Equipment Qualification

The Installation Qualification (I.Q.)/Operation Qualification (O.Q.) validation technique advocated by Shatto [10] and Landes [11] highlights the types of problems that are likely to be encountered.

The I.Q. part would encompass such items as the suitability of the building; services (e.g., air and water); the materials of construction of the equipment; and the suitability, positioning, accuracy, and calibration of instruments.

The O.Q. section should cover generally an investigation of control of the variables occurring with any piece of equipment or operation. The temperature distribution in a sterilizer and the chamber speed of a comminuting mill are two such examples of these variables. Useful examples of detailed studies are presented in the areas of steam [12], ethylene oxide [13], and radiation steriliza-tion [14]. Additional information about these topics is also given in Chap. 3.

With respect to nonsterile products, equipment qualification (I.Q. and O.Q.) may be performed in much the same way as that detailed for sterile product manufacturing equipment; however, aside from that similarity, differences emerge, since validation of existing products can then be performed either by prospective or retrospective means. The differences between these two types of approaches are explained elsewhere in this book.

C. Priority of Work

Having decided on the scope of the validation department's operation, it is advisable then to make a list of the categories of products that are to be tackled in order of importance or priority. An example of such a priority list is given below.

Large volume parenterals
Small volume parenterals
Ophthalmics and biologicals
Sterile solids
Low-dose/high-potency oral solids
Other tablets and capsules
Oral liquids and topicals

This priority list is basically one that has been advocated by Arumbolo [15] and Nash [16].

Products that can cause the most problems if they are not manufactured by completely controlled processes are given at the top of the list; however, it should be stressed that validation and quality of all of the products are important.

Another method of determining work priorities is to rank the products by dollar volume sales. Validation work should then be started on products that are at the top of the sales list.

This method is most easily applied to solid and liquid dosage form products. It has the benefit of first validating those processes that influence the largest portion of the total production volume; however, most pharmaceutical companies have an extensive line of products with only a small percentage of the products producing a large percentage of the dollar volume sales. This means that the greatest benefit of prospective validation will be for those top products, and other means of validation (retrospective) could be used for the remainder.

Generally, prospective validation means following a method of manufacture closely and employing an increased sampling, testing, and checking of products and manufacturing equipment at various points during production. The sampling, testing, and checking plan would be over and above what is considered normal practice.

Retrospective validation can be defined as the study of products that have been manufactured for a considerable time by a well-established process using only the data gathered routinely from those products. This indicates that the manufacturing equipment is of the correct construction, is well controlled, and is fitted with suitable, calibrated instruments.

Companies could also apply prospective and retrospective data validation concepts as an integrated package. This strategy would seem to be the most beneficial, cost effective, and logical. Hence, a decision must be made as to the direction of validation for existing products. If retrospective data are used, the appropriate statistical expertise must be generated. Normally, this will mean using data bases that may require computer as well as statistical inputs. If prospective means are used, the additional testing load imposed on the Quality Assurance analytical laboratory must be considered.

Whatever method is chosen for the existing products, it is strongly recommended that prospective validation concepts be applied to the introduction of new products. This should take into account information that has been gathered during optimization work both on pilot- and production-sized batches. Details of this type of work are given in Chap. 5.

V. MANPOWER REQUIREMENTS

A. PMA Questionnaires

Having decided on a direction, the next question that arises is related to the manpower requirements for the work. A reasonable idea of the number of people required to perform validation work on nonsterile oral and topical drugs can be extracted from the responses to the 1978 and 1981 PMA (Pharmaceutical Manufacturers Association) questionnaires on the subject [17,18]. Comparison of these two documents shows that the percentage of firms with a formal written validation program increased from 12% in 1978 to 57% in 1981. This figure was expected to increase to over 80% during 1982, giving an indication of the increase in the number of companies involving themselves in this type of work.

On manpower requirements to implement a validation group, over 60% of the respondents in 1981 were expecting to use up to 5 people, and a further 20% were using between 5 and 10 people. Unfortunately, these responses are not correlated with the number of products manufactured by the companies. Responses to the question of manpower required to sustain the same validation program showed that just under 80% of the companies were using or expecting to use between 1 and 5 persons.

In 1981, the majority of respondents indicated that their validation programs were either not yet started or less than 25% complete; however, the results are somewhat dichotomous, for over 30% of the respondents stated that their work was between 50 and 75% complete.

The number of persons working on new and existing product validation and their affiliated departments were given in detail in the 1981 questionnaire. The only significant differences between the responses for new and existing drugs were that R&D or technical service departments had more involvement with the validation of new products. Basically, the involvement of the production, engineering, and quality-assurance departments was the same irrespective of product type.

B. Independent Survey

Unfortunately, there are no documents from the primary parenteral organization that parallel the PMA surveys. To develop some understanding of the validation concepts within the parenteral manufacturing industry, a survey was conducted among companies involved in the Validation Discussion Group that is organized by several east coast pharmaceutical manufacturers.

Tables 1 and 2 give details of the approximate number of products, their breakdown by structure, and the numbers of validation personnel employed for sterile and nonsterile product validation, respectively. The results of this investigation showed that only two types of structure were being used: dedicated groups and task forces.

Table 1 shows that, of the seven sterile product manufacturers interviewed, six organized their work using the dedicated group system and only one used the task force concept. The figures for 10 nonsterile product manufacturers in Table 2 show that seven were using dedicated groups and three, task forces.

From these two tables, it is apparent that there are more persons working on sterile than on nonsterile products. This is seen as an indication of the relative importance of these two aspects.

Understandably, the number of persons working on sterile products may vary in a cyclic fashion because some companies have validation workers employed full time for a short time period on particular projects, e.g., qualification of new buildings. Even so, there are still more persons employed on validation of sterile than nonsterile products. For this reason, any correlation between the number of products and number of validation personnel is difficult.

This survey indicates that a group numbering between three and six employees is necessary for validation in a corporation with a pharmaceutical line of about 200 products. Obviously, some companies are trying to perform validation work in a shorter time span than others, and the number of employees engaged in validation would be higher in these companies.

The ratio of professional to technical staff is in most cases about 2 to 1 for work on both sterile and nonsterile products.

One incontrovertible fact came out of the survey: validation on sterile products was universally called prospective. Validation performed on nonsterile forms was almost entirely retrospective for existing products and prospective for new products.

Table 1 Numbers of Employees Engaged in Validation of Sterile Products

Structure	Approximate number of products	Number of employees Professionals[a]	Number of employees Technicians[b]	Approach
Dedicated group	170	6	4	Prospective
Dedicated group	50	3	1	Prospective
Dedicated group	100	4	2	Prospective
Dedicated group	40	22[c]	—	Prospective
Dedicated group	50	8	3	Prospective
Dedicated group	15	1	2	Prospective
Dedicated group	40	16	—	Prospective

| | | Members drawn from | | | | |
Structure	Approximate number of products	Q.A.	R&D	Engineering	Manufacturing	Approach
Task force	55	1	—	1	1	Prospective

[a]Professional employees have college degrees, typically in one of the following areas: chemical engineering, chemistry, pharmacy, microbiology, or computer science.
[b]These figures do not include secretarial assistance. Most structures were supported by between ½ and 2 clerical employees.
[c]Includes employees in validation aspects of a new sterile manufacturing building.

Table 2 Numbers of Employees Engaged in Validation of Nonsterile Products

Structure	Approximate number of products	Number of employees		Approach
		Professionals[a]	Technicians[b]	
Dedicated group	150	3	2	Retrospective
Dedicated group	35	2½	—	Retrospective and prospective
Dedicated group	200	2½	—	Retrospective. Prospective for new products
Dedicated group	130	2	1	Prospective
Dedicated group	210	2	1	Retrospective
Dedicated group	75	4	2	Prospective and retrospective
Dedicated group	200	3	—	Retrospective

		Members drawn from				
		Q.A.	R&D	Engineering	Manufacturing	
Task force	45	1	—	1	1	Retrospective
	190	3	—	3	3	Retrospective
	80	1	—	1	1	Retrospective

[a]Professional employees have college degrees, typically in one of the following areas: chemical engineering, chemistry, pharmacy, microbiology, or computer science.

[b]These figures do not include secretarial assistance. Most structures were supported by between ½ and 2 clerical employees.

C. Qualifications

The educational backgrounds of personnel involved with validation work vary. A significant number working in sterile product validation are biologists or microbiologists. This was the only obvious point of difference between those employed on validation of sterile and nonsterile products. Other professional employees were found to be pharmacists, chemists, and chemical engineers.

Some employees working on validation have been trained in statistics, computer programming, or systems analysis work. Those with the latter qualifications were mainly involved in handling the large quantity of data that is generated in retrospective validation and multipoint recorder work.

The need for employees with these diversified educational backgrounds is understandable. The validation group's responsibilities require a complete understanding of technical equipment, equipment control, instrumentation and testing, and product sampling and testing that will be encountered.

Types of equipment control can range from simple, fixed speed through manual and semiautomatic to computer or microprocessor. That this diversity of equipment control exists means that there is a vast difference in the type and quantity of data that may be gathered for validation testing.

Ideas about the most complex of these types of equipment control are given by Fraade [19] and Foster [20].

Sheth [21] gave several insights into the technical aspects of data-gathering.

As Fraade [19] points out, the use of computer-controlled equipment in the pharmaceutical industry is common. If this type of control can be used to gather data for validation purposes, this will influence the type and number of employees that will be necessary for validation work.

VI. PROTOCOLS

In the context of validation, protocol means: a document that gives details of the critical parts of the manufacturing process, the parameters that should be measured, their allowable range of variability, and the manner in which the system will be tested. For clarification, two examples will be discussed, one from the sterile and the other from the nonsterile area of manufacturing.

In the case of sterile products, the general philosophy of validation needs clarification. A description of which department is to work on what pieces of equipment should be written before starting on validation work. This should cover the type of approach and the number of replicate batches required to be studied.

A general heat sterilization protocol should encompass certification of equipment (i.e., Installation Qualification), heat distribution over the empty sterilizer chamber, placement of bioindicators, heat penetration into components, and the length of time at temperature. Each of the important parameters must have an acceptable range associated with it (e.g., 121 ± 1 °C). The sterility of the final product should then be tested at various load patterns under the required conditions.

As with sterile product protocols, those for nonsterile products should also cover equipment certification. Beyond that, the two types of protocol obviously differ. Nonsterile solid-dosage form product protocols should cover such items as acceptable limits for equipment operating parameters (e.g., rpm for chamber and feed rates in milling, blender shell and intensifier bar rpm for blending), and sampling procedures for granulations. Specifications should also be available for the testing of active ingredients, particle size, and bulk density, if such tests are applicable.

In both of these cases, the results of the recorded parameters should be compared with the figures set down in the testing protocol and information available from scale-up work. The acceptability of the results must then be determined. In other words, the results are compared with a yardstick that has been set down before testing has started. If necessary, equipment, manufacturing methods, and measurement techniques may then be altered to suit the intended purpose, and the reasoning behind the change must be documented.

VII. DOCUMENTATION

The documentation required during validation organization is an essential part of the work. Several types are necessary and are exemplified as follows:

1. Report to Pilot Plant (RPP) covering R&D experiences of the formulation department
2. General Technical Report (GTR) covering Pilot Plant experiences during scale-up
3. Report for Product Specifications (RPS)
4. Manufacturing directions used by production departments
5. GTR detailing validation work during scale-up
6. GTR covering the initial production batches and the validation work performed at full scale
7. Standard Operating Procedures (SOP)
8. Revised RPS, if necessary

It should be noted that many of these report names are specific to Wyeth Laboratories. Similar documents should exist for any pharmaceutical manufacturing organization.

To explain some of these documents, the RPP will be prepared by the scientific personnel in the Research and Development department who have been producing laboratory-scale batches. The report will contain a history of the product development, the formula and manufacturing directions used at laboratory scale, the results obtained from product testing, and stability studies. This type of report should be considered background material that would be applied to validation work.

Next the GTR document details experience gained at pilot scale and includes validation-type work. From these reports, RPS documents are written to provide the formula, manufacturing directions, and testing standards that are intended to be used for full-scale production lots. The approval system for these specifications includes heads of research and development, quality assurance, and production departments. The RPS system assumes a very important role in the control of production parameters at Wyeth Laboratories. It is designed so that the information generated during R&D formulation, pilot plant scale-up, and full-scale trials and validation work is eventually incorporated into the documents followed during the production of trade material.

The batch records, formula, and manufacturing directions are then written for production purposes from the approved RPS documents.

The validation work at full scale is performed on the initial trade batches of material, and the document produced can then take into consideration all of the information gained during the preproduction stage. The number of batches of material investigated varies, depending on the complexity of the process. Generally, the pharmaceutical industry recognizes that this work should be performed on at least three batches of material.

During this type of work, standard operating procedures would be implemented or updated for equipment used in product manufacture. Further, production operators require training to ensure consistency of operation of the equipment.

Finally, revised RPS documents may be required if it is necessary to use a new piece of equipment (or to alter the method of use of an existing item) during the manufacturing procedure. Some further comments about the types of change in the production of solid-dosage form products that necessitate revalidation were given by Jeater [22].

This documentation scheme, especially parts concerning the RPS, manufacturing directions, and SOP, has the overall effect of controlling changes. This is in agreement with Georges [23], who described the necessity of controlling changes to processes that have previously undergone validation. This publication presented some details of the type of questions to be asked by individuals judging the suitability of changes. It was recommended that changes should be reviewed by responsible departments. The work should be followed in a formal fashion and modifications should be made only if the changes are formally approved.

Overall, it can be seen that there is a wealth of documentation that is available for validation purposes.

REFERENCES

1. Guillemoteau, J-Y., *Organizing for Validation—Manufacturing Division*. Proceedings of the Pharmaceutical Manufacturers Association Seminar Program on Validation of Solid Dosage Form Processes, Atlanta, Georgia (May 1980).

2. Greer, W. J., *Organizing for Validation—Quality Assurance Standpoint*. Proceedings of the Pharmaceutical Manufacturers Association Seminar Program on Validation of Solid Dosage Form Processes, Atlanta, Georgia (May 1980).

3. Meyer, R. J., *Validation of Products and Processes from a Production, Quality Control Viewpoint*. Proceedings of the Pharmaceutical Manufacturers Association Seminar Program on Validation of Solid Dosage Form Processes, Atlanta, Georgia (May 1980).

4. Simms, L. L., *Validation of Existing Products by Statistical Evaluation*. Proceedings of the Pharmaceutical Manufacturers Association Seminar Program on Validation of Solid Dosage Form Processes, Atlanta, Georgia (May 1980).

5. Primm, T. M., *Organizing for Validation—Engineering Division*. Proceedings of the Pharmaceutical Manufacturers Association Seminar Program on Validation of Solid Dosage Form Processes, Atlanta, Georgia (May 1980).

6. Papariello, G. J., *Organizing for Validation—Process Development R&D Division*. Proceedings of the Pharmaceutical Manufacturers Association Seminar Program on Validation of Solid Dosage Form Processes, Atlanta, Georgia (May 1980).

7. Federal Register, Department of Health, Education and Welfare, Food and Drug Administration, Human and Veterinary Drugs, Current Good Manufacturing Practices, Rockville, MD (September 29, 1978).

8. Proceedings of PMA Seminar on Validation of Solid Dosage Form Processes, Pharmaceutical Manufacturers Association, Atlanta, Georgia (May 1980).

9. Reports from 4th European Seminar on Quality Control in Pharmaceutical and Cosmetic Industries—Validation of Manufacturing Processes, University of Geneva, Switzerland (September 1980).

10. Shatto, P. F., *A Systems Approach to Validation*. Presentation at Purdue University Management Science Conference for Pharmaceutical Industry, W. Lafayette, IND (September 1977).

11. Landes, J., *Process Validation Concepts and Their Application to Overseas*. Stat-A-Matrix Conference, Edison, New Jersey (November 1981).

12. Parenteral Drug Association, Technical Monograph No. 1. *Validation of Steam Sterilization Cycles*, Philadelphia, PA (May 19, 1978).

13. Association for the Advancement of Medical Instrumentation (AAMI). *Recommended Practice Guidelines for Industrial Ethylene Oxide Sterilization of Medical Devices. Process Design, Validation and Routine Sterilization*. Published by AAMI, Arlington, Virginia (December 1981).

14. Anger, C. B., *Radiation Sterilization Validation for Dosimetric Release, Medical Device and Diagnostic Industry*, Santa Monica, CA (September 1981), pp. 47–79, 74.

15. Arumbolo, A. S., *In-process Quality Control in the Manufacture of Essential Drugs, Drug Development and Industrial Pharmacy 5*: 523, Marcel Dekker, New York, NY (1979).

16. Nash, R. A., Stat-A-Matrix Conference, Edison, New Jersey (November 1981).
17. Pharmaceutical Manufacturers Association, *Survey into Process Validation of Non-sterile and Topical Drugs, Summary of Reponses* (May 1978).
18. Pharmaceutical Manufacturers Association, *Survey-Process Validation on Non-sterile and Topical Drugs, Summary of Responses* (February 1982).
19. Fraade, D. J. (ed.), *Automation of Pharmaceutical Operations, Pharmaceutical Technology Publications*, Springfield, Oregon (January 1983).
20. Foster, B. S., An Automated Granulating Process, *Pharm Tech* 6:8, 32–36 (August 1982).
21. Sheth, H., *Guide to Designing and Installing a Data Acquisition System, Chilton's Instruments and Control Systems*, Vol. 54, No. 11, pp. 57–61, Radnor, PA (November 1981).
22. Jeater, J. P., and Cullen, L. F., *Revalidation—Why, How, When?* Proceedings of the Pharmaceutical Technology Conference, New York (September 1982).
23. Georges, W. D., *Pharmaceutical Validation Change Control, Pharmaceutical Engineering*, Vol. 1, No. 1, pp. 24–25, Tampa, FL (February–April 1982).

3

Sterilization Validation of Sterile Products: Fundamentals

Michael J. Akers *Eli Lilly and Company, Indianapolis, Indiana*

Neil R. Anderson *Marion Merrell Dow, Inc., Kansas City, Missouri*

I. INTRODUCTION

Sterile products have several unique dosage form properties, such as freedom from microorganisms, freedom from pyrogens, freedom from particulates, and extremely high standards of purity and quality; however, the ultimate goal in the manufacture of a sterile product is absolute absence of microbial contamination. The emphasis of this chapter will be the validation of the sterilization processes responsible for achieving this goal.

Unlike many dosage form specifications, the sterility specification is an absolute value. A product is either sterile or nonsterile. Historically, judgment of sterility has relied on an official compendial sterility test; however, end-product sterility testing suffers from a myriad of limitations [1–4]. The most obvious limitation is the nature of the sterility test. It is a destructive test; thus, it depends on the statistical selection of a random sample of the whole lot. Uncertainty will always exist as to whether the sample unequivocally represents the whole. If it were known that one unit out of 1000 units was contaminated (i.e., contamination rate = 0.1%) and 20 units were randomly sampled out of those 1000 units, the probability of that one contaminated unit being included in those 20 samples is 0.02 [5]. In other words, the chances are only 2% that the contaminated unit would be selected as part of the 20 representative samples of the whole 1000-unit lot.

Even if the contaminated unit were one of the 20 samples selected for the sterility test, the possibility still exists that the sterility test would fail to detect the contamination. The microbial contaminant might be at too low a concentration to be detectable during the incubation period or might not grow rapidly enough or at all because of media and incubation insufficiencies.

If microbial growth is detected in a sterility test, this may reflect a false-positive reading because of the problem of accidental contamination of the culture media while performing the sterility test. The problem of accidental contamination is a serious, yet unavoidable limitation of the sterility test.

The Food and Drug Administration (FDA) published guidelines pertaining to general principles of process validation [6]. General concepts and key elements of process validation considered acceptable by the FDA were outlined. A major point stressed in the guidelines was the insufficiency of relying solely on end-product sterility testing alone in ascertaining the sterility of a parenteral of a sterile product lot. Greater significance should be placed on process validation of all systems involved in producing the final product.

These major limitations demonstrate that reliance on end-product sterility testing alone in ascertaining the sterility of a parenteral product may lead to erroneous results. One purpose of validation in the manufacture of sterile products is to minimize this reliance on end-product testing. Three principles are involved in the validation process for sterile product:

1. To build sterility into a product
2. To demonstrate to a certain maximum level of probability that the processing and sterilization methods have established sterility to all units of a product batch
3. To provide greater assurance and support of the results of the end-product sterility test.

Validation of sterile products in the context of this chapter will refer to the confirmation that a product has been exposed to the appropriate manufacturing processes and, especially, to the appropriate sterilization method yielding a batch of product having a known degree of nonsterility.

II. PROCESS OF MICROBIAL DESTRUCTION

Regardless of the type of lethality induced by a sterilization process—whether it be heat, chemical, or radiation—microorganisms, upon exposure to adequate levels of such treatments, will die according to a logarithmic relationship between the concentration or population of living cells and the time exposure or radiation dose to the treatment. This relationship between the microbial population and time may be linear or nonlinear, as seen in Fig. 1. The D value, or the time or dose required for a one-log reduction in the microbial population, may be calculated from these plots.

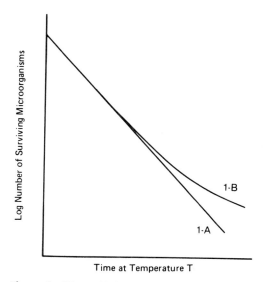

Figure 1 Linear (1-A) and nonlinear (1-B) survivor curves.

A. *D* Value

The *D* value is a single, quantitative expression of the rate of killing of microorganisms. The *D* term refers to decimal point in which microbial death rates become positive time values by determining the time required to reduce the microbial population by one decimal point. This is also the time required for a 90% reduction in the microbial population. Hence, the time or dose it takes to reduce 1000 microbial cells to 100 cells is the *D* value. The *D* value is important in the validation of sterilization processes for several reasons:

1. It is a specific kinetic expression for each micororganism in a specific environment subjected to a specific sterilization agent or condition. In other words, the *D* value will be affected by
   a. The type of microorganism used as the biological indicator*
   b. The formulation components and characteristics (e.g., pH)

---

*Biological indicators (BIs) are live spore forms of microorganisms known to be the most resistant living organisms to the lethal effects of the particular sterilization process. For steam sterilization, the most resistant microorganism is *Bacillus stearothermophilus*. Spore forms of this microorganism are used as the BI for steam sterilization validation. BIs for other sterilization processes are identified in the USP XXII/NF XVII, pp. 1625–1626.

c. The surface on which the microorganism is exposed (glass, steel, plastic, rubber, in solution, dry powder, etc.)

d. The temperature, gas concentration, or radiation dose of the particular sterilization process.*

2. Knowledge of the D value at different temperatures in heat sterilization is necessary for the calculation of the Z value (see p. 29)

3. The D value is used in the calculation of the biological F value (see p. 29)

4. Extrapolation of the D value from large microbial population values to fractional (e.g., 10^{-x}) values predicts the number of log reductions a given exposure period will produce.

   D values are determined experimentally by either of two methods, the survivor-curve method or the fraction-negative method [7,8]. The survivor-curve method is based on plotting the log number of surviving organisms versus an independent variable such as time, gas concentration, or radiation dose. The fraction-negative method uses replicate samples containing identical spore populations treated in an identical manner and determining the number (fraction) of samples still showing microbial growth after treatment and incubation. Fraction-negative data are used primarily for determining D values of microorganisms exposed to thermal destruction processes. The following discussion concentrates on D values calculated by the survivor-curve method.

   Data obtained by the survivor-curve method are plotted semilogarithmically. Data points are connected by least-squares analysis. In most cases the equation used is the first-order death rate equation,

$$\log N = a + bt \tag{1}$$

where N is the number of surviving organisms of time t, a is the Y intercept, and b is the slope of the line as determined by linear regression. The D value is the reciprocal of the linear slope,

$$D = \frac{1}{b} \tag{2}$$

Many microorganisms produce nonlinear survivor curves such as 1-B in Fig. 1. The cause of nonlinear survivor curves has been explained by several theories, such as the multiple critical sites theory [9], experimental artifacts [10], and the heterogeneity of spore heat resistance [11]. Mathematical models for concave survivor curves have been developed by Han et al. [12]. They are quite complicated. For example, the D value for a nonlinear survivor curve can be calculated from the following equation:

---

*Therefore, stating that the D value = 1 minute, for example, is meaningless unless all of the above factors have been identified.

$$D = \frac{1}{\log C_0} - \frac{[1 - \alpha]t - [\alpha Be^{(-t/B-1)}]}{\log C_t} \qquad (3)$$

where C_0 and C_t are initial and final concentrations of spores, t is the time exposure at constant temperature, α is a constant related to the secondary slope of the concave curve, and B is a parameter obtained from the Y intercept extrapolated from the second slope. It is far easier, while less accurate, to apply linear regression to fit the survivor curve data statistically to a straight line and calculate the D value and level of confidence in that calculated value from the slope of the linear line.

A product being validated for sterility should be associated with a characteristic D value for the microorganism either most likely to contaminate the product or most resistant to the process used to sterilize the product. The employment of BIs in the validation of sterile products has the purpose of assuring that the sterilization process that causes a multiple log reduction in the BI population in the product will most certainly be sufficient in destroying all other possible viable contaminants.

B. Z and F Values

These terms, heretofore, have been applied exclusively in the validation of heat-sterilization processes. The Z value is the reciprocal of the slope resulting from the plot of the logarithm of the D value versus the temperature at which the D value was obtained. The Z value may be simplified as the temperature required for a one log reduction in the D value:

$$Z = \frac{T_2 - T_1}{\log D_1 - \log D_2} \qquad (4)$$

Figure 2 presents thermal resistance plot for a Z value of 10°C, the accepted standard for steam sterilization of *B. stearothermophilus* spores, and for a Z value of 20°C, the proposed standard [13] for dry-heat sterilization of *B. subtilis* spores. These plots are important because one can determine the D value of the indicator microorganism at any temperature of interest. In addition, the magnitude of the slope indicates the relative degree of lethality as temperature is increased or decreased.

Mathematical derivation of the Z value equation permits the calculation of a single quantitative expression for effective time exposure at the desired temperature for sterilization. The F value measures equivalent time, not clock time, that a monitored article is exposed to the desired temperature, e.g., 121°C. F values are calculated from the following equation:

$$F = \Delta t \sum 10^{(T-T_0)/Z} \qquad (5)$$

where Δt is the time interval for the measurement of product temperature T and T_0 is the reference temperature; e.g., $T_0 = 121$°C for steam sterilization. The

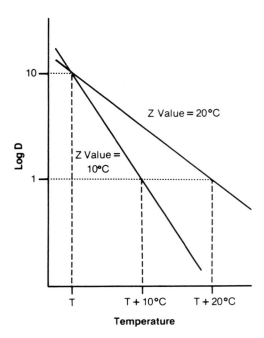

Figure 2 Thermal resistance plots of log D versus temperature, showing slopes equivalent to $Z = 10°C$ and $Z = 20°C$.

F value is shown in Fig. 3. Another equation for the F value as depicted in Fig. 3 is given in the following expression:

$$F = \int_{t_1}^{t_2} L \, dt \tag{6}$$

where $L = 10^{(T-T_0)/Z}$, which is the lethality constant integrated over time limits between time 1 and time 2. Integrating Eq. (6) between two time points will yield the area under the $10^{(T-T_0)/Z}$ versus time curve as seen in Fig. 3.

The more familiar F_0 equation is specific for a Z value of 10°C and a T_0 value of 121°C:

$$F_0 = \Delta t \, \Sigma \, 10^{(T-121)/10} \tag{7}$$

An example of a manual calculation of F_0 value is presented in Table 1.

The F_0 value is mentioned both in the USP XXII/NF XVII and in the CGMPs for large volume parenterals (LVPs). Both sources indicate that the steam steriliza-tion process must be sufficient to produce an F_0 value of at least 8 min. This means that the coolest location in the sterilizer loading configuration must be exposed

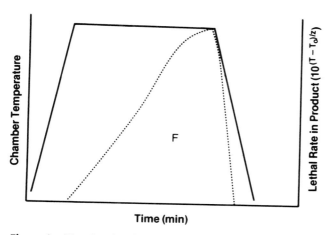

Figure 3 Plot showing the difference between chamber temperature versus time (———) and lethal rate in the product versus time ($\cdots\cdots$). F is the area under the dotted-line curve.

Table 1   A Manual Calculation of F_0 Value

Sterilization time (min)	Product temperature (°C)	$10^{(T-121)/10}$
5	100	0.008
6	103	0.016
7	106	0.032
8	109	0.063
9	112	0.126
10	115	0.251
11	118	0.501
12	121	1.000
13	121	1.000
14	121	1.000
15	118	0.501
16	115	0.251
17	112	0.126
18	109	0.063
19	106	0.032
20	103	0.016
21	100	0.008
		$F_0 = 5.000$ min[a]

[a] $F_0 = \Delta t$ (Σ of lethal rates) $= 1 \times 4.994 = 5.0$ min; Δt is the time interval between successive temperature measurements.

to an equivalent time of at least 8 min of exposure to a temperature of at least 121°C. Unless the D value is known, however, the number of log reductions in the microbial indicator population will not be known. This is why knowledge of the D value is of extreme importance in determining the log reduction in the microbial bioburden.

The equation used for determining the microbial log reduction value is derived as follows:

$$D_t = \frac{t}{\log A - \log B} \tag{8}$$

where t is the heating time at a specific temperature, A the initial number of microorganisms (bioburden or microbial load), and B the number of surviving microorganisms after heating time t. By defining t in Eq. (8) as the equivalent time exposure to a given temperature T, Eq. (8) then may be expressed as

$$D_T = \frac{F_T}{\log A - \log B} \tag{9}$$

When Eq. (9) is rearranged to solve for the microbial reduction value:

$$\log A - \log B = Y_n = \frac{F_T}{D_T} \tag{10}$$

As an example, if $F_T = 8$ min and $D_T = 1$ min, the microbial reduction value $Y_n = 8$, or the process has been sufficient to produce 8 log reductions in the microbial population having a D value of 1 min at the specified temperature T.

C. Probability of Nonsterility

Pflug [14] has suggested that the term *probability of a nonsterile unit* be adopted to define products free of microbial contamination. This term mathematically is B in Eq. (10). Thus, solving for B,

$$B = \text{antilog} \left(\log A - \frac{F_T}{D_T} \right) \tag{11}$$

The expression 10^{-6}, commonly used in sterilization validation, is the B term in Eq. (11). What this means is that after an equivalent time-exposure period of F_T units, the microbial population having an initial value of A has been reduced to a final B value of 10^{-6}. Statistically, this exponential term signifies that one out of 1 million units of product theoretically is nonsterile after sterilization exposure of F_T units. For example, if 10^6 microorganisms having a D value of 1 min at 121°C are placed in a container and the container exposed to 121°C for an equivalent time of 12 min,

$$B = \text{antilog} \left(\log 10^6 - \frac{12 \text{ min}}{1 \text{ min}} \right) = 10^{-6} \tag{12}$$

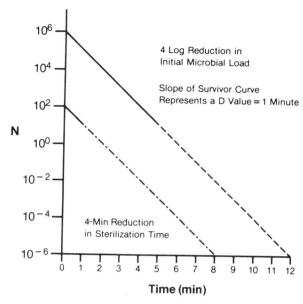

Figure 4 Survivor curves showing the effect of decreasing the microbial load (A) from 10^6 to 10^2 on the time required to achieve a probability of nonsterility (B) of 10^{-6}.

Probability of nonsterility may be extrapolated from the D value slope when plotting the log of the microbial population versus time (equivalent time at a specific temperature), as shown in Fig. 4.

Manipulation of the A, F_T, and D_T values in Eq. (11) will naturally produce different values of B. Accordingly, if it is desirable that B be as low as possible, this may be accomplished in one of three ways: 1) reducing the bioburden (A) of the bulk product, 2) increasing the equivalent exposure time (F_T), or 3) employing a microorganism with a lower D value at the specified temperature. Since option 3 most likely is impossible, as the most resistant microorganisms of a fixed D value must be used in sterilizer validation, one must either employ techniques to assure the lowest possible measurable microbial bioburden prior to sterilization or simply increase the sterilization cycle time.

III. BASIC PRINCIPLES IN THE VALIDATION OF STERILE PRODUCTS

The key to successful validation in sterile product processing, as in any of type of process validation, is being systematic in the theoretical approaches to validation, the performance of the actual validation experiments, and the analysis and documentation of the validation data.

A. Theoretical Approaches

Generally, five basic steps are necessary to validate any manufacturing process [15]:

1. Written documentation
2. Manufacturing parameters
3. Testing parameters
4. In-process controls
5. Final product testing

In sterile product manufacturing, five major steps are involved in approaching the validation of a sterile process [16]. These are outlined below using thermal sterilization as the example process.

1. Select or define the desired attributes of the product. Example: The product will be sterile.
2. Determine specifications for the desired attributes. Example: The product will be sterilized by a sterilization process sufficient to produce a probability of nonsterility of one out of 1 million containers (10^{-6}).
3. Select the appropriate processes and equipment. Example: Use microbial kinetic equations such as Eq. (11) to determine the probability of nonsterility. Select cleaning equipment and container component procedures designed and validated to reduce the product bioburden to the lowest practical level. Select an autoclave that can be validated in terms of correct operation of all mechanical controls. Use the appropriate types of thermocouples, thermal sensing devices, biological indicators, and culture media to conduct the validation tests.
4. Develop and conduct tests that evaluate and monitor the processes, equipment, and personnel.
    Examples:
    a. Determine microbial load counts prior to container filling.
    b. Determine D and Z values of biological indicator organism.
    c. Perform heat distribution studies of empty and loaded autoclave.
    d. Perform heat penetration studies of product at various locations in the batch.
5. Examine the test procedures themselves to ensure their accuracy and reliability.
    Examples:
    a. Accuracy of thermocouples as a function of variances in time and temperature.

b.   Repeatability of the autoclave cycle in terms of temperature and F value consistency.
c.   A challenge of the sterilization cycle with varying levels of bioindicator organisms.
d.   Reliability of cleaning processes to produce consistent low-level product bioburdens.

Each validation process should have a documented protocol of the steps to follow and the data to collect during the experimentation. As an example, App. I presents a protocol for the validation of a steam sterilization process.

Upon completion of the experimental phase of validation, the data are compiled and evaluated by qualified scientific personnel. The results may be summarized on a summary sheet, an example of which is shown in Table 2. Once a process has been validated, it must be controlled to assure that the process consistently produces a product within the specifications established by the validation studies. As shown in Table 2, documentation should present original validation records, a schedule of revalidation dates, and data from the revalidation studies. The interval between validation studies strictly depends on the judgment of the validation team based on experience and history of the consistency of the process.

The remainder of this chapter will address validation approaches and procedures for the five basic methods of sterilization. Other sterile product processes subject to validation but not covered in this chapter are listed with available references in Table 3.

Table 2   Steam Sterilization Process Summary Sheet

Autoclave identification number or letter: P6037
Location: building 22, floor 1
Tag No.: 896101
Validation date: 10-14-83
Revalidation date: 4-14-84
Description of process validated: load containing filling equipment and accessories not to exceed 102 kg
Temperature set point for validation: 121.0°C
Temperature range for validation: ±0.5°C
Cycle validated: 35 min
Validation records stored in archives: A105-11
Revalidation records stored in archives: C314-70

Table 3 Major Processes Other Than Sterilization Processes Validated in the Manufacturing of Sterile Products

Process	Reference(s)
Cleaning of containers and closures	17–19
Cleaning of production equipment	20
Water systems	21
Air systems	22
Compressed gases	—
Pressure and vacuum systems	23
Facilities	24,25
Filling machine accuracy and consistency	25
Calibration of instruments, sensors, measuring devices, and equipment	—
Sanitization and cleaning agents	—
Depyrogenation of rubber closures	—
Bulk manufacturing processes; e.g., weighing, temperature, pH, mixing, time limitations, storage conditions, etc.	—
Container/closure integrity	—
Lyophilization cycles	—
Product stability	—
Product specifications	—

IV. VALIDATION OF STEAM STERILIZATION CYCLES

A. General Considerations

The literature contains more information on steam sterilization validation than any other process in the sterile product area. One reason was the publication of the proposed CGMPs for LVPs in June 1976. Actually, the FDA had been surveying the LVP industry long before the proposed CGMPs for LVP regulations were published. One of the major areas of concern was sterility and the heat sterilization processes for achieving sterility. Thus, at least three sections of the proposed CGMPs for LVPs contain statements related to steam sterilization validation. Although these regulations have not become officially and legally valid, they are taken seriously by the parenteral industry. Table 4 summarizes CGMP-LVP statements pertaining to steam sterilization validation.

The key expression used in steam sterilization validation is F_0. Interestingly, despite the familiarity of this term, it is still misunderstood or misused in the parenteral industry. The main purpose of the F_0 value is to express in a single, quantitative term the *equivalent time* at which a microbial population having a Z value of 10°C has resided at a temperature of 121.1°C. The time units here are not clock time units. Rather, F_0 time is a complete summary of the time the indicator

Table 4 Statements Concerning Sterilization Cycle Design and Validation in the Proposed Good Manufacturing Procedures for LVPs

---

Section 212.240
Procedure for steam sterilization must be sufficient to deliver an F_o of 8 or more.

Section 212.243
Testing of the sterilization processes requires:
1. A maximum microbial count and a maximum microbial heat resistance for filled containers prior to sterilization.
2. Heat distribution studies for each sterilizer, each loading configuration, every container size, using a minimum of 10 thermocouples.
3. Heat penetration studies using product of similar viscosity as that packaged in container studied. Locate slowest heating point in the container. Use 10 or more containers, each with a suitable biological indicator and submerged thermocouple. F_o value is determined beginning when the sterilizer environment has established itself as shown by reproducible heat distribution studies and specific sterilizer temperature has been achieved, and ending when cooling has been initiated.

Section 212.244
Statements on sterilization process design
1. Procedures required to establish uniform heat distribution in the sterilizer vessel. Temperatures must be held at ±0.5°C from the time the product achieves process temperature until the heating portion completed.
2. Verify uniformity of heat distribution for each loading pattern.
3. Temperature of the product and the sterilizer must not fall below the minimum that has been established for the prescribed sterilization process.
4. Establish the time requirement for venting the sterilizer of air.
5. Establish the product come-up time to the desired temperature.
6. Establish the cooling time.

---

organism spent during the entire cycle at a temperature of exactly 121.1°C plus a fraction of the times spent at temperatures below 121.1°C, plus a multiple of the times spent at temperatures greater than 121.1°C. F_0 is a summation term, as exemplified in Fig. 3 and Table 1. F_0 is a time value that is referenced to 121.1°C. It includes heat effects on microorganisms during the heating and cooling phases of the cycle, taking into account that heat effects below 121.1°C are not as powerful in destroying microbial life as the effect found at 121.1°C.

F_0 values may be calculated in several ways. The basic way is by manually recording the temperature of the monitored product at specific time intervals, substituting the recorded temperature for T in Eq. (7), solving the exponential part of the equation for all temperatures recorded, and then multiplying by Δt. This was done in Table 1. Alternatively, and more expediently, a computer program can integrate the temperature and time data to obtain the F_0 value. This approach is now widely used because of the availability of programmable multipoint recorders that record temperature and solve the F_0 equation on an accumulative basis.

F_0 values may be solved using the biological approach, i.e., Eq. (9). The approach is used when D_{121} and A are accurately known and a desired level of survivor probability (B) is sought. In this case, Eq. (9) is rearranged as

$$F_0 = D_{121}(\log A - \log B)$$

For example, if $D_{121} = 1.0$ min, $A = 10^6$, and $B = 10^{-6}$, F_0 is calculated to be

$$F_0 = 1(\log 10^6 - \log 10^{-6}) = 12 \text{ min}$$

Thus, the cycle must be adjusted so that the F_0 value calculated by physical methods (time and temperature data) will be at least 12 min.

An approach for solving F_0 values involves the use of a chemical indicator, called Thermalog S,* which is calibrated in terms of F_0 units. The device has been described by Witonsky [26] and evaluated by Bunn and Sykes [27]. Thermalog strips are placed in the containers being steam sterilized. Each strip contains a chemical sensor that responds to increasing saturation steam temperature. The millimeter distance advanced by the chemical sensor is linearly related to the F_0 value $(T_0 = 121°C, Z = 10°C)$. The advantages of using this device lie in its replacing biological indicators in the validation and monitoring of steam sterilization cycles and its ability to assess F_0 in any part of the sterilizer load however inaccessible to conventional thermocouple monitoring devices. The main disadvantage is the paucity of available data proving the sensitivity and reliability of the chemical indicator system.

With the main emphasis being the validation of a steam sterilization cycle based on the achievement of a certain, reproducible F_0 value at the coolest part of the full batch load, procedures for validation of a steam sterilization process will now be discussed.

B.   Qualification and Calibration

1.   Mechanically Checking, Upgrading, and Qualifying the Sterilizer Unit

The functional parts of an autoclave are shown in Fig. 5. Simmons [28] has adequately addressed this issue. Utilities servicing the autoclave must be checked for quality, dependability, proper installation, and lack of contamination. The major utility of concern here is steam. All equipment used in studying the steam sterilizer, such as temperature and pressure instrumentation, must be calibrated.

---

*Bio Medical Sciences, Fairfield, NJ.

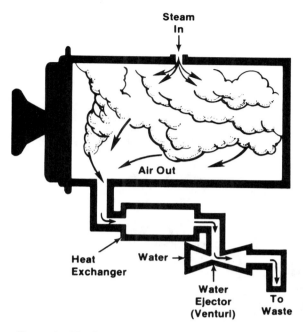

Figure 5   The functional parts of a modern autoclave. (Courtesy of American Sterilizer Company, Erie, Pennsylvania.)

2. Selection and Calibration of Thermocouples

Thermocouples obviously must be sufficiently durable for repeated use as temperature indicators in steam sterilization validation and monitoring. Copperconstantan wires coated with Teflon are a popular choice as thermocouple monitors, although several other types are available.

Accuracy of thermocouples should be ±0.5°C. Temperature accuracy is especially important in steam sterilization validation because an error of just 0.1°C in temperature measured by a faulty thermocouple will produce a 2.3% error in the calculated F_0 value. Thermocouple accuracy is determined using NBS traceable constant temperature calibration instruments such as those shown in Fig. 6. Thermocouples should be calibrated before and after a validation experiment at two temperatures: 0°C and 125°C. The newer temperature-recording devices are capable of automatically correcting temperature or slight errors in the thermocouple calibration. Any thermocouple that senses temperature more than 0.5°C away from the calibration temperature bath should be discarded. Stricter limits, i.e., <0.5°C, may be imposed according to the user's experience and expectations.

Figure 6 Modern equipment employed in the calibration of thermocouples used in sterilizer validation studies. (Courtesy of Kaye Instruments, Inc., 15 De Angelo Drive, Bedford, Massachusetts.)

Temperature recorders should be capable of printing temperature data in 0.1°C increments.

3. Selection and Calibration of BI

The organism most resistant to steam heat is the bacterial spore former *B. stearothermophilus*. Other indicator organisms have been employed, but *B. stearothermophilus* spores are by far the most commonly used BIs in validating steam sterilization cycles.

Since the main purpose of BIs is to assure that a minimum F_0 value has been achieved in the coolest location of the autoclave load, the D_{121} and Z values of the BI must be accurately known. Whether BIs have been prepared by the manufacturer or purchased commercially, laboratory D values must be calculated [29].

Spore strips or spore suspensions are used in the validation studies. The number of microorganisms per strip or per ml of suspension must be as accurately known as the D value.

Precautions should be taken to use proper storage conditions for *B. stearo-*

thermophilus BIs. Storing in the freezer appears to provide a more stable resistance profile for the shelf life of the indicator [30].

If one knows the D value, the BI concentration or population (A), and the desired probability level of nonsterility (B), the minimum F_0 value that must be achieved by the sterilization cycle for the particular load can be calculated. For example, if $A = 10^6$ and $B = 10^{-6}$, and laboratory studies determine the D value for *B. stearothermophilus* in the product to be sterilized to be 0.4 min ($F_0 = 0.4(12) = 4.8$ min), a minimum F_0 value of 4.8 min should be achieved at the worst-case location during heat-penetration studies. The USP XXII requires a steam sterilization process to deliver an F_0 value of 8, unless experimental data prove the adequacy of cycles providing F_0 values less than 8.

C. Heat-Distribution Studies

Heat-distribution studies include two phases: 1) heat distribution in an empty autoclave chamber and 2) heat distribution in a loaded auto-clave chamber. Between 10 and 20 thermocouples should be used per cycle. Thermocouples should be secured inside the chamber according to a definite arrangement (e.g., see Fig. 7); Teflon tape can be used to secure thermocouples. The trips where the wires are soldered should not make contact with the autoclave interior walls or any metal surface. One thermocouple each should remain in an ice bath and high-temperature oil bath during each cycle for reference when the temperature-monitoring equipment has the capability for electronically compensating each temperature measurement against an internal reference. Heat-distribution studies following the initial study may employ fewer thermocouples as the cool spot in the

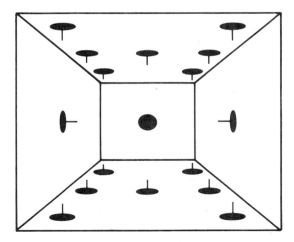

Figure 7 Suggested locations for thermocouples on a single shelf for heat-distribution studies in heat sterilizers.

chamber and in the load is identified. The key is to identify, on a reproducible basis, the location of the cool spot and the effect of the load size and/or configuration on the cool spot location. Most experts suggest the study of the minimum and maximum load size in the proper configuration in elucidating where the cool spot is located.

The difference in temperature between the coolest spot and the mean chamber temperature should be not greater than ±2.5°C [7].* Greater temperature differences may be indicative of equipment malfunction.

D. Heat-Penetration Studies

This is the most critical component of the entire validation process. The success of a validated cycle depends on determining the F_0 value of the cold spot inside the commodity located at the cool spot previously determined from heat-distribution studies. The container cold spot for containers ≥100 ml is determined using container-mapping studies. Thermocouple probes are inserted within a container and repeat cycles are run to establish the point inside the container that is coldest most of the time. It is this exact point which is monitored during heat-penetration studies.

Again, the minimum and maximum loading configurations should be studied. Thermocouples will be placed both inside and outside the container at the cool spot location(s), in the steam exhaust line, and in constant-temperature baths outside the chamber. The F_0 value will be calculated based on the temperature recorded by the thermocouple inside the container at the coolest area of the load. Upon completion of the cycle, the F_0 value will indicate whether the cycle is adequate or if alterations must be made. Following the attainment of the desired time-temperature cycle, cycles are repeated until the user is satisfied with the repeatability aspects of the cycle validation process. Statistical analysis of the F_0 values achieved at each repeated cycle may be conducted to verify the consistency of the process and the confidence limits for achieving the desired F_0 value.

Pflug [31] claims there are three critical times associated with all wet heat sterilization processes:

1.   A minimum F value
2.   A design F value
3.   A sterilization process time

The minimum F value is based only on microbial spore destruction. It is believed that F_0 = 8 min is a realistic minimum value, since most mesophilic spore-forming microorganigms have D values ≤ 0.5 min at 121°C. Even if D_{121} = 1.0 min, the spore log reduction value according the Eq. (10) would be 8.

---

*In fact, a difference ≥1.0°C gives rise to the suspicion of air-stream mixtures in the chamber.

The F value used in the design of a sterile cycle may greatly exceed the minimum F_0 of 8. An $F_0 = 12$ min will provide a 50% safety factor that will take into account additional time that may be required for steam to penetrate certain containers in middle or cool locations of the autoclave.

The sterilization process time is determined from the design F value and the product heat transfer data. The sterilization cycle design must be based on the heating characteristics of the load and of containers located in the slowest heating zone of the load. The variation in the rate of heating of the slowest heating zone must be known, so this variation must be determined under fully loaded conditions. The effect of load-to-load variation on the time-temperature profile must also be determined. Then, the statistically worst-case conditions should be used in the final sterilization process design.

The final step in steam sterilization validation is the establishment of a monitoring program to ensure that the validated cycle remains essentially unchanged in the future. Cycle monitoring usually involves the use of thermocouples to measure heat penetration at the cool spot location and to verify that the design F_0 value has been reached.

Any changes in the load size, load configuration, or container characteristics (volume, geometry, etc.) must be accompanied by repeat validation studies to prove that the cool spot location has not changed or, if it has, that it receives the design F_0 time exposure from the sterilization cycle used.

V. VALIDATION OF DRY-HEAT STERILIZATION CYCLES

A. General Considerations

Two types of dry-heat sterilization systems are utilized in the pharmaceutical industry today. They are the conventional hot air oven and the tunnel system. The major difference between the two systems, as far as validation is concerned, is the belt or line speed variable with the tunnel system.

The key to validating a dry-heat sterilizer is to prove its repeatability. This means that the unit can consistently perform under a given set of conditions to generate materials that are sterile, pyrogen free, and particulate free. Repeatability in dry-heat sterilization obviously involves consistency and reliability in attaining and maintaining a desired temperature. The desired temperature must be reached in all areas of the heating chamber. There will always be an area in the chamber that represents a cold spot, that is, an area that is most difficult to heat up to the desired temperature. This cold spot must be identified so that validation studies involving thermocouple monitoring and microbial challenges can be done at this location. If certain key GMP features of the dry-heat sterilizer are not controlled, with time the cold spot within the sterilizer will change and the key element of validation repeatability cannot be achieved. Simmons [32,33] has discussed the

Table 5 Key Process Features to Control Prior to
Validating Dry-Heat Sterilizers

Batch (oven)	Tunnel sterilizer
Intake air system	Positive pressure to entrance
Exhaust air system	Even distribution of heat
Internal air circulation	Belt speed recorder
Exhaust HEPA filter	HEPA filtered cooling air
Static pressure gauge	Exhaust HEPA filter
Heater current	Heater current
	Particulate control

GMP features of both the batch oven and tunnel sterilizer that must be controlled *before* doing any validation studies. These are listed in Tables 5 and 6. Without control of these processes, as Simmons has clearly stated, validating or even qualifying a dry-heat sterilizer is a total waste of time and money.

As with any sterilization process, the first step in dry-heat sterilizer validation involves qualification of all the equipment and instrumentation used. This step includes examination and documentation of all utilities, duct work, filters, and

Table 6 Basic Equipment Performances That Must Be Verified Prior to
Calibration-Validation Studies

Function	Dry heat process			
	Convection batch	Convection continuous	Conduction batch	Radiant continuous
Electrical logic	×	×	×	×
Cycle set point adjustment	×	×	×	×
Vibration analysis	×	×	×	×
Blower rotation	×	×	×	×
Blower rpm	×	×	×	×
Heater elements	×	×	×	×
Air balance	×	×	×	×
Air balance ability	×	×	×	×
Door interlocks	×			
Commodity interlocks		×		
Gasket integrity	×	×		
HEPA filter integrity	×	×		×
Belt speed		×		×
Heat shields			×	×

control valves or switches for the oven or tunnel unit, and the calibration of the instrumentation used in validating and monitoring the process. Instruments used are [33]:

1. Temperature recorders and thermocouples
2. Constant-temperature baths
3. Amp meters
4. Monometers
5. Dioctylphthalate generators
6. Particle counters
7. Velometers
8. Tachometers

Calibration should be conducted on a regular interval basis. Simmons [33] recommends a regular calibration interval of every 3 months.

Validation studies conducted on dry-heat sterilizers can be divided into two basic components. One component envelops all the physical processes, which must be validated, such as temperature control, air particulate levels, and belt speeds. The other component is the biological constituent, which would involve studies that prove the process destroys both microbial and pyrogenic contaminants.

B.   Batch Oven Validation

1. Air balance determination. In an empty oven, data are obtained on the flow rates of both intake and exhaust air. Air should be balanced so that (a) positive pressure is exerted to the nonsterile side when the door is opened and (b) air velocity across and up and down the opening of the door is ±50 FPM of the average velocity (measured 6 inches from the side wall on the air supply wall).
2. Heat distribution of an empty chamber. Thermocouples should be situated according to a specific predetermined pattern. Repeatability of temperature attainment and identification of the cold spot can be achieved if the temperature range is ±15°C at all monitored locations. Heat-distribution studies can also be conducted as a function of variable air flow rates through the hood ducts and as a function of the gas flow rate to the sterilizing burners. A suggested thermocouple placement pattern per shelf in an empty oven is presented in Fig. 7.
3. Heat-penetration studies. These studies should be designed to determine the location of the slowest heating point *within* a commodity at various locations of a test load in the sterilizer. The test load should be the maximum size of load anticipated. Thermocouples are placed in the commodities located in the areas likely to present the greatest resistance to reaching the desired temperature. Minimum and maximum temperatures as defined in the process specifications should be studied. Normally, three replicate cycles are run at

each temperature. The cold spot must not move during the replicate studies. Firm identification of the most difficult location for heat to penetrate will represent the area to be used for the biological challenge studies. Other variations in the cycle affecting heat penetration at the cold spot can be studied, and these might include (a) test load variations, (b) temperature set point variations, and (c) variations in the time of exposure.

4. Mechanical repeatability. During all these studies, mechanical repeatability in terms of air velocity, temperature consistency, and reliability and sensitivity of all the oven and instrumental controls must be verified.

C. Tunnel Sterilizer Validation

Principles as described above for the physical process validation of batch ovens apply also in the validation of tunnel sterilizers; however, in addition to the variables affecting batch oven validation, tunnel sterilizers have an extra variable-belt speed. This variable can be held constant by maintaining the same belt speed throughout the validation process and not changing it after validation has been completed.

1. Air Balance Determination

Proper and even air balance is more critical to a tunnel sterile process than a batch oven process. Since the items being sterilized are moving, they are exposed to different air systems, e.g., heating zone and cooling zone. Air flow must be balanced in order to provide a gradual decrease in air temperature as items move along the conveyor. In the absence of a critical balance of air dynamics, either the items will not be cooled sufficiently once they exit the tunnel or they will be cooled too quickly, causing the glass to shatter and contaminate the entire tunnel area with particles. In fact, the major problem in validating tunnel sterilizers is the control of particles. Not only are the items exposed to great extremes in temperature, but also the conveyor belt is a natural source of particulates because metal is moving against metal.

Adjustments in the air source should be made to obtain a controlled flow of air within the tunnel and across the entrance and exit openings. Air must be particulate-free as it enters the tunnel area; therefore, all HEPA filters in the tunnel must be DOP tested and certified prior to validation studies.

2. Heat-Distribution Studies

Thermocouples used in tunnel sterilizer validation must be sufficiently durable to withstand the extremely high ($\geqslant 300°C$) temperatures in the heating zone area of the tunnel. Heat-distribution studies should determine where the cold spots are located as a function of the width of the belt and height of the tunnel chamber. Trays or racks of ampules or vials should be run through the tunnel and thermocouples placed at strategic locations among the containers.

Bottle-mapping studies may also be conducted during this phase [32]. The purpose of these studies is to determine possible locations inside the container that are most difficult to heat. The loading configuration should be identical to what will be used in production cycles. The major difficulty in doing these studies is the avoidance of thermocouple wire hang-ups. Thermocouples must be long enough to be transported through the entire tunnel. A special harness for thermocouple wires should be constructed for feeding these wires into and throughout the tunnel.

Repeatability of the thermal process must be demonstrated during these studies. Peak temperature readings should remain within ±10°C across the belt for at least three replicate runs.

3. Heat-Penetration Studies

Prior to microbial challenge testing of the tunnel sterilization, heat-penetration studies must be completed in order to identify the coolest container in the entire load. Results of heat-distribution studies should aid in predicting where the coolest location within the load should be. Thermocouples should be deposited at or near the coolest point inside the container as determined previously from bottle-mapping studies. Normally, the coolest point inside the container is at the juncture of the bottom of the container and the sidewall. The container inner surface should be in contact with the thermocouple tip because the objective is to sterilize the inner walls of the container, as well as the inner space.

Three to five replicate runs for each commodity size and every loading configuration should be done using 10 to 20 thermocouples distributed throughout the load. Careful analysis of the temperature data after each run will be invaluable in the determination of the cool spot and the repeatability of the process using the minimum number of replicate runs.

4. Mechanical Repeatability

Tunnel sterilizers must demonstrate mechanical repeatability in the same manner as batch ovens. Air velocity, air particulates, temperature consistency, and reliability of all the tunnel controls (heat zone temperatures, belt speed, and blower functions) must be proved during the physical validation studies.

D. Biological Process Validation of Dry-Heat Sterilization Cycles

If a dry-heat process is claimed to produce sterile commodities, microorganisms known to be most resistant to dry heat must be used to prove the ability of the dry-heat cycle to destroy them at the coolest location in the load. If the dry-heat process is claimed to produce both sterile and pyrogen-free commodities, validation studies must be done using both microorganisms and microbial endotoxins. It is the strong opinion of many, including the authors, that biological validation of dry-heat cycles should be based on the destruction of endotoxin rather than on the destruction of microorganisms because of the enormous dry heat resistance of endotoxin compared to microorganisms [34]. To satisfy the FDA, however, microbial challenges continue to be done.

With both microorganism and endotoxin challenges, the cool spot identified in the heat-distribution and heat-penetration studies will be the logical location to run the microbial challenge tests. Containers inoculated with microbial cells or endotoxin will be situated adjacent to identical containers into which thermocouples are secured to monitor temperature. Temperature profiles must not deviate from temperature data obtained in earlier studies.

The goal of the biological validation process depends on the nature of the process. If the process is intended to sterilize only, the probability of survival approach is used. In this case, validation studies must determine a dry-heat cycle that will assure that the probability of survival of the microbial indicator is not greater than 10^{-6}. If the process is intended to sterilize and depyrogenate, which occurs when the materials can withstand excessive heat, the overkill approach is used. The goal here is to validate a heating cycle which can produce a 12-log reduction in the biological indicator population.

Equations that apply for determining log reductions or survival probabilities as Eq. (11) and (12), respectively. Information that must be known prior to initiating biological validations include the D value of the biological indicator to be used, the change in its heat resistance as temperature is changed (Z value), and the presterilization microbial load on the commodity being sterilized. Methods for obtaining these values have been adequately described with ample references in the Parenteral Drug Association technical report on dry heat validation [13].

The most widely used biological indicators for dry heat have been spores of *B. subtilis*; however, spores of other bacterial species may be used if they are shown to have greater resistance to dry heat. At 170°C, even the most resistant microbial spore form will have a D value of 6 to 10 min. At temperatures required to depyrogenate, microbial spores will have D values of only a few seconds.

The acceptable Z value for microbial dry-heat resistance is 20°C [13]. This value is used primarily in programming computerized temperature-detection devices, which take temperature data from thermocouple monitors and compute F values as seen with Eq. (6). The Z value used for endotoxin dry-heat resistance is 54°C [34]. The greater Z value for endotoxin demonstrates the greater resistance of endotoxin to dry heat.

A suggested step-by-step sequence in the microbial validation of a dry-heat process for sterilizing and depyrogenating large volume glass containers by a convection batch oven is presented. Procedures for the validation of a tunnel sterilization process have been reported by Wegel [35] and Akers et al. [36].

1.   The overkill approach is selected for the validation study. This eliminates the need for bioburden and resistance studies. The objective is to ensure that the coolest area in the loading pattern, as determined in earlier heat-penetration

and heat-distribution studies, receives sufficient heat to cause a 12-log reduction in the biological indicator chosen.
2. Select the type of biological indicator to be used in monitoring process lethality. Calibrate the biological indicator in its carrier medium (strip or suspension).
3. Place spore carrier in approximately 12 glass bottles located at the previously determined coolest area of the oven. Bottles adjacent to the inoculated bottles should contain thermocouples for monitoring purposes.
4. Run a complete cycle using the desired loading pattern for future dry-heat overkill cycles.
5. After the cycle, aseptically transfer the spore strip to vessels of culture media. If spore suspensions were used, aseptically transfer the inoculated bottles to a laminar air flow work station and add culture media to the bottles. Use appropriate positive and negative controls.
6. Determine the number of survivors by plate-counting or fraction negative methods [13].
7. Use Eq. (10) to determine the number of spore log reductions (SLRs):

$$SLR = \frac{F_{170}}{D_{170}}$$

As described in the PDA Technical Report No. 3, p. 48 [13], the overkill approach usually yields extremely high F values. A minimum F value can be estimated by assuming one positive unit. In this case, if 12 challenge bottles were used and if it is assumed that $D_{170} = 1.5$ min, $Z = 20°C$, $A = 1 \times 10^8$, and $B = 12/11$ then

$$F = D_{170}(\log A - 2.303 \log B)$$
$$F = 1.5(8 - 0.087)$$
$$F = 11.87 \text{ min}$$

Therefore, an equivalent time exposure at 170°C of 11.87 min will produce an SLR value of

$$SLR = \frac{11.87}{1.5} = 7.9$$

If an SLR of 12 were desirable, the process cycle would be extended to achieve an F_{170} value of at least

$$F_{170} = 1.5(12) = 18 \text{ min}$$

If a temperature of 200°C were used and thermocouples located at the coolest area of the load showed that the bottle interior equaled 200°C or greater for 15 minutes, the F_{170} value would be at least:

$$F_{170} = 15 \times 10^{[(200-170)/20]} = 474 \text{ min}$$

It is because of these enormous F_{170} values obtained during overkill cycles that several experts strongly advocate the use of endotoxin challenge studies instead of microbial tests.

E. Endotoxin Challenge in the Validation of Dry-Heat Sterilizers

The most controversial aspect of endotoxin challenge testing is how much endotoxin challenge to use. The PDA [13] suggests using a level of endotoxin in excess of the level expected in the item being subjected to the dry-heat cycle. Simmons [33] suggests the use of 10,000 ng endotoxin. Akers et al. [37] used only 10 ng endotoxin.

Another unresolved aspect of validation based on endotoxin destruction is the extraction of dried endotoxin from the commodity for testing by the limulus amebocyte lysate (LAL) test. Studies must verify that endotoxin placed in containers being dry-heat sterilized can be extracted quantitatively. Otherwise, false-negative LAL tests will be suspected.

The step-by-step procedure for the endotoxin validation of a dry-heat process may be as follows:

1. Inoculate commodity samples with a known amount of endotoxin, e.g., 10–100 ng *Escherichia coli* lipopolysaccharide, obtainable from several commercial sources. The endotoxin should be contained in a volume of water equal to the residual water volume following the washing procedure used prior to sterilization.
2. Thermocouples should be placed in commodities adjacent to those containing endotoxin for temperature monitoring and correlation with LAL test results.
3. Endotoxin destruction should be ascertained at the coolest location of the load. Load configurations should be identical to those used in the microbial validation studies.
4. Several endotoxin challenge samples should be done per cycle, and the studies must be adequately replicated (3–5 repeats).
5. Following the dry-heat cycle, aseptically transfer the units, containing endotoxin to an aseptic area for extraction procedures, sampling, and conducting the LAL test. Sampling procedures and LAL test methodology have been described elsewhere [38,39].
6. *F* values required for endotoxin destruction at various temperatures and/or cycle time-temperature variations can be determined using a Z value of 54°C [34] and the following equation:

$$F_{endo.} = \Delta t \sum 10^{(T-170)/54}$$

This approach was used by Akers et al. [37].

When the validation studies described in this section have been completed, all data are analyzed and a decision is made concerning their acceptability. If acceptable, the entire validation procedure and all appropriate supporting data are documented in a bound manual. If the studies are unacceptable, because of unsubstantiated claims of the process or lack of reproducibility, further testing must be performed or process variables changed followed by additional validation studies.

The final document will be reviewed and approved by various plant disciplines—engineering, microbiology, production etc.—before the dry-heat sterilizer is considered fully validated and released for use.

VI. VALIDATION OF ETHYLENE OXIDE STERILIZATION CYCLES

Ethylene oxide (EtO) has been a sterilant for over 40 years. Yet, while much attention in the literature has been focused on validation of heat sterilization cycles, EtO cycle validation has received relatively little attention. Undoubtedly, a major reason is the inability to define accurately the kinetics of microbial death upon exposure to EtO. This is a result of the complexity of the process, in which not one but three variables—heat, EtO concentration, and relative humidity—must be controlled in order to determine D values of microorganisms when considering EtO sterilization.

The discussion of EtO validation in this section reflects largely what has been written on this subject since 1977. Several good references [40–44] have significantly contributed to the rationale, design, and implementation of validation programs for EtO sterilization cycles.

Five variables are critical to the EtO process. They are EtO concentration, relative humidity, temperature, time, and pressure/vacuum. Temperature is the easiest variable to measure and monitor. Therefore, temperature is used as the indicator of the worst-case location within the loaded EtO sterilizer. Once the worst-case location is identified, the validation studies are conducted with the goal of inactivating a known concentration of indicator microorganisms in the worst-case location using a specific loading pattern with a specific EtO cycle with all variables defined and controlled.

The procedure for EtO cycle validation can be described in eight steps:

1. Address the products specifications and package design. What is the chemical nature of the components of the product? Do there exist long and/or narrow lumens that will represent barriers to EtO permeation? How dense are the materials through which EtO gas must permeate? What is the nature of the primary and secondary packaging? Where are dead air spaces within the package and within the load? By addressing questions such as these, the problems in validating the EtO cycle can be anticipated and solved at an early stage in the validation process.

2. Use a laboratory-sized EtO sterilizer during early phases of the validation process as long as the sterilizer is equipped with devices allowing variability in vacuum, relative humidity, temperature, gas pressure, timing, and rate of gassing the chamber. Involve production sterilizer experts in these early phases of the EtO validation process.

3. Verify the calibration of all instrumentation involved in monitoring the EtO cycle. Examples include thermocouple and pressure gauge calibration, gas leak testing equipment, relative humidity sensors, and gas chromatographic instrumentation.

4. Perform an extensive temperature distribution study using an empty sterilizer. Identify the zones of temperature extremes; then use these locations for monitoring during loaded vessel runs. Monitoring will be accomplished using both thermocouples and biological indicator spore strips. The most common biological indicator for EtO cycle validation is *B. subtilis* var. *niger*. Concentration of these spores per strip usually is 10^6. Significant spore survival results will indicate the need to increase the cycle lethality parameters. It is also prudent to analyze gas concentration at periodic intervals during the distribution studies.

5. Do a series of repetitive runs for each sterilization cycle in an empty vessel in order to verify the accuracy and reliability of the sterilizer controls and monitoring equipment. Thermocouple locations should be basically the same for all the heat-distribution studies.

6. Do a series of repetitive heat-distribution and heat-penetration runs using a loaded EtO sterilizer. The sterilizer should be an industrial unit in order to ascertain the cycle requirements that will yield consistent and reliable assurance that all components of the load will be sterile. The validation procedure should include data collected on both partial- and full-load sizes. The loading design should be defined at this point. Dummy loads closely resembling the actual packaging can be used to test cyclic parameters. Thermocouples and biological indicators should be placed in a statistically designed format throughout the load, including areas within the dummy packaged products. The number of loading patterns, repetitive runs, and the daily timing sequence of events should all be based upon prior knowledge and experience. At this point and before proceeding further, the data should verify the following questions:

    a. What is the concentration of EtO released into the vessel?
    b. What is the concentration of water vapor in the vessel?
    c. What is the range of temperature distribution throughout the loaded vessel?
    d. How much EtO is consumed during the cycle?
    e. What are the rates of creating a vacuum and applying pressure?
    f. What D value should be used for the biological indicator employed?

g. Does the selected cycle sterilize the product, and what is the estimated probability of nonsterility?

7. Tests should be conducted on the final packaged product. The protocol applied should be one that leads to minimal interruption of the standard manufacturing operations of the facility. Intermediate pilot plant studies should be carried out to simulate large-scale industrial sterilization cycles. The EtO cycle documentation should be integrated into a single protocol. An example of one protocol is as follows:

a. Use approximately 10 biological indicators per 100 cubic feet of chamber space.

b. Place these indicators throughout the load along with thermocouples at the same locations.

c. Use at least three sublethal exposure cycle times, each in triplicate; then define the required EtO exposure times using D value calculations. The exposure time should be increased by an additional 50% to add a safety factor.

d. Perform three or more fully loaded sterilization cycles at the selected exposure time, monitoring these cycles with thermocouples and biological indicators.

e. Concomitantly, perform EtO residual tests on the materials exposed to the desired exposure cycle times from full-load runs.

8. Institute a documented monitoring system primarily relying on biological indicators with lesser reliance on end-product sterility testing.

VII. VALIDATION OF RADIATION STERILIZATION PROCESS

The major objective in validating a radiation sterilization process, regardless of whether the mode of radiation is cobalt-60, cesium-136, or electron beam, is to determine the D value of the indicator microorganism used to monitor the process. With radiation sterilization, the D value is defined as the dose of radiation in Mrads necessary to produce a 90% reduction in the number of indicator microbial cells. The D value depends on such factors as temperature, moisture, organism species, oxygen tension, and the chemical environment and/or physical surface on which the indicator microorganism is present. D values of different organism species in different suspending media are summarized in Table 7 [45].

Bacillus pumilus spores at the USP XXII choice as the biological indicator for radiation sterilization. If a probability of nonsterility of 10^{-6} is specified for a system sterilized by radiation and the D value of *B. pumilus* in that system is 0.20 Mrad, a radiation dose of 1.2 Mrads would produce a 6-log reduction in the concentration of *B. pumilus* spores. Greater probability allowances (e.g., 10^{-3}) would permit lower radiation doses.

A five-step approach to use in the development of radiation sterilization

Table 7 Radiation Resistivities (Expressed as *D* Values) of Various Microorganisms

Species	*D* value (Mrad)	Presence of a "shoulder" (Mrad)	Medium
Anaerobic spore formers			
Clostridium botulinum[a]			
Type A NCTC 7272	0.12	0.9–1.0	Water
Type B 213	0.11	0.9–1.0	Water
Type D	0.22	0.25–0.35	Water
Type E Beluga	0.08	0.25–0.35	Water
Type F	0.25	0.25–0.35	Water
Clostridium sporogenes[a]			
PA 3679/S2	0.22	0.25–0.35	Water
NCTC 532	0.16	0.25–0.35	Water
Clostridium welchii (*perfringens*)[a]			
Type A	0.12	0.25–0.35	Water
Type B	0.17	0.25–0.35	Water
Type F	0.20	0.25–0.35	Water
Clostridium tetani[a]	0.24	0.25–0.35	Water
Aerobic spore formers			
Bacillus subtilis[b]	0.06	—	Saline + 5% gelatin
Bacillus pumilus E 601[c]	0.17	1.1	Water
Vegetative bacteria			
Salmonella typhimurium R 6008[d]	0.13	0.4	Phosphate buffer
Escherichia coli[e]	0.009	—	Phosphate buffer
Pseudomonas species[d]	0.003–0.006	—	Phosphate buffer
Staphylococcus aureus[e]	0.02	—	Phosphate buffer
Molds			
Aspergillus niger[b]	0.047	—	Saline + 5% gelatin

[a]Roberts, T. A., and Ingram, M., *J. Food Sci. 30*:879 (1965)
[b]Lawrence, C. A., Brownell, L. E., and Graikoski, J. T., *Nucleonics 11*:9 (1953).
[c]Van Winkle, W., Borick, P. M., Fogarty, M., in *Radiosterilization of Medical Products*, IAEA, Vienna (1967).
[d]Thornley, M. J., IAEA Tech. Rept. Series 22 (1963).
[e]Bellamy, W. D., and Lawton, E. J., *Ann. N.Y. Acad. Sci. 59*:595 (1955).
Source: Adapted from Ref. 45.

cycles has been proposed by the Health Industry Manufacturers Association (HIMA) [46]:

1. Determine microbial load on preirradiated products.
2. Determine the D value for natural flora on the product.
3. Determine the D value using biological indicators on the product to make certain that the natural flora are not more radioresistant than the biological indicator.
4. Determine the D value of biological indicator spore strips placed within the product. Determine the location of the lowest radiation dose point within the product. Then determine the dosage required for a 10^{-6} probability of nonsterility for the product.
5. Determine whether the D value for the biological indicator varies as a function of the dose rate. With cobalt-60, dose rate differences are not of much concern (variance of 0.1–0.5 Mrad/h), whereas electron beam sterilization might produce dose rate variances of several Mrads per minute!

The microbiological studies above are conducted to establish the appropriate dose level to be used to sterilize each specific product or commodity to an acceptable level of statistical nonsterility. These studies should be conducted following qualification of the irradiation facility. HIMA [46] has suggested major items to be included in the qualification phase of the validation scheme for radiation sterilizer installation:

1. Specifications of the irradiator equipment—description, materials used, instrumentation, etc.
2. Drawings of the equipment and the entire facility
3. Licensing agreement and supporting documentation from both the Atomic Energy Commission and the appropriate state
4. Reliability and calibration of the dosimeter system
5. Radiation source strength when the sterilization cycle is validated through D value determination
6. Speed of conveyor belt
7. Dose rate

If it is assumed that the radiation sterilizer equipment and facilities have been qualified and microbiological studies have been conducted as outlined above, the next step in the validation process is the complete evaluation of the radiation sterilization cycle. Tests are conducted to determine the effect of minimum and maximum product density on the ability of the minimum or nominal radiation dose, determined during the microbiological studies to produce a given log reduction in the biological indicator population, to sterilize the load. For example, it was found that a 0.2-Mrad dose of cobalt-60 will produce a 1-log reduction in the population of *B. pumilus*. The microbial load of a one-package polyvinyl chloride (PVC) device (intravenous administration site) was estimated to be approximately 1000. A probability of a nonsterility level of 10^{-6} is desired. Therefore, theoretically, the minimum dose necessary to produce a 9-log reduction in the microbial population is 1.8 Mrad.

Validation tests must be conducted in such a manner that the following questions are answered:

1. Is the nominal radiation dose sufficient to destroy *B. pumilus* spore samples at relatively high concentration (e.g., 10^8 spores per ml or per strip) using a minimum load of product (minimum density)?
2. Is the nominal radiation dose sufficient to destroy *B. pumilus* spore samples at relatively high concentration (e.g., 10^8 spores per ml or per strip) using a maximum load of product (maximum density)?
3. What is the radiation sterilization efficiency; that is, how much of the applied dose is actually absorbed by the product?
4. What is the isodose profile for each irradiated item; that is, what is the dose of radiation absorbed, as a function of the location within the product being irradiated? What is the radio between the highest and lowest doses absorbed within the product?
5. What is the effect of conveyor loading conditions and line speeds on the amount of radiation absorbed?

As these questions are answered, adjustments probably will be made in the process. For example, it might be concluded that a higher radiation dose is required for adequate exposure to all points of a particularly large and/or dense container system. The loading size or pattern may have to be reduced to permit adequate sterilization at a given dose level. Once all process parameters have been defined through preliminary testing, the tedious but essential task of proving consistency, repeatability, and reliability of the radiation sterilization cycle must be established. Test records, data work sheets, and monitoring systems schedules must be kept and organized for easy retrieval and analysis.

While radiation sterilization cycles are validated based upon the achievement of sterility, many other factors must be considered in the utilization and approval of the radiation sterilization process. Such factors include the effect of irradiation on 1) the physical appearance of the container system and its contents, 2) stability of the active ingredient, if present, and 3) safety of the irradiated material.

VIII. VALIDATION OF STERILIZING FILTERS

A. Introduction to Filtration

The following definitions will be helpful in using this section. *When filter is used as a verb* "to filter," it means to pass a solid-liquid mixture through a permeable medium to cause a separation of the two. *Filter when used as a noun* refers to a device for carrying out filtration, and it consists of the filter medium and a suitable holder for constraining and supporting it in the fluid path. The permeable material that separates solid particles from the liquid being filtered is called the *filter medium*. The *unit operation of filtration*, then, is the separation of solids from a liquid by passage through a filter medium. In many instances, the filter, including the permeable medium; the means for passing liquid through the medium; and the process piping are all referred to by the term *filter system*.

In general, filtration objectives can be separated into four basic categories: to save solids and reject liquids, to save liquids and reject solids, to save both liquids and solids, and to reject both liquids and solids [47].

As a filtration process proceeds, generally under an applied driving force of pressure, solids are removed by and begin to accumulate on the filter medium. The liquid portion continues to move through the filter medium and out of the filter system. The separated liquid is referred to as the *filtrate*. The amount of pressure applied to accomplish the filtration depends on the filtration resistance. *Filtration resistance* is a result of the frictional drag on the filtrate as it passes through the filter medium and the accumulated solids. In equation form,

$$\text{Filtration rate} = \frac{\text{pressure}}{\text{resistance}} \tag{13}$$

Permeability is often referred to as a measure of liquid flow through a filter system and is the reciprocal of the filtration resistance.

During filtration, as the particulate buildup continues on the filtration medium, the filtration resistance increases, or, in other words, the filtration permeability decreases. The capacity of a system, expressed in time, volume of liquid fed, or amount of solids fed, depends on the ability of the system to maintain acceptable permeability.

When operating a filtration system, it is important to note the following general relationship:

$$\text{Retention} \times \text{permeability} = \text{constant} \tag{14}$$

Therefore, in attempting to have a certain degree of filtration efficiency or retention, a high rate of filtration, and the lowest possible cost, it is necessary to make a compromise with one or more of the above factors. A high permeability or low resistance for large filtration flow rates requires a filter medium of low retention efficiency. A highly efficient retention will have low permeability, low flow rates, and higher filtration costs.

B. Sterile Filtration

Production of parenteral drugs requires that the product be sterile. In many cases, terminal sterilization by heat, ethylene oxide gas, or ionizing radiation is used to render a product sterile; however, certain products are not stable when exposed to heat, gas, or radiation, and they must be sterilized by other means. Filtrative sterilization is suitable in such cases. Indeed, the practice of sterile filtration is not limited to labile preparations. Unlike the other forms of sterilization, filtration sterilizes by the removal of the bacteria from the product rather than by inducing a lethality to the microorganism. Filtration is straightforward and reliable; it removes particulate matter other than microbiological; it avoids possible pyrogenicity owing to the presence of dead bacteria in the dosage form; it is cost effective and energy efficient; and it allows convenient and flexible manufacturing systems and schedules with low capital investment [48].

Sterile filtration processes are employed to sterile-filter a product prior to filling it aseptically into its final containers. Bulk drug solutions are sterile-filtered prior to aseptic crystallization, thus eliminating the possibility of having organisms within the bulk drug crystals. The bulk drug can then be processed into a dosage form aseptically or further processed to be terminally sterilized. Other filtrative operations reduce the organism content of a final product prior to terminal sterilizations [49].

As noted earlier, a highly efficient retentive media will have low permeability, low flow rates, and higher filtration costs than other less retentive filter media. The highly retentive filter media used for sterilization have a short useful life because they clog very easily. Consequently, most filtration processes cannot be efficiently or economically carried out without the use of prefiltration. Prefiltration filter media are used to protect and thus lengthen the useful life of the final membrane filter media by collecting the bulk of the particulate material so that the membrane filter media must filter out only a small portion of the particulate. Prefiltration media are normally depth-filter media having a relatively wide pore and size distribution. A properly selected prefilter must meet the following conditions: 1) it must be retentive enough to protect the final membrane filter medium; 2) the prefilter assembly must not allow fluid bypass under any condition; 3) the prefilter system must be designed to make use of the prefilter medium; 4) it must have the best retention efficiency (with depth-filter media low pressure differentials and low fluid flux, accomplished by a multielement parallel design, are best); and 5) the prefilter medium must be compatible with the solution and not leach components into the solution or absorb components from the solution [50]. One note of caution needs to be mentioned in reference to lengthening membrane filter media life. Organism grow-through can become a problem if filtration takes place over an extended period of time. During filtration, bacteria continuously reproduce by cell division and eventually find their way through the filter medium to contaminate the filtrate. For this reason, the USP states that prolonged filtration must be avoided [51], and the proposed current good manufacturing practices for large-volume parenterals state that final filtration of solutions shall not exceed 8 hours [52].

Sterilization by filtration is a major unit operation used in aseptic processes. Aseptic processes require the presterilization of all components of the drug product and its container. Then all of the components are brought together in a controlled aseptic environment to create the finished sterile product sealed within its container/closure system. The level of sterility attained by an aseptic procedure is a cumulative function of all the process steps involved in making the product. Therefore, the final level of sterility assurance for such a product cannot be greater than the step providing the lowest probability of sterility. Each step in the aseptic process must be validated to known levels of sterility assurance.

This part of the chapter will concentrate on that portion of the aseptic process wherein the drug product is sterilized by filtration. From the earlier discussion, sterile filtration is perhaps a misnomer, since the "sterile" filtrate is almost always processed further under aseptic conditions, which involves a risk of contamination [53]. Therefore, to speak of drug product sterilization by filtration as being as final a processing step as the steam sterilization of a product could possibly lead to erroneous assurances or assumptions. Since a sterile filtrate can be produced by filtration, however, we will continue to refer to the process as product sterilization by filtration.

The primary objective of a sterilizing filter is to remove microorganisms. The filter medium used to accomplish such an efficient retention may be classified as one of two types—the reusable type or the disposable type.

The reusable filter media are made of sintered glass, unglazed porcelain, or diatomaceous earth (Table 8). Because these filter media may be used repeatedly without being destroyed, they are less costly; however, the use of reusable filter media demands that the media be cleaned perfectly and sterilized prior to use to prevent microbial contamination and chemical cross-contamination. Even after exacting and painstaking cleaning processes have been used on reusable filter media, most companies using sterile filtration have decided that the risk of contamination is still great and prefer the use of the disposable media that are used

Table 8 Reusable Sterilizing Filter Media

Type	Manufacturer	Comments
Diatomaceous earth candles	Allen Filter Company, Toledo, OH	Fragile to handling, adsorptive alteration of solutions, difficult to clean, leachables, large pore size
Unglazed porcelain candles	Selas Corp. of America, Flotronics Division, Huntingdon Valley, PA	Fragile to handling and thermal shock, difficult to clean
Sintered glass	Kimble Division, Owens, Illinois, Toledo, OH	Fragile to handling and thermal shock, low pressures required, difficult to clean, smallest pore 4–5.5 μm.

once and then discarded. The remainder of our discussion will concern the disposable media, often referred to as membrane filter media.

Membrane filter media are available from several different manufacturers and are made from many different materials (see Table 9). Filter media consist of a matrix of pores held in a fixed spatial relationship by a solid continuum. The pores allow the product solution to pass through the medium while retaining the unwanted solid particles and microorganisms. The size of filter medium pores to retain microorganisms must be quite small. The 0.20- or 0.22-μm pore size filter media are considered to be capable of producing sterile filtrates.

The characteristics of a given membrane filter medium depend on its method of manufacture: whether by phase separation of casting solutions, by adhesion into an organic union of matted fibers, or by track etching of solid films [54]. The retention of microorganisms by the various membrane media, while not fully understood, has been investigated by numerous researchers who have indicated that several mechanisms are responsible. The dominant mechanism of retention is sieve retention. Particles larger than the pore size of the filter medium are retained on the medium, and as large particles are retained, pore openings can become bridged and thereby effectively reduce the filter medium's pore size. Other possible mechanisms of retention are adsorption of the particles to the medium itself, entrapment in a tortuous path, impaction, and electrostatic capture [55]. The importance of these latter retention mechanisms has not been fully determined, and on the whole filtration sterilization is treated as depending on the steric influences of the sieve retention mechanism. The problem with assuming a sieve retention mechanism is that a sieve or screen has uniform openings, whereas a membrane filter medium does not. The filter medium has a distribution of pores, albeit narrow, rather than pores of a single size. In addition, thinking in terms of a sieve or screen conjures up a vision of precisely measured and numbered openings. Precise methods for computing both numbers and the actual sizes of pores in a filter membrane medium are not available.

Many approaches have been taken in an attempt to measure the size of membrane filter media pores. Flow measurements, both of air and of water, have been made. Mercury intrusion under high pressure has been employed, and pore sizing using either molecular templates or particles, including bacteria of known size, has been tried. The numerical values for pore sizes from these methods are based on a derivation from a particular model selected. Each of the various models has difficulties and shortcomings, and a pore size designation based on one method does not necessarily mean that a filter medium with the same designated size but from a different method really is the identical size [56]. More important, relating such a designated pore size to the membrane's ability to retain certain size particles may be anywhere from merely uncertain to misleading. Therefore, a given membrane filter medium with a designated pore size of 0.2 micron should not be thought of as "absolutely retaining all particles greater than 0.2 micron"

Table 9 Selected 0.2/0.22 μm Membrane Filter Media

Composition	Mfg.	Designation	Thickness (μm)	Porosity (%)	Flow Rate, H_2O (ml/min/cm^2) (pressure diff. 10 psi)	Autoclavable
Mixed ester of cellulose	Millipore[a]	MF-Millipore	150	75	21	Yes
	Nuclepore[b]	Membra-fil	150–200	75	18	Yes
Cellulose acetate	Millipore	Celotate	150	71	16	No
	Sartorius[c]	—	120	—	18	Yes
	Gelman[d]	—	130	—	35	No
Nitrocellulose	Nuclepore	—	150–200	72	17	Yes
	MFS[e]	—	140	72	20	Yes
	Sartorius	—	130	—	18	Yes
	Whatman[f]	WCN	140	72	20	Yes
Polytetrafluoroethylene	Millipore	Fluoropore	175	70	20	Yes
	Nuclepore	Filinert	150–200	70	20 (methanol)	Yes
	MFS	Teflon	—	78	15 (methanol)	Yes
	Sartorius	PTFE	65	—	9 (isopropanol)	Yes
	Gelman	Teflon TF200	175	—	15 (methanol)	Yes
	Whatman	WTP	—	78	15 (methanol)	Yes
Nylon	Pall[g]	Ultipor N$_{66}$	—	—	—	Yes
Polyvinylidene fluoride	Millipore	Durapore	125	75	12	Yes
Polycarbonate	Nuclepore	—	10	10	15	Yes
Regenerated cellulose	Sartorius	—	90	—	18	Yes
	Gelman	Alpha Metricel-200	65	—	28 (acetone)	Yes
Polyamide	Sartorius	—	140	—	18	No
Acrylonitrile/PVC/nylon	Gelman	Acropore AN200	125	—	20	No

[a]Millipore Corporation, Ashby Road, Bedford, MA 01730.
[b]Nuclepore Corporation, 7035 Commerce Circle, Pleasanton, CA 94566.
[c]Sartorius Filters, Inc., 26576 Corporate Ave., Hayward, CA 94545.
[d]Gelman Sciences, Inc., 600 South Wagner Rd., Ann Arbor, MI 48106.
[e]Micro Filtration Systems, 6800 Sierra Court, Dublin, CA 94566.
[f]Whatman Laboratory Products, 9 Bridewell Place, Clifton, NJ 07014.
[g]Pall Trinity Micro Corporation, Cortland, NY 13045.

without challenging the medium with a known size particulate. In fact, filter media should not be thought of as "absolute retentive" devices at all. It has been demonstrated that under certain operational conditions or with certain bacterial challenges, 0.2 micron–rated membrane filter media can be penetrated by bacteria. Filter media companies do challenge their products to ensure retention efficiency to sterility [49,57].

In addition to the pore size–particle size retention relationship problems mentioned above, other factors can influence a filter medium's retention characteristics. Absorptive retention can be influenced by the organism size, organism population, pore size of the medium, pH of the filtrate, ionic strength, surface tension, and organic content. Operational parameters can also influence retention, such as flow rate, salt concentration, viscosity, temperature, filtration duration, filtration pressure, membrane thickness, organism type, and filter medium area [58].

The complexity of the sterile filtration operation and the current good manufacturing practices regulations require the validation of sterilizing filter systems. The validation of a sterile filtration operation can be complex, with many operational parameters and their interactions needing to be identified, controlled, and predicted for each end product to demonstrate that sterility is adequately achieved by the filtration process. In the commonly used steam sterilization process, the heat parameters are identified and in-process controls specified such that a level of sterility assurance can be reproducibly obtained. In steam sterilization, the important parameter of heat, measured by temperature, can be accurately measured and continuously monitored to ensure the operational integrity of the autoclave; however, unlike steam sterilization, filtration sterilization cannot be monitored on a continuous basis throughout the process.

The important aspect of filtration sterilization, the membrane filter medium—its pore size, pore size distribution, integrity, and capacity—cannot be monitored during use. Therefore, the prediction that a filter membrane, given a certain set of operational parameters, will produce a sterile filter is critical. The only way to test a membrane filter medium's ability to retain bacteria is to challenge the medium with bacteria. Unfortunately, after a challenge with bacteria the filter membrane cannot be used again. Therefore, nondestructive tests need to be developed by which a filter can be tested as to its suitability for bacterial retention. Consequently, the approach in filter system validation has been to establish a reproducible relationship between a membrane's pore size and its bacterial retention efficiency. The thinking is that, once such a relation is established, a nondestructive physical test can be developed by which each filter membrane medium can be tested and its bacterial retention efficiency assured. Testing of the membrane can then be performed both before and after use, and if the test results are satisfactory, the filtration process can be deemed to have been carried out successfully.

C. Nondestructive Physical Tests for Pore Size Characterization

The theoretical basis for characterizing a membrane filter medium pore size and pore size distribution is based on the fact that a wet medium is impermeable to the bulk flow of a test gas until a certain pressure is attained that is sufficiently high to force the wetting liquid from the medium's pores. The pressure at which the transition from a nonflow to a bulk-flow situation occurs can be estimated in the following manner. First, the assumption must be made that the pores in the medium can be characterized as parallel cylindrical capillaries of circular cross section perpendicular to the membrane surface. Even though membrane pores are not normally found to be cylindrical, the assumption is made that they can be treated as cylindrical equivalents [59]. The transition pressure, P, can be estimated by equating the forces holding liquid in the cylindrical pores and the pressure forcing the liquid out of the pores.

In a given capillary of diameter (D) filled with a liquid that wets the capillary surface (Fig. 8) at any point along the circumference, the force component resisting the removal of the liquid is given by

$$f_r = \gamma \cos \theta \tag{15}$$

where

f_r = point resistance force component
γ = surface tension of the liquid
θ = contact angle of the liquid and the capillary wall

The total resisting force F_r is found by multiplying the point force, f_r, by the circumference.

$$F_r = \pi D f_r \tag{16}$$
$$F_r = \pi D \gamma \cos \theta \tag{17}$$

The resisting force, F_r, and the opposing transition pressure, P, can be equated, resulting in

$$P = F_r \tag{18}$$

$$\frac{\pi D^2}{4} = \pi D \gamma \cos \theta \tag{19}$$

$$P = \frac{4\gamma \cos \theta}{D} \tag{20}$$

For almost all practical purposes, the liquid wets the capillary wall so that the $\cos \theta$ is taken as unity and the equation simplifies to

$$P = \frac{4\gamma}{D} \tag{21}$$

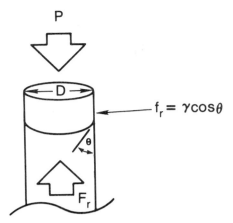

Figure 8 Capillary filled with a liquid that wets the capillary surface.

For example, by Eq. (21), the transition pressure for 0.2-μm cylindrical pores is

$$P = \frac{4\gamma}{D}$$

$$P = \frac{4 \times 72 \text{ dyne/cm}}{0.2 \ \mu\text{m}}$$

$$P = 1440 \times 10^4 \text{ dyne/cm}^2$$

$$P \text{ (in psi)} = 1.440 \times 10^7 \text{ dyne/cm}^2 \times 1.450377 \times 10^{-5} \text{ psi/dyne/cm}^2$$

$$P = 209 \text{ psi}$$

The cylindrical capillary model predicts that the size of the largest pore present in a membrane filter medium is inversely proportional to the pressure at which bulk flow of a test gas is not present.

The bubble point test is a popular single-point physical integrity test for disc filter membranes based on Eq. (21). A filter medium is wetted with a liquid, and test gas pressure is slowly raised until a steady stream of bubbles appears from a tube or hose attached to the downstream side of the filter and immersed in water (Fig. 9). The pressure at which the bubbles first appear is recorded as the bubble point and is related to the largest pores in the filter medium. A pore size can be calculated from Eq. (21); however, it must be realized that the bubble point test does not measure the actual pore size, but only allows correlation of the measured capillary equivalent with some dimensional characteristic of the pore structure of the membrane medium [56,60].

The bubble point test, while popular, has some deficiencies that must be

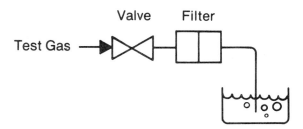

Figure 9 Basic bubble point test setup.

realized. First, there is variation in the operator detection of the test end point, that is, the first appearance of gas bubbles rising in the liquid. Some operators are able to see smaller bubbles than others. In a recent study, a panel of seven observers recorded the initial detection of a steady stream of air bubbles rising from a capillary held under water as the air pressure was gradually increased. The observers, who had received different degrees of training, identified the simulated bubble point as occurring at air flows of 5 to 50 ml/min corresponding to air pressures of 34 and 38 psi, respectively, for a 90-mm disc filter membrane [61].

In Eq. (21), the surface tension of the liquid (γ) is an important parameter in determining bubble point pressures, and it predicts that liquids of different γ values will have different pressures for the bubble point. In addition, it is a common assumption in Eq. (21) that the contact angle (θ) is 0, indicating a complete wetting of the filter medium by the test liquid. Tests have shown that this might not be a valid assumption in all instances [62]. Different medium materials show different bubble point values using the same test liquid. The change in wettability can affect testing before and after autoclaving. Autoclaving has been shown to wash away filter medium surfactants and thereby decrease the wettability, thus decreasing the bubble point pressure. Autoclaving has also been shown to decrease the hydrophobicity of a medium, thereby increasing the wettability of a membrane resulting in a higher posttest bubble point pressure [63].

As pressure is increased above the bubble point pressure, pores of decreasing size have the liquid forced out and this allows additional bulk flow of the test gas. By measuring and comparing the bulk gas flow rates of both a wetted and a dry filter medium at the same pressure, the percentage of the bulk gas flow through the medium pores that are larger than or equal to the size tested may be calculated. By increasing the test pressures in very small increments and determining the flow contribution of the corresponding pore size increments, it is possible to determine a pore size distribution for the filter medium [64,65].

The pore size distribution determination is illustrated in Fig. 10. Again, the pore size distribution determination method does not result in the actual mem-

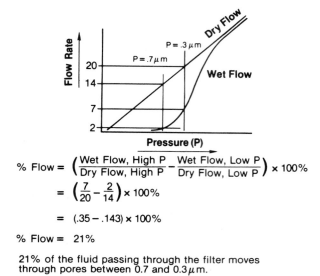

$$\% \text{ Flow} = \left(\frac{\text{Wet Flow, High P}}{\text{Dry Flow, High P}} - \frac{\text{Wet Flow, Low P}}{\text{Dry Flow, Low P}}\right) \times 100\%$$

$$= \left(\frac{7}{20} - \frac{2}{14}\right) \times 100\%$$

$$= (.35 - .143) \times 100\%$$

$$\% \text{ Flow} = 21\%$$

21% of the fluid passing through the filter moves
through pores between 0.7 and 0.3 μm.

Figure 10 Pore size distribution determination example. (From Ref. 64.)

brane pore size and pore size determination. It does, however, give a means of
comparing different filter media. A narrow pore size distribution is required for
effective filtration and filtration validation.

Another integrity test referred to as the pressure hold test makes use of the fact
that below the transition pressure no bulk flow of the test gas takes place.
Therefore, in a pressure hold test, once a filter system is in place and the filter
medium wetted, pressure is applied to the system and then shut off and sealed. If
there are no leaks in the system or holes in the membrane larger than the
corresponding test pressure used, the pressure should remain constant. If the
pressure drops, there is a leak somewhere in the system that should be corrected.
The pressure hold test is popular in testing filter assemblies and systems in
production situations before and after filtration as a quick integrity check of the
system.

Another problem with the use of the bubble point test develops as one begins
to test large volume disk-type membranes (293 mm) and the pleated cartridge-
type filter media that have large surface areas available for filtration. Bubble point
measurements are inaccurate with these high-surface-area filters because of
several problems. With the larger systems, enough test gas can go into solution
under the test pressure to form visible gas bubbles when the solution reaches the
downstream side of the filter and the test pressure is released. Observers, seeing
the pressure release bubbles, would record the pressure at that point in the

experiment as the bubble point and hence mark the filter medium as a failure because the bubble point pressure was low, indicative of large pore sizes in the membrane medium. With the cartridge systems, initial bubble point gas bubbles tend to rise within the core of the filter rather than leave the filter. In this case, the first appearance of the bubbles is viewed at a pressure level higher than the real transition pressure, and defective cartridges could be approved for use when really unsuitable [63].

With large-surface-area membrane filter media, the interpretation of the true bubble point can be further complicated because of the diffusion of the test gas through the media. Because the filter media are more than 70% void space, a liquid-wetted membrane is virtually a thin film of liquid across which a test gas will diffuse, governed by Fick's law:

$$Q = \frac{D(C_1 - C_0)\phi}{h} \tag{22}$$

where

Q = molar flux of test gas per unit area and unit
D = diffusion coefficient for the gas-liquid system used
ϕ = void fraction of the filter medium used
h = thickness of the membrane
C = concentration of the gas; 1 = upstream, 0 = downstream

Because the solubility of the gas in the liquid is low by virtue of Henry's law, the solubility can be expressed in terms of pressure:

$$C_1 - C_0 = H(P_1 - P_0) \tag{23}$$

where

H = solubility coefficient for the gas-liquid system
P_1 = upstream pressure
P_0 = downstream pressure

The the downstream side of the filter vented to the atmosphere, $P_0 = 0$. With the appropriate substitution, Eq. (22) can be rewritten as:

$$Q = \frac{DHP\phi}{h} \tag{24}$$

where P = applied test pressure upstream.
For a given test D, H, ϕ, and h would be constant. Therefore,

$$Q = KP \tag{26}$$

and Q should be predictable for a given pressure. As long as the transition pressure is not reached, Q and P should be linearly related.

Figure 11 shows the wet-flow properties of three hypothetical membrane filter media. Each filter medium is made of the same material, has the same thickness, and total void fraction. Media A and B have the same oversized pore size but A has a broader pore size distribution. Medium C has a pore size smaller than A and B with a narrow pore size distribution.

The diffusion flow test is not without its difficulties or potential problems, however; if the filter traps liquid and essentially forms a secondary liquid layer in addition to the medium, the diffusional flow will, of course, be decreased. A test pressure that is too low will not be able to differentiate between good media and media that will pass bacteria because the test pressure will be below even the largest pore bubble point; the only flow reading obtained will be diffusional flow through the support media, and they will be almost identical for each size medium [66]. The recommended single-point diffusion test pressure is 80% of the bubble point. To run such a diffusion test, the medium to be tested is placed in its filter assembly and the medium is thoroughly wetted with a liquid and the filter assembly drained. Pressure from a test gas, generally air or nitrogen, is then slowly increased up to approximately 80% of the estimated bubble point pressure for the given medium and liquid used. The resulting flow of test gas is then quantitatively measured. In the past few years, the sophistication of equipment to run this test has steadily increased to a point that now some firms offer automatic instruments for the running of diffusion tests [67].

Diffusion tests have been complicated by the diffusion coefficient's being changed for the gas-liquid system after the membrane has been autoclaved [63]. With the introduction of additional layers of media material to large cartridge filters, additional problems have also arisen. The additional media can possibly affect the drainage of liquid from the filter prior to flow testing. If all of the liquid is not removed, the possibility exists for additional liquid layers to reduce the

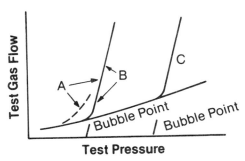

Figure 11 Diffusional wet-flow characteristics of three hypothetical membranes. (From Ref. 48.)

diffusion effectively or for thicker liquid layers in the medium to retard diffusion. The additional medium material itself adds thickness and therefore decreases diffusional flow. The reduced diffusion readings, in turn, could mask larger pores and flaws if this is not dealt with in designing the tests [60]. Additional nonlinearity with the pressure–gas flow relationship has been reported as attributable to a process known as liquid thinning. As the test gas pressure is increased to near the true bubble point of the medium but not below it, the average thickness of liquid held in the medium decreases. The amount of gas diffusion per unit pressure, therefore, increases, and the relationship becomes nonlinear [66].

The search for the ideal nondestructive test of a sterilizing filter system is still proceeding. One new suggestion has been proposed to use test gas pressures above the bubble point. In the meantime, the wise user of filter systems for sterilization will test in as many ways as possible and correlate for physical tests with bacterial challenge tests.

There are additional characteristics of filter media that need to be addressed in a total validation scheme for filter systems. While a thorough discussion of them is beyond the scope of this discussion of sterilization, they are mentioned below. Particles and soluble materials can be rinsed from various process filter media and must be considered as contaminating any parenteral preparation. Therefore, steps should be taken to isolate, identify, and eliminate these contaminating substances prior to use. Solid extractables have been shown to be pieces of the filter medium itself (media migration) or "cutting" debris. Soluble contaminants in parenterals have been isolated from filter aids, from upstream prefilters, and from the sterilizing filter medium itself. In general, extractables from a membrane filter medium can be categorized into either plasticizers or surfactants. The surfactants found have been nonionic ethylene oxide adducts, polyvinylpyrrolidone, long-chain fatty acid–substituted polyethylene glycol, and alkylated cellulose. The plasticizers have been found to be glycerol or polyethylene glycol [68]. The filter media should also be tested for compatibility with each parenteral drug product, presence of induced nonpyrogenicity, and biological toxicity.

D. Bacterial Challenge Test

Microbiological challenging of a filter is the only true means of determining the bacterial retention properties of the system. Such a test is sensitive because of the large number of organisms used and because the organisms self-replicate and allow even low numbers of bacteria that might pass through a filter system to make themselves known.

Filter media are not repetitive-use items, and although used for more than one lot in production, the media are usually discarded after some predetermined number of uses or time. Therefore, it is impossible to test every filter medium individually, since the challenge test is a destructive test. The nondestructive tests, therefore, require a high degree of correlation with a retention test. When such correlated tests are established and controls maintained, filtration users can depend on filtration to produce a sterile parenteral product.

The level of sensitivity of the challenged test is dependent on the challenge organism, culture environment of the organism, challenge level of the organism, test volume filtered, challenge rate or the duration of the challenge test, and pressure used during the challenge test [69,70].

The Health Industry Manufacturers Association (HIMA) is in the process of developing a standardized microbial challenge procedure to be used in challenging sterilizing filter systems. While the proposed guidelines developed by the HIMA task force are by no means complete or official, they do provide a convenient outline of current industry thinking concerning sterilizing filter bacterial challenge testing [71].

The challenge organism utilized in filter testing is *Pseudomonas diminuta* (ATCC 19146). The rationale for using *P. diminuta* follows the same logic as used in choosing *B. stearothermophilus* for steam sterilization testing. *B. stearothermophilus* is resistant to heat and, therefore, severely challenges the lethality given by an autoclave. Because filtration is a removal process, the most resistant organism to filtration would be the smallest known bacterium. *P. diminuta* has been adopted for several reasons. First, the organism is quite small. The gram-negative rod-shaped cell has a mean diameter of 0.3 μm. The bacteria were first isolated when found to consistently pass through 0.45-μm filter membranes to contaminate filtered protein solutions. The organism can be grown to high cell densities in a short period of time, and with proper culturing the cells are small and arranged singly. In addition, *P. diminuta* shows only limited biochemical activity. A growth curve for *P. diminuta* in saline-lactose broth (SLB) at $30°C$ is shown in Fig. 12. The initial lag time lasts about 3 h. In the exponential growth phase, the organism has a population doubling time (generation time) of 2.6 h and an instantaneous growth rate constant (μ) of 0.27 h^{-1}. The growth curve levels off in the stationary phase at approximately 10^7 cells/ml [72].

For reproducible challenge tests, care must be taken in culturing and handling the bacteria to maintain bacterial cells of equal morphology. Studies have shown that differences in cell morphology can be produced by using different growth media or by the use or nonuse of agitation during culturing. *P. diminuta* grown in trypicase-soy broth (TSB) without agitation produces a cell that is distinctly rod shaped, having a length-to-diameter ratio of 2 to 5. Grown in the same TSB medium but with 200 rpm agitation, *P. diminuta* was more dense and had longer cells with a length-to-diameter ratio of about 4. In addition, the cells tended to form clusters of from 3 to 8 cells each. *P. diminuta* grown in SLB without agitation are found to have a length-to-diameter ratio of 1 to 2.5 and are arranged singly [72].

The growth state of a *P. diminuta* culture is also important in obtaining the

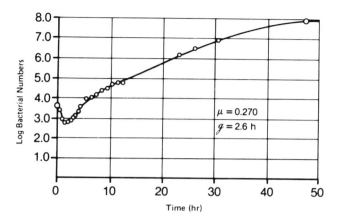

Figure 12 Growth curve of *P. diminutia* (ATCC 19146) in saline-lactose broth incubated without agitation at 30°C. (From Ref. 72.)

smallest cell size on a reproducible basis. *P. diminuta* cells are observed to increase in cell size during the lag phase and become smaller during the declining growth period. Therefore, challenge cells for retention testing are most appropriate when in the early stationary phase of growth. Early stationary phase rather than late stationary phase is taken to reduce the chance of the challenge culture containing nonviable cells and cellular debris, which could prematurely clog the test filter medium.

Maintenance of a pure culture of *P. diminuta* must be done in such a manner as to keep the probability of mutational changes that might alter cellular characteristics to a minimum.

The microbial challenge test can be performed on a particular filtration medium, whether disk or cartridge type, by following these general steps:

1. Sterilize the filter system. Figure 13 shows a hypothetical test system for a disk filter medium.
2. Integrity test the filter medium using a sterile 0.1% peptone solution or saline solution to wet the medium. The wetting solution also serves as a negative control sterility check. The entire wetting solution is forced through a sterility control filter, incubated, and checked for sterility.
3. The bacterial challenge suspension is placed in the appropriate container and the test filter medium is challenged.

The challenge suspension should have a microbial concentration of 10^7 *P. diminuta* per square centimeter of effective filter area (EFA). Many challenge levels have appeared in the literature: 10^7 per 100 ml for 1400 liters, 10^5–10^7

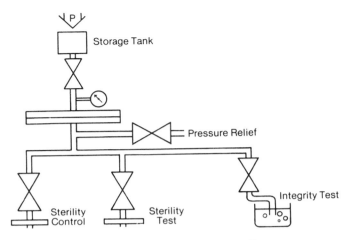

Figure 13   Hypothetical disk-filter bacterial challenge test apparatus.

per ml, $2-4 \times 10^5$ per liter per min, $1.2 \times 10^{12}-1.9 \times 10^{13}$ per liter, and 10^8 per cm^2 EFA [53,57,69,70,72–75]. Much discussion has also appeared in the literature concerning the challenge level and the potential adverse effects of excessive levels of challenge bacteria [73]. The rationale for the 10^7 *P. diminuta* per cm^2 EFA challenge is that while this level of bacteria might not challenge every membrane pore (approximately 10^8 pores per membrane medium), it is enough to challenge any oversized pore. Since the flow through pores varies as the fourth power of the radius of the pore, a larger fraction of the total flow is carried by the larger pores. Therefore, it is felt that at the 10^7 challenge level enough increased flow will pass through any oversized pores that challenge bacteria will inevitably encounter an oversized pore, pass through, and indicate a negative test. The 10^7 level is also under the filter-clogging concentration [10,24].

The challenge suspension should be forced through the test medium at a pressure differential greater than 2 kg/cm^2 (approximately 30 psi) for disk filters and at fluxes of greater than 2 liters per 0.1 m^2 up to around 3.86 liters per 0.1 m^2 for cartridge-type filters [69–72]. A pressure relief valve on the downstream side of the filter should be provided to allow maximum pressure differentials. The suggestion has also been made that the pressure be applied full strength immediately rather than a gradual buildup in order to stress the filter system further [72].

4.   The entire volume of the challenge filtrate is subsequently forced through a sterility test filter system and incubated in the same manner as the negative control filtrate.

5. A postchallenge integrity test is performed.
6. The challenge test results are then observed. The challenge tests are considered invalid if the negative control contains any organisms. The filter system is considered to have failed the test if the filtrate contains any test organisms.

E. Retention Efficiency

In the past, several terms have been coined to describe the retention efficiency of the filter system: *beta value, microbiological safety index, reduction ratio,* and *titer reduction ratio* [69,70,74,76]. The proposed HIMA guidelines introduce a new filter retention efficiency term, the *log reduction value* (LRV) and defines it as the logarithm to the base 10 of the ratio of the number of organisms in the challenge suspension to the number of organisms in the filtrate.

$$\text{LRV} = \log \frac{N_0}{N} \tag{26}$$

$$\text{LRV} = \log N_0 - \log N \tag{27}$$

where

$$\text{LRV} = \log \text{reduction value}$$
$$N_0 = \text{number of organisms in the challenge}$$
$$N = \text{number of organisms in the filtrate}$$

With a sterile filtrate, the term $\log N$ becomes $\log 0$, which is undefined and is eliminated from the expression. The LRV is then expressed as being equal to or greater than N_0.

$$\text{LRV} \geqslant \log N_0 \tag{28}$$

For example, if a 293-mm diameter disk filter system having an EFA of 530 cm^2 is challenged and the $10^7/\text{cm}^2$ level is used, the total challenge to the filter is 5.3×10^9 organisms. If a sterile filtrate is assumed the LRV would be calculated and reported as follows:

$$\text{LRV} = \log 5.3 \times 10^9 - \log 0$$
$$\text{LRV} \geqslant 9.72$$

The probability of passing a single organism through this filter system, or in other words, the probability of nonsterility (PNS) can be calculated by the following equation:

$$\text{PNS} = \frac{N}{N_0} \tag{29}$$

For the above example, the PNS is calculated as

$$\text{PNS} = \frac{1}{5.3 \times 10^9} = 1.89 \times 10^{-10}$$

Equations (27) and (29) can be used to calculate the total PNS of replicated experimental filter challenges. For example, five filter membrane media are to be challenged at the following *P. diminuta* levels.

18×10^9 9×10^9

5×10^9 14×10^9

12×10

The total challenge (N_0) is 5.8×10^{10}, and the assumption is made that the filtrate for each is sterile. The LRV then is

$$\text{LRV} = \log N_0 - \log N = \log 5.8 \times 10^{10} = 10.76$$

The PNS then is calculated to be

$$\text{PNS} = \frac{N}{N_0} = 1.72 \times 10^{-11}, \qquad N = 1$$

These equations may be used to calculate an estimate of the degree of nonsterility associated with a particular filtration process. In order to determine such a sterility assurance associated with the process, some knowledge of the initial microbiological bioburden of the product to be sterilized must be known. If it is assumed that the microbiological bioburden of a product is 10^4 organisms and the product is to be sterilized by filtration through filters from the example above, the PNS is the sum of all the probabilities of all of the combinations of the 10^4 organisms passing through the filter. The expression for this is

$$\text{PNS} = \sum_{n=1}^{N_0} P_i \tag{30}$$

where

N_0 = the bioburden of the product
P_i = probability of i organisms passing the filter medium
$n = 1, 2, \ldots i$

In other words, the PNS is equal to the probability of one organism passing the filter plus the probability of two organisms passing the filter, etc. With the bioburden level greater than one organism, however, there result many combinations of sets or organisms that can have a probability of passing the filter. The probability of all combinations of one organism passing a filter with a given retention efficiency from a bioburden level N_0 can be written as

$$P_1 = \frac{N_0!}{\dfrac{(N_0 - 1)!1}{1 \times RV}} \tag{31}$$

where

$$RV = \text{reduction value}$$

Or in logarithmic form:

$$\log P_1 = \log\frac{N_0!}{(N_0 - 1)!1} - LRV \tag{32}$$

Similarly, the probability of all combinations of i organisms passing the filter is

$$\log P_i = \log\frac{N_0!}{(N_0 - i)i} - i(LRV) \tag{33}$$

When Eq. (30) is expanded into the format of Eqs. (32) and (33), the following expression results:

$$\log PNS = \Sigma\left[\left(\log\frac{N_0!}{(N_0 - 1)!1} - LRV\right) + \cdots \right. $$
$$\left. + \left(\log\frac{N_0!}{(N_0 - i)!i} - iLRV\right)\right] \tag{34}$$

In a convergent series, as is Eq. (34), the bracketed quantity representing $P_1 \gg P_2 \gg \cdots P_i$ can be approximated by using P_1 only. Therefore, Eq. (34) can be simplified to

$$\log PNS = \log\frac{N_0!}{(N_0 - 1)!1} - LRV \tag{35}$$

This simplifies further to

$$\log PNS = \log N_0 - LRV \tag{36}$$

A sterility assurance (SA) can be calculated from

$$SA = 1 - PNS \tag{37}$$

By way of example, the LRV for the previous five-filter example was 10.76. If a product having a bioburden, N_0, of 10^4 organisms is to be filtered, the PNS can be calculated using Eq. (36).

$$\log PNS = \log N_0 - LRV = 4 - 10.76 = -6.76$$
$$PNS = 1.74 \times 10^{-7}$$

The SA can be calculated then by Eq. (37) where

$$SA = 1 - PNS = 1 - 1.74 \times 10^{-7}$$
$$SA = 0.9999998 \quad \text{or a } 99.99998\% \text{ assurance of sterility}$$

Terminally sterilized parenteral products have a level of SA in the range of 0.999999. If we assume that are example solution has 100 organisms per liter, how much could we filter before the SA dropped below 0.999999? By using Eq. (37):

$$SA = 1 - PNS$$
$$PNS = 1 - .999999 = 10^{-6}$$

When we substitute into Eq. (36) and rearrange

$$\log N_0 = \log PNS + LRV = -6 + 10.76 = 4.76$$
$$N_0 = 57,544 \text{ organisms}$$

When we use the following relationship

$$N_0 = C \times V \tag{38}$$

where

N_0 = the bioburden of the product
C = the bioburden concentration per unit volume
V = the volume of the product

then

$$V = \frac{N_0}{C} = \frac{57,544 \text{ organisms}}{100 \text{ organisms/liter}}$$
$$V = 575.44 \text{ liters}$$

Therefore, 575.44 liters can be filtered before going below an SA of 0.999999.

Data generated by the Millipore Corporation show that a mixed cellulosic ester membrane filter medium with an average bubble point of 3.44 kg/cm^2, when challenged with an average of 2.78 $\times$ 10^7 organisms/cm^2, had an average LRV of 9.96. Millipore claims that 20 years of quality control testing has confirmed that mixed esters of cellulose filter media having a minimum bubble test of 3.3 kg/cm^2 or greater will quantitatively retain 10^7 P. diminuta/cm^2 EFA at a differential pressure of 2.6 kg/cm^2. Such is the type of correlative data that are needed to validate each product for filtration sterilization [71].

F. Aseptic Processing

The filter SAs of membrane media are several orders of magnitude higher than that associated with the entire aseptic fill process. Aseptic fill processes are validated by simulating production conditions and using a bacterial culture medium as the product. This process simulation test is commonly referred to as a "media fill" (MF). While an in-depth study of MF is beyond the scope of this chapter, an introduction to some of the parameters of concern is appropriate. A number of factors have an impact on an efficient aseptic filling process test: equipment, environment, personnel, and procedures.

The production facilities should be checked to ensure that all installed equipment satisfies the engineering and quality design criteria and that it is functioning properly. In the performance of an MF test, it is important that everything be conducted just as a normal production run. All equipment normally used should be used. All equipment should be cleaned, sanitized, sterilized, handled, and assembled in a normal manner.

The environment of an aseptic filling operation must be monitored and controlled. The aseptic filling room environment is the last occasion for environmental contamination of the product. Such contamination could come from viable organisms suspended in the air or from manipulative procedures in which component handling leads to contamination. Microbiological monitoring is the most common form of environmental monitoring with prescribed action levels. It should be reoutinely conducted for production and MF runs. In addition, the monitoring system should be routinely checked to ensure such things as proper instrument calibration and use of effective growth media. The MF test does cause some concern in that it introduces into the aseptic area a substance that is designed to support microbial growth. Therefore, adequate care must be taken to clean up the production area after MF testing.

Personnel in the aseptic area probably represent the greatest source of contamination. All persons, therefore, must have a working knowledge and understanding of the aseptic filling process. Aseptic area operator training programs should be designed to cover such areas as personal hygiene, growing techniques, manipulative techniques, safety, and cleaning procedures. In addition to process validation, some companies utilize MF tests to ensure operator adherence to aseptic techniques.

As for the frequency of MF testing, there appears to be no industry standard. A 1974 PMA survey [77] found that MF testing frequently varied, ranging from daily to yearly, and that different processing areas in many cases were subjected to different testing frequencies.

The number of containers used for an MF test should represent some time–normal production rate relationship. The number of containers used should allow the MF test to be of sufficient duration to determine properly the contamination rate. The vials or ampules used should be the same size and type as in a normal production run on the particular line being tested. The Pharmaceutical Manufacturer's Association (PMA) survey showed that the number of containers used in MF testing again varies with each company, with a minimum of 100 containers to a maximum of 40,000 containers being reported!

The efficacy of the MF test rests on the ability of the culture medium to grow contaminating organisms. Therefore, many factors must be carefully considered in the manufacture, sterilization, and incubation of the culture medium for an MF test. Table 10 lists some culture medium selection considerations. For additional information, the reader is referred to the Parenteral Drug Association Technical Monograph No. 2, *Validation of Aseptic Filling for Solution Drug Products* [78].

From the PMA survey, a single type of medium was generally used for MF testing within a given company. The most commonly used was fluid thioglycollate medium. Other media used are tryptone glucose yeast extract (TGYE), brain-heart infusion (BHI), soybean casein digest agar (SCD), and trypticase-soy broth (TSB). Once the medium has been filled into the sample containers, the samples are to be incubated upright at suitable conditions. Two temperature ranges, 20 to 35°C and 30 to 35°C, for 7 to 14 days were reported to the PMA survey. If there is a positive contamination response to the MF test, the identity of the organisms should be determined and an attempt to correlate the organism with the environmental sources should be made. In looking for positive contamination responses, contaminated containers should be checked for evidence of container/closure damage. Such damage compromises the integrity of the dosage form and should not be considered in the MF evaluation.

A company must establish rigid accept-reject limits for a media fill test which will initiate some sort of corrective action should an unacceptable level of contaminating organisms be found. A widely accepted contamination level for MF test is 0.3%, suggested by the World Health Organization in 1973 [79]; a 0.1%

Table 10 Considerations in Selecting Culture Media for Product Simulation Tests

Manufacture
 Type of medium
 Physical properties of meduim
 Concentration of medium
 Presterilized use or sterilized during MF test
Sterilization
 Steam sterilization
 Filtrative sterilization
Incubation
 Test container fill and storage techniques
 Storage time
 Storage temperature
 Test analysis
 Positive contamination controls

level is suggested as a goal to strive for. Again, the PMA survey showed that the reject limit varied with each company and the reported percentage of contamination accepted ranged from 0.1 to 1%, with the majority of the firms using the 0.1 to 0.3% levels.

For an aseptic filling process utilizing sterile filtration, the level of sterility assurance is a cumulative function of all of the unit operations involved in the manufacturing system. The final level of sterility cannot be greater than the unit operation providing the lowest probability of sterility. Adherence to a program that will enable the validation of the sterilizing filtration unit operation will add much to the process validation objective of assuring that all of the steps in an aseptic process are collectively functioning to yield a product that can be claimed to be sterile at a known level of sterility assurance.

APPENDIX I: EXAMPLE PROTOCOL FOR VALIDATION OF THE STERILIZATION PROCESS IN A STEAM AUTOCLAVE

Reference No. _____
Date _____

   I.   Purpose:
        To provide the method to be used for the validation of the sterilizing process using an autoclave containing _____ .
   II. Scope:
        This procedure applies to all steam autoclaves used to process filling equipment, package components, or final containers. The procedure will be implemented under the following conditions:
        A.   The validation of sterilization processes using saturated steam as the sterilant
        B.   Prior to production use of a new autoclave
        C.   A change in load design or weight that would result in a load that is more difficult to sterilize.
   III. References:
        A.   USP XXII
        B.   CFR title 21, subchapter E.
   IV. Responsibility:
        Process validation department
   V.   Autoclave identification:
        Make _____
        Location _____
        Tag no. _____
        Mfg. serial no. _____

VI. Load identification:
    A. Description

    B.   Weight of load: _____
VII. Cycle parameters:
    No. of pre-vac pulses _____
    Sterilization:
        Temp set point _____
        Temp range _____
        Exposure time _____
        Dry time _____
VIII. Equipment and materials:
    A. Recording potentiometer
    B. Thermocouples and lead wire harness
    C. Compression fitting for autoclave access port
    D. *B. stearothermophilus* biological indicators _____
IX. Procedure:
    A. Place 10 thermocouples in the load at the 10 slow-to-heat points, as determined previously on prot. no. _____ (penetration TC).
    B. Place thermocouples exterior and near to the penetration TC and exposed to the chamber steam (distribution TC).
    C. Place one BI at each of the slow-to-heat penetration locations.
    D. Load autoclave.
    E. Extend TC out of autoclave and attach to recording potentiometer.
    F. Position one TC by controller recorder sensor.
    G. Close autoclave door.
    H. Perform function check of TC. Replace any defectives.
    I. Replace autoclave recording chart with a new one, if appropriate.
    J. Check to make sure cycle parameters are set.
    K. Set potentiometer for a _____-min scan cycle.
    L. Initiate sterilization cycle and potentiometer cycle at the same time. Time _____
    M. Allow cycle to continue until it is complete. Record the following:
        Time process start _____
        Time sterilization cycle on _____
        Sensor TC read _____
        Time sterilization cycle complete _____
        Chamber pressure at cycle initiation _____
    N. Time cycle complete _____
    O. Collect all potentiometer, control, and computer control records and place with this protocol.

P. Have computer graph results and calculate F_0 delivery.
Q. After load has cooled, remove BI and have tested.
R. Incubate BIs in incubator at 55°C for 48–56 h.
    Date on _____
    Date off _____
S. Similarly, place an untreated control into incubator as in (R) above.
    Date on _____
    Date positive _____
    Read by _____
    Date _____
X. Results:
BI

_____
        Read by _____
        Date _____
F_0 delivery
        high _____
        low _____
XI. Signatures of operators conducting study:
    _____ date _____
    _____ date _____
    _____ date _____
    _____ date _____
XII. Protocol reviewed by: _____ date _____
XIII. Conclusions:

APPENDIX II: MEDIUM CONSIDERATIONS IN PRODUCT SIMULATION TESTS

The efficacy of the product simulation test rests on the ability of the culture medium–manufacture, sterilization, incubation—to grow contaminating bacteria. The following outline is from the Parenteral Drug Association, Technical Monograph No. 2, *Validation of Aseptic Filling for Solution Drug Products* [78] concerning growth media, which should be consulted for additional details.

5.2.1. Medium Considerations for Use in Product Simulation Tests
    (a) Type of Medium
        A number of general microbiological growth media are available and may be used in a process simulation program. In general, when selecting a medium for use, the following considerations should be made:
        Selectivity—The medium should have low selectivity; i.e., it should

support the growth of a broad spectrum of organisms including fungi and yeasts.

Clarity—The medium should be clear to allow for ease in observing turbidity.

Filterability—Medium should not contain agar or high levels of suspended solids when a filtration process is used.

Soybean casein digest (SCD)* is currently one of the most frequently used media, due to its low selectivity and relatively low cost; however, a partial listing of acceptable media would also include the following:

- Tryptone glucose yeast extract (TGYE)*
- Brain heart infusion (BHI)*
- Alternate (NIH)* thioglycollate—(if an anaerobic growth medium is desired)

(b) Medium Concentration

The medium of manufacturer's recommended concentration, should be used when preparing media for process simulation tests unless other concentrations can be shown empirically to be equivalent.

(c) Medium Utilization

In conducting process simulation tests, there are two basic alternative techniques available:

1. Use unsterilized medium and filter the medium through the normal sterilizing membrane hooked directly to the filing equipment. The media may be prefiltered to reduce bioburden and increase filtration efficiency.

2. Presterilize the medium in a separate operation. After verification of medium sterility (such as examining the bulk medium for absence of growth), use the medium in the process simulation test. For the test, pass the sterilized medium through normal processing equipment.

(d) Medium Sterilization

Medium for use in a process simulation test can be rendered sterile using either moist heat (autoclaving) or filtration. The method chosen depends on the availability of suitable equipment, and the information desired from the study.

1. Sterilization with Steam

When using this approach it is recommended that:

- The medium should be solubilized and dispensed into vessels with suitable closures to allow for filtered gas exchange, and

---

*Use only if testing for anaerobiosis of thioglycollate medium.

for subsequent dispensing at the filling line. The vessel should, if possible, be identical to regular production equipment.
- The medium should be exposed to steam under pressure in a validated sterilization cycle to achieve at least a 10^{-6} probability of survival of organisms within the medium.
- Medium should be cooled slowly to prevent excessive boiling.
- Medium is ready for use immediately upon cooling. It should be inspected for clarity prior to use.

2. Sterilization by Filtration
When using this approach it is recommended that:
- Medium be solubilized at an elevated temperature (50°C) to facilitate dissolution of the solids.
- Filtration be conducted under normal production conditions using a sterilizing grade of filter with adequate prefiltration to increase final filter throughput and life.
- Medium may be stored in bulk vessels following filtration to ensure that adequate aseptic technique was used.

5.2.3. Media Incubation Parameters
(a) Technique
The filled container with medium should be gently rotated immediately prior to incubation so that all surfaces, including the closure (if any), are wetted by the medium. The container should be incubated in an upright position with the closure uppermost. This posture minimizes the migration of closure ingredients which might affect the growth promoting characteristics of the medium.
(b) Time
Media, in the sealed container as delivered from the production line, should be incubated for a minimum of 14 days.
(c) Temperature
Process simulation test containers should be incubated at suitable incubation parameters.
The temperature should be monitored throughout the test period and should be maintained within the specified range for the test period. Deviations from the specified range should be evaluated and countered with appropriate action.
(d) Positive Controls
These should be incubated under identical incubation conditions as the test containers.

5.2.4. Test Controls
The growth-promoting ability of the medium in the final filled containers

should be demonstrated using filled control containers challenged with low levels of microorganisms.

(a)   Microorganisms

Compendial microorganisms—the microorganisms referenced in the USP for sterility test growth promotion tests—are suitable for use as controls. These include the following:

- *Bacillus subtilis* (spores) ATCC #6633 or *Micrococcus lutea* ATCC #9341
- *Candida albicans* ATCC #10231
- *Bacteroides vulgatus* ATCC #8482* or *Clostridium sporogenes* (spores) ATCC #11437*

As an alternative to compendial microorganisms, isolates frequently encountered in the manufacturing environment may be used to challenge the medium.

A combination of compendial organisms and indigenous organisms may be used as controls. In all cases, however, microorganisms used in growth promotion testing should include both bacterial and fungal species.

(b)   Challenge Parameters

Challenge levels not to exceed 100 cells per container should be used in an attempt to simulate low-level contamination.

Dilutions of actively growing or frozen stock cultures may be used.

A viable count via a pour plate or spread plate should be obtained for the final dilution of each microorganism to verify the challenge level.

Growth promotion studies should be carried out in duplicate for each type of microorganisms and each type of container system.

Incubation parameters should be identical to those of the test medium.

(c)   Interpretation of Results

Medium is acceptable if growth is observed in at least one of the two test containers for all of the challenge microorganisms.

If no growth is observed in both of the challenged containers, one repeat test may be conducted to rule out laboratory error. On the repeat test, both containers must support growth.

REFERENCES

1.   Mascoli, C. C., Should end-product sterility testing continue? *Med. Device Diag. Ind.* 3:8–9 (1981).

2. Bowman, F. W., The sterility testing of pharmaceuticals. *J. Pharm. Sci. 58*:1301–1308 (1969).

3. Ernst, R. R., West, K. L., and Doyle, J. E., Problem areas in sterility testing. *Bull. Parenter. Drug Assoc. 23*:29–39 (1969).

4. Knudsen, L. F., Sample size of parenteral solutions for sterility testing. *J. Amer. Pharm. Assoc. Sci.* ed. *38*:332–337 (1949).

5. Brewer, J. H. In *Antiseptics, Disinfectants, Fungicides, and Sterilization*, 2d ed., Redish, G. L. (ed.), Lea & Febiger, Philadelphia, pp. 160–161 (1957).

6. Food and Drug Administration, "Guideline on general principles of process validation," FDA, Rockville, MD (1984).

7. Validation of Steam Sterilization Cycles, Technical Monograph No. 1, Parenteral Drug Association (1978).

8. Pflug, I. J., and Holcomb, R. G., Principles of thermal destruction of microorganisms. In *Disinfection, Sterilization and Preservation*, 2d ed., Block, S. S. (ed.), Lea & Febiger, Philadelphia, pp. 933–944 (1977).

9. Moats, W. A., Kinetics of thermal death of bacteria. *J. Bacteriol. 105*:165–171 (1971).

10. Stumbo, C. R., *Thermobacteriology in Food Processing*, Academic Press, New York (1965).

11. Han, Y. W., Death rates of bacterial spores: nonlinear survivor curves. *Can. J. Microbiol. 21*:1464–67 (1975).

12. Han, Y. W., Zhang, H. I., and Krochta, J. M., Death rates of bacterial spores: mathematical models. *Can. J. Microbiol. 22*:295–300 (1976).

13. Validation of Dry Heat Processes Used for Sterilization and Depyrogenation, Technical Report No. 3, Parenteral Drug Association (1981).

14. Pflug, I. J., Sterilization: science, not art. *Med. Device Diag. Ind.* (March 1981), pp. 8–9.

15. Barry, I. R., Process validation: a U.S. viewpoint. *Manuf. Chem.* (Jan. 1983), pp. 34–35.

16. Process validation in drug manufacture. *Drug Cosmet. Ind.* (Aug. 1980), p. 46.

17. Feldsine, P. T., Ferry, E. W., Gauthier, R. J., et al., A new concept in glassware depyrogenation process validation, *J. Parenter. Drug Assoc. 33*:125–131 (1979).

18. Korczynski, M., Concepts and issues: container/closure microbial validation. *J. Parenter. Drug Assoc. 34*:327–285 (1980).

19. Wood, R. T., Validation of elastomeric closures for parenteral use: an overview. *J. Parenter. Drug Assoc. 34*:286–295 (1980).

20. Grimes, T. L., Fonner, D. E., Griffin, J. C., et al., An automated system for cleaning tanks and parts used in the processing of pharmaceuticals. *Bull. Parenter. Drug Assoc. 31*:179–186 (1977).

21. Kuhlman, H. C., Technical processes in the production of water for injection. *J. Parenter. Drug Assoc. 35*:54–59 (1981).

22. Gross, R. I., Testing of laminar flow equipment. *J. Parenter. Drug Assoc. 32*:174 (1978).

23. Duberstein, R., and Howard, G., Sterile filtration of gases: a bacterial aerosol challenge test. *J. Parenter. Drug Assoc. 32*:192–198 (1978).

24. McQuillen, D. F., Design and testing of pharmaceutical sterile rooms. *Pharm. Tech.* (Nov. 1981), p. 44.

25. Prout, G., Validation and routine operation of a sterile dry powder filling facility. *J. Parenter. Drug Assoc. 36*:199–204 (1982).

26. Witonsky, R. J., A new tool for the validation of the sterilization of parenterals. *Bull. Parenter. Drug Assoc. 31*:274–281 (1977).

27. Bunn, J. L., and Sykes, I. K., A chemical indicator for the rapid measurement of F_0 values. *J. Appl. Bacteriol. 51*:143–174 (1981).

28. Simmons, P. L., Sterilizer validation. *Pharm. Tech. 2*:69–70 (1979).

29. Caputo, R. A., and Mascoli, C. C., The design and use of biological indicators for sterilization-cycle validation. *Med. Device Diagn. Ind.* (Aug. 1980), p. 23.

30. Reich, R. R., Whitbourne, J. E., and McDaniel, A. W., Effect of storage conditions on the performance of *Bacillus stearothermophilus* biological indicators. *J. Parenter. Drug Assoc. 33*:228 (1979).

31. Pflug, I. J., Monitoring the sterilization process. In *Syllabus for Introductory Course in the Microbiology and Engineering of Sterilization Processes*, 2d ed., Parenteral Drug Association, Philadelphia pp. 19.2–19.4 (1978).

32. Simmons, P. L., Validation of dry heat sterilizers. *Pharm. Eng.* (May–July 1981), p. 38.

33. Simmons, P. L., Hot Air and Continuous Sterilization, Pharmaceutical Manufacturers Association, p. 27 (1978).

34. Tsuji, K., and Harrison, S. J., Dry-heat destruction of lipopolysaccharide: dry heat destruction kinetics. *Appl. Environ. Microbiol. 36*:710–714 (1978).

35. Wegel, S., Short time sterilization of glass materials under ultraclean conditions. *Bull. Parenter. Drug Assoc. 23*:122–135 (1974).

36. Akers, M. J., Avis, K. E., and Thompson, B., Validation studies of the Fostoria infrared tunnel sterilizer. *J. Parenter. Drug Assoc. 34*:330–347 (1980).

37. Akers, M. J., Ketron, K., and Thompson, B. F value requirements for the destruction of endotoxin in the validation of dry heat sterilization/depyrogenation cycles. *J. Parenter. Drug Assoc. 36*:23–27 (1982).

38. Cooper, J. F. Principles and applications of the limulus test for pyrogen in parenteral drugs. *Bull. Parenter. Drug Assoc. 29*:112–117 (1975).

39. International Symposium on Pyrogenicity, Innocuity and Toxicity Test Systems for Biological Products, *Dev. Biol. Stand. 34* (1977).

40. Robertson, J. H., Townsend, M. W., Allen, P. M., et al., Validation of ethylene oxide sterilization cycles. *Bull. Parenter. Drug Assoc. 31*:265–273 (1977).

41. Valenti, L., A validation program for ETO sterilization. *Med. Device Diagn. Ind. 1*:15 (1979).

42. Halleck, F. E., Principles for the validation of ethylene oxide sterilization cycles. *Med. Device Diagn. Ind. 2*:27 (1980).

43. Simmons, P. L., ETO sterilizer validation. *Pharm. Eng. 1*:13 (1981).

44. Caputo, R. A., Rohn, K. J., and Mascoli, C. C., Biological validation of an ethylene oxide sterilization process. *Dev. Ind. Mic. 22*:357–362 (1981).

45. Silverman, G. J., and Sinskey, A. J., Sterilization by ionizing radiation. In *Disinfection, Sterilization and Preservation*, 2d ed., Block, S. S. (ed.), Lea & Febiger, Philadelphia, p. 552 (1977).

46. Report No. 78-4.2, Medical Device Sterilization Monographs, Sterilization Cycle Development, Health Industry Manufacturers Association (1978).

47. Shoemaker, W. In *What the Filter Man Needs to Know About Filtration*, AICHE

Symposium Series, No. 171, Vol. 73, Shoemaker, W. (ed.), AICHE, New York, pp. 1-3 (1977).

48. Schroeder, H. G., and DeLuca, P. P., *Pharm. Tech.* *4*(11):80 (1980).
49. Wallhausser, K. H., *Drugs Made Ger.* *19*:85 (1976).
50. Tracen, B., *Pharm. Tech.* *5*(11):62 (1982).
51. *The United States Pharmacopeia XX*, Mack Publishing Co., Easton, PA, p. 1038 (1980).
52. *Federal Register 41*(106):2214 (June 1, 1976).
53. Wallhausser, K. H., *J. Parenter. Drug. Assoc.* *33*(3):156 (1979).
54. Lukaszewicz, R. C., and Meltzer, T. H., *J. Parenter. Drug Assoc.* *33*(5):246 (1979).
55. Lukaszewicz, R. C., and Fisher, R., *Pharm. Tech.* *5*(5):49 (1981).
56. Lukaszewicz, R. C., Tanny, G. B., and Meltzer, T. H., *Pharm. Tech.* *2*(11):77 (1978).
57. Howard, Jr., G., and Duberstein, R., *J. Parenter. Drug Assoc.* *34*(2):95 (1980).
58. Lukaszewicz, R. C., and Meltzer, T. H., *J. Parenter. Drug Assoc.* *33*(4):187 (1979).
59. Jacobs, S., *Filtration and Separation 9*(5):525 (1972).
60. Johnston, P. R., and Meltzer, T. H., *Pharm. Tech.* *4*(112):49 (1980).
61. Johnston, P. R., Lukaszewicz, R. C., and Meltzer, T. H., *J. Parenter. Sci. Tech.* *35*(1):36 (1981).
62. Meltzer, T. H., and Meyers, T. R., *Bull. Parenter. Drug Assoc.* *25*(4):165 (1971).
63. Olson, W. P., Martinez, E. D., and Kern, C. R., *J. Parenter. Sci. Tech.* *35*(5):215 (1981).
64. Standard Test Method for Pore Size Characteristics of Membrane Filters for Use with Aerospace Fluids, ASTM F316-80, Part 25, American Society for Testing and Materials, Philadelphia, pp. 872–878 (1981).
65. Marshall, J. C., and Meltzer, T. H., *Bull. Parenter. Drug Assoc.* *30*(5):214 (1976).
66. Reti, A. R., *Bull. Parenter. Drug Assoc.* *31*(4):187 (1977).
67. Olson, W. P., *Pharm. Tech.* *6*(5):42 (1982).
68. Olson, W. P., Briggs, R. O., Garanchon, C. M., et al., *J. Parenter. Drug Assoc.* *34*(4):254 (1980).
69. Olson, W. P., *Pharm. Tech.* *3*(11):85 (1979).
70. Reti, A. R., and Leahy, T. J., *J. Parenter. Drug Assoc.* *33*(5):257 (1979).
71. Dawson, F. W., Leahy, T. J., and Manalan, D. A., "Validation of Sterilizing Filters," presented at Nordiska Foreningen for Relighetsteknik och Rena Rum, Goteborg, Sweden (May 4, 1981).
72. Leahy, T. J., and Sullivan, M. J., *Pharm. Tech.* *2*(11):65 (1978).
73. Price, J. M., and Pauli, W. A., *Bull. Parenter. Drug Assoc.* *30*(1):45 (1976).
74. Johnston, P. R., and Meltzer, T. H., *Pharm. Tech.* *3*(11):66 (1979).
75. Pall, D. B., *Bull. Parenter. Drug Assoc.* *29*(4):192 (1975).
76. Pall, D. B., and Kirnbauer, E. A., "Bacteria Removal Prediction in Membrane Filters," presented at 52d Colloid and Surface Science Symposium, University of Tennessee, Knoxville (June 12, 1980).
77. Korcyznski, M. S., "Industrial Survey of Media Fill Practices in Aseptic Filling Operations," presented at the 2d PMA Seminar Program on Validation of Sterile Manufacturing Processes: Aseptic Processing, Atlanta (March 1-2, 1979).
78. Validation of Aseptic Filling for Solution Drug Products, Technical Monograph No. 2, Parenteral Drug Association, Philadelphia, pp. 16–21 (1980).
79. Sterility Testing and Sterility Testing of Pharmaceutical Preparation and Biological Substances, World Health Organization, Geneva, Switzerland (1973).

4

Sterile Products Validation

Karl L. Hofmann, Jr. *Pharmaceutical Group, Technical Operations, Bristol-Myers Squibb Company, Syracuse, New York*

I. INTRODUCTION

The student of statistics will appreciate the difficulty of successfully predicting the outcome of trials wherein several independent variables interact to affect the final result. Such is the case with sterile products. Validation of the manufacture of sterile pharmaceutical products is an extremely complicated process involving numerous activities that can be grouped for the purpose of discussion into four factors: process, facility, equipment, and personnel. Validation, then, can be viewed as the sum total of these factors, or validation = process + facility + equipment + personnel.

The object of the validation project is proof of reliability of the manufacturing process in its entirety. With this point in mind, this chapter will describe the interactions of the various elements of the validation equation contained in the factors mentioned above.

The individual topics have been described in great detail in the literature. This chapter intends to define the essential elements for consideration in a well-planned and well-executed validation project.

II. FACILITY DESIGN AND CONSTRUCTION

Much has been written about the design and construction of facilities intended for the manufacture of sterile products. No two facilities are identical, but all high-quality installations share common design features.

Control of the environment within the aseptic or clean areas of the facility is the most important design criterion [1]. This is accomplished by 1) filtering the air supply to reduce or eliminate particulate contaminants; 2) maintaining higher air pressures (positive pressure) within the critical areas to minimize infiltration of airborne contaminants from outside air; 3) providing smooth, easily cleanable surfaces on equipment, floors, walls, and ceilings to minimize the opportunity for collection of particulates and growth of microorganisms; and 4) providing temperature and humidity controls appropriate to the product being manufactured.

A modern aseptic production facility contains a series of zones or regions of different degrees of cleanliness, designed to create barriers to the ingress of contamination from the exterior noncontrolled environment into the most critical enclosure, where sterile products are manipulated [2].

The "cleanest" areas will be supplied with air at the highest positive pressure differential with respect to ambient conditions. The various zones can be classified according to standards such as FED-STD-209D [3], which provide guidance for air cleanliness in terms of particle size and quantity permissible per cubic foot of air.

Table 1 lists the maximum permissible counts for particles of sizes equal to or greater than those shown in the table for each classification listed:

Since personnel and materials must enter and leave the facility, buffer zones are established to provide access while minimizing the ingress of contaminants. Traffic control, sterile nonshedding garb, aseptic technique, and cleaning and decontamination procedures play important roles in maintaining the proper conditions. A modern parenteral drug manufacturing facility layout is shown in Fig. 1.

Higher air flows and special room finishes distinguish the critical enclosures from the less critical rooms. For example in Fig. 1 the most critical enclosure is the "sterile filling" room, where the product and sterilized components are manipulated and exposed to the room environment. High-Efficiency Particulate Air (HEPA)–filtered air supplying in excess of 20 complete changes per hour creates

Table 1 Particulate Count Limits by Area Class [3]

Area class	Particle size (μm)				
	0.1	0.2	0.3	0.5	5.0
10	350	75	30	10	NA
100	NA	750	300	100	NA
1000	NA	NA	NA	1000	7
10000	NA	NA	NA	10000	70
100000	NA	NA	NA	100000	700

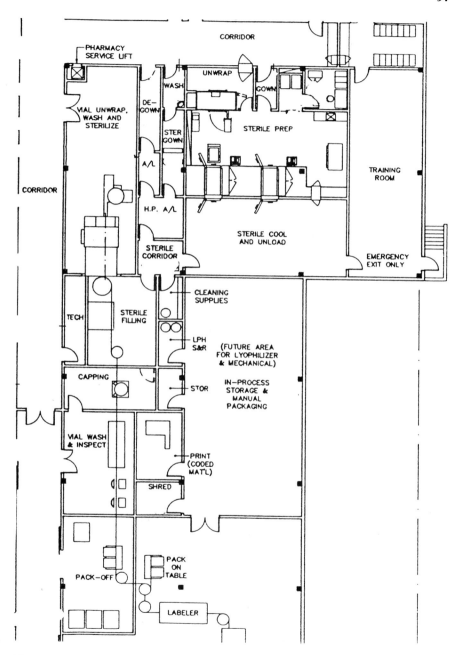

Figure 1 Sterile drug manufacturing facility.

an environment corresponding to Class 100 or better [2]. The room is maintained at a pressure differential (ΔP) of approximately 0.05 in. H_2O gauge with respect to the adjacent areas. The absolute pressure differential with respect to ambient air pressure could be in the range of 0.10 to 0.15 in H_2O.

The adjacent "sterile corridor" in Fig. 1 is also designated as a controlled area or "clean room"; however, it is not as critical as the sterile filling room because product and sterilized components are not normally exposed to the environment. Nevertheless, the design provides for air pressure differentials, air cleanliness of Class 10,000 or better, and room finishes typical of a clean room.

Special design features such as separate entrances and exits assist in maintaining the environment. The progressively higher controls from the noncontrolled corridor into the wash room, sterile gowning room, and high-pressure airlock serve to create a buffer to the sterile filling room. Air flow, in a direction from the controlled to the noncontrolled rooms, sweeps airborne particles away from the critical enclosures.

Clean rooms like the sterile filling, sterile corridor, sterile cool, and unload rooms in Fig. 1 are constructed using a smooth, durable flooring such as epoxy terazzo with walls and ceilings made from seamless PVC such as MIPOLAM®.

Less critical regions like the "vial unwrap, wash, and sterilize" room are finished with less expensive materials like troweled epoxy flooring, epoxy-painted walls, and Mylar-faced paneled ceilings.

Finally, the noncontrolled rooms, such as the final packaging and labeling areas, which pose no challenge to exposed product or sterilized containers and closures, might have ceramic tile floors and bases, epoxy-painted gypsum walls, and ceilings of latex-painted gypsum board or suitable panels.

III. PRINCIPLES OF STERILIZATION

The single most important objective in the validation of sterile products is achievement of sterility in the product. This goal can be realized consistently only if the container-closure system, the product contact surfaces of equipment, and the environment are likewise free of viable microorganisms. Depending on the nature of the item to be sterilized, various treatments can be employed.

A. Methods

Procedures commonly used to achieve sterilization of product, product contact components, and equipment include moist heat, dry heat, chemical (e.g., glutaraldehyde, chlorine, iodine, hydrogen peroxide, quaternary ammonium salts, and phenolic compounds), sterilization by gases (e.g., ethylene oxide, propylene oxide, β-propiolactone, and formaldehyde), filtration, ionizing radiation, or ultraviolet radiation [4].

Each treatment acts to destroy microbes in a unique manner with a different degree of effectiveness. For example, certain chemical treatments are effective against vegetative forms of microorganisms (e.g. ethyl alcohol) but relatively harmless to the spore forms (see Section VII,A of this chapter). Other treatments may not be suitable for certain product substrates. For example, steam sterilization may have a deleterious effect on certain types of plastic. The sterilizing medium must be effective against the known or suspected bioburden but not harmful to the item undergoing sterilization.

B. Microbial Destruction

Independent of the mechanism of action of the sterilization process, a unique and predictable relationship exists between the number of survivors in a given population of microorganisms and the time of exposure to the sterilizing medium or size of a radiation dose.

Although the rates of death may or may not be linear in all cases, mathematical expressions [5] have been developed to define the process to enable prediction of the probability of nonsterility. These expressions require a definition of terms:

1) *D value*: A unit of time important in describing microbial death kinetics for heat, chemical, and radiation sterilization processes. The term can be defined by the mathematical expression [6]

$$D = \frac{U}{\log N_0 - \log N_u}$$

where U is the exposure time under a given set of temperature and other conditions or the magnitude of the radiation dose, N_0 is the original bioburden, and N_u is the remaining population after time (or dose) U. For practical purposes the D value is the time required (under a given set of conditions) to reduce the bioburden by 90% or one log unit.

2) *Z value*: This is a temperature term that defines the resistance of a particular microorganism under a given set of conditions. The Z value is expressed mathematically as [5]

$$Z = \frac{T_2 - T_1}{\log D_1 - \log D_2}$$

where T_2 and T_1 are two different temperatures and D_1 and D_2 are the corresponding D values. The Z value is the slope of the logarithm of the thermal death time plotted against temperature. For practical purposes it is the difference in temperature (°C or °F) required to change the D value by 90% or one log unit.

3) *F value*: This time unit indicates the equivalent amount of time delivered by a thermal process at a particular temperature, with respect to a reference tempera-

ture and a specific Z value. The general term F is again defined by a mathematical expression as [5]

$$F = \Delta t \sum 10^{(T-T_0)/Z}$$

where t is time in minutes for the interval at temperature T with a specified Z.

4) F_0: The more commonly used term F_0 has application in steam sterilization, where the reference temperature is defined as 121.1°C with a Z value, based on the spore form of the microorganism *B. stearothermophilus*, of 10°C. F_0 can be derived from the general expression above by substituting the reference values for T_0 and Z into the equation. It is also derived from the expression [6]

$$F_0 = D_{121}(\log N_0 - \log N_u)$$

which terms have been defined above.

Another equation is useful in calculating the F_0 delivered in a process at a given temperature over a span of time [4]

$$F_0 = \int_{t_1}^{t_2} 10^{(T-T_0)/Z} dt$$

Example 1. To determine the F_0 delivered by a process at a temperature different from the reference temperature (121°C), we can integrate this expression with respect to time. If T is 125°C with t_1 at 1 minute and t_2 at 5 minutes, the expression becomes

$$F_0 = 10^{(T-T_0)/Z} * t]_{t_1}^{t_2}$$

Substituting values as above for T_0 and Z and completing the calculation,

$$F_0 = 2.5119(5 - 1) = 10.05 \text{ min}$$

In other words, 4 minutes treatment at 125°C is equivalent to more than 10 minutes at 121°C.

Having established some relationships as expressed in the equations for F, D, Z and F_0, we can focus on the purpose of the mathematical manipulations— namely determination of the probability of nonsterility of the product.

Although courts have held that articles deemed to be sterile must be sterile in the absolute, the industry and the regulatory bodies (e.g., FDA) for practical purposes deal with the concept of sterility on a probabilistic basis. The sterilization process must be proved to deliver a treatment that will provide a certain statistical probability of a nonsterile unit.

Example 2. To determine the probability of survival of a single microorganism after a sterilization treatment, we can define a term P as the absolute value of N_u expressed as a fraction. Rearranging the expression listed above, we can write

$$\log N_u = \log N_0 - \frac{F_0}{D_{121}}$$

Then

$$P = N_u = \text{antilog}\left(\log N_0 - \frac{F_0}{D_{121}}\right)$$

If a particular sterilization process delivers an F_0 of 9 minutes and the initial bioburden N_0 is 10^3 microorganisms with a D_{121} of 1 minute, the probability of survival of a single microorganism is calculated to be 10^{-6}.

IV. UTILITY QUALIFICATION

Much of the emphasis on validation of sterile products is placed on the sterilization process(es), rather than the facility supporting systems, e.g., utilities, equipment, and cleaning procedures. This is not inappropriate because the sterilization processes are critical to the manufacture of sterile products. However, no manufacturing operation can be considered under complete control without qualification of every system that can potentially affect product quality.

This task must be undertaken in a systematic way to be successful. Earlier in the chapter it was shown that the design of the facility is critical. Likewise, individual utilities require qualification.

The GMP regulations [8] do not provide specific directives or guidelines concerning qualification of utilities. However, the requirements for features such as temperature and humidity controls, HEPA filtration, environmental monitoring, cleaning, disinfection, and maintenance are explicitly mentioned. 21 CFR 211 (Subpart C, Buildings and Facilities, and Subpart D, Equipment) [8] implies that systems having an impact on product quality must be properly qualified.

Several different utility systems are necessary to operate a manufacturing plant, but only a few have direct or incidental product contact and therefore require qualification. The most important of these are heating ventilation and air conditioning (HVAC), water (including clean steam), and compressed gases. Other utilities, such as electricity, plant steam, and lighting, are obvious requirements but not considered process critical [10].

The style and approach to facility qualification may differ from firm to firm, but the principles of a well designed qualification program are similar. Typical programs begin with installation qualification (IQ). The IQ is described in a written protocol that contains these key elements:

1. Equipment or system specifications
2. Spare parts list
3. As-built drawings
4. Wiring diagrams
5. Piping and installation diagrams
6. Installation certification statement

Although IQ is a relatively straightforward procedure for a new facility, it should be carefully executed. The IQ documentation is the proof that the equipment (utility) actually met the design specifications from the original engineering documents, was installed in accordance with approved drawings and plans, and was properly connected to the required services (electrical, steam, chilled water, etc.). IQ documentation is invaluable whenever modifications to the installation are required for facility upgrade or expansion.

Following completion of the IQ, the equipment or system is subjected to operational qualification (OQ). This is a more rigorous exercise in which the object is to ascertain that the equipment or system being tested performs in accordance with design specifications throughout the full operational range(es). The OQ protocol contains

1. A full system description
2. Calibration certification documents
3. Testing plans
4. Acceptance criteria
5. Full record of testing results
6. Certification statement

A. Heating Ventilation and Air Conditioning (HVAC)

The term HVAC is an engineering acronym for one of the most critical utilities in the manufacture of sterile products. As discussed in the previous section, the supply of filtered air under positive pressure is the single most important means of maintaining control of the environment in an aseptic manufacturing environment.

Features of the HVAC system that affect product quality (sterility) and therefore require qualification include:

1. HEPA filter integrity
2. Airborne particle control
3. Air flow direction
4. Room air pressure differentials
5. Temperature and humidity control

1. HEPA Filter Integrity

The primary element in the HVAC system for the purpose of controlling air cleanliness in the aseptic environment is the HEPA filter. These specialized devices are manufactured by several vendors, including Cambridge Filter Co. and American Air Filter Co.

a. Design: Although the filter may be constructed of different materials dependent on the manufacturer and the customer's needs, it typically consists of a series of glass fiber sheets, folded accordion style to create a large surface area. The sheets or elements are held apart by aluminum separators and contained within a metal or plywood frame, attached with bonding material such as polyurethane foam or RTV silicone [2].

b. Certification: Certification by the filter manufacturer is normally required for units that are to be installed in a pharmaceutical plant. The testing done by the vendor will certify that the filter is capable of removing all particulate matter equal to or greater than 0.3 μm in size with an efficiency of 99.97%. This testing alone, however, does not suffice to qualify the HVAC system.

c. Installation: Virtually all modern sterile product-manufacturing facilities are designed with filters installed at the terminus of the ductwork of the air supply to the aseptic enclosure, preferably flush with the ceiling (terminal filter). Proper installation must be verified by testing. A certified filter that is improperly installed will not perform as intended and provides a false sense of security that the air supply is being properly filtered to remove contaminants from the noncontrolled technical areas.

d. Integrity testing: A popular method for certifying integrity of the filter installation uses a polydisperse aerosol, created by blowing air through liquid dioctylphthalate (DOP), introduced into the upstream ductwork, followed by scanning the entire downstream side of the filter face and periphery with a probe nozzle of an aerosol photometer. This testing, described in detail in technical publications [7,9], will identify "leaks" caused by damage due to mishandling or faulty construction. Small leaks can be repaired with a suitable silicone-based compound without removing the filter.

Each filter and each installation must be tested in this fashion before the facility can be considered qualified from the standpoint of the cleanliness of the air supply.

All measurements and testing are done in compliance with the written protocols for either IQ or OQ as appropriate, with data and test results properly recorded.

2.   *Airborne Particle Control*

After completion of the testing described above, the workstation enclosures must be certified in terms of designed air cleanliness classifications. As mentioned earlier, FED-STD 209 D [3] provides new guidelines for area classifications. The workstation classification must be confirmed by actual particle counting and sizing, using suitable electronic equipment such as optical particle counters.

Particle count surveys should be performed over extended time intervals and under a variety of operational conditions to determine if the enclosure consistently meets its design classification. One procedure used by a sterile bulk powder manufacturer to verify the design criteria for its Class 100 workstations is described below.

a. Procedure: Particle count/size data were obtained over a 3-month period at random times during the day, using an HIAC/ROYCO particle counting apparatus. A total of 566 data points were collected for analysis from seven different room enclosures within the aseptic suite. The particle counts selected for analysis were those sized at 0.5 μm and larger per cubic foot of air sample per minute of sampling time.

The data were analyzed individually by room (enclosure) and collectively to determine the probability distribution of the number of occurrences of particle counts within selected intervals sizes of 5 particles per interval. Intervals were defined as interval 1, 0–5 particles; interval 2, 6–10 particles, etc. (see Table 2). A histogram (Fig. 2) was prepared to determine the shape of the distribution curve and hence the type of distribution.

Actual count data were tabulated by the number of occurrences per interval and assigned a weighted count, which is defined as the product of the number of occurrences and the interval midpoint (see Table 2). The sum of all the interval-weighted counts, divided by the total number of occurrences, produced the weighted average count for the entire population. This number was assigned an "interval ratio" corresponding to the interval decimal equivalent for the count

Table 2 Determination of Distribution, Maximum Counts All Rooms

Interval number	Count range	Occurrences ×	Rng midpt =	Weighted count	Percent of total occurrences
1	0–5	139	2.5	347.5	24.6
2	6–11	79	8.5	671.5	14.0
3	12–17	80	14.5	1160	14.1
4	18–23	54	20.5	1107	9.8
5	24–29	50	26.5	1324	8.8
6	30–35	38	32.5	1235	6.7
7	36–41	29	38.5	1116.5	5.2
8	42–47	20	44.5	890	3.5
9	48–53	21	50.5	1060.5	3.5
10	54–59	13	56.5	734.5	2.3
11	60–65	12	62.5	750	2.2
12	66–71	7	68.5	479.5	1.2
13	72–77	7	74.5	521.5	1.2
14	78–83	7	80.5	563.5	1.2
15	84–89	4	86.5	346	0.8
16	90–95	5	92.5	462.5	0.9
17	96–101	1	98.5	98.5	0.2
Totals		566		12,869	99.9

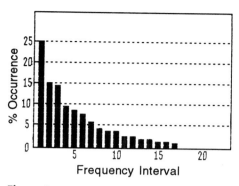

Figure 2

range (see the following section on data analysis). Only the maximum counts per minute taken over a sampling interval of several minutes were utilized in order to characterize a worst-case situation.

The shape of the curve generated from the histogram suggests an exponential probability distribution of the general form

$$f(x) = \lambda e^{(-\lambda x)}$$

b. Data analysis:

1. Weighted average count: $12{,}869/566 = 22.74$
2. Interval ratio: $E\{x\} = 4.79$ (note: this is the expected value of the random variable x)
3. λ value $= 1/E\{x\} = 0.209$

To determine the probability that an individual sampling experience will generate a count of less than 100 particles per cubic foot per minute, P is defined as $P\{x \leqslant 17\}$ (interval no. 17) or $P\{x \leqslant 98.5\}$ (midpoint count of interval no. 17). The cumulative probability function is then

$$F\{x\} = P\{x \leqslant 17\} = \sum_{0}^{x} \lambda e^{(-\lambda x)} \tag{1}$$

Since the exponential distribution is a continuous function it is easily evaluated using calculus.

Equation (1) is then integrated with respect to x:

$$F\{x\} = \int_{0}^{x} \lambda e^{(-\lambda x)} \, dx \tag{2}$$

$$F\{x\} = \lambda \left[-\frac{1}{\lambda} e^{(-\lambda x)} \right]_{0}^{x}$$

$$F\{x\} = -e^{(-\lambda x)} - (-e^{(-0)})$$

and

$$F\{x\} = 1 - e^{(-\lambda x)}$$

Substituting values for λ and x (the 17th frequency interval), the cumulative probability distribution becomes

$$F\{x\} = 1 - e^{(-0.209*17)} = 1 - 0.02864$$
$$F\{x\} = 0.9714$$

In summary, the study shows the probability that a random sample of particle counts within the controlled enclosures will be less than 100 for particles equal to or greater in size than 0.5 μm is *97.14%*.

3. Air Flow Direction

Other factors involving the air supply need to be considered. Some installations are designed to provide unidirectional flow [3], previously known as "laminar flow," directly above or adjacent to work areas where product is to be exposed.

Determination of unidirectional flow involves measuring the parallelism of air flow emanating from the HEPA filter throughout the work zone. This can be accomplished using an isokinetic smoke generator and measuring devices to determine offset from straight-line flow, either vertical or horizontal. Procedures, equipment, and limits are defined in the technical literature [9].

4. Room Air Pressure Differentials

The importance of maintaining air pressure differentials in the enclosures of the aseptic suite within the ranges specified in the design plans cannot be over-emphasized. Reversal of air flow, which can occur if the relative room pressures are upset, can allow contaminated air from a noncontrolled region into the clean room, thus defeating the purpose of the HEPA filtered air supply.

Most enclosures in the aseptic processing suite are not airtight because of the need for conveyor lines and pass-through openings, so there is very real opportunity for contamination from the noncontrolled adjacent manufacturing areas and particularly overhead uncontrolled technical areas.

The only way to ensure that contamination is excluded is to maintain positive pressure within the controlled room. This is accomplished by controlling the rate of room exhaust to maintain an excess of incoming air over the return or exhaust air, thus creating a pressure differential with respect to an unpressurized room. Within the aseptic suite the various rooms are rated with respect to degree of cleanliness (see Section II).

Special monitoring devices known as Magnahelic or Photohelic gauges measure the pressure differentials across a diaphragm and depict the value in terms of inches of water or some other convenient scale. These instruments are very accurate and sensitive to very small changes in pressure differential. Typically, they are connected directly to an alarm system that will cause a visual signal (flashing light) or an audible signal (alarm buzzer) and/or trigger a recording device to report a deviation outside a prescribed range of pressure differential.

Qualification of these devices and systems is a matter of calibrating the instruments against a certified standard and verifying that alarms will function properly if operational ranges are exceeded.

5. Temperature and Humidity Control

Control of temperature and humidity within enclosures utilized for aseptic processing is specifically mentioned in the GMP regulations [8]. However, little or no explanation is provided in the regulations as to why such control is important to the production of sterile dosage forms.

Experience tells us, however, that failure to control temperature within a fairly narrow range can have an adverse impact on personnel comfort, which could lead to improper aseptic technique and hence product contamination. Excessive temperature within the enclosures can also induce germination of latent spores on equipment and other surfaces, thus increasing the area bioburden. This is especially likely if the high temperature is combined with moisture due to high humidity. Poor flow characteristics and erratic weight control can occur during the filling of sterile powders if temperature and humidity exceed prescribed ranges.

Many of the newer facilities are equipped with computer-controlled environmental systems that automatically maintain temperature and humidity within narrowly defined limits. These systems undergo installation and operational qualification testing similar to that performed for the critical utilities mentioned above. Such testing and subsequent documentation provide assurance that the control system(s) will reliably maintain an environment suitable for production of sterile products.

B. Water

Production of sterile pharmaceutical dosage forms is heavily dependent on the quality of water used to formulate product or to clean components, equipment, and surfaces within the aseptic enclosure. Various names are associated with types of water that have undergone specialized treatment to achieve certain characteristics or levels of quality required for a particular use. These include potable water, soft water, deionized water, purified water USP, water for injection USP, and sterile water for injection USP.

Water quality is usually defined in terms of chemical and bacteriological purity, particulate matter content, and endotoxin levels. Potable water is normally from the municipal water system, which may have been treated with chlorine to control microbiological growth. Soft water and deionized water have undergone ion-exchange or similar treatment to eliminate unwanted ionic species such as

Mg^{2+} and/or Ca^{2+}. Purified water, water for injection, and other types of water meeting compendial [11] specifications are produced by either ion exchange, reverse osmosis, distillation, or a combination of such treatments.

1. System Design

A poorly designed or maintained system will not produce water of the desired quality in a reliable manner. Because reliability is the essence of validation, a system having unsatisfactory design or maintenance features cannot be validated.

Analysis of the feedwater before designing a water treatment system is essential. Every effort should be made to take into account seasonal variation in the feedwater source and to determine the best design to achieve the desired water quality [13]. A typical source or feedwater analysis is shown in Table 3.

Certain design features of a water system have come to be recognized as standard for the pharmaceutical industry. Because control of particulate matter and microbial growth are critical to the water system, many firms have chosen the following typical specifications for their purified and water for injection (WFI) systems:

Table 3 Water Analysis

Temperature	55°F
PH	6.8
Total hardness	133 ppm
Total dissolved solids	211 ppm
Conductivity	280 µohm-cm
Color	20 alpha units
Turbidity	0.61 NTU
Iron	< 0.04 ppm
Manganese	0.060 ppm
Copper	0.050 ppm
Zinc	0.149
Nitrate	13.8 ppm
Silica	12.3 ppm
Free CO_2 as $CaCO_3$	12.67
Calcium	34.2 ppm
Magnesium	10.1 ppm
Sodium	13.1 ppm
Potassium	3.56 ppm
Chloride	33 ppm
Sulfate	58 ppm
Carbonate alkalinity as $CaCO_3$	0.02
Bicarbonate alkalinity as $CaCO_3$	39.97
Hydroxide alkalinity as $CaCO_3$	< 1.0

1. Storage vessel fabricated at 316L stainless steel, jacketed to maintain not less than 80°C, with interior surfaces mechanically polished or electropolished to eliminate inclusion sites where deposition of an electrolytic substance could initiate corrosion.
2. Distribution system should consist of a continuously recirculating loop from the storage vessel, connecting all points of use without branching and returning to the storage vessel. The system should meet 3 A sanitary standards, be sloped to drain, with product contact surfaces polished to a finish similar to the storage vessel. Piping should be joined by certified tungsten inert gas (TIG) welded connections or the less desirable method of sanitary clamp fittings.
3. Recirculation pumps should have double mechanical seals using WFI as the lubrication and barrier fluid.
4. Valving should be diaphragm, ball, or plug types with connections, and construction materials, suitable to pharmaceutical use (e.g., 316L stainless steel and Teflon) [2].
5. Storage vessels and distribution piping should be designed for sterilization from a clean steam source capable of pressurizing the entire system.
6. Storage vessel vent filters should be hydrophobic [12] and microbially retentive, rated at least 0.45 μm maximum mean porosity.
7. Points of use connections from the distribution loop should not create "dead legs" or regions where water is stagnant within the piping. Any heat exchangers should be installed at points of use and be of a double-tubesheet design, which is likewise suitable for steam sterilization.

2. Qualification and Validation

As with the other utilities, the installation qualification and operational qualification precede the actual validation. Many firms undertake the validation as a series of separate studies of each component of the entire system. In other words, the WFI system may consist of the municipal water supply treated by a sand filter, carbon bed, cation-anion exchanger, mixed bed deionizer, ultrafiltration unit, microbial retentive filters, distillator (or reverse osmosis unit), and distribution system, including the storage tank, pumps, valves, heat exchangers, and associated piping.

Each station of the treatment train is designed to impart certain quality characteristics to the "product" water that leaves that station. Understanding the reason for each treatment is the basis for the validation program. For example, the sand filter, if used, is designed to clarify the water. Therefore a simple comparison of particulate matter levels of the feedwater and effluent is the essential element of the validation of the sand filter.

Likewise, the demineralization or deionization step is intended to eliminate undesirable anions or cations by replacing them with hydrogen or hydroxyl species. Effectiveness of this treatment can be verified by simple chemical testing.

Each treatment is intended to improve the quality of the feedwater to the next station, thereby reducing the loading on each station and contributing to the efficiency of the entire system. The sequence or order of each treatment is very important. For example, removal of silica or other scale-forming impurities from the feedwater prior to distillation is critical to preserving the useful life of the evaporator.

The validation protocol provides a detailed description of sampling locations and requirements, testing methodology, and test limits or specifications. Because piping and installation diagrams of typical water systems can be very detailed and confusing to nonengineers, a simplified sketch of the sampling points, identified by a numbering system, will be of great help to the personnel conducting the sampling. Typical layouts for a USP purified water system and a USP water for injection system are presented in Figs. 3 and 4 [13].

Sampling points, indicated by the numbered locations in the diagram, provide the means of verifying whether each treatment station is effectively controlling the water quality. Sampling and testing can be performed daily during qualification and validation. When the system is in routine use, following the validation, the testing frequency can be reduced to a weekly schedule for monitoring purposes.

Table 4 indicates typical test requirements for each of the sampling points for the USP purified water system depicted in Fig. 3.

Water samples from points numbered 2–10 in the WFI system depicted in Fig. 4 should meet specifications for water for injection, USP. An action guideline of not more than 10 colony-forming units (CFU)/100 ml for bacteriological purity is suggested. As with the purified water system, the sampling and testing frequency for the WFI system is defined in the protocol and can be reduced after the system is qualified and validated.

C. Compressed Gases

Various kinds of compressed gases (e.g., nitrogen, oxygen, and carbon dioxide) may be found in the sterile drug manufacturing plant; however, as an example only compressed air will be discussed.

Compressed air is one of the utilities that may have direct or incidental product contact and therefore requires qualification. The types of contaminants found in compressed air, not surprisingly, are the same as those found in the ambient environment. These may include microorganisms (e.g., bacteria, molds, and viruses), moisture, particulate matter, and possibly pyrogens. Undesirable levels of hydrocarbons from compressor lubricants may be found if the compressor is not of the oil-free type.

A well-designed compressed air system eliminates or substantially reduces the levels of these contaminants. Components of such a system include:

1. An oil-free compressor—typically a rotary screw, multiple-stage design.

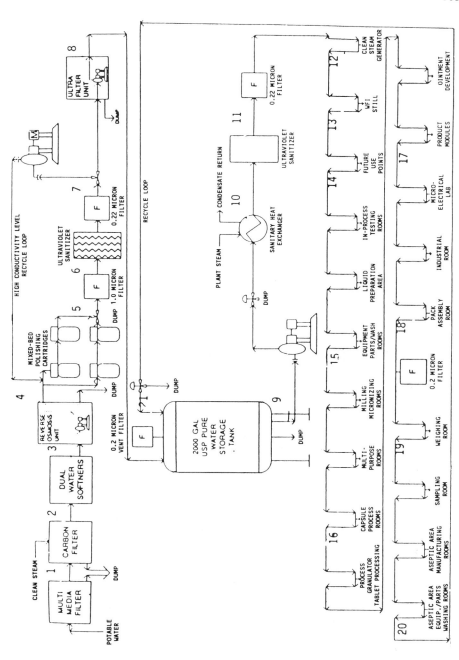

Figure 3 USP purified water system.

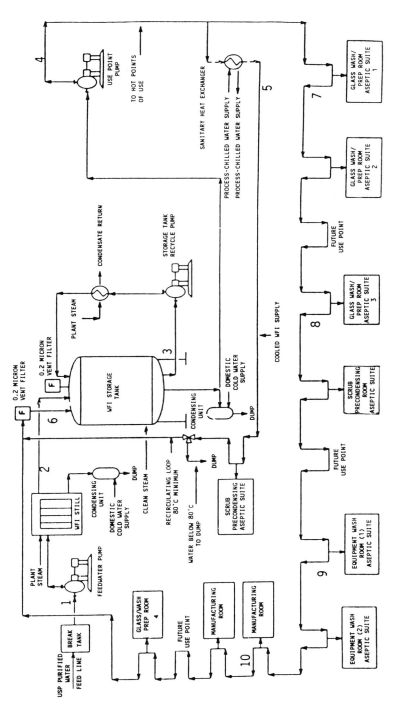

Figure 4 USP WFI system flow diagram.

106

Table 4 Sampling and Testing Requirements

Sample point	Location	Specification
1	In line downstream from multimedia filter	Potable water specification, including: Chlorine content 0.2–3.0 ppm Microbial content < 500 CFU/ml Absence of visible particulate matter
2	In line downstream from carbon filter	Potable water specification except chloride— USP purified water limits
3	In line downstream from water softeners	Potable water specification, including: Calcium and magnesium ≤ 10 ppm
4	In line downstream from reverse osmosis unit	USP purified water specification, including: Microbial count ≤ 100 CFU/ml Absence of coliform and *Pseudomonas* sp.
5	In line downstream from mixed-bed polishing cartridge	USP purified water specification, including: Microbial count ≤ 100 CFU/ml Absence of coliform and *Pseudomonas* sp.
6	In line downstream from 1.0 μm filter	USP purified water specification, including: Microbial count ≤ 100 CFU/ml Absence of coliform and *Pseudomonas* sp.
7	In line downstream from 0.2 μm filter	USP purified water specification, including: Microbial count ≤ 50 CFU/ml Absence of coliform and *Pseudomonas* sp.
8	In line downstream from ultrafilter	USP purified water specification, including: Microbial count ≤ 50 CFU/ml Absence of coliform and *Pseudomonas* sp.
9–21	Locations as depicted	USP purified water specification, including: Microbial count ≤ 50 CFU/ml Absence of coliform and *Pseudomonas* sp.

2. An oil-coalescing filter to trap any liquid hydrocarbons or water.
3. A dryer to remove condensed moisture and reduce levels of gaseous hydrocarbons.
4. A filtration unit to eliminate gross particulate matter such as fibers and metal particles.
5. A sterilizing filter rated at 0.2 μm.
6. A sanitary design receiver tank and distribution piping sloped for proper drainage.
7. Instrumentation suitable for monitoring the temperature, pressure, and volume or flow rate in the system.

In addition the compressor should be sized to deliver peak demands that will not exceed 75 to 80% of its rated capacity.

Table 5 Compressed Air—Quality Attributes

Contaminant	Limit
Hydrocarbons	Less than 5 mg/m^3
Water Vapor	Dewpoint less than 0°C
Microorganisms	Less than 0.1 CFU/ft^3

1. Qualification

Installation and operational qualification work includes verification of temperature, pressure and flow rates, instrument calibration, and thorough flushing of the entire system to remove oil, metal particles, and other contaminants.

2. Validation

The type of testing and acceptance limits listed in the validation protocol may vary from firm to firm; however, compressed air with product contact should be tested for the quality attributes listed in Table 5.

Analysis for hydrocarbon content involves passing a known quantity of compressed air through a suitable filter, extracting any retained hydrocarbons from the filter into a suitable solvent, and quantitatively analyzing the extract using a validated spectrophotometric (or equivalent) procedure (see Appendix, Section VIII). A diagram of a filtration apparatus suitable for in-line sample collection is shown in Figure 5.

Water content or dewpoint can be determined by various procedures, including an electrolytic hygrometer technique, frost point analysis, or a piezoelectric sorption hygrometer procedure [14].

Microbial content can be analyzed by passing a measured quantity of compressed air into a suitable neutral medium such as a phosphate buffer (pH 7) and filtering the medium through a 0.22-μm membrane. The filter membrane is then transferred to a Petri dish containing a general-purpose medium such as trypticase soy agar (TSA), which is then incubated at temperatures and times suitable to detect the presence of bacteria, mold, and yeast.

During validation testing the air quality can be evaluated for various other contaminants [14], some of which are indicated in Table 6.

V. EQUIPMENT QUALIFICATION/VALIDATION

A. Container Preparation

The quality of sterile products is directly dependent on the care taken at each step of their manufacture to ensure freedom from particulate matter, impurities, microbial contamination, and pyrogenic substances. A very important aspect of

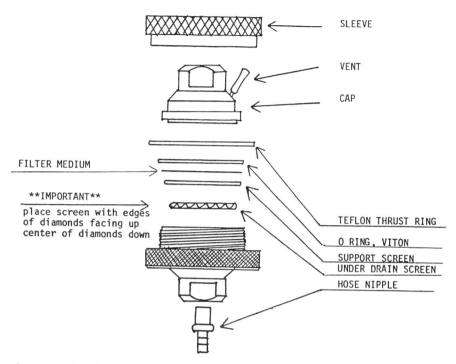

Figure 5 Filtration apparatus suitable for in-line sample collection.

the process is cleaning of the product container. The immediate drug product container and closure system is the physical barrier between external contaminants and the sterile drug substance. It is the primary means of ensuring that the drug maintains its quality for the entire shelf life.

Parenteral drug containers are typically fabricated from glass (bottles, vials, syringes, or ampules) or plastic (bottles, bags, vials, or syringes). Regardless of the nature of the container, contaminating substances such as paper fibers, cellophane particles, atmospheric dust particles, molding adjuvants, lubricants, glass fragments, viable microbes, and pyrogenic materials must be eliminated from the containers before they are used in the filling operation.

The design of the cleaning equipment should conform to the requirements of the GMPs in that it will not be "reactive, additive, or absorptive so as to alter the safety, identity, strength, quality or purity of the drug product" [8]. Container-washing equipment should be constructed of high-quality (304 or better grade) stainless steel suitably polished to resist corrosion from the high water temperatures normally experienced in the equipment.

Table 6 Typical Compressed Air Quality Attributes

			Type I	
Limiting characteristics	A	B	C	D
% O_2 (v/v), balance predominantly N_2[a]	atm	atm	atm/ 19.5–23.5	atm/ 19.5–23.5
Water		none condensed	[b]	[b]
Hydrocarbons (condensed) in mg/m^3 of gas at NTP[c]		none	5	5
Carbon monoxide			50	20
Odor				
Carbon dioxide				1000
Gaseous hydrocarbons (as methane)				
Nitrogen dioxide				
Nitrous oxide				
Sulfur dioxide				
Halogenated solvents				
Acetylene				
Permanent particulates				

[a]The term "atm" (atmospheric) denotes the oxygen content normally present in atmospheric air; the numerical values denote the oxygen limits for synthesized air.

[b]The water content of compressed air required for any particular grade may vary with the intended use from saturated to very dry. If a specific water limit is required, it should be specified as limiting dewpoint or concentration in ppm (v/v). Dewpoint is expressed in temperature °F at one atmosphere absolute pressure (760 mmHg). To convert dewpoint °F to °C, ppm (v/v), or mg/liter.

[c]No limits are given for condensed hydrocarbons beyond grade E since the gaseous hydrocarbon limits could not be met if condensed hydrocarbons were present.

The utility services should consist of high-quality water, i.e., filtered deionized (USP purified), for the initial wash cycle and water for injection USP quality water for the final rinse cycle. Likewise, other services such as compressed air should be suitably filtered and obtained from an oil-free compressor. The steam supply should meet "clean steam" quality in that its condensate should conform to specifications for water for injection USP.

The suitability of the design and utility services is established during the IQ and OQ phases of qualification discussed earlier in this chapter. Important criteria for a typical washer include

(gaseous)					Type II (liquid)	
Grades						
E	F	G	H	J	A	B
atm/	atm/	atm/	atm/	atm/	atm/	atm/
19.5–23.5	19.5–23.5	19.5–23.5	19.5–23.5	19.5–23.5	19.5–23.5	19.5–23.5
b	b	b	b	1 −10.4°F		b
5						
10	5	5	5	1		5
						None
500	500	500	500	0.5		5
	25	15	10	0.5		10
		2.5	0.5	0.1		0.5
				0.1		
		2.5	0.5	0.1		0.5
		10	1	0.1		0.5
				0.05		0.5
						−.15

Water: quality, temperature, pressure, and flow rate
Steam: quality and pressure
Compressed Air: quality and pressure

The duration of the prewash, washing, final rinse, and flush cycles must be established during validation and maintained within suitably narrow ranges to ensure repeatability.

Containers should be subjected to testing prior to beginning the validation phase to determine the type and extent of contaminants normally found. These could include some or all of the items listed above for glass and plastic containers. Any or all of these contaminants, if not removed from the containers, may compromise the drug product quality to varying degrees. The drug product manufacturer is responsible for removing or reducing these substances from the surface of the containers to levels considered safe for their use in the drug product.

A significant question arises at this point. What levels are considered safe and acceptable? The answer(s) to this question can be very complicated, because many experts disagree. The medical community has studied the effects of intravenous injection of parenteral solutions containing particulate matter. Pulmonary micro-emboli, thrombi, and granulomas have been reported [11].

Solutions that are contaminated with viable microorganism and/or pyrogenic substances pose obvious risks to the patient. Clearly, every reasonable effort must be made by the manufacturer to rid the container of contamination from any source.

The USP has provided guidelines [11] in terms of quantity and size limits for particulate matter in containers of small-volume parenterals. However, these limits apply to liquid or constituted solutions of the drug product rather than the container itself. Because the drug product itself often contributes significantly to the total level of particulate matter, essentially no guidelines are available for container cleanliness.

Fortunately, gross contamination of the containers received from the vendor is uncommon. Through well-controlled manufacturing processes and special pack-aging and shipping containers, most of the major vendors now produce a relatively clean product. Nevertheless, quantifiable levels of contaminants are still observed and their removal by a consistently repeatable process must be validated.

1. Mechanism of Cleaning

Modern cleaning equipment functions principally through mechanical cleaning action. This means that contaminants are removed forcibly by the action of flowing water, steam, or air against the surface(s) of the container.

Although detergents would enhance removal of certain organic contaminants such as oils, lubricants, and grease, their use is not recommended. These agents function by solubilizing the nonpolar portion of the organic contaminant in the long-chain fatty acid portion of the detergent molecular complex, while the ionic carboxyl portion dissolves in the water phase, creating a stable emulsion. Deter-gent residuals create yet another concern in validating the cleaning process. Because the container manufacturers take precautions to minimize the level of contaminants on the parenteral containers, the use of detergents is not necessary in most applications.

Ultrasonic techniques have come into use for a number of applications in cleaning parenteral containers. The principle of these treatments is again mechani-cal action. The equipment develops rapid, alternating pressure pulses in the fluid contained within a basin or sink in which the item to be cleaned is submerged. A force is created by the collapse of a cavity or "hole" in the cleaning fluid directly on the surface(s) of the containers; this action serves to loosen contaminants, which can then be rinsed away.

Simple air jet and vacuum cleaning techniques have been employed with limited success. These techniques should be used with caution because there is a potential to create more contamination within the container rather than eliminate it. This happens because the air stream moving across the container surface at high velocity in relatively dry conditions creates a static charge of considerably high potential by stripping electrons from the container surface. Any oppositely charged particles in the immediate environment are attracted and cling tenaciously to the container surface. Many of these systems are so poorly designed that they simply create zones of turbulence within the container that tend to move the particulate contaminants around and redeposit them at another spot within the container.

2. Validation

One practical approach to validating the cleaning process is to establish a known level of challenge contaminant, which is applied or "spiked" into numbered or otherwise identified containers, which then undergo a typical cleaning cycle. Typical contaminants include visible and subvisible particulate matter, chemical, microbiological, and pyrogen challenges.

After the wash cycle, the spiked container is evaluated by suitable testing to determine the amount of residual contaminant. The "before" and "after" numbers can be compared to establish an efficiency number based on the original level of contaminant. For example, a 50-ml vial, type 1 glass on position, is "spiked" with approximately 1000 particles of a size equal to or greater than 25 μm. The vial is then subjected to the cleaning process and evaluated to determine the residual particulate levels. Approximately 10 particles of the original 1000-particle challenge remains on the surface. This finding is interpreted as follows:

1000 particles (original challenge) $-$ 10 particles (residual after cleaning) $=$ 990 particles removed by cleaning.

$$\frac{990}{1000} = 0.99 \times 100 \text{ or } 99\% \text{ efficiency for the cleaning process}$$

It is important to establish the type and quantity of contaminants in order to design a testing or validation program that is meaningful. An unnecessarily rigorous challenge may be difficult or impossible to eliminate using the normal cleaning cycle and may lead to a false conclusion about the suitability of the cleaning equipment and system. Conversely, failure to determine whether the cleaning system can successfully eliminate or substantially reduce high levels of typical contaminants is likewise inappropriate.

One parenteral drug manufacturer conducted a validation study by evaluating the removal of four different types of contaminants. The equipment being evaluated was a Strunck vial washer manufactured by Robert Bosch Corp. The four challenge contaminants were particulate matter, NaCl, a suspension of *B. stearothermophilus* spores, and a control standard endotoxin (CSE). Methodology and principles of application of these challenges as well as detection procedures and levels of acceptability are described in the following subsections.

a. Particulate matter: The pretreatment particulate matter content of various different-sized containers was determined by flushing the interior surfaces of the containers with particulate-free deionized water. The rinse water was analyzed for subvisible contaminants, at the ≤ 10 μm and ≤ 25 μm levels, by HIAC-ROYCO. Finally, the rinse water was passed through a 0.45-μm membrane disk filter. Visible particles trapped on the filter surface were examined by low power optical microscopy for counting, sizing, and characterization. In this manner the average quantity, size, and type of particulate contamination per individual vial were determined.

b. Chemical: As a qualitative test of washing efficiency, a solution of NaCl was added to selected vials. The vials were swirled to coat the inner surface of each container and the solution evaporated to dryness. Test vials were then subjected to the normal wash cycle followed by addition of a solution of $AgNO_3$ to detect the presence of Cl^-. Any residual NaCl would ionize in the presence of water to form the chloride ion, which would then react with silver ion to create insoluble AgCl, which can be detected visually.

c. Microbiological: Bioburden loading levels were determined by a membrane filtration procedure prior to washing and also after the spiking to confirm that the desired challenge level was achieved. Following the cleaning cycle, the same procedure was used to evaluate residual bioburden. To recover the residual contaminants, sterile peptone water USP was used to rinse the entire inner surface of each vial. Results are reported as CFU per vial.

d. Endotoxin: Pyroburden was determined by validated limulus amebocyte lysate (LAL) techniques both before and after treatment in the washer to confirm preexisting and challenge levels. It is expected that pretreatment pyroburdens will be low, and removal of a known challenge of pyrogen in the cleaning procedure provides assurance that subsequent dry-heat depyrogenation will eliminate any preexisting contamination.

Table 7 shows the summarized results of a series of trials for the Strunck vial washer using three different sizes of glass vials and 50 vials per trial.

B. Closure Preparation

The most common type of primary closure used in conjunction with glass containers for parenteral drugs is the elastomeric closure, or plug. As with the container itself, the closure must be sterile, pyrogen free, and free from contaminants that could adulterate the drug substance, because the closure is likely to be in direct contact with the drug at some time during the storage, handling, or use of the dosage unit.

Accordingly, it rests with the drug manufacturer to determine the nature and extent of typical contaminants found on these articles as received from the closure manufacturer and to design and validate a system for reliably removing or reducing these contaminants to an acceptable level.

Table 7 Strunck Vial Washer Validation Summary

Test	Vial size (cm³)	Average prewash loading (A)		Average prewash spike (B)		Post treatment residuals (C)		Reduction factor (log B − log C)	
		≥10 μm	≥25 μm	≥10 μm	≥25 μm	≥10 μm	≥25 μm	≥10 μm	≥25 μm
I. Particulate matter test	8.2	76	10	1300	110	7.5	1	2.23	2.04
	15	82	8.5	1500	125	10	0	2.18	2.10
	20	130	10	1750	140	16	2.5	2.04	1.75
						*No visible particulate matter			
II. NaCl test	8.2	NA		150 μg/vial		0+/50		NA	
	15			250 μg/vial		0+/50			
	20			250 μg/vial		0+/50			
III. Bioburden Test	8.2	0.32 CFU/vial		10³ CFU/vial		0.04 CFU/vial		4.4	
	15	0.36 CFU/vial		10³ CFU/vial		0.05 CFU/vial		4.3	
	20	0.60 CFU/vial		10³ CFU/vial		0.08 CFU/vial		4.1	
IV. Endotoxin Test	8.2	≤0.25 EU/vial		10³ EU/vial		≤0.25 EU/vial		3.6	
	15	≤0.05 EU/vial		10³ EU/vial		≤0.25 EU/vial		3.6	
	20	≤0.05 EU/vial		10³ EU/vial		≤0.25 EU/vial		3.6	

1. Closure Contaminants

A number of undesirable substances could be present on the surface or sorbed into the matrix of the closures, but the predominant contaminants are particles of the closure matrix itself, usually butyl, other rubber compounds, metallic particles from the closure templates, microorganisms, endotoxins, and template lubricants, which are usually organic in nature. In addition, various extractable substances used in the formulation of the elastomeric closure can present problems. These extractable substances include activators such as ZnO, MgO, and stearic acid; curing agents like sulfur and phenolic compounds; accelerators like amines and thiazoles; and antidegradants such as dithiocarbamates and various ketones and aldehydes [15].

Knowing the types of contaminants likely to be associated with the closures upon receipt from the vendor, it remains to devise suitable procedures for removing them. Throughout the industry numerous techniques have been devised to eliminate unwanted contaminants from parenteral closures. Surfactants such as sodium lauryl sulfate and treatment with solvents such as acetone have been utilized to remove debris and organic substances and to kill bacteria, viruses, and fungi. Detergents have the capability to reduce the ionic, van der Waals, and hydrophobic interactions causing weakening of the bonds between the lipid A portion of lipopolysaccharide, or surface endotoxins, and the closure surface, thus facilitating their removal [16].

2. Validation

Experience has shown that the difficulty of removing certain of these cleaning agents far outweighs their usefulness in treating elastomeric closures. As a result, most parenteral manufacturing firms simply utilize a high-quality water wash/rinse treatment before siliconization and sterilization.

Contaminants on the surface of the elastomeric closures as received from the vendor should be identified and quantified before developing a treatment cycle. This work is necessary to facilitate measurement of the effectiveness of the treatment in terms of absolute elimination or substantial reduction of an unwanted contaminant and to indicate the need for changing cycle parameters when desired results are not achieved.

Closure sterilization, following the cleaning cycle, is typically done by autoclaving with saturated steam. The temperatures achieved in such treatments are not sufficient to eliminate significant endotoxin contamination.

Therefore, the validation of any cleaning procedure must include testing for residual endotoxin, particulate matter, and any adventitious contaminant determined during the pretreatment examination. Achieving sterility during the cleaning cycle is not an absolute requirement; however, the bioburden remaining should not present a significant challenge to the subsequent sterilization process and should be considered in the development of those treatments.

The usual IQ and OQ as described for utilities precede the validation and serve as the basis for design of the validation study. As with other utilities and equipment, the validation protocol provides the scope of the work through the acceptance criteria, test results, and conclusions.

Washing equipment designed for cleaning elastomeric closures is normally constructed of high-quality, corrosion-resistant, stainless steel (e.g., 304 or 316L rating) and polished to eliminate surface imperfection. These washers are serviced with high-quality water, e.g., WFI USP grade, at elevated temperatures. Certain designs incorporate a silicone treatment as part of the cycle to facilitate handling of the closures during the actual filling operation.

As with any procedure that is to be validated, the cleaning process must be reproducible. Many modern closure washers operate on the principle of mechanical agitation of the components within the load to dislodge the sorbed or lightly attached particulate matter and remove this debris without redeposition on another portion of the load. This feature is extremely important.

Some units are controlled by microprocessors that regulate such parameters as water temperature, water pressure or flow rate, introduction of clean steam or air, wash cycle time, rinse cycle time, addition of silicone oil, and drying (if necessary).

Many manufacturers use equipment that combines the steps of washing, siliconization, and sterilization in a continuous operation. Such a treatment is desirable because it minimizes the time the closures are held in a wet condition. If sterilization does not follow the washing step immediately, the components must be thoroughly dried to eliminate the likelihood of microbial growth and/or formation of pyrogens. Closures should be handled in such a manner as to minimize the potential for contamination from the cleaning operation through the filling and sealing steps.

C. Steam Sterilization

Sterilization of product and equipment by saturated steam is one of the most widely used treatments in the parenteral drug industry. It is a very efficient procedure and is the method of choice for products and articles that can withstand the treatment.

1. Mechanism of Action

Microbial destruction is brought about by cleavage of intramolecular hydrogen bonds between proteins, which effect a rearrangement of the spatial orientation of the molecule. This change destroys the molecule's functionality, which is dependent on its highly specialized structure [26,27].

Considerable research on the subject has shown that bacterial spores, particularly those of *Bacillus* and *Clostridium* species, are resistant to thermal death.

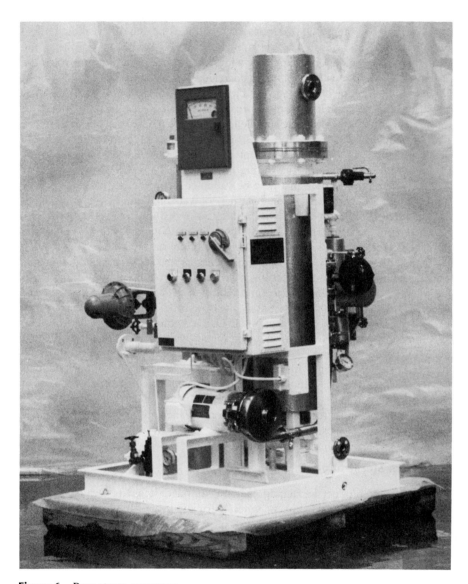

Figure 6 Pure steam generator.

Because the rate of microbial death appears to follow first-order reaction kinetics, predictions of microbial destruction can be made using mathematical models.

The destruction of the highly resistant spores is dependent on the presence of moisture for hydration of the spore and denaturation of nucleic acids and proteins. It is, therefore, essential that saturated steam be employed as the sterilant. Dry-heat treatments can be utilized, but the temperature and time parameters are much greater than those for saturated steam.

Heat transfer from saturated steam to the chamber environment is much more effective than that from dry heat or superheated steam. Heat of condensation is transferred to the load, thus raising its temperature and hydrating any adventitious microorganisms on the surfaces of articles to be sterilized.

2. Equipment

During the IQ and OQ phases, various features of the autoclave are checked for proper function. These include the pressure vessel for conformance to appropriate ASME codes, door safety interlock system, the chamber for design and finish, the chamber and jacket steam traps, temperature control monitoring and recording equipment, timers, vacuum pumps, jacket and chamber pressure indicators, any associated vent filters, and the steam supply to the chamber.

A pure or "clean" steam supply for the treatment chamber is essential. A pure steam generator produces and supplies saturated steam meeting WFI specifications, at the proper pressure and temperature. A typical unit is shown in Fig. 6.

The plant steam supply, usually of lower quality, can be supplied to the chamber jacket provided there is no physical interconnection between the chamber and jacket.

3. Cycle Development

Many steam sterilization cycles are designed as "overkill" treatments. Since the population and heat resistance of the microorganisms in the load may be unknown, large F_0 values are required to ensure that the treatment is successful. The articles selected for sterilization must be heat stable. Because a typical challenge to the cycle incorporates biological indicators of *B. stearothermophilus* at a population of 10^6 with a D value (121°C.) of approximately 1 minute, a 10^{-12} theoretical spore reduction must be achieved to provide overkill assurance.

Most manufacturing firms seek to target sterilizing temperatures in excess of 121°C, which provide the higher F_0 values in a shorter time. For example, a 5-minute treatment in chamber at 125°C, assuming a z value of 10°C, provides the equivalent of an F_0 of 12.6 minutes. This follows from the expression

$$F_0 = \int_{T_0}^{T} L \, dt \qquad\qquad (4)$$

where $\quad L = 10^{(T-T_0)/z}$
$\qquad\quad T_0 = 121°C$

$$T = 125°C$$
$$t = 5 \text{ minutes}$$
$$z = 10°C$$

then
$$F_0 = 5 \times \text{antilog} \, 0.4$$
$$= 12.6 \text{ min}$$

Using the slightly elevated temperatures, F_0 values in the range of 30 to 60 minutes are not uncommon and the desired level of overkill assurance is achieved with cycles of relatively short duration, e.g., 15–20 minutes, without product degradation.

Validation studies depend heavily on accurate determination of the heat resistance or D value of the indicator microorganism. Vendors normally supply a certificate of population and D value with each lot of biological indicators; however, it is important to verify the D value using a square-wave retort device. The nature of the substrate that is impregnated with the spore suspension and the method of preparation and storage conditions can have significant effects on the performance of the indicator in actual trials.

4. Validation

On completion of the IQ and OQ, the validation studies will consist of replicate runs for temperature distribution, container mapping (if appropriate), and heat penetration. These studies should be performed sequentially because the information obtained from each trial is utilized to determine cycle parameters and loading patterns for the subsequent trials.

a. **Temperature distribution:** The chamber cold spot or slowest heating location is determined during the empty chamber, temperature distribution study. Usually this point is found in or near the chamber drain, generally considered to be the coldest point in chambers of uncomplicated geometry.

Cold spot determinations should be performed on representative loads evaluating both the expected maximum and minimum patterns for production use. Determination of a consistent cold spot in a particular loading configuration should be a guide for the placement of thermocouples for routine production cycle monitoring.

Approximately 15 to 20 thermocouples, depending on the chamber volume, properly calibrated before and after each run, should be utilized during the empty chamber studies and subsequent loaded chamber cycles to provide a data base upon which a meaningful statistical analysis can be performed. The thermocouples should be distributed according to a placement diagram that ensures representative coverage of all horizontal and vertical planes within the chamber. During the empty chamber and loaded chamber distribution studies, the thermocouples should be suspended in free space within the chamber, not in contact with any solid surface, in order that temperatures determined truly represent the sterilizing medium [27].

Any significant spread of temperatures during the empty chamber studies is indicative of an equipment problem, such as leakage, which may allow air entrapment within the chamber. The Parenteral Drug Association [28] suggests that deviation of more than ±2.5°C from the chamber mean temperature is undesirable. The entrapped air serves as insulation preventing uniform heat transfer within the chamber. If such a condition is detected during the empty chamber studies it must be corrected before continuing.

b. Container mapping: Container mapping or cool point studies should be performed if the load consists of large-volume liquid containers. This work can be conducted in a laboratory retort rather than the production sterilizer because the objective is to determine whether any particular location within the container heats significantly more slowly than other locations rather than to the temperature uniformity within the equipment. Significant errors due to thermocouple mass and baffling effects make this study difficult in containers smaller than, for example, 100 ml. The relatively small mass of such containers, however, serves to allow uniform heating and thus makes container mapping studies unnecessary in the smaller containers.

c. Heat penetration: These studies establish the slowest-heating locations within the product load. This information is critical to proper evaluation of the cycle characteristics. Because the objective is to sterilize the entire product load, the location(s) that are slowest to attain sterilizing temperatures determine the length of the sterilizing cycle. Thermocouple placement should be done with the intent of testing locations that would present the most difficulty to penetration of steam due to the design of the article, placement within the load, or size of the container. Biological indicators should be colocated with the thermocouples in accordance with a diagram in the protocol, similar to that prepared for the temperature distribution study. The faster-heating regions will achieve a treatment that is higher than the designed minimum F_0 for the overkill approach, which is another reason to ensure the load is heat stable.

d. Data analysis: Data from the heat penetration runs should be analyzed statistically to determine that the desired F_0 is achieved throughout the chamber with an appropriate level of confidence.

Table 8 presents data from five typical consecutive heat penetration runs showing the accumulated F_0 values from each of 15 thermocouple locations for the entire length of the cycle. Note: the target or desired minimum F_0 is 25 minutes.

The data are analyzed to determine the 95% confidence interval for the mean of the F_0 for each individual run and the 95% confidence interval for the minimum F_0 values across the five runs.

Table 8 F_0 Values by Thermocouple Location (No.)[a]

RUN	1	2	3	4	5	6	7	8	9	10	11	12	13	14	15
1.	28	29	32	33	27	28	27	26	31	31	32	34	33	32	29
2.	29	31	33	29	28	31	31	28	32	31	31	29	30	31	30
3.	29	32	34	31	29	32	31	29	31	30	30	31	29	33	29
4.	28	31	33	30	29	31	31	30	30	32	33	33	29	33	32
5.	30	32	31	32	29	28	31	27	31	32	32	32	30	31	32

[a]Using the expression $X - \dfrac{St}{\sqrt{n}} < u < X + \dfrac{St}{\sqrt{n}}$.

The expression used is

$$X - \frac{St}{\sqrt{n}} < u < X + \frac{St}{\sqrt{n}}$$

where u = population mean
X = sample mean
S = sample standard deviation
n = sample quantity and
t = value of the t distribution for the sample size at the 95% confidence level, equal to 2.145 (individual run) and 2.776 (across all runs)

We can calculate the 95% confidence interval for the mean of F_0 values for each run and, more important, evaluate the 95% confidence level for the minimum F_0 values across all runs. See Table 9.

The data from Table 8 suggests that the cold spot is point 8, which, except in run 4, consistently displayed the lowest accumulated F_0 values. The 95% confidence limit, calculated from the above expression, shows that the lowest F_0 value expected within the load, at the cold spot (point 8) will be 26.0 minutes. Stated another way, there is more than a 95% level of confidence that the minimum F_0 value in any cycle that meets specified parameters, with a consistent load pattern, will be greater than the required overkill value of 25 minutes.

Table 9 Summary of Confidence Intervals

Run	n	S	X_{15}	95% CI for u
1.	15	2.6	30.1	28.7–31.5
2.	15	1.4	30.3	29.5–31.1
3.	15	1.6	30.7	29.8–31.6
4.	15	1.6	31.0	30.1–31.9
5.	15	1.6	31.0	30.1–31.9

5. Terminal Sterilization

Terminal sterilization of aseptically filled drug products has been actively solicited by the Food and Drug Administration when it can be shown that such treatment will not cause product degradation. Nevertheless, such treatments do not tend to be overkill treatments because the heat lability of the drug product is of paramount concern.

Cycle parameters should be carefully selected to provide the necessary lethality to any preexisting bioburden plus the desired sterility assurance level (SAL) without causing product degradation. For this reason, knowledge of the product bioburden and heat stability of the product is essential. The activation energy E_A and mechanism of heat degradation [27] for the product under consideration should be known so that sterilization temperature and time parameters can be coordinated to minimize degradation.

During the cycle development work, various combinations of time and temperature treatments should be evaluated for their effect on product stability. The same delivered F_0 can be achieved with lower temperatures and longer times or vice versa; however, if activation energy is a key factor in product degradation, a longer cycle at lower temperatures may be appropriate. This is not a general rule. Other products may suffer deleterious effects from a prolonged treatment at a lower temperature, while being unaffected by the short-time, higher-temperature procedure. Although the heat contribution from the heat-up and cool-down phases of the cycle is less significant in terms of delivered F_0, it should be considered in the overall heat treatment received by the product.

The activities associated with qualification and validation of terminal sterilization are similar to the overkill steam sterilization procedures; however, the additional concerns related to product stability require a carefully planned and executed project.

D. Ethylene Oxide Sterilization

Despite the concerns of various agencies about the hazardous properties of ethylene oxide (EtO), it continues to be used as a sterilant in the pharmaceutical industry, as well as in many hospitals and laboratories. Many products and components cannot withstand the rigors of sterilization by saturated steam, ionizing radiation, chemical action, or dry heat, and the only suitable alternative is EtO.

The colorless gas with a molecular weight of 44.05 is also known as 1,2-epoxyethane and as dimethylene oxide. It has the following structure:

$$H_2C-CH_2$$
$$\diagdown \quad \diagup$$
$$O$$

The various physical and chemical properties of EtO and its mechanism of action have been well characterized and defined in the literature. It is typically supplied as a mixture with halogenated hydrocarbons (12% EtO and 88% Freon 12) or carbon dioxide (20% EtO and 80% CO_2). Although 100% EtO is available, there is an associated explosion hazard.

1. Toxicity

Ethylene oxide has long been identified as a toxic agent. It is this very toxicity that creates the excellent properties as a sterilant.

The material has acute effects in humans, such as epidermal irritation, eye and respiratory irritation, and various gastrointestinal disturbances. Chronic and long-term toxic effects include respiratory infections, anemia, and possible mutagenic and carcinogenic activity.

Government agencies such as the National Institute of Occupational Safety and Health (NIOSH) have studied the effects of worker exposure to hazardous substances in the workplace and have issued recommendations for limitations on their use. As a result, worker exposure limits for EtO were reduced to 1 ppm on a time-weighted basis in 1985. Short-term exposure limits (STEL) of 5 ppm have also been prescribed by the regulating agencies.

2. Usage

Components commonly used in production of sterile drug products that lend themselves to sterilization by EtO include vent filters with polypropylene housings, membrane filters, Tygon tubing, clean room garb, plastic caps, and many types of medical devices used in conjunction with administration of sterile drugs. Actual drug products are not typically treated with EtO because of its mechanism of action as a strong alkylating agent.

Use of EtO as a sterilant poses several challenges to the individual or group assigned the task of validation, because several process parameters must be carefully controlled and evaluated to achieve the desired results on a reproducible basis. These are the:

1. Nature, size, and arrangement of the component load
2. Concentration of EtO in the sterilizer chamber
3. Chamber temperature
4. Moisture level of the product load
5. Exposure time

Although it is not strictly a criterion for sterilization validation, GMP requires evaluation of residuals or by-products of the EtO sterilization process. Ethylene oxide can react with chlorine or chloride ion to form ethylene chlorohydrin, which can remain deposited within the product-component load. Excess moisture in the form of water can react with gaseous EtO to create ethylene glycol. The relative toxicity of these substances has been widely disputed, but there is no disagreement that their presence in the sterilized components must be minimized. This issue has been addressed by the regulatory agencies, which have proposed maximum residual levels of these products.

Aeration of the load at slightly elevated temperatures with repeated air exchanges (air flushes) is a typical procedure for eliminating these unwanted contaminants. The cycle should be designed to eliminate formation of liquid water during the prehumidification phase and remove water vapor and excess ethylene oxide promptly by evacuation after the exposure phase.

3. Process Variables

Validation of EtO sterilization is not a straightforward process. Several variables are involved.

The *load configuration* is a variable that has received limited attention in the literature. Goods to be sterilized by EtO are generally wrapped in a gas-permeable covering, such as TYVEK®, which permits removal of air during the vacuum phase and penetration by EtO and steam during the sterilization phase. It is important that this covering material be 1) able to withstand the temperatures and pressures developed during the cycle, 2) resistant to physical deterioration, and 3) capable of preserving the sterility of its contents after the treatment by creating a barrier of microorganisms.

Placement of the packages for sterilization within the load is generally accomplished by means of racks or shelves that permit good flow patterns for evacuation of air and subsequent charging with steam and EtO mixture. Care must be exercised to avoid creating dead zones in the load, which create barriers for the sterilant.

Load configurations or patterns should remain consistent between treatments and be in conformance with the configurations subjected to validation studies. Alteration of these patterns by changing the placement, wrapping material, quantity of items per load, or type of component from the pattern(s) subjected to validation study can result in loss of sterility assurance.

Temperature is a critical variable for EtO sterilization. For example, it has been reported that at lower temperatures, e.g., 40 to 50°C, temperature affects the rate of the EtO alkylation reaction and hence the rate of lethality according to first-order kinetics. In other words, a temperature increase raises the cycle lethality in a directly proportional manner. A typical cycle temperature range is 45–55°C. However, elevated temperatures may shift the reaction equilibrium toward polymerization of EtO rather than alkylation, thus effectively stopping its sterilizing action.

Likewise, *ETO concentrations* of the order of 300 to 600 mg/L have shown similar first-order kinetics, effectively doubling the reaction rate with a similar increase in concentration. This relationship holds true until the concentration reaches approximately 1200 mg/L, at which point the reaction rate no longer follows this rule.

Another extremely important variable is *moisture in the sterilizing chamber*. Pretreatment of the sterilizer load under conditions of elevated temperature and humidity is critical to effective sterilization. The action of the water vapor, usually in the form of steam, is to effect hydration of any proteinaceous material, which in turn causes swelling of cell surfaces of microorganisms and exposure of the active sites to the alkylating action of the EtO.

Moisture levels between 45 and 60% RH are desirable. Lower levels do not provide sufficient hydration, which inhibits the action of the sterilant, and higher levels may lead to condensation, saturating the goods with water and formation of ethylene glycol.

Once the desired conditions of gas concentration, temperature, and humidity within the load have been achieved, the exposure phase, another critical process variable, begins. Generally, the longer the exposure, the more effective the treatment. However, excessive exposure times can lead to formation of large quantities of EtO by-product residuals and may require longer aeration times after the cycle.

No guidelines can be given for optimum exposure times because the other process variables, described previously, together with the nature and configuration of the product load interact to determine the length of the exposure phase.

4. Validation

Because EtO sterilization is so dependent on the several interacting factors described above, process control becomes much more important. The equipment, i.e., sterilizer, associated controls, and instrumentation, must be thoroughly reliable and properly calibrated during validation and in subsequent production use.

Many modern sterilizers are equipped with integral programmable microprocessors or computers that continually monitor the critical process variables through signal inputs from sensors located in the sterilizer chamber. The microprocessors then control the critical process variables by opening or closing various valves to regulate steam pressure, vacuum, EtO concentration, or temperature as appropriate. This feature ensures cycle repeatability. Documentation is provided on a real-time basis to verify that conditions are maintained within acceptable ranges throughout the cycle.

Concentration of EtO within the chamber, as we have seen, directly affects the effectiveness of the treatment. This concentration can be determined in two ways.

1) Since the chamber pressure under charge with the sterilant mixture is the sum of the pressures of EtO and the diluent gas, it is necessary to correct that number to determine the contribution of the EtO alone. Once the EtO pressure is known, the concentration is easily calculated using an expression derived from the ideal gas law:

$$PV = nRT \qquad\qquad (5)$$

Gillis [17] has developed an expression that makes use of a constant that accounts for the contribution of the diluent gas.

$$EtO_{conc.} = \frac{KP}{RT} \tag{6}$$

In Eq. (6), K has a value of 1.20×10^4 mg/g-mol for the 12:88 EtO–Freon 12 mixture, P is the absolute chamber pressure in atmospheres, T is chamber temperature (kelvin), and R is the gas constant (0.08205 atm liter/g-mol K). If the EtO/Freon ratio does not change and temperature is held constant, the EtO concentration is directly proportional to the chamber pressure and easily calculated. By rearranging Eq. (6) one can determine what chamber pressure is necessary to obtain a particular EtO concentration.

For example, to obtain an EtO concentration (E) of 650 mg/L at a chamber temperature of 50°C we could write:

$$P = \frac{ERT}{K} \tag{7}$$

then

$$P = \frac{650 \text{ mg/L} \times 0.08205 \text{ atm L/g-mol K} \times 323 \text{ K}}{1.20 \times 10^4 \text{ mg/g-mol}}$$

and

$$P = 1.44 \text{ atm}$$

This value is the absolute chamber pressure, which is equivalent to 0.44 atm above ambient or a gauge pressure of approximately 13.2 in. Hg.

2) The calculated concentration of EtO can and should be verified by sampling the environment in the chamber and analyzing by gas chromatography. To permit continuous monitoring during production use and facilitate validation, many modern sterilizers are equipped with sampling ports that allow collection of samples of the gaseous chamber environment. Once the gas chromatographic equipment is calibrated with a standard gas, the mole percent of the sample is determined and converted to mg/L by use of a suitable scale factor.

Consumption of EtO during a cycle can be verified by weighing the container supplied by the EtO vendor before and after the cycle. Quantities consumed from run to run should be relatively consistent if cycle parameters and load patterns are not varied.

Moisture content within the chamber can be calculated through pressure measurement when the entire environment consists of water vapor, such as after steam injection following a prevacuum phase. However, it is more common to employ direct-reading dew point hygrometers or gas chromatography (GC). As with use of GC for EtO determination, care must be exercised to obtain representative samples.

Although the approaches to EtO validation differ from firm to firm, many of the principles are similar. The following are general considerations:

1. Carefully evaluate the material and type of packaging to be sterilized. EtO is corrosive to certain items and the packaging and design of the items to be sterilized must be accessible to the sterilant mixture.
2. Cycle development studies should be done in sterilizers with features similar or identical to those of the production units so that similar conditions of concentration, humidity, and temperature can be achieved. Ideally, development work should be performed in the actual production unit.
3. Validation studies should make use of biological indicators in the form of desiccated spores of *Bacillus subtilis* var. *niger*, impregnated on paper carriers (spore strips). These indicators should be verified by testing to contain a population of 10^6 viable spores. D values for typical sterilizing conditions (600 mg/L EtO, 54 ± 2°C, and 40–60% RH) typically are in the range of 2.5 to 4.5 minutes.
4. Temperature distribution studies should be performed on an empty chamber to determine the location of regions or zones that are slow to heat. These locations should be selected for monitoring with thermocouples and biological indicators during the loaded chamber studies. One formula uses a minimum of 10 thermocouples colocated with biological indicators in chambers up to 200 ft^3 in volume. For larger chambers an additional biological indictor-thermocouple pair is used for each increment of 30 ft^3 up to a maximum of 30 pairs per chamber load.
5. Loaded chamber studies for each particular loading pattern, to determine heat penetration, should follow the empty chamber runs. The objective of this series of studies is to determine effectiveness of heat transfer within the actual packages. Thermocouples and biological indicators should be placed at locations within the packages that represent the greatest impediment to the penetration of the sterilant.
6. When development cycles are complete, at least three successful consecutive validation cycles using the production unit, with identical cycle parameters except for total exposure time, should be completed for each loading configuration, including full and partial loads. Typically, the exposure phase for routine production is twice the time used in the validation trials.

E. Dry-Heat Sterilization

1. General Considerations

Dry-heat sterilization-depyrogenation is a commonly used procedure because of the general availability of equipment and the relative simplicity of the treatment.

These procedures are favored because they do not involve unwanted environmental and safety concerns associated with other forms of sterilization such as EtO and radiation.

Materials suitable for this treatment must be heat stable, such as glassware, metal containers, equipment, instruments, and certain oils. Plastic and rubber materials would be destroyed by the excessive temperatures achieved during the treatments.

Typical equipment for dry-heat treatment is either a continuous-type unit or a batch-type unit. The heat sources may be hot air forced convection, infrared, or flame sterilizers. Dry heat at suitable temperatures will sterilize by incineration living vegetative or spore forms of bacteria, viruses, molds, yeasts, etc., but its most important use in the industry is depyrogenation.

Endotoxin, a lipopolysaccharide associated with the outer membrane of gram-negative bacteria, is a high-molecular-weight complex often reaching a mass of 10^6 daltons (da). The lipid A moiety [22] produces various toxic reactions in animals, such as pyrogenicity, neutropenia, and leukocytosis. The endotoxin is destroyed by oxidation at a rate that follows nonlinear second-order kinetics [23,24].

2. Qualification and Validation

Installation qualification and operational qualification are critical to the successful validation of dry-heat sterilization and/or depyrogenation equipment. Items for inclusion in a typical IQ protocol include [25] records, equipment descriptions, utility connections, door gaskets, critical and noncritical instruments, heaters, blowers, baffles, filters, and lubricants. Each may affect the proper function of the unit and must be properly installed.

Likewise, the OQ must consider temperature-monitoring and -controlling instruments, cycle timers, door interlocks, heaters and blowers, cooling coils, belt speed controllers and recorders (for continuous process units), and data loggers.

It is common practice in the industry to combine the treatments of washing and sterilization-depyrogenation in one unit. Such units have the capability of producing washed, sterile, and pyrogen-free containers on a continuous basis to supply modern high-speed filling equipment.

Following the wash treatment, the vials are transferred by a conveyor belt to a tunnel supplied with heating devices to raise temperatures, by convective heat transfer or infrared radiation, in the heating zone to 300 to 350°C. Following heat treatment, the container temperatures are lowered to approximately ambient conditions by using cool filtered air before transfer onto the conveyor to the filling equipment.

One such installation is shown in Fig. 7.

This type of arrangement has practical value for larger installations with high production volumes. Batch-type sterilizer-depyrogenation equipment is more

Figure 7 Washing and sterilization-depyrogenation unit. (Courtesy of Bristol-Myers Squibb Company.)

flexible for accommodating different sizes of containers or equipment but is less efficient in that additional handling is required with the concomitant opportunity for contamination.

Continuous-type units are installed with the vial loading end located in a less clean or controlled environment and the discharge end inside the clean room controlled region. Air flow through the tunnel is from the clean region toward the less clean region. Typically, air quality in the tunnel should be designed to meet Class 100 requirements or better.

a. Endotoxin destruction: Treatments designed as overkill procedures deliver heat treatment well in excess of that required to inactivate 1000 EU of *Escherichia coli* endotoxin, which is a typical challenge level used by many manufacturers. USP has recommended a 3-log reduction in endotoxin challenge using a limulus amebocyte lysate reagent with greater than 0.15 EU/ml sensitivity [11].

Validation studies with either continuous-type or batch-type units include empty chamber testing and full and partial load studies. During the empty chamber runs the uniformity of temperature throughout the treatment chamber is determined through a temperature profile. Data-logging devices such as those manufactured by Kaye Instruments provide a real-time report of temperatures at selected points with a high degree of accuracy.

Temperature spread evident in the empty chamber runs that exceeds the range provided in the protocol, or which the manufacturer indicates should be met, is indicative of failure or malfunction of heating elements or air circulation devices (blowers or fans). Any such conditions must be corrected and the studies repeated until an acceptable temperature distribution profile is obtained. Another value of the empty chamber runs is identification of the cold or slowest-heating point or points within the chamber or tunnel.

As with the previously discussed methods, it is the cold spot(s) that determines the placement of temperature-monitoring and -controlling devices, i.e., thermocouples, for loaded chamber studies and subsequent routine usage.

Complete records of the empty chamber runs, including thermocouple placement diagrams, heating and cooling times, temperatures profiles by location, heater settings, belt speeds, environmental conditions, and pertinent observations, are maintained with the validation documentation.

Partially and fully loaded chamber testing follows the empty chamber studies. In this sequence various different configurations or loading patterns of typical items for dry-heat treatment are placed into the batch-type unit in a manner similar to the loading plan that will be used during routine production. It is very important that each loading configuration be tested during this phase, because the nature of items being treated, mass of the load, and placement within the chamber will interact to affect the heat distribution profile.

The complete range of sizes and types of glass containers used in routine production should be evaluated at various belt speeds in the continuous-type units to ensure that each extreme of usage planned for routine production is tested. Normally concern is directed toward achieving minimum temperatures at the container surface with the monitoring thermocouples. However, excessive temperatures should be avoided due to the possibility of inducing thermal stress fracturing in the glassware after it is returned to ambient temperatures. This problem is prevalent in molded glassware but has also been reported in tubing ware to a lesser extent.

Because the load acts as a heat sink, the articles do not reach the desired temperatures as quickly as does the air in the empty chamber studies. Conversely, the articles do not cool rapidly either. Accordingly, these time lags must be taken into account during cycle development.

Although all heating of the articles has an effect in destruction of microorganisms or endotoxins, only time during which the articles have achieved a certain minimum temperature is normally considered for the purpose of calculating F_H. This point is illustrated in Table 10, for which the following definitions and assumptions are made:

1. F_H is the equivalent time at a reference temperature T_0
2. The reference temperature is defined as 250°C.
3. Z is established at 54°C.
4. $F_H = \int_{t_1}^{t_2} 10^{(T-T_0)/Z} dt.$

Table 10 Comparison of F_H Values at Different Temperatures

Temperature (°C)	150	200	250	300	350
Time required to deliver equivalent of 1 minute at T_0 of 250°C (minutes)	71	8.4	1	0.12	0.01
Equivalent time at 250°C (minutes)F_H	0.014	0.12	1	8.4	71

b. Particulate contamination: Another issue for validation is testing for particulate matter in the air supply to the treatment chambers of the batch type or continuous type. The excessive temperatures developed in these regions in earlier models caused damage to the HEPA filters through which the air supply to the chambers is filtered. The filters then shed particles of bonding material or filter matrix into the air stream, creating contamination.

Design improvements have included strategic placement of heating and cooling elements to achieve desired temperature conditions without damage to the filters and ensuing contamination of the air supply. The schematic for one such unit is shown in Fig. 8.

Validation studies on a recent installation using a particle counter set to determine 0.5-μm particles within the heating chamber of a newer design batch-type oven indicated that the unit is capable of approaching a Class 100 environment at temperatures in excess of 250°C during the treatment cycle. See Table 11.

F. Radiation Sterilization

The radiation used for commercial sterilization is ionizing radiation normally produced by decay of radioactive isotopes of cobalt (^{60}Co) or cesium (^{136}Ce), which produce gamma rays. A similar effect for the purpose of sterilization is achieved by electron beam accelerators e.g., Van de Graaff generators or linear acclerators [18].

This particular method of sterilization requires highly specialized equipment and entails a number of problems associated with environmental and safety concerns. For these reasons, sterile product, pharmaceutical, and medical device manufacturers do not usually perform radiation sterilization on site but rather employ a specialized contractor to perform the service on their products.

1. Mechanism of Action

Bacteria and other microorganisms are susceptible to the effects of high-energy secondary electrons, which, in the case of those produced by Compton scattering of gamma rays from radioactive decay, can have energies as high as 1.25 MeV. This energy is far in excess of that required to alter the chemical bonds of living microbes. The secondary radiation acts by 1) directly destroying chemical bonds

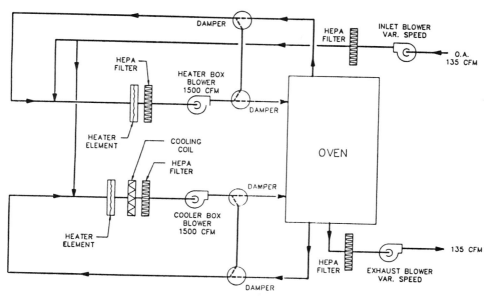

Figure 8   Dry heat oven—air supply.

in the DNA of the microorganism or 2) creating toxic chemical substances as a result of the radiation, such as H_2O_2 from any water source within the load.

A very important consideration for manufacturers who choose radiation sterilization is the issue of product compatibility. The ionizing radiation produces free radicals, which cause chemical change. Because the free radicals recombine rapidly, their effect in causing chemical changes is usually rapid. However, in the case of certain plastic substances, e.g., polypropylene, which may be utilized in the product carrier or as a container for the dosage form, the effects are longer term, creating permanent discoloration or other undesirable changes [19].

Another difference in the use of ionizing radiation is in the establishment and expression of D values for indicator microorganisms. In most other types of sterilization processes this value is expressed in units of time, given a set of specific environmental conditions within the sterilizing chamber. In the case of radiation the value is expressed in Mrads necessary to effect a 1-log reduction (90%) in the number of viable indicator organism cells surviving the treatment. One rad is equivalent to the absorption of 100 ergs per gram of substrate; one Mrad is 10^6 rads.

A number of different organisms, e.g., *Clostridium* sp, *Bacillus subtilis*, *Salmonella* sp., *E. coli*, and *Pseudomonas* sp., have been evaluated for specific

Table 11 Particle Counts During Operation[a]

Time	Particle level	Comments	Time	Particle level	Comments
10:07 A.M.	4106	Start of cycle		10	
	2477			3	
	1732		11:39 A.M.	10	
:12	533			5	
	287			11	
	271		:44	281	
:16	166			7	
:18	45			16	
	65			3	
	60		:49	10	Start of soak
:25	81	Heating damper		3	period
	54	100% open		16	
	45			6	
	31			10	
:31	21		:56	12	
	70			12	
	35			10	
	33		12:00 P.M.	12	
				5	
:52	10			12	
	25			3	
:59	30		:10	2	
11:00 A.M.	10			3	
	10			16	
	7			7	
	5		:15	3	
:06	12			3	
	3			2	
	5		:20	9	
:12	9			2	
	9		:22	6	Soak period
:17	9			7	over
	22		:25	39	
	6			21	
	10			9	
	4			4	
:26	4			12	
	18		:32	0	
	12			1	
	7			8	

[a]Met one particle counter set for 0.5 μm, 1 CFM zero check O.K. (4,6,2), room approx. 2500. Particle level througout oven cycle.

resistance to this treatment, but the indicator of choice is *Bacillus pumilus* E601 [20].

2. Qualification and Validation

In selecting a suitable radiation treatment for sterilized product there are several considerations:

The sterilization equipment should be operationally qualified according to guidelines acceptable to the regulatory bodies and the industry. Such guidelines have been established by the Health Industries Manufacturers Association (HIMA) and include such considerations as:

1. Complete description of the irradiation equipment including installation diagrams and construction materials.
2. All appropriate licensing documents for the Atomic Energy Commission and other governmental agencies.
3. Certification of the radiation source strength for gamma source sterilization [21].

Establish the suitability of radiation treatment with the particular product by a series of well-planned stability studies in accordance with a written protocol. Normally the product should be subjected to a dosage of at least twice the anticipated dose level requirement.

The pretreatment bioburden should be known.

Dosage should be determined by one of the following methods [11]:

1. Testing pure cultures of resistant microrganisms and using inoculated product, e.g., spores of *B. pumilus*, in a fractional experimental cycle approach to determine the D_{10} value of the biological indicator. Extrapolation of the data leads to determination of the appropriate dose to obtain a certain desired microbial survivor probability.
2. Testing the radiation resistance of the natural heterogeneous microbiological bioburden and proceeding with a series of sublethal cycles to establish the desired dosage.
3. Characterizing the microbial population from representative samples of product from different batches or production runs and applying a standard dose setting, based on literature-determined radiation resistance, for the particular population.
4. Using a series of incremental dose exposures to obtain a dosage such that 1 of 100 articles will be nonsterile. The dosage to obtain the desired probability of survival is then determined by extrapolation.

Establishing product loading patterns, evaluating the dose distribution throughout the load, and calibrating the dosage timer are the key elements in validating the radiation sterilization procedure.

Specific procedures for handling the loads during shipment to and from the contractor to preclude mixup, afford accountability, and prevent posttreatment contamination need to be established and agreed on by both parties.

The validation protocol and subsequent processing standard operating procedures (SOP's) should be specific and detailed, describing the biological indicator placement, desired sterility assurance level (SAL), conveyor speed, and dosage rate.

G. Filling Equipment

The types of equipment used to meter sterile dosage forms into their final containers are highly specialized and diverse in design. Indeed, some units may be prototype equipment specially designed for a sterile drug product manufacturer's particular needs.

1. Design Characteristics

There are several features that all types of filling equipment must share in order to perform effectively. Some of these are:

1. The product contact surfaces must be compatible with the product and of a suitable design to minimize product contamination [6].
2. The equipment must be capable of delivering the product into the container with an accuracy of fill that exceeds the product requirements.
3. Product contact parts must be capable of withstanding repeated sterilization treatments, preferably by steam autoclave procedures.
4. Moving parts should be contained within a suitable housing to the extent possible to prevent exposure to the aseptic environment. The need for lubricating fluids should be minimized by use of limited friction bearing surfaces whenever possible and contained within enclosures to prevent leakage to the environment.
5. Equipment should be designed for ease of changeover and cleaning.
6. The rate of filling should be readily controllable by the operator to allow for differences in product filling characteristics.

For the purpose of this discussion, only liquid and powder filling will be characterized.

2. Qualification and Validation

Once the IQ and OQ work is complete and the equipment is deemed suitable from a compatibility and contamination perspective, the validation work essentially becomes a study of filling variability at various filling rates. Note: The topics of process simulation/media filling and viable and nonviable particle control are covered in Section VII.

Validation protocols for filling accuracy should specify the number and duration of filling runs for each size and fill configuration, the filling rates, and the limits for filling variability considered acceptable to the manufacturer.

The purpose of the validation work is to determine a filling configuration, i.e., line speed, fill quantity, and container size combination, that will provide the optimum line speed while maintaining acceptable filling variability. Generally, the higher the filling rate, the poorer the filling accuracy.

a. Liquid filling: Generally speaking, liquids can be metered into dosage containers with greater accuracy than powders. The liquid filler may operate on the principle of positive displacement of the product from a filling cylinder by means of a piston or plunger, thus achieving fill accuracies of the order of 1 or 2% relative standard deviation (RSD), depending on the unit fill volume. Factors that affect fill accuracy include product specific gravity, if filling by volume, viscosity, product temperature, dissolved air from mixing or agitation, and leakage from the filling head [41].

b. Powder filling: The nature of the powdered dosage form does not readily lend itself to accuracy in metering. For this reason the filling equipment has special features in order to enhance the speed and accuracy of the filling process. A schematic of a typical filler for sterile powders is shown in Fig. 9.

A quantity of powder is drawn from a storage hopper, into a "port" or cylinder of known volume, contained in a circular filling wheel. The quantity of powder, or "shot," is held in place by vacuum as the fill wheel continues to rotate until it is positioned directly over the opening of a vacuum funnel. At this point the powder is forced into the funnel opening by a charge of sterile air or nitrogen and continues to fall into the product container assisted by gravity and funnel vibration [42].

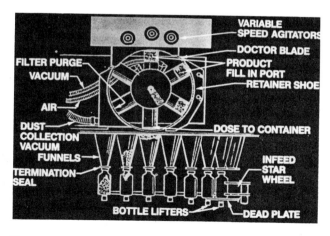

Figure 9 Continuous-motion rotary filler.

Several factors can affect the accuracy of powder filling equipment [42]:

1. Physical characteristics of the powder
2. Powder hopper agitation speed
3. Vibration rate
4. Vacuum setting
5. Powder hopper level
6. Machine filling speed

Of the several factors, perhaps the most important are the particle size and bulk density of the powder [43]. Poor flow characteristics lead to erratic fill control even if all other factors are well controlled.

The validation work should lead to the discovery of equipment settings for the optimum control of these variables to permit consistent filling accuracy at reasonable machine speeds. With experience gained through several machine trials, filling RSDs of 3 to 5% can be achieved, depending on the nature of the product and the fill quantity. See Fig. 10.

The experience gained through repetitive trials in this example resulted in a 76% decrease in filling weight RSD with an accompanying increase of 66% in filling speed.

**BRISTOL LABORATORIES DIVISION
BRISTOL-MYERS COMPANY**

QUALIFICATION DATA -- SUMMARY SHEET

Equipment: Model CMR-048   Samples
Product: Sodium Cephapirin   Per Trial: 250
List No: 7613-20   Target
Vial Size: 100CC   Fill Weight: 21.90GM

RELATIVE STANDARD DEVIATION
OF FILL WEIGHT BY MACHINE TRIAL

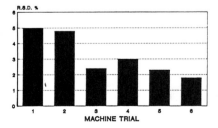

MACHINE SPEED IN V.P.M.
BY MACHINE TRIAL

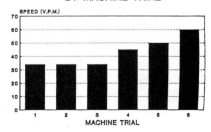

Figure 10   Machine filling speed and RSDs of powder filling equipment.

H. Sealing/Capping Equipment

1. Vial Capping Equipment

Capping refers to the application of an aluminum seal to a vial of sterile dosage form once its primary closure (plug) is in place. This seal helps ensure sterility of the unit by preventing movement of the primary closure, thus maintaining continuous contact between the closure and container surfaces. The seal or cap is normally crimped into position over a flange in the lip finish of the vial with sufficient pressure to prevent slippage.

Adequacy of the container-closure system is determined through stability studies during the development work and is not the subject of the validation project for the equipment. It is the objective of this phase to demonstrate that the sealing/capping equipment will consistently apply the overcap in such a manner that integrity of the unit is ensured.

A typical capping unit is the RW500, manufactured by West Company, which is used for application of aluminum seals in the sizes 20 and 28 mm. See Fig. 11.

For consistent operation, proper adjustment of upper and lower spring pressures for each individual spindle is essential to ensure that each unit is properly sealed. These ranges must be maintained during the operation of the unit. Operation with lower than specified pressures may result in loose seals, and excessive pressures can cause vial breakage. A log sheet for recording setup spring pressures is shown in Fig. 12.

Several types of tests have been described to evaluate the effectiveness of the container closure system. These are briefly described:

1. The leakage test, as defined by the Defense Personnel Support Center [44], requires inversion of the filled sealed containers, storage at room temperature and elevated conditions, and visual examination for evidence of leakage.
2. System integrity can be evaluated using soybean-casein digest (SGD) media filled into the container closure system, followed by incubation and macroscopic examination for contamination [45].
3. Challenge by immersion in a suspension of E. coli at a concentration of 10^8 CFU/ml, followed by incubation and examination for evidence of growth within the containers [46], is another method.
4. An aerosol challenge procedure has been described [47] that requires immersion of vials containing a suitable sterile culture medium into a confined chamber with an aerosol concentration of approximately 10^3 microorganisms per cubic foot of chamber volume. The vials are held under specified conditions of pressure, temperature, and relative humidity for a predetermined exposure time, followed by evaluation for microbial growth.
5. Finally, a closure displacement test was developed [46] in which a digital micrometer with a spring force tester is used to accurately determine the force

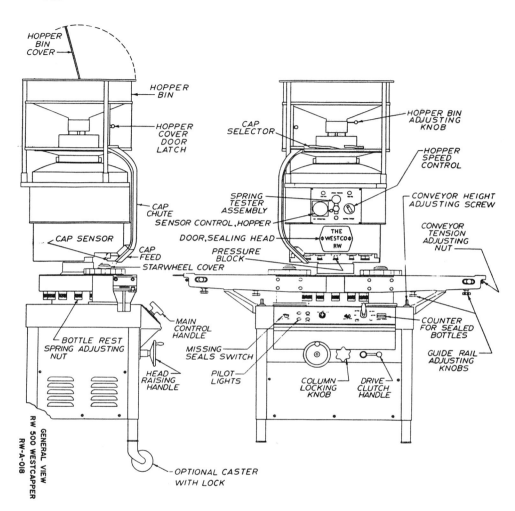

Figure 11 Typical capping unit. (Courtesy of West Company.)

MEASUREMENT OF SEALING PRESSURES ON THE WEST CAPPERS IN THE STERILE FILLING DEPARTMENT

DATE_____TIME_____CAPPER #_____

VIAL SIZE/STOPPER/CAP_____

	HEAD #											
	1	2	3	4	5	6	7	8	9	10	11	12
UPPER SPRING PRESSURE												
LOWER SPRING PRESSURE												

Comments, Adjustments made, etc._____

Performed by_____ Reviewed by/Date_____

SEALING PRESSURE GUIDELINES - TABLE OF SPRING PRESSURES (POUNDS)

Seal Used	Upper Spring Pressure	Lower Spring Pressure
20 mm	28 - 35	18 - 24
28 mm	20 - 28	10 - 24

Figure 12 Log sheet.

necessary to compress a sealed closure over a predetermined distance. The required force is correlated to the tightness of the seal.

Of these five procedures, the closure displacement test is the most practical for routine production and evaluation of the capping equipment.

2. Ampul Sealing Equipment

There are three generally accepted procedures for evaluating the performance of ampul sealing equipment [46]. Two of these methods involve a dye leakage test; the third is a electronic test that measures the relative difference in capacitance between intact units and unsealed units.

1. The vacuum dye leak test requires the units to be submerged in a solution containing a highly visible dye, in a chamber, for a specified time period under vacuum. Vials are removed, washed, dried, and visually inspected for evidence of dye migration into the ampuls.
2. The autoclave dye process likewise utilizes a solution of dye in which the units are submerged. However, in this case the ampuls are subjected to an autoclave procedure, followed by the rinsing, drying, and inspection.

Both procedures have drawbacks, such as a requirement for subjective judgment during inspection and variation in the rate of dye migration with changing conditions of pressure and size of the leak or fracture.

3. Densok of Japan [46] claim the capability of detecting pinholes as small as 0.5 μm in glass ampuls using the principle of electronic capacitance. The procedure involves placing the test unit between two electrodes of high differential potential. The completely sealed ampul will exhibit a higher capacitance, which results in a difference in current reading on the equipment that identifies the "leaker." The sensitivity of the equipment must be adjusted for each size and product.

    As with any test procedure, specifications must be developed for the equipment, number of samples, and acceptance criteria for each evaluation, taking into consideration the product characteristics and the size and type of each presentation.

VI. PROCESS VALIDATION

A. Compounding

After completion of development and scale-up work, a process formulation should be run on the production equipment under normal production conditions to complete the qualification project. These series of batches are usually considered "validation" lots and are subjected to extensive sampling and testing in accordance with a validation protocol.

Many sterile products are not as complicated from a formulation standpoint as are certain oral dosage forms, such as tablet and capsule mixes; however, certain principles of validation apply equally to any formulation.

1. Prospective Process Validation

Jeater and Jacobs [39] have defined several steps to be taken for full-scale validation work. The planning and execution of a validation project are fully described in the validation protocol, which includes the following areas of consideration:

1. A definition of critical steps in the manufacturing process for study during the validation work. This selection of critical steps should be limited to procedures that could have significant effects on product quality, e.g., pH adjustment, rate of crystallization, blending or mixing times, temperature control, filtration rates, milling or comminution rates, and screen sizes.

The validation phase is not the place for development work and process optimization. The range of variable process parameters should be narrowly defined with the target at the midpoint of the range whenever possible. For example, a pH adjustment should be defined as "adjust solution to pH of 5.6,

Table 12 Blend Potency (mg/g)

Set	1	2	3	4	5	6	7	8
Top	25	26	24	27	28	24	26	24
Middle	27	23	25	26	27	23	25	26
Bottom	28	27	26	24	25	24	24	27

range 5.5 to 5.7, using. . . ." For the work to be considered validated, the results must be repeatable and consistent. This is best achieved by controlling the process variables and strictly defining process limits.

2. A sampling plan that will provide sufficient data for statistical analyses, if necessary, with descriptions of the sampling equipment, quantities, containers, method of identification, technique, and testing schedules. Provision for duplicate samples should be made to verify technique and serve as a backup in the event samples or data are lost or destroyed. The sampling plan should be representative of all critical steps and the final product, but it need not be extensive. For example, powder blend uniformity can be established with a relatively small number of samples (e.g., 6–10), depending on the size of the blending equipment or container. Although 25–30 samples may provide a subjective sense of assurance, the increased sample size yields limited improvement in the statistical significance, especially when testing costs are considered.

The data in Table 12 represent the potency values for a sterile blend obtained from samples taken at various points within the container.

These data were examined in two ways: (1) consideration of all data points and (2) consideration of every third data point. The results are listed in Table 13. Analysis of the full number of samples would improve the lower limit of the 95% confidence interval by only 0.7 mg/g or 2.7%, compared to the value of the mean, yet the analytical testing cost would be significantly higher.

3. Complete analyses of all raw materials are performed and included in the

Table 13 Statistical Summary

Statistic	All data	Every third point
Average potency	25.5	25.5
No. of samples	24	8
Sample Std. Dev.	1.414	1.50
Relative standard deviation	5.54%	5.89%
95% confidence interval for the mean (t distribution)	24.9–26.1	24.2–26.8

validation records. Use of materials from previously qualified alternative vendors should be considered. Any raw material not meeting all appropriate specifications should not be utilized in the validation lots.

    4.   Acceptance criteria based on product specifications are defined for in-process and final dosage form stages. These requirements may include derivation of statistically significant confidence levels for certain parameters, which would not be routinely verified during production. However, the expected level of performance should be similar to that anticipated for routine production. In other words, the validation batches should be representative of the quality expected during regular operation.

    5.   Validation lots or batches are manufactured under normal production conditions, i.e., by regularly assigned production operating personnel (not technical services or product development staff), using production equipment and the SOP that describes steps for routine full-scale production lots.

    6.   Complete in-process records are maintained and included in the validation documentation. These are control charts, process parameter charts (e.g., temperature-pressure-vacuum), and calibration or standardization records for critical equipment and instruments, such as pH meters.

    7.   If appropriate, data analysis using statistics is performed to determine whether acceptance criteria have been met. Any exceptions are noted, explained, and justified.

2. Retrospective Process Validation

Essentially an analysis of historical data from batch documents, retrospective process validation can be a very effective tool in demonstrating process control [40]. This method may be useful in the case of products with large production volume, for which there exists a wealth of data in the batch documentation that can be analyzed to assess product performance. This approach must be used with care, however. Seemingly subtle or unimportant changes in the manufacturing process, raw materials, or even analytical procedures, taken individually or collectively, can have a significant impact on product attributes. A change control program is essential to prevent unauthorized deviations from the previously validated process.

    Many firms make use of trend analysis for product attributes, which is available from computer files on a real-time basis. With the capability of exhibiting data in a variety of presentations, the effect of a change such as a new source of a particular raw material is readily visualized. These tools also facilitate the annual review of drug quality standards required by the GMP regulations.

B. Lyophilization

Pharmaceutical formulations are subjected to lyophilization for two primary reasons: 1) lack of assurance of stability in the liquid, or reconstituted, state and

2) ease of metering or filling a solution, followed by lyophilization, over conventional dry powder filling. Blood serum and plasma, certain vaccines, antibiotics, and hormones are typical of the products that lend themselves to this type of treatment [28].

1. Practical Application

Lyophilization, also known as freeze drying or cryodesiccation, is essentially a six-step process:

1. Metering a solution of the drug into a dosage form container
2. Freezing the product solution
3. Applying a vacuum
4. Removal of solvent by sublimation
5. Final drying of the product
6. Sealing the dosage form container

The resulting product is stored in this desiccated state until needed for administration, at which time it is reconstituted with the appropriate solvent.

A typical lyophilization process for a pharmaceutical product in aqueous solution is outlined below:

1. Prepare a solution of the active drug compound and necessary excipients, and sterilize the solution by filtration.
2. Aseptically fill suitable vials with the batch or lot, with each vial containing a precisely measured amount of solution, and then insert specially designed elastomeric closures partway into the vial openings.
3. Under aseptic conditions, transfer the batch to the lyophilization chamber and rapidly freeze the vials and contents to a temperature of approximately −50°C. Rapid freezing produces smaller crystals, which are readily reconstituted [29].
4. Warm the product in the vials to a temperature slightly below the freezing temperature and apply a vacuum, usually in the range of 10–100 μm Hg. It is critical to the process that the pressure-temperature conditions be maintained below the eutectic point to ensure that drying takes place entirely by sublimation. (Note: The eutectic point, also known as the triple point, is the condition of temperature and pressure at which gas, liquid, and solid phases are in equilibrium. See Figure 13 for the vapor pressure curve for water [30]. Point O is the eutectic point.)
5. Initial drying takes place through removal of water by sublimation. The driving force is the temperature difference between the relatively warmer product and the lyophilizer condenser, usually maintained at −50 to −60°C, which causes the solvent in the product to have a higher vapor pressure than the condensing surface environment. The rate of volatilization is increased by

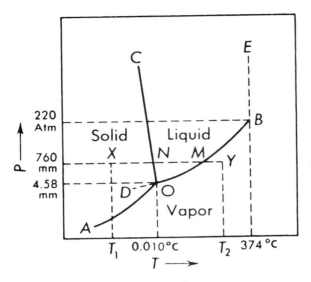

Figure 13 Vapor pressure curve for water.

application of vacuum, which lowers the product surface temperature through the latent heat of vaporization.

6. Secondary or final drying takes place after the ice is removed, eliminating the possible formation of liquid solvent, by raising the shelf temperature and heating the product to drive off any adsorbed solvent. Drying is complete when the moisture content reaches a level that ensures stability [31].

The essential features of a typical freeze dryer are shown in Figure 14 [32].

The product is frozen by the action of a refrigerant such as Freon circulated through the chamber shelves from the compressor through piping inside the shelves. Once the product is thoroughly frozen, the chamber and condenser are evacuated by the vacuum pump, and the condenser compressor lowers the condenser temperature below that of the product. Heat is applied to the shelves from electric resistance coils or recirculating hot water, to raise the product temperature to begin the primary drying process.

2.   Qualification and Validation

The complex interdependence of the various utilities and services necessary to operate a lyophilization system leaves little tolerance for poor design, improper installation, or innacurate instrumentation. For example, should the coolant for the refrigeration units exceed specified temperature limits, condenser temperature could rise, possibly raising system pressure due to a decrease in the condensation

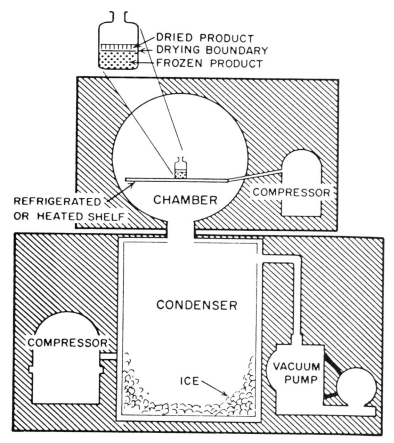

Figure 14 Typical freeze dryer.

rate, which could lead to a rise in product temperature above the phase-transition point [37]. This could cause product melting or collapse of the cake.

Instrumentation such as vacuum pressure gauges must be sensitive and accurate but also rugged to withstand the rigors of the various temperature and pressure extremes during the lyophilization and chamber sterilization treatments.

The manufacturer must ensure that the equipment and instruments do not lose integrity to avoid contamination of the lyophilization chamber. For example, hydraulic fluid from the vial stoppering mechanism or vacuum pump oil must be prevented from entering the chamber [38].

During the OQ the following specialized checks should be conducted:

1. Maximum chamber vacuum under no load.
2. Chamber leak rates under vacuum and pressure.
3. Shelf temperature control, i.e., temperature variation
4. Vacuum pumping rate
5. Chamber heating and cooling rates under no-load conditions to establish a reference point for future study
6. Condenser cooling rate
7. Refrigerant integrity test to verify coolant does not leak into the chamber
8. Condenser drying rate to establish the maximum rate of drying of which the unit is capable
9. Stoppering mechanism functionality to verity that the mechanism will properly insert the vial stoppers over the entire range of sizes to be used.

The actual validation project includes three general requirements.

1. At least three complete production-sized lots of each formulation should be manufactured in strict accordance with the manufacturing SOPs. Each lot must meet specification for all quality attributes and qualify for release, without reprocessing. In addition to the product specifications other attributes, particular to lyophilized products should be verified. These may include: uniformity of cake, cake color, cake height, reconstitution time, moisture content (if not a product specification), and short term (accelerated) and long term stability [31,37].
2. Validation of the lyophilizer cleaning and sterilization processes should be accomplished. Particular care should be taken to verify that there is no back-migration of contaminants, either from adjuvant fluids integral to the equipment or by cross-contamination from previous product. Although some manufacturers continue to employ EtO as a sterilant, the industry trend is toward the use of saturated steam under pressure. Therefore, the equipment must be capable of undergoing this treatment. Typically, an overkill approach using a sufficient number of thermocouples and biological indicators is the method of choice (see Equipment Qualification C).
3. Finally, some type of process simulation or media fill testing to verify the adequacy of the sterilization procedure and the aseptic manipulations involved with product filling, transfers, and lyophilization needs to be performed.

Although there is widespread agreement in the industry regarding the need for such testing, there are diverse views and lack of consensus on the extent of process simulation that is most appropriate. For example, many manufacturers do not freeze the media, because it is suspected that this treatment could damage or kill adventitious vegetative organisms, which could lead to erroneous false-negative conclusions.

As a general guideline, three simulations of at least 3000 units each should be performed with an acceptance criterion of not more than 0.1% contamination on the individual tests. The simulations should be reasonably rigorous, including all manipulations the product will undergo, such as filling, initial stopper placement, transfer, cooling, vacuum, heating, and final stoppering. The medium used for the process simulation should be capable of supporting growth of bacteria, both aerobic and anaerobic, and fungi, and each lot should be subjected to the USP XXII Growth Promotion Test [11]. (See also Section VIIE.)

C. Filtration Sterilization

Certain products may be altered beyond acceptable limits by the effects of heat, radiation, or chemical exposure and are thus not good candidates for sterilization by steam, dry heat, ethylene oxide, or radiation. For liquids and gases, removal of microorganisms through filtration provides a nondestructive, efficient means of sterilization. For the purpose of this discussion, only the membrane- and cartridge-type systems used for aseptic filtration of solutions intended for final dosage forms will be described. The features and advantages of each type are shown in Table 14 [33].

1. Filtration Systems

Filtration systems intended to produce a sterile, particulate-free solution generally employ a prefilter in conjunction with the final or "sterilizing" filter. The prefilter is designed simply to remove gross particulate contamination to prevent "loading" the final filter. Without prefiltration the final filter would become clogged with debris from the solution and the filtration rate would be reduced.

Prefilter systems are an integral part of the filtration "train" and must be selected with care. The media have a relatively wide range of pore sizes, which significantly reduces the particulate level in the solution to be filtered while maintaining a high filtration rate.

The prefilter media must be compatible with the solution to be filtered and

Table 14 Sterilizing Filters—Summary of Features

Cartridge type	Membrane type
More surface area, e.g., 5 ft^2 per element	Surface area limited, e.g., 0.55 ft^2 for a 293-mm plate
Ease of replacement, few parts	Disassembly required with numerous parts
Compatibility studies required for end caps, media support, O-rings, and sealants	Only the gasket material requires compatibility test
Bubble point integrity test may not be suitable for high-surface-area filters	Diffusional flow and bubble point integrity tests are suitable

installed in a suitable housing to prevent any solution leakage or bypass [35]. Filter media types vary depending on the application [36]. For example, cellulose acetate and polyvinylidine difluoride (Kynar) have application for protein solutions and polysulfone is more suitable for aqueous solutions. Polytetrafluoroethylene (Teflon) and nylon membranes are relatively inert and suitable for filtration of gases and solvents.

Manufacturers assign ratings to their products based on a nominal maximum pore size, which in turn leads to a rating or designation of the filter medium as "absolute" or "sterilizing" if it meets certain criteria. The testing procedures employed by the vendors are typically indirect procedures such as measurement of flow rates of the filtrate through the system, which allow prediction of a nominal pore size based on a mathematical model.

Filter media are designed to separate solid particles of small dimensions, e.g., bacteria, from the filtrate, rendering the product free from contamination. Numerous articles have been published on the mechanism of filtration sterilization, most of which agree on the following five mechanisms [34]:

1. Sieve retention—the most important mechanism
2. Adsorption
3. Impaction
4. Entrapment within the matrix
5. Electrostatic capture

The only true measurement of a filter's capability to remove microorganisms from a solution is a challenge test using a standard organism such as *P. diminuta* (ATCC 19146), which is a gram-negative rod-shaped cell with an average diameter of 0.3 μm. Since this procedure is by nature a destructive test, other models were developed and have been shown to be reasonably reliable in correlating a filter membrane's pore size and bacterial retention efficiency. These procedures, designed for use with a filtration system in situ, are nondestructive and are typically performed as integrity tests before and after use of the membrane.

2. Nondestructive Testing

Two procedures have evolved as the methods of choice for nondestructive filter integrity and filtration efficiency verification. These are the bubble point test and the diffusion or pressure hold test. A third procedure, which is a more recent development, is a combination of the bubble point and pressure hold tests.

a. Bubble Point Test: The most common procedure, the bubble point test, is based on a mathematical model in which the pores in a filter medium matrix are assumed to be cylindrical capillaries with spherical cross sections. A simple expression for bubble point calculations derives from surface chemistry, particularly capillary phenomena. The Laplace equation relates the differential pressure required to force liquid from a wetted spherical cylindrical pore, or capillary, to the surface tension of the wetting liquid and the pore geometry. This model predicts that the pressure is equal to twice the surface tension of the wetting fluid divided by the radius of spherical curvature. This relationship is stated mathematically in Eq. (8).

$$P = \frac{2\gamma}{R} \tag{8}$$

$$d = 2R \cos \theta \tag{9}$$

Figure 15 depicts a hypothetical pore with uniform dimensions from which another expression is derived. In the figure, P1 is the pressure of the gas forcing the liquid through and out of the pore, P2 is the resistance to that force from the capillary pressure phenomena, θ is the contact angle of the wetting fluid with the side of the capillary pore, R is the radius of curvature of the liquid interface, and d is the pore diameter. By combining these expressions and rearranging terms, the desired mathematical relationship is derived:

$$P = \frac{4\gamma \cos \theta}{d} \tag{10}$$

Since the capillary is presumed to be completely wetted, the contact angle becomes zero and the equation simplifies to

$$P = \frac{4\gamma}{d} \tag{10'}$$

This model is an oversimplification of the actual situation, but it is useful because it shows that pressure required to force a liquid through a capillary pore is inversely proportional to the pore size and dependent on the wetting liquid surface tension.

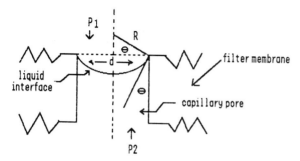

Figure 15   Hypothetical capillary pore.

The bubble point test has several shortcomings that must be considered when employing the procedure to verify integrity of the filtration system and filter efficiency ratings.

1. The filter must be completely wetted by the test liquid or erroneous results will be obtained.
2. Since the filter integrity test is generally performed on a system set into place for production use, operator training is critical. The test must be conducted without breaking the sterility of the system, in accordance with a written protocol to ensure consistent results.
3. Pretreatment of the filter matrix by autoclaving alters the wettability of the filter material by leaching out surfactants, thus altering the bubble point reading.
4. Accuracy of the pressure gauges is critical for correct interpretation of the test results.
5. Surface tension of the liquid being filtered is a key factor in determining bubble point, so the test liquid must be one for which the manufacturer has determined a bubble point value or, alternatively, testing should be done to correlate the bubble point for the product to be filtered. For example, most filter manufacturers rate their products using water. Many liquids that have ionic species in solution, hence greater polarity than water, exhibit a higher surface tension and hence a higher bubble point than does water on the same filter.
6. Large-surface-area membrane filters such as a 293-mm disk can lead to dissolution of the test gas in the liquid under pressure on the upstream side of the filter. The gas will then migrate in solution to the downstream side on the filter, where the pressure is lower, at which point the gas leaves the solution and forms bubbles. Appearance of these bubbles at a lower pressure than expected for the test filter can lead to the erroneous conclusion that the filter is damaged or not properly rated.

Despite these shortcomings, the bubble test procedure is a valuable in-process aid for the filter manufacturer and will reliably detect damage or improper filter rating for the pharmaceutical manufacturer. Extensive experience in the field has shown a membrane rated at 0.22 μm maximum mean porosity will produce bubble point test pressures greater than 40 psi [33].

b. Diffusion flow testing: One of the inaccuracies that plague the bubble point test has given rise to the diffusion flow procedure. Fick's law relates the rate of flow of a test gas in solution through a filter membrane to the concentration gradient of the gas in solution (across the media), the diffusion coefficient, and a void volume factor. Shown in equation form, this is

$$Q = D\phi\frac{dc}{dx} \tag{11}$$

where D = diffusion coefficient for the test gas-liquid system
         ϕ = void volume factor (as much as 60–70%)
         dc/dx = is the concentration gradient across the media
         Q = is the flow rate or molar flux of the test gas

The differential expression dc/dx can be rewritten as $(C_1 - C_0)/t$, where C_1 is the upstream gas concentration, C_0 is the saturation concentration on the downstream or low-pressure side, and t is the membrane thickness. Then:

$$Q = \frac{D(C_1 - C_0)\phi}{t} \tag{12}$$

Henry's law relates the concentration gradient to the pressure differential across the membrane, ΔP. This is

$$C_1 - C_0 = H \Delta P \tag{13}$$

In a given system the factors D, H, t and ϕ are constant, so:

$$Q = K \Delta P \tag{14}$$

which says that the molar flux of the test gas is directly proportional to the applied pressure while the test pressure is below the bubble point. This relationship is shown in Fig. 16. At point A the linear relationship ends as diffusional flow changes to mass flow at the bubble point.

c. Bubble point–pressure hold test: One equipment manufacturer has developed a testing procedure that incorporates both the pressure hold and bubble point tests. The operator shoud bear in mind several important considerations if this testing is to be successful:

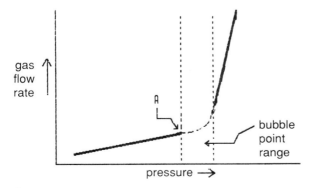

Figure 16   Gas flow rate–pressure relationship.

1. Diffusional flow testing should be conducted at test pressures sufficient to cause diffusional flow but at no more than 80% of the rated bubble point pressure.
2. All air should be vented from the system to allow complete wetting of the filter medium.
3. The filter should be completely wetted with the test fluid before attempting to proceed. If the test fluid is different from the fluid being filtered, the latter should be completely purged from the system.
4. Criteria for flow rate or pressure decay should be established and followed. For example, a determination of less than 10% change in flow rate per minute at a given test pressure could be indicative of a successful test.
5. Testing should be continued to the bubble point to verify the criteria stated by the vendor for diffusional flow (or pressure hold-decay) and bubble point.

One device that performs both the pressure hold (decay) and the bubble point procedures in a single operation is the Sartocheck. A graphical representation of the test is produced for inclusion in the manufacturing documentation as evidence of successful integrity testing. A typical print is shown in Fig. 17.

When failures occur after the test protocols are precisely executed on properly designed and calibrated equipment, other factors must be considered [33]:

1. Actual defective or improperly rated filter media. Manufacturing defects or damage caused by mishandling or mislabeling of the filter at the vendor.
2. Damaged support equipment such as dents in the O-ring channel of a cartridge filter.
3. Damaged or otherwise defective gasketing.

I.   DATE: 11Jul89
II.   TIME: 1530 h
III. FILTER TYPE: Millipore GSWP
                     293 mm disk
IV.   FILTER NUMBER: 321
V.   TEST SPECIFICATIONS:
      a. Bubble Point: NLT 45 psig *(3.1 bar)
      b. Pressure Hold @37.7 psig, *(2.6 bar): no obvious pressure loss in 10 min hold
VI.   TEST RESULTS:
      a. Bubble Point: 57.3 psig
      b. No pressure loss @ 37.7 psig, 10 min hold
VII. FILTER INTEGRITY VERIFIED
           BY: ngs
*Conversion factor: 1 bar = 14.51 psi.

Figure 17

4. Distortion of the support structure of a cartridge filter, softening of the sealant, or warping of a membrane support plate caused by the heat from the autoclave cycle. These are among the most common causes of test failures.

VII. ENVIRONMENTAL QUALIFICATION

A. Area Decontamination

The effort spent in qualification and validation of the utilities, equipment, and processes that make up a sterile product manufacturing operation is wasted unless the manufacturing environment is maintained under control at all times during production.

Area decontamination begins with cleaning. Many chemical agents that are good cleaners do not have effective antimicrobial properties. To be an effective cleaner, a chemical should be a surfactant. An agent such as Duponol is effective in removing quantities of residual product from equipment surfaces, floors, and walls; however, this treatment needs to be followed by a suitable sanitizer or disinfectant to complete the task.

Antimicrobial agents have very different characteristics that should be thoroughly understood by the user in considering their suitability for a particular application. A good general-purpose antimicrobial agent will have a wide range of effectiveness on both vegetative and spore forms of bacteria, viruses, and fungi. It should be noncorrosive, nontoxic, stable, have good residual action, and be inexpensive. Such an agent does not exist. Many have several desirable characteristics but fall short in other areas.

1. Sanitizing Agents

In general, sanitizing agents can be classified on the basis of the primary active ingredient [48]:

1. Chlorine-containing compounds, e.g., sodium hypochlorite. These are effective against a variety of microorganisms and relatively inexpensive but tend to be corrosive to metals and have limited residual effect.
2. Alcohols, e.g., isopropyl alcohol. This class is effective against vegetative forms but not against spores. The alcohols do not leave residues and can be somewhat effective as cleansing agents. Higher-molecular-weight, branched-chain alcohols tend to be more effective.
3. Iodine-containing compounds, e.g., Betadyne®. Agents in this class are expensive, have good stability, and are effective, but they have a marked tendency to stain certain porous surfaces.
4. Quaternary ammonium compounds [49], e.g., MIKRO QUAT®. The class is noncorrosive, exhibits good surface activity, has limited broad-spectrum effectiveness, and is expensive.

5. Aldehydes, e.g., alkaline glutaraldehyde. These compounds have a marked odor, show good broad-spectrum activity at low pH, are relatively stable, and are noncorrosive.

6. Peroxides, e.g., hydrogen peroxide (3–6%). Agents in this class lack stability, particularly in the higher concentrations, are effective against vegetative forms with limited activity on spores, and are corrosive to certain metals.

7. Phenols, e.g., LPH. Compounds in this category are effective against vegetative forms, have a moderate odor, and tend to leave residuals.

To meet a variety of needs, a manufacturer may require a sanitization program using a number of different agents. For example, a cleansing treatment, using a quaternary compound, might be followed on a periodic basis with a sporicidal agent such as glutaraldehyde or sodium hypochlorite.

2. Qualification and Validation

The validation project should include a study to evaluate the effectiveness of the agents chosen for use in the facility. The testing should include a challenge by the most resistant types of microorganisms found in the environment. Cultures of various challenge organisms in high-concentration suspensions are inoculated onto nonporous surfaces, which are then immersed in the sanitizer solution for various incrementally increased time intervals. The residual population is determined by harvesting the residual challenge at the end of each exposure interval and culturing in a suitable medium, followed by incubation and examination. The study is continued until a contact interval is found for which there is no evidence of microbial activity. This information serves as a guide in establishing the application times for routine use.

It is extremely important to include suitable controls in such studies to avoid false-negative conclusions attributed to bacteriostasis or fungistasis rather than pure cidal effects. Sanitizer solutions should be prepared according to written procedures using clean equipment and purified water (if dilution is necessary). They should be stored in appropriate containers and discarded in accordance with established expiration periods. Sanitizing agents should be applied in a consistent manner using techniques that ensure adequate coverage and contact time.

Typical methods of application for exposed surfaces are wiping with a sterile sponge or cloth, direct application to floors using a sterile mop, and aerosolization to achieve contact with remote surfaces and the air-handling ductwork.

The work leading to the selection of the sanitizing agent is important, but the actual procedure that will be followed by the operators is the process to be validated.

The SOP detailing the decontamination frequency, schedules, agents, specific methods of sanitizer preparation, and application is the validation protocol. A known challenge of surface contaminants may be appropriate. When the sanitizer has been applied and has remained in contact with the surface for the predetermined contact time, a sample of the residual microbiological load is determined by suitable means (see Section VIII, D).

B. Nonviable Particulate Monitoring

The quantity and size of particulate matter in the environment of the enclosures within the aseptic suite are normally determined by optical particle counters. Equipment such as the instruments made by HIAC/ROYCO and Climet Industries is typical. See Fig. 18.

The principles of operation of these instruments are similar. Air is drawn into a chamber of the instrument at a measured rate. Individual particles in the air sample are introducted into a focused beam of light within the chamber. Any particles present will cause the light to be scattered at a particular angle. This light-scattering effect is sensed by a photodetector tube. With suitable amplification and rectification of the resulting signal, the quantity and size range of particles present in the sample are displayed on the equipment.

Nonviable particulate matter testing is performed in accordance with a written protocol which stipulates that replicate determinations be made at different times

Figure 18 Optical particle counter. (Courtesy of Met One.)

of the day when the area is at rest (i.e., no production activity) and also during periods of full operation, to simulate the maximum or worst-case challenge to the environment.

In the case of sterile powder filling operations, the background counts from product in the environment during periods of operation may lead to erroneous conclusions about the cleanliness classification of the environment. Most manufacturers perform the particle counting by simulating all normal activities, e.g., personnel movement and equipment operation, *except* for manipulation of the product. (Section IV.A presents one approach for evaluation of particle count information.)

C. Surface Sampling

The residual population of viable microorganisms on a surface in the aseptic processing area after decontamination is a measure of the effectiveness of the disinfection procedure. The determination is made in concert with the decontamination validation. Rodac or contact plate sampling and swab sampling are two methods of obtaining this information.

1. RODAC (Replicate Organism Detection and Counting)

A sterile 60-mm Petri dish containing a semi-solid medium nutrient agar with a convex surface is pressed directly onto the previously decontaminated surface to be tested. The medium is then incubated for a predetermined period and the plate is examined for evidence of growth. Contamination is reported in terms of colony-forming units (CFU) per plate. The plate is of standard size, and if the assumption is made that any contamination is uniformly distributed, the results can be extrapolated to determine the residual bioburden on the entire surface. Since residual medium is left on the surface, a suitable cleansing procedure is necessary after testing [50].

The written protocol should describe in detail the methods, techniques, media, incubation period, acceptance criteria, and number of tests required to validate the decontamination procedure. Typically, a replicate series of decontamination procedures is performed, followed in sequence by RODAC testing, and the results are reported in the validation documentation.

2. Swab Testing

Another way to collect information about microbial contamination on surfaces is to use sterile cotton swabs moistened with sterile peptone water, WFI, or phosphate buffer. Using sterile forceps and aseptic technique, an area of predetermined size, e.g., 60–100 in.^{2}, is wiped with a sterile swab. The swab is then aseptically transferred to a tube containing a suitable diluent. The tube is then agitated to suspend any viable microorganisms and aliquots are plated in a semisolid medium to obtain *quantitative* results.

For purely *qualitative* determination, the medium in the tube can be observed for after a few days of incubation. Appearance of turbidity indicates the presence of viable microorganisms on the test surface. Results are typically reported as simply positive or negative.

D. Airborne Viable Particulate Monitoring

Three current techniques for obtaining samples of the air within the aseptic environment will be described:

1. *Fallout or settling plates*. This is a good qualitative procedure for monitoring over an extended period of time. Irregular air flow patterns within the aseptic environment reduce the effectiveness of this technique for meaningful quantitative measurement; however, ease of use and evaluation make it a good routine monitoring aid. Cautions to be observed include proper evaluation of the medium for growth promotion characteristics and possible desiccation of the medium when exposed to the relatively arid conditions within the aseptic suite, leading to false-negative interpretations.
2. *RCS (Reuter centrifugal sample)*. This is a good quantitative procedure that is gaining widespread acceptance. A known quantity of air, based on a sampling rate, is drawn into contact with sterile nutrient agar contained in shallow cups in a holder placed inside the instrument. After a suitable exposure period the medium is incubated, and results can be expressed in terms of CFU per ft^3 of air volume. Media can be selected to detect aerobes or anaerobes. Efficiency of the RCS appears to increase with particle size.
3. *Slit-to-agar and cascade plates*. These are additional techniques having a degree of quantifiability and size selectivity for airborne viable particulates. Associated problems include the possibility of desiccation of media and selectivity.

E. Aseptic Filling

Although it is possible to devise a validation program for aseptic filling without the use of media fills [51], the technique provides the best direct evidence of the microbiological quality of the operation and the environment. An outline of a media filling procedure suitable for validation of a sterile powder filling operation is provided below:

1. *Frequency*
   a. Before use of a new or renovated facility.
   b. At least once every 6 months for all operational filling lines and each production shift.
   c. All vial sizes should be evaluated.

    d. Each operator assigned to the aseptic filling area should participate at least once a year.

2. *Quantity*. At least 3000 units should be filled and additional units should be prepared to serve as positive and negative controls as stipulated in the protocol.

3. *Medium*. A broad-spectrum medium such as TSB is normally used; however, another selective medium can be substituted if deemed appropriate to determine the presence of anaerobes. Medium should be preincubated to ensure its sterility before use.

4. *Reconstitution*. Addition of sterile reconstitution fluid should be performed on line rather than in the microbiology laboratory to avoid ambiguity in the interpretation of any subsequent evidence of contamination. A suitable liquid filling apparatus should be placed in line immediately downstream of the powder filler before application of the closure and seal. Use of suitable antibiotic inhibitors, e.g., penicillinase, should be considered as appropriate to the product line.

5. *Incubation*. A period of 7 days at 30–35°C to detect bacterial growth, followed by 7 days at 20–25°C for molds, is considered appropriate.

6. *Growth promotion*. Growth should be evident using a challenge inoculum of 10 to 100 microorganisms as described in the USP Growth Promotion Test.

7. *Acceptance criteria*. A contamination rate less than or equal to 0.1% of the total number of filled units is considered acceptable. Any media run showing more than 0.1% contamination is cause for investigation. If the investigation cannot confirm the source of contamination as being unrelated to the filling operation (e.g., contaminated media), the filling equipment should be re-sterilized, the area decontaminated, and the media fill repeated until results are acceptable.

See Section VI.B for additional comments concerning media fill validation of lyophilization.

Validation of media fill for a liquid product follows essentially the same procedure as for the dry powder, except in this case the vials are filled with a predetermined quantity of a suitable sterile medium such as USP fluid soybean casein digest medium [51]. The requisite positive and negative controls are prepared, and growth promotion tests are performed in accordance with the protocol requirements.

VIII. DOCUMENTATION

Although the validation project is the sum of numerous subsets of projects, tasks, and tests, the entire documentation package should be collated into a complete document or set of documents that contains all pertinent information. This is necessary for a comprehensive review for acceptance by the quality control unit and will also serve to facilitate an FDA inspection.

The documents should consist of tables of contents, summary statements, data tables, discussion of results, conclusions, and acceptance statements. The need for proper tabulation and indexing is paramount because the volume of documentation associated with a typical facility qualification is likely to be substantial.

APPENDIX: ANALYSIS OF OIL MIST

I. *Summary of Procedure*
    1.0 Air samples are collected using 37-mm membrane filters.
    2.0 Oil mist is extracted from the filters with carbon tetrachloride.
    3.0 The carbon tetrachloride solution is analyzed for oil content using infrared spectrophotometry to measure the CH absorbance near 2940 cm^{-1}.

II. *Range, Precision, Sensitivity, and Limit of Detection*
    1.0 For a 100-liter air sample, the working range is linear up to at least 15 mg/m^3 and can be extended by dilution.
    2.0 Sensitivity is approximately 35 μg ml/0.1 absorbance unit and varies depending on the actual oil being analyzed. Precision is estimated to be 5% RSD.
    3.0 The detection limit varies slightly with oil types, but is approximately 2 μg oil/ml, which corresponds to 0.3 mg/m^3 for a 100-liter air sample.

III. *Precautions*
    1.0 Filters must be handled with care to avoid any oil or smoke contamination since this method is sensitive to any CH-containing compound.
    2.0 All handling of CCl_4 should be performed in a hood. Waste samples should be properly labeled and held for disposal in accordance with EPA requirements.

IV. *Apparatus*
    1.0 Sampling equipment. The sampling unit for the filter-collection method has the following components.
        A. The filter unit, consisting of the filter medium supported by a backup pad and 37-mm three-piece cassette filter holder secured with tape or a shrinkable band.
        B. Personal sampling pump. A calibrated personal sampling pump whose flow can be determined to an accuracy of ±5% at the recommended flow rate. The pump must be calibrated with a representative filter holder and filter in the line.

   C. Thermometer.
   D. Manometer.
   E. Stopwatch.
  2.0 Mixed cellulose ester membrane filter, 0.8 μm pore size or filter, 5.0 pore size, 37-mm diameter.
  3.0 Infrared spectrophotometer, double-beam dispersive, with scanning capabilities in the 3400–2700 wavenumber region.
  4.0 Glassware
   A. Scintillation vials with plastic-lined caps for desorption of samples.
   B. Volumetric flasks for preparing standards, 50 ml.
   C. Transfer pipets.
   D. Reagent dispenser, 15 ml delivery capacity for adding solvent to samples.
   E. Two 1-cm optical cells, infrared quartz with Teflon stoppers mounted in demountable cell holders.

V. *Analytical Reagents*
  1.0 Carbon tetrachloride, distilled reagent grade.
  2.0 Stock solution, 10 mg/ml. Weight 0.500 g of oil into a 50-ml volumetric flask and dissolve with CCl_4 to volume. Working standards should be prepared fresh in CCl_4 in the range of 1 to 100 μg oil/ml.

VI. *Procedure*
  1.0 Preparation
   A. Wash in detergent solution and follow with tap water and distilled or deionized water rinses. Dry.
   B. Rinse with distilled CCl_4 and allow to dry.
  2.0 Collection and Handling of Samples
   A. Assemble the filter unit by mounting the filter disk and backup pad in the filter cassette and securing the cassette with tape or shrinkable band.
   B. Connect the exit of the filter unit to the pump with a short piece of flexible tubing.
   C. Turn on pump to begin sample collection. The flow rate, times, and/or volume must be measured as accurately as possible. A minimum sample of 100 liters should be collected.
   D. Sample cassettes should be shipped in a suitable container to minimize contamination and prevent damage in transit. Care must be taken during storage and shipping that no part of the sample is dislodged from the filter or that the sample surface be disturbed in any way.

E. With each batch of samples, one filter, labeled as a blank, must be submitted. No air should be drawn through this filter.

F. An unused, undiluted sample (5–10 ml is sufficient) of the oil being used must be collected and sent to the laboratory for use as a standard material in the analysis. To prevent contamination, the bulk should not be shipped in the same container as the samples.

3.0 Analysis

A. Use tweezers to transfer sample and blank filters into individual scintillation vials, exercising care to avoid contaminating the filters with oil from hands. Add 15.0 ml CCl_4 and cap the vial. Allow vials to stand for 30 minutes with occasional agitation. At this point the oil is in solution and the samples are ready for analysis.

B. Fill both cells with distilled CCl_4 and scan the region from 3400 to 2700 cm^{-1}. All scans should be done in absorbance mode, if available. Otherwise, data must be converted to absorbance units.

C. Fill one cell with sample or blank filter extracts, one at a time and scan each solution against CCl_4 in the reference beam.

D. The absorbance at the wavenumber of the peak used to plot the calibration curve, generally about 2940 cm^{-1}, is measured and used to determine the oil concentration from the calibration curve prepared from the bulk samples (Section VI.2.0.F).

VII. *Calibration and Standardization*

1.0 Prepare appropriate dilutions of the stock solution with CCl_4 to obtain working standards in the range 1–100 μg/ml.

2.0 Transfer the working standards to a 1-cm cell and record an infrared spectrum of the region from 3400-2700 cm^{-1} for each standard. A calibration curve is constructed by measuring the peak height of the largest absorbance peak and plotting this value against concentration in μg/mL.

VIII. *Calculations*

1.0 Blank values, if any, should first be subtracted from each sample.

2.0 The concentration of oil in the air sampled can be calculated as mg oil/m^3 (C) as follows:

$$C = \frac{K \times V}{V_s}$$

where K = concentration of oil from calibration curve in μg oil/ml

$V =$ final volume (ml) of sample analyzed including any dilution factor

$V_s =$ volume of air in liters sampled at 25°C and 760 mm Hg

REFERENCES

1. McQuillen, D. F., Design and Testing of Pharmaceutical Sterile Rooms, *Pharmaceutical Technol.* Vol. 5, p. 45 (Nov. 1981).
2. Keller, A. M., Environmental Factors in the Design of a Parenteral Facility. In: *Pharmaceutical Dosage Forms: Parenteral Medications*, Vol. 1. Avis, K. E., Lachman, L., and Lieberman, H. A. (eds.), Marcel Dekker, New York, pp. 355–425 (1984).
3. Federal Standard Clean Room And Work Station Requirements, Controlled Environment. FED-STD-209D, June 15, 1988.
4. Block, S. S., *Disinfection Sterilization and Preservation*, 3d ed., Lea & Febiger, Philadelphia, Chapters 1–9,11, 14 (1983).
5. Akers, M. J., and Anderson, N. R., Validation of Sterile Products. In: *Pharmaceutical Process Validation*, Vol 23 Loftus, B. T., and Nash, R. A. (eds.), Marcel Dekker, New York, pp. 31–35 (1984).
6. Avis, K. E., and Akers, M. J., Sterilization. In: *Theory and Practice of Industrial Pharmacy*, 3d ed., Lachman, L., Lieberman, H., and Kanig, J. (eds.), Lea & Febiger, Philadelphia, pp. 619–623,668 (1986).
7. Document No. F 91, American Society for Testing and Materials, 1916 Race Street, Philadelphia, PA 19103.
8. Good Manufacturing Practices and Proposed Exemptions for Certain OTC Products, Human and Veterinary Drugs, 21CFR211, Federal Register, Friday, September 29, 1978.
9. IES-RP-CC-006-84-T, Testing Clean Rooms, Institute of Environmental Sciences, 940 East Northwest Highway, Mount Prospect, IL 60056.
10. Simmons P. L., The Impact of International GMP's on the Drug, Device and Diagnostics Industries, Chapter 8, Graphics Marking Systems, Inc., Tampa, FL (1985).
11. The United States Pharmacopeia, USP XXII/ The National Formulary, NF XVII, 1990, United States Pharmacopeial Convention, 12601 Twinbrook Parkway, Rockville, MD 20852.
12. Brown, P. W., "Storage and Distribution of Distilled Water, LVP's," Proceedings of the PMA Water Seminar Program, Pharmaceutical Manufacturer's Association, Atlanta, GA (1982).
13. Meyrick, C. E. Practical Design of a High Purity Water System, *Pharmaceutical Eng.* 9(5) 20–27 (1989).
14. Pamphlet G-7.1 ANSI Z86.1–1973, American National Standard, Commodity Specification for Air, 2d ed., Compressed Gas Association, New York (1973).
15. Bondi, H., and Olson, W. P., *Closure Cleaning and Sterilization in Aseptic Pharmaceutical Manufacturing*, Interpharm Press, Prairie View, IL pp. 63–73 (1987).

16. Wood, R. T., *J. Parenteral Drug Assoc. 34*: 286–294 (1980).
17. Gillis, J. R., Ethylene Oxide Sterilization and Validation for Practical Pharmaceutical Aseptic Production. In *Validation of Aseptic Pharmaceutical Processes*, 3d printing, Carleton, F. J., and Agalloco, J. P. (eds.), Marcel Dekker, New York, pp. 364–365 (1986).
18. Anderson, N. R., Container Cleaning and Sterilization. In *Aseptic Pharmaceutical Processing*, Olson, W. P., and Groves, M. J. (eds.), Interpharm Press, Prairie View, IL pp. 11,40,41 (1987).
19. Dietz, G. R., Validation of Cobalt 60 Radiation Sterilization. In *Validation of Aseptic Pharmaceutical Processes*, 3d printing, Carleton, F. J., and Agalloco, J. P. (eds.), Marcel Dekker, New York, pp. 378–379 (1986).
20. Akers, M. J., and Anderson, N. R., Validation of Sterile Products. In *Pharmaceutical Process Validation*, Vol. 23, Loftus, B. T., and Nash, R. A. (eds.), Marcel Dekker, New York, pp. 60–61 (1984).
21. Medical Device Monographs, Sterilization Cycle Development, Report No. 78-4.2, Health Industries Manufacturers Association.
22. Pearson, F. C., Pyrogens and Depyrogenation: Theory and Practice. In *Aseptic Pharmaceutical Manufacturing*, Olson, W. P., and Groves, M. J. (eds.), Interpharm Press, Prairie View, IL, pp. 76–77 (1987).
23. Tsuji, K., and Harrison, S. J., *Appl. Environ. Microbiol. 36*:710–714 (1978).
24. Tsuji, K., and Lewis, A. R., *Appl. Environ. Microbiol. 36*:715–719 (1978).
25. Burns, L. A., and Heffernan, G. D., Dry Heat Sterilization and Depyrogenation Validation and Monitoring. In *Validation of Aseptic Pharmaceutical Processes*, 3d printing, Carleton, F. J., and Agalloco, J. P. (eds.), Marcel Dekker, New York, pp. 329–333 (1986).
26. Perkins, J. J., *Principles and Methods of Sterilization in Health Sciences*, Charles C. Thomas, Springfield, IL (1973).
27. De Santis, P. and Rudo, V. S. Validation of Steam Sterilization in Autoclaves. In *Validation of Aseptic Pharmaceutical Processes*, 3d printing, Carleton, F. J., and Agalloco, J. P. (eds.), Marcel Dekker, New York, pp. 286,287,307–311,315 (1986).
28. Rankell, A. S., Lieberman, H. A., and Schiffman, R. F., Drying. In *Theory and Practice of Industrial Pharmacy*, 3d ed., Lachman, L., Lieberman, H. A., and Kanig, J. L., Lea & Febiger, Philadelphia, pp. 62–63 (1986).
29. Groves, M. J. *Parenteral Technology Manual*, 2d ed., Interpharm Press, Prairie View, IL, p. 74 (1989).
30. Maron, S. H., and Prutton, C. F., *Principles of Physical Chemistry*, 4th ed., Macmillan, New York, p. 350 (1965).
31. Jennings, T. A. Validation of the Lyophilization Process. In *Validation of Aseptic Pharmaceutical Processes*, 3d printing, Carleton, F. J., and Agalloco, J. P. (eds.), Marcel Dekker, New York, pp. 596,603 (1986).
32. Gennaro, A. R., (ed.), *Remington's Pharmaceutical Sciences*, 17th ed., Mack Publishing Co., Easton, PA, p. 1538 (1985).
33. Errico, J. J., Validation of Aseptic Processing Filters. In *Validation of Aseptic Pharmaceutical Processes*, 3d printing, Carleton, F. J., and Agalloco, J. P. (eds.), Marcel Dekker, New York, pp. 440,455–457 (1986).
34. Lukasziewicz, R. C., and Fisher, R., *Pharmaceutical Technol. 5*(5):49 (1981).

35. Akers, M. J., and Anderson, N. R., Validation of Sterile Products. In *Pharmaceutical Process Validation*, Vol. 23, Loftus, B. T., and Nash, R. A. (eds.), Marcel Dekker, New York, p. 65 (1984).

36. Olson, W. P., Sterilization of Small-Volume Parenterals and Therapeutic Proteins by Filtration. In *Aseptic Pharmaceutical Manufacturing*, Olson, W. P., and Groves, M. J. (eds.), Interpharm Press, Prairie View, IL, pp. 110–111 (1987).

37. Trappler, E. H., Validation of Lyophilization. *Pharmaceutical Technol.* 13(1):56–60 (1988).

38. Lee, J. Y., GMP Compliance for the Lyophilization of Parenterals: Part II. *Pharmaceutical Technol.* 12(11):38–43 (1988).

39. Jeater, J. P., and Jacobs, R. A., Validation of New Formulations. In *Validation of Aseptic Pharmaceutical Processes*, 3d printing, Carleton, F. J., and Agalloco, J. P., (eds.), Marcel Dekker, New York, p. 518 (1986).

40. Trubinski, C. J., and Majeed, M., Retrospective Process Validation. In *Pharmaceutical Process Validation*, Vol 23, Loftus, B. T., and Nash, R. A., (eds.), Marcel Dekker, New York, p. 178 (1984).

41. Boylan, J. C., Liquids. In *Theory and Practice of Industrial Pharmacy*, 3d ed., Lachman, L., Lieberman, H. A., and Kanig, J. L. (eds.), Lea & Febiger, Philadelphia p. 476 (1986).

42. Hofmann, K. L., Sterile Powder Filling—The Learning Curve. *J. Parenteral Sci. Technol.* 40(5):200 (1986).

43. Prout, G., An Introduction to Aseptic Filling of Sterile Powders. In *Aseptic Pharmaceutical Manufacturing* Olson, W. P., and Groves, M. J., (eds.), Interpharm Press, Prairie View, IL, p. 170 (1987).

44. Federal Specifications, PP-C-186 C, November 10, 1976, Containers, Packaging & Packing for Drugs, Chemical and Pharmaceutical, Defense Personnel Support Center, Directorate of Medical Material, Philadelphia.

45. Frieben, W. R., Folck, R. J., and Derisser, A. J., *J. Science and Technol.* 36:112–116 (1982).

46. Levine, C. S., Validation of Packaging Operations. In *Validation of Aseptic Pharmaceutical Processes*, 3d printing, Carleton, F. J., and Agalloco, J. P. (eds.), Marcel Dekker, New York, pp. 561,564,565 (1986).

47. Korczynski, M. S., Evaluation of Closure Integrity. In *Aseptic Pharmaceutical Manufacturing*, Olson, W. P., and Groves, M. J. (eds.), Interpharm Press, Prairie View, IL, pp. 188–189 (1987).

48. Wilson, J. D., Validation of Sanitation. In *Validation of Aseptic Pharmaceutical Processes*, 3d printing, Carleton, F. J., and Agalloco, J. P. (eds.), Marcel Dekker, New York, pp. 389–391 (1986).

49. Petrocci, A. N., Surface-Active Agents: Quaternary Ammonium Compounds. In *Disinfection, Sterilization and Preservation*, 3d ed., Block, S. S. (ed.), Lea & Febiger, Philadelphia, p. 325 (1983).

50. DeVecchi, F., Validation of Air Systems Used in Parenteral Drug Manufacturing Facilities. In *Validation of Aseptic Pharmaceutical Processes*, 3d printing, Carleton F. J., and Agalloco, J. P. (eds.), Marcel Dekker, New York, p. 157 (1986).

51. Agalloco, J. P., Validation of Aseptic Filling Operations. In *Validation of Aseptic Pharmaceutical Processes*, 3d printing, Carleton, F. J., and Agalloco, J. P., (eds.), Marcel Dekker, New York, pp. 655–656 (1986).

5

Validation of Solid Dosage Forms

Jeffrey S. Rudolph   *ICI Pharmaceuticals Group, Wilmington, Delaware*

I. INTRODUCTION

The concept of process validation from its beginnings in the early 1970s through the regulatory aspects associated with current good manufacturing practice (CGMP) regulations and the application thereof to various analytical, quality assurance, pilot plant, production, and sterile produce considerations will be discussed elsewhere in this book. In this chapter, emphasis will be placed on the validation of solid dosage forms, from the early stages of product development through pilot scale-up and the manufacturing process. The objective is to present an overview and to discuss aspects of validation in terms of pharmaceutical unit operations, i.e., those individual technical operations that comprise the various steps involved in product design and evaluation. The focus of the discussion will be on tablets, but consideration will also be given to hard-shell gelatin capsules.

All pharmaceutical scientists, whether in development, quality assurance, production, or regulatory affairs, are familiar with the axiom that quality is not tested into a product but rather is built into a product. This is an important concept, since it serves to support the underlying definition of validation, which is a systematic approach to identifying, measuring, evaluating, documenting, and reevaluating a series of critical steps in the manufacturing process that require control to ensure a reproducible final product. Dr. Chao [1] has enumerated four key elements that form the basis of a prospective process validation program:

1. Definition of the desirable attributes of the drug product or components thereof as well as those characteristics that are not desired
2. Establishment of limitations or constraints for these attributes
3. Determination of the controls or testing parameters that will be measured or tested
4. Initiation of studies to establish control or boundary limits for those key attributes that influence the product, process, quality, and performance

These criteria represent a logical progression of activities encompassing the development of a pharmaceutical product.

There are several important reasons for validating a product and/or process. First, manufacturers are required by law to conform to CGMP regulations. Second, good business dictates that a manufacturer avoid the possibility of rejected or recalled batches. Third, validation helps to ensure product uniformity, reproducibility, and quality [2–4].

Most discussions of product and process validation that have occurred in recent articles [5–7] or have been the subject of presentations at meetings have concentrated on validation associated with the full-scale manufacture of pharmaceutical processes and how equipment processing variables affect the overall quality of the finished product. Although this is certainly an important aspect of product validation, validation of numerous earlier aspects of development are critical to the subsequent phases of the process.

Without proper characterization, specification, and control of these earlier development steps, the foundation will be weak and will not support the evolving product when it is challenged during the formal validation of pilot and production batches.

II. VALIDATION OF RAW MATERIALS

The validation process of a solid dosage form begins with a validation of the raw materials: both active ingredients and excipients [8]. Variation in raw materials is one of the major causes of product variation or deviation from specification. The active ingredient may represent the most uncontrollable component in the complete product/process validation scheme, as key physical properties such as particle size and surface area may not be completely defined this early in the sequence. Oftentimes, the synthesis of the new drug substance is not completely defined at this early stage.

The preformulation program initiated during the early exploratory phase of product development is rarely considered part of validation, but it represents one of the more critical steps in the development cycle. Characteristics such as drug morphology, particle size, surface area, color, and other physical/chemical characteristics are important in assessing drug availability and reproducibility of subsequent manufacturing processes [9]. For example, a water-insoluble drug, in order to achieve rapid dissolution and in vitro availability, is usually milled or micronized to achieve the desired particle size range [6]. The particle size is usually inversely related to surface area and, therefore, large surface areas (5000–10,000 cm^2/g) are created during a particle reduction process. Particle size is directly interrelated to several key processing variables. Several of the most significant are flow, blend uniformity, granulation solution/binder uptake, compressibility, and lubricant efficiency [10]. In order to achieve a uniform blend of active ingredient with other formula components, either for subsequent wet granulation or direct compression processing, it is critical that the active ingredient be compatible with the other ingredients in terms of particle size, density, and shape in order to permit a random distribution of ingredients within the blend prior to compression. If the milling or micronizing process is not controlled and properly validated so as to achieve a reproducible particle size distribution, irregularities in blend distribution will result in content uniformity problems of the final dosage form [11].

Another manufacturing characteristic that may be affected negatively by not validating the active ingredient particle size distribution is the volume of granulating solution or binder needed to produce a properly agglomerated mass. A greater volume of granulating agent will be needed to wet mass a powder bed comprised of finely divided particles than is needed for coarser particles of the same substance. If the particle size/surface area ratio is not controlled and a specific amount of granulating solution is not stated in the product manufacturing directions, then, in some cases, the wet mass will be overwet, resulting in erratic drying properties (case-hardening, insufficient dried product); or, in contrast, it will be too dry and will not form proper particle aggregates, resulting in poor granulation flow, poor tablet compressibility, and content uniformity problems with the final dosage form.

The concept of particle control and the validation thereof is also extremely important for excipients used in solid oral dosage forms. Excipients can represent less than 1% of a tablet formula or as much as 99%. It is no less important to validate the critical characteristics of the 1% material than of an excipient used in larger quantities. Two specific examples illustrate this point.

1.   Magnesium stearate is used as a lubricant to reduce friction when removing the solid dosage form from its molding process. It is well known that the action of magnesium stearate is highly dependent on its particle size and ability to delaminate its "deck of cards" configuration when stress is applied, thus creating a slipping action that relieves the applied stress [12]. It is also well known that when magnesium stearate is used in excess, the disintegration and dissolution characteristics of the final tablet or capsule are usually hindered as a result of a hydrophobic coating of the formula components. This coating action can also be achieved by using a small particle size or greater surface area lubricant which,

when used in the same percent concentration as a lower surface area lubricant, more efficiently coats the surface of the particles, thus creating more hydrophobicity and subsequent drug-release problems. It is critical to validate the particle size/surface area characteristics of a supplier's grade of magnesium stearate to ensure that there is relatively good assurance that the stearate is uniform lot after lot. Also, when an alternate source of stearate is sought, it is critical to check the particle size/surface area characteristics to ensure that these parameters do not vary significantly from the primary source material. If these criteria are different, a more in-depth study, possibly using an instrumented tablet machine, would be appropriate to ensure that alternate source stearate does not cause compression or ejection problems. Also, dissolution testing would also be an appropriate companion test, again to ensure that the new stearate did not create in vitro drug release problems.

2.   The importance of validating a raw material can also be illustrated in the case of dyes used to impart a color to a tablet. Consider the use of an aluminum lake dye that is dry-blended into a direct compression tablet formulation. In order to achieve an even color distribution, the colorant should be added using a geometric addition or preblend approach. Unless the dye is available as a finely divided, large surface area material that is free from agglomerates and has a soft texture the resulting tablets will be mottled and have areas of high dye concentration, which may yield a speckled tablet appearance. The validation of colorant raw materials using such techniques as particle size analysis, surface area measurements, and Hegman gauge testing is critical to ensure that all lots of dye material received will repeatedly perform in a successful manner when incorporated into pharmaceutical dosage forms.

A comprehensive program for establishing validation and control procedures for raw materials is critical if one hopes to achieve a product that meets all of the final product criteria batch after batch.

Variations in raw materials constitute one of the major sources of problems confronting the pharmaceutical development scientist, production supervisor, or quality control chemist. Variations in materials occur among different suppliers of the same product depending on the method of transportation chosen, the exposure of materials to undesirable conditions (heat, humidity, oxygen, light), the reliability of the supplier, and the individual supplier's conformance to regulatory requirements in terms of facilities, personnel, operating procedures, and controls. In addition to the important physical characteristics of particle size, surface area, etc., mentioned previously, the manufacturer should check the supplier's assay procedure as part of its own validation program. Other chemical characteristics, such as water content, residue on ignition, and heavy metals, should also be monitored.

The steps involved in the validation of a raw material or excipient follow those sited in the CGMPs and involve formal written documentation of those procedures and methods used.

1. Each raw material should be validated by performing checks on several batches, preferably three, from the primary supplier as well as the alternate supplier. The batches chosen should be selected to represent the range of acceptable specifications, both high and low.

2. Depending on the susceptibility of the raw material to aging, either physical, chemical, or microbiological stability should be assessed. This is especially true for liquid or semisolid ingredients where interaction with the container or permeability of the container to air and moisture could have a detrimental effect on the raw material.

3. Once the samples of raw materials have been selected as having fallen into an established, acceptable range of specifications and stability, it should be used to manufacture a batch of final dosage form. It may be appropriate to manufacture several lots of final product with raw material at the low and high ends of the specification limit. Such testing would be especially useful when it is known that the product may be sensitive to small changes in the characteristics of the excipients or active ingredient.

4. The final step of raw-material validation should involve an on-site inspection of the supplier to review the vendor's manufacturing operations and control procedures. The reliability of each vendor and how well each conforms to regulatory requirements must also be determined.

III. ANALYTICAL METHODS VALIDATION

The topic of analytical methods validation will be discussed elsewhere in this book in great depth. It is important, however, to enumerate the key elements of this subject at this time. Unless a suitable analytical method, or series of methods, is available to assess the quality and performance of a solid dosage form, then the validation program will have limited validity. The following list of analytical criteria must be assessed prior to beginning any validation program:

1. Accuracy of method—ability of a method to measure the true value of a sample.

2. Precision of method—ability of a method to estimate reproducibility of any given value, but not necessarily the true value.

3. In-day/out-of-day variation—does the precision and accuracy of the method change when conducted numerous times on the same day and repeated on a subsequent day?

4. Between-operator variation—repeat the precision and accuracy studies within the same laboratory using the same instrument but different analysts to challenge the reproducibility of the method.

5. Between-instrument variation—how will different instruments within the same laboratory run by the same analyst affect the accuracy and precision of the method?

6. Between-laboratory variation—will the precision and accuracy of the method
    be the same between the development and quality-control laboratories?

A collaborative study between various analytical methods chemists who developed the analytical method and the analytical chemists in the quality control laboratory who must routinely run the method will help to ensure the validity and ruggedness of the analytical method. If characteristics of the analytical method are found to be less than optimum or if deficiencies arise during testing, the method should be returned to the originating chemist for reevaluation.

It is important, when a method is being developed, that the analytical methods development chemist be cognizant of the laboratory conditions to which his methods will be conducted in a quality control setting.

The methods chemist must be able to make the method work when operating conditions of time, instrument limitations, and other techniques that could "baby" the method are not used. Normal operating conditions in quality control laboratories require a robust method that can be run routinely by different chemists on different instruments in a high-throughput mode. In some cases, the method should be automated to take advantage of greater laboratory efficiency. It is the responsibility of the analytical methods development chemist to build these important elements into the methods.

The responsibilities for suitable validated analytical methods, however, do not rest solely in the analytical method development group. Today, the analytical function uses new and sophisticated chromatographic and other instrumental techniques that require a high level of technical expertise. It is the responsibility of quality control management to ensure that its staff is adequately trained and its laboratories properly equipped so that new analytical methods can be properly translated from an analytical methods group to the quality control department. A mutual understanding of each other's responsibilities and limitations is necessary in order to develop the trust that is required between these two important functions.

IV. DEFINITION AND CONTROL OF PROCESS VARIABLES

Process validation can be defined as a means of challenging a process during development to determine which variables must be controlled to ensure the consistent production of a product or intermediate. It also provides the means for an ongoing quality audit of the process during the marketing phase of the product to ensure its compliance with these specifications. It is based on the concept that the process employed has been optimized, so that data generated through the testing program may be considered credible and evaluated for consistency, as well as relevance. The activity starts when the pharmaceutical development department begins its work. Pertinent data or information is collected during the preformulation stage, and additional inputs are generated during formulation development and evaluation, process development, and during full-scale manufacture. The information gathered in all four stages is evaluated to determine which parameters in the process can be used as possible tools to show that the product is under proper control. Once this is done, some other major steps in the development of a validation program are as follows:

1. Obtaining test data to determine the numerical range of each parameter— e.g., assess the tablet hardness over a series of batches that achieves an acceptable friability, disintegration, and dissolution.
2. Establishing specification limits from the test data derived for a given parameter—based on the data collected, using statistical techniques determine the extremes of acceptable hardness (high and low) that would provide 95% assurance that the friability, disintegration, and dissolution specifications would be met (upper and lower control/release limits).
3. Determining how well the specification limit indicates that the process is under control—challenge the process by producing product at the extremes of the specification limit to ensure *all* product specifications are met.
4. Certify the equipment that is used in obtaining the data and controlling the process—ensure that equipment operating conditions, e.g., rpm, temperature, power utilization, are within specification limits under variations of product load.

Once this has been done, one can proceed to actual product testing utilizing these parameters and their specifications to validate that the process will produce acceptable product. Each product may have its own idiosyncracies requiring special tests, but generally the tests that would be required for all solid dosage forms in process validation are as follows:

1. Moisture (total volatile) content as "dry" granulation—Has the granulation solvent been removed to a sufficient extent during the drying operation (usually less than 1% moisture)?
2. Content uniformity of the blend and the final dosage form—across the blend or batch profile sampling at various points. Does the content uniformity comply with compendial standards (± 15% of labeled amount) or other internal standards? Is there demixing during the tablet manufacturing operation, e.g., segregation during flow of granulation from a storage bin?
3. Hardness—the relationship between tablet hardness, thickness, friability, and release characteristics must be clearly defined.
4. Disintegration and dissolution where appropriate—important to ensure proper drug release characteristics (in vitro availability) and batch-to-batch uniformity.
5. Friability—an important characteristic to interrelate to the extent tablets will chip, crack, or "dust" during the packaging operations.

6. Weight variation—throughout the batch sampling. Normally attempt to achieve a weight variation of less than 5% from the average. If this is not achieved, problems related to poor granulation flow and equipment problems may be suspect.
7. Granulation particle size distribution—an extremely important parameter that affects tablet compressibility, hardness, thickness, disintegration, dissolution, weight variation, and content uniformity. This parameter should be monitored throughout the tablet validation process.

These key test parameters are the yardsticks by which the major processing variables in solid dosage forms are evaluated. These variables include mixing time and rpm in blenders and granulators; solvent addition rates in granulators; time, temperature, and air flow conditions in dryers and coaters; screen size and feed rate in mills; tablet machine speed and compression force in tablet presses; and machine speed and fill volume in encapsulators. Process validation testing is generally done on the first three batches of product made in production size equipment. Therefore, revalidation testing is only done when a "significant" change has occurred. A significant change is one that will alter the in-process or final product specification established during the validation program or a change in formula, process, or equipment.

V. GUIDELINES FOR PROCESS VALIDATION OF SOLID DOSAGE FORMS

Numerous factors should be considered when developing and validating solid dosage forms. Figures 1 and 2 are flowcharts for the validation of new and existing processes. As a means of providing a broader overview of these validation criteria, I have established the following possible guidelines or check list for tablets and dry-filled capsules for inclusion in an in-depth program of solid dosage form validation.

I. Compressed and coated tablets
  A. Tablet composition: provide the reason for the presence of each ingredient in the formula.
    What are the "normal" properties of each ingredient? Are these properties used or changed in the formula under study?
    What are the characteristics of the initial powder blends, the wet and/or dry granulations and the final blends?
    Density: "loose" and "tap".
    Particle size distribution.
    Surface area.
    Flow properties, e.g., contact angle.
    Moisture content, if applicable.

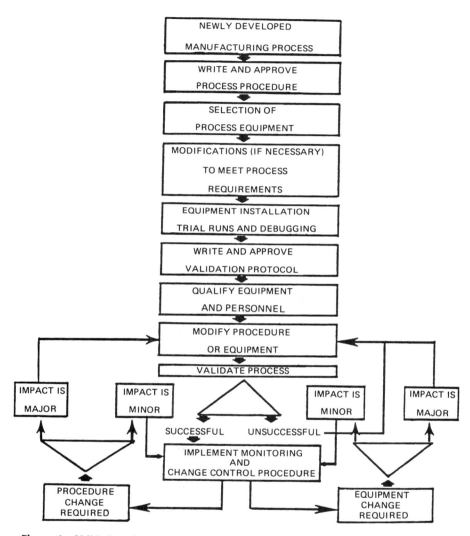

Figure 1 Validation of new processes. (Courtesy of ICI Pharmaceuticals Group, Wilmington, Delaware.)

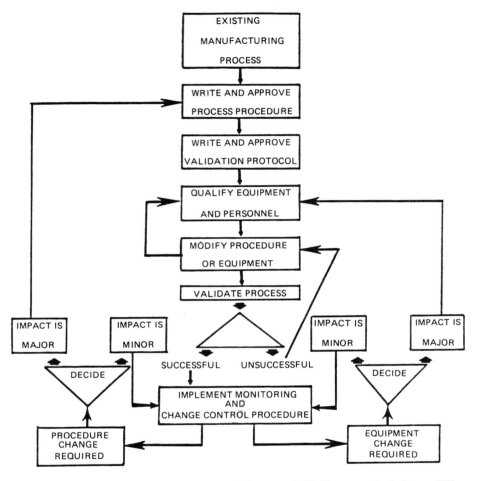

Figure 2 Validation of existing processes. (Courtesy of ICI Pharmaceuticals Group, Wilmington, Delaware.)

Solubility of active ingredient at various pH values in aqueous or hydroalcoholic systems.
B. Process evaluation and selection: determine the processing steps needed for the initial scale-up.
   1. Blending operations (as applicable). Determination of the optimal blending time based on:
      a. Does extensive blending cause demixing and segregation of components? This is important, especially if the particle size and/or density of the powder/granulation varies widely.

b. What tests are used to assess the uniformity of the final product? Content uniformity, weight variation testing?
2. Is the granulation adequately blended to achieve the desired distribution of active ingredient in the overall mix (e.g., direct compression formulations) or simply to add a tablet lubricant to the final stage? The type of blender, length of blending operation, and intensity of shear during the blending operation will be different depending on the objective.
3. Determine time of "unmixing," i.e., time to lose uniformity—powder blends and granulations can become segregated on blending as a result of particle size or density differences. For example, in a direct compression formula in which the active agent is micronized (5 microns) and the excipients are granular (500–1000 microns).
4. Check for a possible interaction between the process and its effect on tablet (core) compression; e.g., tablet machine table rpm will affect dwell time (the time the powder mass is under compression by the tablet punches), which can ultimately affect hardness, friability, dissolution, etc. In general, an increased dwell time will result in a harder tablet; however, if the tablet machine cam system does not permit gradual compression, air may be entrapped in the tablet, resulting in capping.
5. Check characteristics of blend:
   a. Bulk density—this will have a significant bearing on tablet thickness and could affect product uniformity (as noted above).
   b. Particle size distribution—a key parameter affecting many product characteristics.
   c. Moisture, if applicable—can be important as related to product physical and chemical stability.
6. Does any ingredient in the formulation affect the density of the final blend to a greater extent than any other ingredient? If this does occur, a well-controlled density specification for that ingredient will be warranted.
7. Color uniformity—the color of a powder blend or compressed tablet can vary as a function of applied stress as this stress can deform and/or deaggregate a drug or colorant affecting the color, hue, intensity, and uniformity.
8. Test different sized loads in the blending apparatus, e.g., 30, 50, and 70% of working volume—undercharging or overcharging a blender can result in poor drug or tablet lubricant distribution.
C. Wet granulation.
1. Evaluation of binder depends on :
   a. Binder concentration—requires adequate binder to agglomerate particles to achieve good granulation flow and compressibility. The binder concentration and volume are interrelated to numerous characteristics of the formulation and process used to manufacture the product. For example, if the granulation is being made using fluid

bed granulation and starch paste has been determined to be the best binder, a dilute paste, capable of being pumped through a spray nozzle, would be desirable. Granulating in a conventional planetary mixer would probably not require this special "low-viscosity" paste.

b. Solubility in granulating solution—the binder should be in solution to exert its maximal agglomeration activity.

c. How it behaves during the drying step; e.g., does it swell; does it become tacky? These characteristics affect the granulation drying rate. A tacky granulation will dry more slowly than one that does not exhibit this characteristic (e.g., povidone vs. tragacanth).

2. Evaluation of mixed granulation.

a. Compare density—wet granulation versus original dry powder. During the wet granulation phase, the granulation may go through a phase where bulk volume increases before it begins to agglomerate. This can result in the granulation bulk volume exceeding the volume capacity of the blender. This density measurement can be made using a weighed quantity of granulation placed in a volumetric flask.

b. Determine the optimum density for powder flow and tablet formulation.

c. Amount of granulating solution required for optimum granulation; use of granulation end-point instrumentation, e.g., an ammeter or wattmeter, is highly desirably.

d. Compactibility of wet granulation—densification during wet granulation is associated with the degree of aggregation of particles and is interrelated to granulation particle size and flow characteristics.

e. Optimal mixing time (for maximum distribution of liquid, etc.)— same as "c" above.

f. Effect of overmixing on physical characteristics, etc.—overmixing can result in overwet granulation, which will create difficulties in wet milling and subsequent drying operations.

3. Evaluation of drying step and dried granulation.

a. Determine the optimal moisture content of the dried granulation. High moisture content can result in (1) tablet picking or sticking to tablet punch surfaces and (2) poor chemical stability as a result of hydrolysis. An overdried granulation could result in poor hardness and friability. Moisture content analysis can be performed using the conventional loss-on-drying techniques or state-of-the-art techniques such as infrared or radio-frequency drying.

b. Particle size distribution of dried granulation—extremely important to ensure good granulation flow and good content uniformity of resultant tablets.

    c. Density of dried granulation—related to tablet thickness; density can vary if particle size distribution changes.

    d. What equipment and/or instrument conditions are required to promote optimal drying?

       i. Air flow—proper air flow is needed to remove moisture-laden air from the wet granulation.

      ii. Inlet temperature—temperature of incoming air to dryer; this is an important factor (along with outlet air) to determine drying efficiency.

     iii. Dryer efficiency and its effect on the product under study—see "ii" above.

     iv. Load to be dried—the greater the load, the more moisture that will have to be removed on drying; in fluid bed drying, a maximum dryer load is that load above which the dryer will not fluidize.

      v. Outlet temperature—see "ii" above.

4. The milling operation for the dried granulation.

    a. Particle size distribution—the type of mill, its speed, and milling screen are key parameters in producing the desired particle size distribution; parameters such as knives or impact impellers, wire mesh, or solid plate screens and product feed rate into the mill significantly affect the particle size distribution of the resultant product.

    b. Dissolution (if applicable)—if the drug is water insoluble, a large particle may cause prolonged dissolution rates—dissolution rate is directly proportional to the surface area of the dissolving particle.

    c. Granule disintegration—larger granules generally disintegrate at a slower rate than smaller granules.

    d. Moisture pickup versus percent relative humidity (24-hr period) re powder flow properties—hygroscopic granulation can result in poor granulation flow, which can lead to poor tablet content uniformity and weight variation problems; the moist granulation creates weak particle-to-particle bonds, which prevents free flow of the granules.

    e. Compressibility (without lubricant and other recommended fillers)—compression of nonlubricated granulation will provide an indication of tablet lubricant needed, as well as requirements for additional tablet binders. An instrumented tablet press can be extremely valuable in these studies, as compressional and ejection forces can be monitored.

5. Tablet (core) compression. In addition to the characteristics noted previously, the following additional product/process characteristics should be evaluated.

a. Appearance—mottled, picking of monogram.
b. Color quality—may need a finer grind of color or a milling step of color with tablet excipient prior to incorporation into final tablet blend to deagglomerate the color properly and facilitate dispersal into the bulk of the tablet granulation.
c. Stability (effect of age on all physical and chemical properties).
d. Moisture pickup versus percent relative humidity (24 hr and 1 week). If moisture pickup exceeds 2 to 5%, such negative effects as tablet softening, increased friability, mottling, abraded monogram, and decreased chemical stability may result.
e. Powder flow from hopper (include observation for "rat hole effect")—interrelated to particle size of granulate and moisture content.
f. Separation or uniformity in feed frame? The centrifugal action of the turntable causes agitation of the granulation in the tablet feed frame, which may result in segregation of coarse and fine particles of the granulation.
g. List special requirements needed, e.g., screen to delump powder— excipients or drugs may be agglomerated after prolonged storage in drums. Need to deagglomerate prior to granulation step to ensure good content uniformity.
h. Optimal speed of tablet press—flow characteristics of the granulation as related to the filling of tablet dies at various tablet machine rotation speeds will affect the tablet weight variation; if the granulation flow characteristics are poor, it may not uniformly fill the die cavities where the dies pass beneath the granulation bed too rapidly.
i. Compare high-speed machine operation with low-speed operation— the rotation speed and/or dwell, time will be significantly different for single station or development tablet presses as compared to machines used in production. All physical characteristics of the resulting tablet should be monitored to ensure translation of product quality during scale-up.

6. Direct compression.
   a. Blending—(NOTE: Operations are the same as those listed in IB (page 176).
   b. Powder characterization—(NOTE: Operations are the same as those listed in IB5 (page 177).
   c. Tablet (core) compression—(NOTE: Operations are the same as those listed in IC5 (pages 179–180).
   d. Tablet coating (if applicable)—(NOTE: Operations are the same as those listed in item 7 below.)

7. Tablet coating (if applicable).
   a. Review the procedure recommended by the formulation group.
   b. Confirm whether the procedure is adequate as related to full-scale equipment, e.g., material handling to and from the coating pan; proper pan load, speed and baffling to achieve good tablet agitation.
   c. Evaluate the coating procedure in at least two different sized pans, e.g., 24-in. and 48-in. pans.
   d. Compare the operations and determine the adequacy of the procedure. Is the pan rpm proper? Is there sufficient tablet bed movement to ensure even distribution of the coating solution onto the tablets? If using a spray system, are the spray nozzles sized properly to ensure even distribution over the tablet bed? To prevent clogging of the nozzles?
   e. Why is the tablet coated? Mask taste, stability, sustained release, product identification?
   f. Effect of sealing solution on the tablet core—surface roughness. If the sealing coat is not smooth, the imperfections are carried through to the final coated tablet.
   g. Integrity of cover resulting from sealer coat—impermeability of the sealed tablet to moisture. A crack in the seal coat will permit moisture from subsequent coating steps to penetrate into the tablet core resulting in decreased stability.
   h. Effect of subcoating solution on sealed core—surface roughness. [Same as (f)].
   i. Determine the application rate of subcoating materials (solution and dusting powder). This is important to ensure a smooth, even coat.
   j. Determine the optimal amounts of materials required per application.
   k. Determine what amounts will be excessive. How many applications are required?
   l. Determine the optimal drying conditions. Drying at too high a temperature can cause crystallization of ingredients during the subcoating and glossing steps.
   m. Test the disintegration time of the partially coated tablet. This test can serve as a quick assessment of coating integrity. If the disintegration time is high, was too much seal coat applied?
   n. Friability of the partially coated tablet. The subcoating operations may have permitted moisture to penetrate the core. One negative effect of this could be a tablet with a higher friability than desired with the result being chipping during subsequent coating steps.
   o. Determine the application rate of the finishing materials. What are the optimal drying conditions?

     p. Tablet polishing.
       i. Coated tablet dimensions.
       ii. Solvent residue.
     q. When film coating is used, additional questions must be answered.
       i. Determine the proper application rate, drying rate, rotational pan speed, and amount of agitation in the pan.
       ii. What is the quantity of solvent residue in tablet?
D. Equipment evaluation.
  1. Blending equipment.
    a. What is the working capacity of equipment?
    b. Does the equipment operate more efficiently with the density of fluffy powders?
    c. What is the working load range, i.e., the proper blender load to ensure good uniformity of blend?
    d. What features does the equipment have for ease of handling of powders, automated charging and discharging, e.g., Vac-U-Max, Gemco valves?
    e. Can the equipment heat the powder blend if needed for application as a dryer as well as a granulator? Is the method of heating electric or steam?
    f. May a vacuum be used with the equipment?
    g. Does the equipment have the capability to wet the powder blend?
  2. Granulating equipment.
    a. What is the working capacity of equipment?
    b. What is the method of mixing, e.g., planetary, plows, choppers, etc?
    c. Does the equipment compact the powder during granulation? Does the process require such equipment?
    d. Does the equipment merely wet the powder—minimal shear to provide for intimate contact between the granulating agent and the powder bed—or does it possess high shear to "work" the granulating solution into the powder blend?
    e. Can the equipment dry the granulation after the granulation is completed? What is the efficiency of drying as compared to more conventional (tray, fluid bed) techniques?
  3. Tablet equipment.
    a. What kind of tablet volume is required to meet the sales forecast?
    b. What is the number of compression stations required to produce the desired quantity of tablets?
    c. What is the compression force range of the equipment? Some products, especially large tablets or slugs, require a significant compression force (greater than 5 to 25 kg).

    d. How long can the equipment operate without routine maintenance? This is related to air dragoff from compression table, compression rolls and ejection cams, lubrication system (oil misting).

    e. How long is the turnaround time for complete cleaning? One shift, two shifts? This downtime can be significant and may affect the need for a multishift tableting operation or numerous tablet machines.

    f. Does the equipment possess automated weight control capability, e.g., Thomas' Sentinel device.

    g. Does the equipment require specialized tooling? Or can the equipment use tooling from other equipment, e.g., length of shafts of tooling, diameter of dies?

    h. Can the equipment perform a specialized function in addition to basic tablet compression, e.g., multilayer tablet compression, compression coating?

    i. What kind of powder feeding capabilities does the equipment have? Can this capability be altered or controlled, e.g., open feed frame, forced below feeder?

4. Tablet coating.

    a. What is the working capacity range of a panload?

    b. Do the coating pans have a "variable drive" capability? This may be needed to achieve proper tablet mixing in the pan so as to achieve a uniform application of coating solution to all the tablets.

    c. Can the angle of the pan's pitch be varied?

    d. What kind of air input (volume and temperature) and vacuum dragoff is required for the coating pan's optimal operation? These utility requirements may exceed the capacities available in the plant.

    e. What is the shape of the coating pan, oval, mushroom, round? The shape characteristic will affect the degree of agitation and direction of tablet flow in the pan. The spray nozzle configuration will have to be designed to ensure adequate spray coverage over the tablet bed.

    f. Is it possible to utilize the equipment for sugar coating as well as film coating? Certainly, if this were possible, capital expenditures would be reduced.

    g. Is it possible to modify the pan with the installation of baffles? Baffles will undoubtedly be needed to ensure good tablet agitation in the pan. If the pan cannot accept baffles, a different design will have to be considered.

II. Dry-filled capsules [13, 14].

  A. General-capsule composition.

    1. Why is each ingredient used in the formulation?

2. What are the "normal" properties of each ingredient—density, particle size, moisture content, etc.?

3. What is the size of capsules and composition of the encapsulating material?

B. Powder properties of powder mix (granulation)

1. Density: "loose" and "tap."
    a. Can processing (or equipment) affect either density measurement?
    b. Which raw materials affect the density most significantly?
    c. Can their specifications be adequately controlled?

2. Particle size distribution.
    a. How does the processing control the particle size distribution?
    b. What is the optimal particle size distribution:
        i. To promote powder flow?
        ii. To aid in capsule filling?

3. Characterize the flow properties.
    a. Does the powder flow freely? Does it form a "rat hole?" Does it become packed? Does it flow uniformly or nonuniformly?
    b. Must the content or ratio of excipients be changed to improve flow?
    c. What are the lubricant requirements of the capsule formulation?

4. Miscellaneous properties.
    a. Moisture content.
    b. Compactibility of powder.
    c. What are the requirements for additives to overcome "difficult to handle" powder properties? Cohesive active ingredient, poor flow—may need to add a glidant, e.g., silica gel.

C. Equipment evaluation.

1. Premixing equipment.
    a. Sifting equipment—This step may be needed to deaggregate formula components when the formulation is a physical mixture of materials rather than a granulation made by wet granulation techniques.
        i. Determine the ability of the equipment to segregate the powder (if applicable).
        ii. Determine whether the equipment can reproduce the particle size distribution of a powder or powder mixture when it is passed through its screen.
        iii. Does the equipment have the capability to force the powder (or mixture) through its screen?
        iv. Does the normal sifting action of the equipment induce electrostatic charges on the powder? This could lead to poor flow and possible segregation.
    b. Mills—If sifting does not produce the required deaggregation, the more intense action of a mill will be required.
        i. Type of milling process, e.g., air attrition, hammer mill?

       ii. Ability to control particle size and particle size distribution?

      iii. Versatility of equipment re speed variability? Feed rate control? Availability of milling screens and impellors?

    c. Miscellaneous equipment (general). Can the equipment control the physical properties of the raw material or final product?

2. Mixing equipment—this equipment is required to blend the formula components into a uniform mix prior to encapsulating.

    a. How versatile is the equipment in mixing very small quantities of powder with large bulk quantities of powder?

    b. What type of equipment is required to achieve the desired mixture?

    c. Should different pieces of equipment be evaluated or compared so as to determine the mixer with the best mixing characteristics?

3. Blending equipment. Determine the type of blending equipment on the basis of physical properties of the final blend and the job required. If possible, compare two (or more) different types of blenders using criteria such as:

    a. Efficiency and reliability of blending (e.g., least liability of unmixing).

    b. Assurance of quality adherence.

    c. Ability to produce powder of proper characteristics needed for encapsulation.

    d. Working range versatility re batch size. If the sales volume increases, can the batch size be increased?

4. Encapsulating equipment. Factors to be considered in selecting the proper encapsulating equipment include:

    a. Expected annual volume of capsules required over the initial period and subsequent time periods.

    b. Flow properties of the powder blend.

    c. Packing characteristics of the powder.

    d. Capsule fill weight.

    e. Variability in fill to be allowed: USP limits? in-house specifications?

5. Miscellaneous equipment.

    a. Polishing and dust removal equipment.

    b. Auxiliary equipment such as feeding equipment, vibrators.

D. Process evaluation. Most of these process parameters have been discussed in the tableting section of this chapter. The same criteria apply to capsules. Does the powder mix lend itself to the encapsulating process? Or is an alternate dosage form more applicable?

1. Mixing. The following should be studied as applicable:

    a. Density before and after mixing.

    b. Particle size distribution beginning, during, and after the complete mixing procedure.

    c. Optimal mixing time for specific equipment.

    d. Uniformity of active ingredient.

    e. Moisture content of encapsulating powder blend. Of individual components.

2. Blending.

    a. Determine the optimal blending time for specific equipment.

        i. Determine the effect of blending time on uniformity.

        ii. Determine the final content uniformity of the blend.

    b. Determine time for "unmixing" or overmixing, if possible.

    c. Determine the maximum and minimum effective blending load.

    d. Determine whether a lubricant is needed and the optimal mixing time required for its incorporation. (NOTE: This mixing may be separate from the process required to blend the other powder ingredients).

    e. Check the blend's density and its particle size distribution.

    f. What ingredients affect the density most? Does the density change during the blending operation?

    g. How does moisture affect the blending operation? Should it be controlled? What kind of testing and what moisture limits are required?

    h. Determine and evaluate specifications for the blend:

        i. Appearance.

        ii. In-process testing as determined under other sections of "blending" evaluation.

        iii. Pertinent identity test(s).

        iv. Assay of active ingredients and any other important excipient.

        v. Moisture pick-up versus percent relative humidity (24-hour period).

    j. Bulk storage conditions recommendations.

3. Encapsulation.

    a. Dusting characteristics of filling powder on equipment. Can these characteristics be controlled?

    b. Disintegration/dissolution properties. Is there any limit on the amount of powder that can be encapsulated? Is the limit determined by dissolution or bioavailability?

    c. Tendency of powder to pack.

    d. Determine what the weight variation is for any given encapsulating machine and formulation.

    e. Content uniformity.

    f. Other physical characteristics such as condition of capsule shell (split body or cap, etc.), quality of gelatin capsule, effect of humidity on "pharmaceutical elegance" of the dosage form.

    g. Powder flow characteristics in hopper.

    h. List special requirements needed to ensure desirable encapsulation characteristics; these requirements should be listed in the "precaution" section of the worksheet.

    i. Stability (effect of age on all properties).
    j. Filling characteristics of powder in capsule, e.g., packed loose.
    k. Polishing or dedusting conditions required.
    l. Printing requirements (before and after filling).

VI. CONCLUSION

The above guidelines and checklist of items to be considered as part of a comprehensive process validation for solid, oral dosage forms should be considered generic. No one validation process can meet the needs of all products or processes. The unique formulation or process characteristics of a particular product and the equipment available to manufacture the product may dictate the need for a specialized validation program. As such, the validation team must identify the product and process characteristics that must be studied and incorporate those special tests into the comprehensive product validation scheme.

The guidelines presented above reflect a portion of the process validation program of Stuart Pharmaceuticals. Our comprehensive validation program also includes guidelines for the validation of semi-solid, suspension, oral solution, and parenteral dosage forms. The program for the validation of raw materials is established by the Raw Material Evaluation Committee, comprising personnel from formulation, process development, analytical, quality control, and purchasing groups. This committee sets priorities and determines the extent to which a new or alternate raw material must be evaluated before it can be considered acceptable for routine acquisition.

Analytical methods validation at Stuart is also handled in a comprehensive manner. A method is not declared acceptable until a collaborative crossover study is conducted between two development laboratories and at least one quality control laboratory to ensure proper precision, accuracy, and efficiency.

In conclusion, validation of a new or existing product involves the efforts of scientists at various stage of the product development program. At times, information obtained during the preformulation activities may represent the start of the program. It is at this stage that raw material testing and analytical methods development are established.

The validation program is expanded as the dosage form is designed and the critical formulation and processing variables are defined. The parameters chosen for a validation program must be relevant indicators of a controlled process. Thus, it is not sufficient merely to devise a test and set specifications for it; rather it is desirable to show some cause and effect relationship between the parameter and the process (discussed in Chapter 7).

Finally, a validation program is really a formalized list of formulation, process, and testing criteria to ensure that by scientific means, the product can be manufactured in a manner to ensure uniformity within a lot, consistency between lots, and conformance to design criteria within defined limits. In my view, most firms had been practicing this scientific approach to dosage form design prior to the advent of what is now considered validation. In today's regulatory climate, a validation program provides the necessary documentation to support a stepwise evaluation of a pharmaceutical process.

ACKNOWLEDGMENT

The author wishes to extend his appreciation to C. B. Rifino, H. Rosenberg, B. A. Spiller, and R. J. Pierce of ICI Pharmaceuticals Group for their advice and technical input.

REFERENCES

1. Nash, R. A., Process validation for solid dosage forms, *Pharmaceut. Technol.* June, 105–107 (1979).
2. Byers, T. E., "Validation: A Systematic Approach to Quality Assurance." Pharm. Tech. Conference, New York (September 1981).
3. Loftus, B. E., "Validation Protocol: The Bottom Line," Proprietary Association—Manufacturing Control Seminar, Cherry Hill, NJ (October 9, 1980).
4. Byers, T. E., "Role of Product and Process Design in Assuring Quality," Good Manufacturing Practices Conference, Cherry Hill, NJ (February 1977).
5. von Doehren, P. J., "An Approach to the Characterization of Solid Dosage Forms," Pharm. Tech. Conference, New York (September 1981).
6. Harpaz, D., "Process Evaluation/Validation of Solid Dosage Forms," Pharm. Tech. Conference, New York (September 1981).
7. Samyn, J. C., "New Product Validation Begins in R&D," PMA Seminar on Validation, Atlanta, GA (May 1980).
8. Berry, I. R., Process validation of raw materials. *Pharmaceut. Technol.* February, 38–39 (1981).
9. Kumkumian, C., OK, Your Candidate Drug Has Activity. Now What? *Chemtech.* March, 178–180 (1980).
10. Rippie, E. G., Mixing. In *Theory and Practice of Industrial Pharmacy*, 2nd ed., Lockman, L., Lieberman, H., and Kanig, J., (eds.), Lea & Febiger, Philadelphia, chapter 16 (1976).
11. Parrott, E. L., Milling. In *Theory and Practice of Industrial Pharmacy*, 2nd ed., Lockman, L., Lieberman, H., and Kanig, J. (eds.), Lea & Febiger, Philadelphia, chapter 15 (1976).
12. Shah, A. C., and Mlodozeniec, A. R., Mechanism of surface lubrication: Excipient mixing on processing characteristics of powders and properties of compressed tablets. *J. Pharm. Sci.* 66:1377–1382 (1977).
13. Rifino, C. B., Guideline for scale-up of dried filled capsules and tablets, Stuart Pharmaceuticals Internal Document, February 17, 1978.
14. Spiller, B. A., Process validation program, Stuart Pharmaceuticals Internal Document, July 28, 1978.

6

Process Validation and Quality Assurance

Carl B. Rifino *ICI Pharmaceuticals Group, Newark, Delaware*

I. INTRODUCTION

In the first edition [1], the introductory chapter discussed the factors that justify the need for documentation of process validation. Such factors included needs associated with current good manufacturing practice (CGMP), the concept of efficient manufacturing processes, the team approach to development and plant introductions, and the planning of activities involving the validation effort itself. The role of quality assurance, however, was not mentioned. This chapter discusses current quality assurance issues that pertain to process validation.

Juran [2] defined quality assurance as the activity of providing, to all concerned, the evidence needed to establish confidence that the quality function is being performed adequately. The definition of process validation is that it is the total activity which shows that the process will do what it is purported to do. The relationship of quality assurance and process validation goes well beyond the responsibility of any quality assurance (QA) function. Nevertheless, it is a fair to say that process validation is a QA tool, because it establishes a quality standard for the specific process.

Before we consider how process validation can be a QA tool, it should be recognized that most pharmaceutical companies develop quality statements as part of their business rationale. This declaration often includes much, if not all, of the following precept [3]: It is the policy of the company to provide products and services of a quality that meets the initial and continuing needs and expectations of the customer in relation to the price paid and to the nature of competitive offerings, and in so doing, to be the leader in product quality reputation.

Quality assurance in pharmaceutical companies embodies the effort to assure that products have the strength, purity, safety, and efficacy represented in the company's new drug application (NDA) filings. For new drug products, quality assurance has also become that effort which is needed to satisfy the consumer or to achieve an established standard of excellence. The total effort requires that sound working relationships be developed among the quality assurance, development, and production departments. Other groups such as engineering may be included in this effort.

In recent years, quality awareness has been stressed as companies seek world-class status for their operations. Such QA programs that have been adopted are outside the scope of this chapter, but they include some of the following factors: certification of suppliers, setting standards for customer satisfaction both within and outside the organization, incorporation of statistical process control (SPC) in manufacturing operations, etc. In addition, the need for quality standards for personnel involved in production, development, and quality assurance work is well recognized. We will limit our discussion to how process validation might be used to develop quality standards.

Although quality assurance is usually designated as a departmental function, it must also be an integral part of an organization's activities. When process validation becomes a general objective of the technical and operational groups within an organization, it becomes the driving force for quality standards in development work, engineering activities, quality assurance, and production. Process validation is valuable to an organization when it consists of good and pragmatic science. To appreciate this concept, one must go beyond Juran's definition of quality assurance. Thus, instead of quality assurance just being an activity that provides evidence to establish confidence that the quality function is being performed adequately, it becomes a measure of the technical group's ability to add value to its work for the sake of its company and its company's customers.

Nash [4] stated that quality assurance was originally "organized as a logical response to the need to assure that cGMPs were being complied with." He concluded that "it is not surprising that process validation became the vehicle through which Quality Assurance now carries out its commitment [5] to cGMPs." In addition, process validation has become the vehicle through which QA shares this commitment with development, production, and engineering.

II. QUALITY ASSURANCE AND THE ORGANIZATION

The quality assurance that exists within an organization rests not only on the management of the quality function but also on the activities that occur on a daily basis in the company's technical and operational functions. These groups are responsible for the training of the personnel to achieve a company culture based on quality. They develop and carry out the procedures that govern the product composition, the manufacturing process, the test criteria, or the operating system which ensures that the quality function is performed adequately.

Jeater et al. [6] outlined the many facets of validation work within a pharmaceutical company. No matter which subject of validation work is undergoing testing, the method of testing (challenge) provides a measure of quality assurance to a company's operations. Furthermore, there is a clear implication that if any tested function is found wanting, corrective action will be taken to assure compliance in the affected area. For example, when personnel are tested for their qualifications and found wanting, training or some other management response is undertaken. Similarly, when the design of a process or facility is inadequate, process improvement, replacement, or preventive maintenance activity usually follows. The other subject areas, such as raw materials and components, procedures, packaging and manufacturing functions, and equipment, would likewise receive appropriate attention.

A. Pharmaceutical Development

This function is responsible for the design of the finished dosage form as well as the qualification of the manufacturing process. Its effort will also become the basis of the documentation required for the preapproval clearance of NDAs, which will be carried out by the Food and Drug Administration (FDA). Thus, the level of quality associated with its scientific performance will greatly affect the product's commercial availability.

Rudolph [7] presented a checklist that could be used to develop an in-depth program for the validation of all solid dosage forms. This type of checklist enables the scientist to determine what data must be collected and which data demonstrate that the process is under control. Table 1 lists a portion of the checklist.

The basis of these checklist points is as follows: to develop knowledge about the formula composition, to develop knowledge about the process and equipment used (Table 2), and to understand the mutual influences of the formula composition and process (or equipment) on each other. They focus on solid dosage forms, but these same activities may also be undertaken for other dosage forms (see Table 3). These checklists are useful to both the formulator and the process technologist for a developmental strategy. They also form the basis for adding value to the work they perform. It is suggested that these checklists should be modified to suit the scope of the development program, making them equally applicable for small or large projects. Furthermore, they are a planning activity, which would also be useful as the basis for the validation protocol.

The quality assurance associated with the pharmaceutical development effort includes the following general functions:

1. To ensure that a valid formulation is designed
2. To qualify the process that will be scaled up to production-size batches
3. To assist the design of the validation protocol
4. To manufacture the biobatches for the clinical program, which will become the object of the FDA's preapproval clearance
5. To work with production and engineering to develop and carry out the qualification program for production equipment and facilities/process systems
6. To develop validated analytical methods to allow:
    a. The stability program to be carried out
    b. The testing of raw materials and finished product
    c. The development of release specifications for the raw materials and finished product
    d. The testing of processed material at certain specified stages

I referred to process validation [8] as the quality assurance of pharmaceutical technology. At the time, I wanted to point out that process validation was validating the manufacturing process, not the product per se. This distinction is made because the product results from the way the process is carried out. Process validation verifies that the process will consistently produce the desired product. Today, the term "validation" is used extensively (as in product validation, methods validation, etc.), yet my focus is still on process validation only. Thus, I will discuss the basic approach that most PV procedures follow to show how the development function achieves the objective of adding value to its work. The steps are as follows:

1. Define the process and determine which process steps are the critical ones. If the technologist has progressed adequately from the checklist stage to the stage where the process is known and understood, these steps should be readily identified.

When the development function looks at the process validation activity as a quality assurance tool, it must view each process step very deeply. The development plan must ensure that the ability and limitations of the process design are known. This can come about only if sound planning occurs at the beginning, which should include dissection of the process into discrete parts and the ability to evaluate them. This has been a very complex task for solid dosage form processes, and herein lies the opportunity for using good pragmatic approaches [9] for the task. It must be understood, however, that perfection should not be the target of the validation effort. Thus, the scientist should evaluate only what can be measured with confidence and each process activity that can be controlled.

2. Define which process variable will be used as the monitoring device of each process step.

Let's look at the wet granulation step, for example. We will want to learn

Table 1 Checklist Leading to the Optimization/Validation of a Solid Dosage Form

A. Tablet Composition: provide the reason for the presence of each ingredient in the formula.
    1. What are the "normal" properties of each ingredient?
    2. Do these properties change in the formula under study?
    3. What are the characteristics of the initial powder blends, the wet/dry granulations and the final blends?
    4. Density: "loose" vs. "tap" of blend.
    5. Particle size distribution of blend.
    6. Surface area of the final blend.
    7. Flow properties, such as contact angle.
    8. Moisture content, if applicable.
B. Process Evaluation and Selection: determine the processing steps needed for the initial scale-up.
    1. Blending operations (as applicable). Determination of the optimal blending time based on:
        a. Does extensive blending cause demixing and segregation of components? This is important, especially if particle size/density of the powder/ granulation vary widely.
        b. What tests are used to assess the uniformity of the final product? Content uniformity, weight variation testing?
    2. Is the granulation adequately blended to achieve the desired distribution of the active ingredient in the mix?
    3. Check for a possible interaction between the process and its effect on tablet core compression.
    4. Check the characteristics of the blend: bulk density; particle size distribution; moisture (if applicable).
    5. Does any ingredient affect the density of the final blend?
    6. What is the blending performance at 30, 50, and 100% of working capacity?

Table 2 Checklist Concerned with Blending Equipment for the Optimization and Validation of Solid Dosage Forms

1. What is the working capacity of the equipment?
2. Is the efficiency of the equipment affected by the density of the material?
3. What is the appropriate working load range to ensure good uniformity and homogeneity of the blend?
4. What material-handling features does the equipment have?
5. Is the equipment capable of wet granulating the powder?
6. Can the equipment heat the powder blend, if it is needed as a granulator-dryer?
7. May vacuum-drying be used to assist in the drying?

Table 3   Checklist on Process Evaluation Leading to Optimization and Validation of a
Liquid Sterile Dosage Form

---

1. Mixing tank
   What kind of agitator system is needed to dissolve all the ingredients efficiently?
   What composition must the tank's product contact points be (e.g., stainless 316L, glass)?
2. Process services
   Does the process require a jacketted tank to heat the product?
   What source of heat is required (e.g., hot water, steam)?
   Does the product require protection from oxygen?
   What other protection does product require during processing?
3. Sterilizing conditions
   Will the product require sterilization of the bulk liquid?
   Is it possible to sterilize the product terminally? Or must the product be aseptically processed?
   How long does it take to reach the sterilizing conditions? How long is the cool down period? Must the batch size be controlled to achieve the needed sterilizing conditions?
4. Container
   What composition is the container?
   Will the container affect or be affected by the product?
   Does the stopper interact with the product during any part of the product's lifetime?
   Will the properties of the stopper or container be affected by heat sterilization?

---

whether it affects the dissolution of the drug, the final blend performance, the drying and milling procedures, and the final tablet compression performance. If quality assurance is to result from the development effort, answers must be had. However, the task cannot be left only to the process development scientist to solve. Thus, the pragmatic approach to the scientific effort would be that the answer be developed through the partnership of the physical pharmacist, the formulator, and the process development engineer (or scientist).

The formulator and the pharmaceutical scientist should determine how drug dissolution can be affected (i.e., would it be affected by the formula composition or by the physical characteristics of the drug or granule?). The process engineer must also determine whether the granulation quality will be affected by the choice of equipment or whether it will affect the milling characteristics or tablet quality. After the preliminary work is satisfactorily completed, the scope of the process engineer's work may become clearer. Thus, if the physicochemical properties of the drug or the formulation are not a factor, the process step alone will become the focus of the scale-up work, which markedly reduces the number of process experiments required.

On the other hand, if the drug or formulation is a factor, it may become necessary to control tightly and measure each facet of the granulation step. This may result in a program that requires close monitoring of the way the granulating fluid is mixed into the batch, the blending of the dry powders prior to granulation, a specific volume of granulating fluid, and the instrumentation needed to control the process itself. If the technical plan includes this kind of evaluation, it will become pragmatic enough to allow either approach. Therefore, the technical plan must first determine whether the formula or process significantly affect the granulation's quality. And if the process step is significant, the plan objective must be to fully understand the process step's capabilities and limitations.

3.   Generate the data. During the development effort, the data generated while the process is being qualified will determine what the specification limits will be for each test. The development/statistical team will choose the "three-sigma" rule of thumb or some other standard criterion to set its specification limits. However, if there are specific cautions needed to ensure against a deviation in product performance, these limits may have to be customized accordingly.

For example, the drug's content uniformity in the final tablet may yield a relative standard deviation greater than 6%, even though the uniformity of the powder blend is much tighter. It may become necessary to control not only the powder blend's uniformity but also its particle size distribution. Thus, in order to meet the necessary criteria for the latter test, it may be necessary to control the blend process by setting tighter specification limits for the former test.

4.   Statistically evaluate the data from the validation effort. Compare the data with the specification limits listed in the protocol. Conformance to these limits is essential, because this effort must also include the determination of whether failure signifies a missing link in the company's understanding of the process. This exercise is especially important when the size of the validation batch is significantly larger than the largest development batch made to date.

5.   The validation function reviews the results of all the validation batches using the protocol as a basis of comparison. In addition, the group will review the equipment qualification work and/or its calibration program.

This total effort will help to ensure the quality of the finished product. This provides a formal turnover mechanism from process development to production and the actual work forms a database for any future technical activity. It follows that it would also be useful as the basis for any future work that may be required on the process, including process improvement, change control, or troubleshooting. Furthermore, documentation of the effort enhances its scientific stature both within the company and, as needed, outside it (e.g., FDA inspections). The main benefits of the validation effort, realized within the organization, are that both the production unit and the quality control group have acceptable reference points to assist them in carrying out their responsibilities.

The example of the wet granulation step demonstrates that good planning of the development effort provides a solid basis for the best understanding of a process. It also demonstrates how the quest to achieve process validation for a process will promote quality assurance. However, another major benefit of process validation is that it requires the personal commitment of the involved individuals to quality assurance by setting validation objectives for them. This extra step makes it necessary for them to accept the quality functions of the organization as their own and to bring good science to process validation. Herein lies the opportunity to evaluate development personnel and the quality of their work, an idea suggested [10] earlier.

Process validation affects a number of job activities that an R&D manager can control or utilize. It offers the manager a job enrichment opportunity for subordinates. By encouraging personnel to evaluate process design and process capability, the manager will seek good science from subordinates. In addition, the organizational goals to prepare for preapproval inspections by FDA personnel would be enhanced by this work. It provides a tool for the manager to evaluate the quality of work coming from each subordinate, e.g., planning work activity, program organization, data development, and overall job performance.

The ultimate benefit of process validation to pharmaceutical development is that it is an approach to demonstrate a quality standard for a given process, whether the batching occurs during development or during the commercial stages of a product's life. This activity has become associated with cGMP, and FDA representatives have stated that batching activity which yields a product intended for ingestion by humankind needs validation data [11]. In the cited guideline, FDA stated that "limited validation . . . should be derived . . . from product and process analogs." Although this recognizes that only limited data would be available in the early development stages, it leaves open the possibility that the database will be increased as additional batches are manufactured.

This approach would seem to be an example of concurrent process validation [12], which fits well when the development function continues its effort to validate clinical manufacturing processes. It is also an opportunity to validate a process when it is used to produce different batch sizes with a given piece of equipment. It may even be possible to employ differently sized equipment (to make different batch sizes) as part of the validation effort. It remains to be determined whether this kind of approach ought to be extended to the commercial validation effort. Later in this chapter, I will discuss the possibility, which is attractive for the company that is totally involved in total quality management (TQM).

B. Production

This department needs process validation for a number of reasons. First, the completed validation program serves as the formal transfer of the process to the production function. Through validation, it would be demonstrated that a controlled process was established. It doesn't guarantee that nothing will go wrong, but it will say what process was validated and it will require that any change must be examined beforehand. In this way, it will require that the organization formally evaluate whether a proposed change warrants a new development and/or validation effort. This will also avoid the comment that the previous validated process is no longer validated.

Process validation is also useful for the production function, because the data generated may also be used as a basis for statistical process control (SPC). SPC is useful for collecting data, but there must be useful limits to control the process variables by allowing standard equipment adjustments to obtain quality product continuously. Validation data enable a company to develop a database to do just that. Furthermore, when normal adjustments no longer control the process variables, the validation data become the basis to judge whether there has been a statistical change in the process. The rational process to such a finding would be a demonstrated need for process improvement or a troubleshooting effort.

Quality assurance in production is the result of careful planning. In their discussion on quality in manufacturing, Ekvall and Juran [13] refer to setup dominance and machine dominance. The former approach seeks to create a highly reproducible process, which would include a means of self-control. The latter is concerned with variability that is caused by the equipment's performance. Many older production processes appeared to rely on the machine-dominance strategy because they relied on in-process checks and adjustments, as needed. However, process validation leans toward setup dominance because this activity seeks to document the fact that the variable process parameters are under control, which means that the in-process test results will be within their specification limits.

In a setup-dominant process, it is important that the development function understand where the setup must be centered (targeted). This information is most useful when instruments can effectively and accurately measure the property of the intermediate material (e.g., powder blend) or dosage unit. This capability is reinforced whenever an instrument reading, outside the given specifications, causes an equipment response (e.g., activation of a servo motor on a tablet press). Caution limits within the normal product limits are established purposefully to effect this kind of control.

Another level of control may be achieved with a tablet press by the proper positioning of each tablet tool with respect to its neighboring tablet tools. For example, the total tool length may become the basis for determining the relationship of each tool. The first step [14] is to grade each tool by measuring the total tool length (upper and lower) and putting them in order from the longest to the shortest tool. In the second step, the tools must be rearranged so that one revolution of the tablet press will yield a complete "sine curve."

[Note: The sine curve designation is the result of a graphical representation of the tool station number on the x-axis and the tool length on the y-axis. The graph shows a maximum (longest tool length) and a minimum (shortest tool length), which are connected by an ever-changing tool length (minimum to maximum) from one compression station to the next. This kind of special setup is especially needed when the output of the monitoring instrument does not develop an independent electrical signal for the compression force of a single station of the tablet press.]

Whenever this kind of activity becomes part of the manufacturing plan, the benefits of the setup-dominant process will be realized. This results because the quality standard, formed by the development function in the performance qualification, is carried over to the production setting. When production then incorporates this standard into its own operating procedures, the quality standard becomes a measurable criterion for performance. Thus, this example clearly shows how this phase of PV would be a quality assurance tool for auditing.

When production develops an operation plan, it will include quality standards that complement the validation effort and are as follows:

1.   Equipment calibration. This quality function for production consists of a viable calibration program for equipment that provides in-process test data or a measurable indication of the controlled process used. This activity is needed so that the manufacturing unit will know whether the equipment is operating consistently during the time period covered by the calibration activity. This effort is also the continuing commitment of production to maintain its equipment as it was documented to perform during its installation qualification (IQ) and operational qualification (OQ) activities.

2.   In-process testing and monitoring. Quality assurance of the production effort also occurs within its inspection plan, which it carries out through in-process testing. The generated data are often collected through the SPC system, but other activities come from in-process testing. The purpose of testing is to provide assurance that the ongoing process is yielding a uniform product and a consistently reproducible process. This effort is also useful when it becomes necessary to investigate the causes of defects or potentially out-of-control conditions.

3.   Training of personnel. This quality function enables management to determine the real productivity level of its personnel, because productivity is no longer just measured in terms of units made. Rather, it concentrates on the number of units made correctly. Training has been viewed as an element of process validation, but the activity probably is more correctly interpreted as being a measure of the validation of an organization's personnel. Thus, training really depends on the production environment of the company; that is, the company evaluates the personnel qualifications and responsibilities needed to carry out its operation and then works out a system to carry it out.

4.   Development of standard operating procedures (SOPs). Training is achieved and maintained through the use of SOPs or operating manuals. The SOP is mainly written to provide a "how to" approach for the activity it covers and to document that approach so that the audit activity will have a basis. SOPs

complement the process validation effort by ensuring that personnel will perform their work in a manner consistent with the objectives of the validation. These SOPs will normally cover the operation, cleaning, and calibration of the operating equipment as well as similar activities with test equipment and other control equipment.

5. Development of a logbook system. Logbooks are another quality assurance vehicle which complement the process validation effort. They are used to document any activity that involves the equipment they cover, e.g., cleaning or maintenance.

6. Use of clear, precise operating instructions, which include the documentation of process performance and verification. A company's system includes the issuance of a master production and control record and the batch production and control record (for each batch). These records document the fact that the company continues to manufacture each batch of product with the validated process of record.

These examples show how quality standards are established in production and how quality improvements may be sought. When process validation is used as a quality assurance tool, these quality standards enhance the potential for maintaining a validated process during routine production. They then will be the basis for QA confidence [2] that the quality function is being adequately performed in production.

C. Quality Assurance

QA functions primarily to monitor the fact that the quality function is being performed. Its role in process validation is readily associated with its main functions. For example, it performs the tests that demonstrate the product's content uniformity. It may also perform the statistical evaluation of the test results to show that the process is reproducible. QA initiates the action to dispose of nonconforming product. It implements the inspection criteria and sets the specifications for product approval or rejection. It analyzes the product complaints to learn how effective its test program has been in preventing rejectable product from reaching the marketplace.

Quality assurance carries out the ongoing stability programs for each product at least once a year. It performs the physical and chemical tests that are used as the basis for approval or rejection of individual batches. In conjunction with setting specification limits as a basis for releasing or rejecting product, it will carry out programs to determine whether the new information is indicating that a change in product or process has occurred. Finally, it performs the analytical tests that are used to generate the validation data required by the protocol.

One approach that QA would use to assure itself that a given process (step) is under control is the effort associated with the concept of process capability. Ekvall and Juran [13] defined the concept as the measured inherent reproducibility of the product turned out by the process. The statistical definition of process capability is that all the measured values fall within a 6-sigma range. The information is used to show that the process is under control over a period of time as well as determine whether there is any drifting or abnormal behavior from time to time. Process validation is a QA tool in this case, because its data will be used as the origin for the data curve developed for the "process capability" concept.

This approach is made possible if the process (step) is demonstrated to be "under a state of statistical control." A number of tests were listed by Ekvall and Juran to learn whether this condition exists. One approach to validating the technique involves the comparison of the process capability curve with the tolerance limits for the product. The intent of the validation is to determine whether the data from the process conform to the state of statistical control. It may also be used to determine whether quality costs can be reduced without changing the process's status.

The technique involves superimposing the tolerance limits on the graphical representation (i.e., distribution curve) of the process capability curve (see Fig. 1). If the curve fits well within the tolerance limits, the inherent reproducibility of the process is considered adequate. However, if the width of the curve straddles the tolerance limits, the inherent reproducibility is considered inadequate. Finally, if the curve is skewed near the right or left limit, the model will predict that defects should occur.

In some respects, this technique is similar to retrospective validation [15–17]. Its value, however, is not as a type of retrospective validation but as a basis to

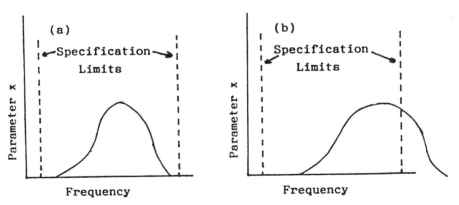

Figure 1 Determination of process capability by graphical approaches. (a) Adequate process; (b) inadequate process control.

require revalidation or suggest other options. The options would include the following: slightly modify the process, revise the tolerances, or sort the product to cull out the defects. Modification of the process may include any change in the process short of substituting a new one. Likely activities would include tooling changes (tablet presses), reordering the sequence of the process steps, or replacement of certain equipment with a similar class type. It should be noted that while quality assurance principles may allow such small changes, NDA filings may not, which means that such an activity would automatically result in revalidation work.

Revision of the tolerances is an option that may be limited, but it is possible, especially if the basis for setting them has changed. For example, tight tolerance limits for tablet hardness or friability may be set, because the available data may require a conservative approach to set them that way. However, after data have been collected over a period of a year, the product experience may suggest that the tolerance range actually should be higher (or lower). The sorting of a product to cull out the defective units is another example when a small change in process is needed. The approach has limited value; but whenever a validated technique to perform the sorting exists, culling out minor defects would be acceptable.

It should be pointed out that some organizations have a different role for quality assurance, especially when the group is part of a quality control department. In such a situation, the regular QC group will handle the testing responsibilities, and a technical services group in QC will handle the data interpretation and other duties. QA then would be involved in audit activities of production, contractor operations, etc. The main concern of a QA audit is that the written SOPs follow cGMP. The second concern is that the actual activities of production and contractor personnel directly follow the written SOPs. Any deviations from cGMP or SOP are recorded and reported to the audit unit. Corrective action is requested, and the completion must be satisfactory to the QA audit team.

Finally, quality assurance is the effort taken to ensure compliance with government regulations for the systems, facilities, and personnel involved with manufacturing products. QA audits will be quite varied in scope to achieve this assurance. These responsibilities include batch record reviews, critiques of product design, process validation activity, and, possibly, audits of other departments' operations.

III. PROCESS VALIDATION AS A QUALITY ASSURANCE TOOL

A. General QA Tools

Up to this point, it was suggested how certain organizational activities might become quality assurance tools. But process validation should be considered the main quality assurance tool, because it not only involves the activities of many organizational units but also centers on proving that the process is under control. It provides documented evidence that the quality function exists for the manufacturing process. It is part of a series of quality assurance activities [8] that pharmaceutical scientists have undertaken to determine objectively what grade of raw materials should be used, how well the materials should be formulated and processed, how well the products stand up during their shelf life, and how well the dosage form behaves in vivo. A brief description of these activities is given in the following:

1. Raw Material Specifications and Their Acceptable Limits

All raw materials are tested before they are used in a pharmaceutical product. These materials must meet quality standards, or meaningful specifications, and their limits must be set so that the use of unsafe, unpure, and inefficacious materials will not be allowed in the product. The control labs will run the tests or have a contractor perform them, but QA will ensure that the lab procedures are properly followed and documented. Furthermore, QA will ensure that no raw materials were released improperly.

2. Product Specifications and Their Acceptable Limits

QA responsibilities are essentially the same for raw materials and final products. All finished drug products are tested to determine if they meet the required quality standards. These tests help to characterize the product so that the QA/QC function can determine whether the product has the proper strength and is safe, pure, and efficacious. Yet these tests do not necessarily build quality into the product.

An analogous situation exists for intermediate mixtures, such as blends or granulations. When these mixtures must meet preset specification limits, pharmaceutical technologists have set them to make sure that the intermediates would meet the same standards that were established for raw materials and products.

3. Product Stability

A stability program is undertaken to determine whether the product will maintain its quality characteristics throughout its shelf life. This effort includes studying the physical and chemical stability of the product under specific environmental conditions, such as ambient room temperature storage, humidity, light, and heat challenges. In addition, its sterility (or microbial character) may be determined under certain conditions.

QA will ensure that the stability profile for a raw material, bulk product, or packaged product is properly documented. In addition, it will ensure that final package labeling includes a statement of the expiration date, which is determined from the stability program. In this latter case, it may only be concerned that the test method used to show that the end is adequate.

4. Bioavailability

Bioavailability has become an important part of the quality assurance effort to "prove" that the product maintains its strength, safety, purity, and efficacy during its shelf life. Since bioavailability was introduced, the scientist has not been satisfied with chemical equivalence between batches of product, and this expanded the quality assurance effort. The study of bioavailability makes it necessary to know how the body's physiology and biochemistry are affected by the drug molecule's availability within it. The drug's concentration in the body fluids, its ability to bind protein, its metabolic rate, its ability to present the active metabolite at the needed site of action, and the body's excretion rate are the tools used to measure the drug's bioavailability.

Thus, knowledge about a product's bioavailability enables the technologist to develop certain quality standards for that product. The concept of using the biobatch (i.e., a product batch used for clinical studies) as a reference enables the sponsor company to seek analytical methods that will show that later batches are similar to the reference batches.

5. Training and Documentation

Responsibilities associated with process validation and quality assurance depend on the training of manufacturing personnel and the documentation of their activities. Such activities help to form the recognized quality standard that a pharmaceutical company builds for its products. These personnel are trained to carry out the standard procedures required by GMP. Documentation includes the writeup/revision of these procedures. Other records document how a batch of product is manufactured, whether unusual incidents or deviations occurred, the existence of reject notices, product complaints, and the investigation and analysis (as needed) of the above abnormalities.

6. Process Validation

This activity is concerned with evaluating the manufacturing process. The undertaking adds an element of quality to the product, because it demonstrates what procedure must be performed and under what conditions the procedure must be carried out. It is often recognized that the equipment used and/or the process step itself may affect the product's bioavailability or its release specifications. Since the purpose of process validation is to provide documented evidence that a process is reproducible and that it will consistently produce a safe, pure, and efficacious product, control of the manufacturing process makes it possible for the quality assurance to be built into the product.

B. Purpose of Process Validation

The kind of effort expended for process validation is largely determined by organizational structure. Whether process validation is managed by a department, a consultant or a committee, the criteria for the program are still the same. These criteria will be examined by the responsible individuals so that the program will be tailored to the character of the process under study. The following questions are recommended in developing a suitable validation protocol:

1. What Is Being Validated?

1. The answer to this question is important, because it is essential that the objectives of the validation activity be clearly stated. This understanding will enable the responsible group to plan the protocol and the test program needed to carry out the validation program. QA requires that the total process validation document include the following [18]:

Data on the installation qualification for the facility and equipment
Data on the operation qualification for the facility and equipment
An account of the understanding on each process step's capability
Documentation approval of the validation activity

Documentation of the IQ is important for QA so that the information will be available for future reviews by QA or an FDA inspector. There are three possible approaches that may be followed. First, the IQ information may be compiled as a standalone document to which other parts of the validation document would refer. The advantage of this approach is that the IQ doesn't get tied into a specific process or product validation. The second approach would have each validation document stand alone, which would mean that the IQ information on the equipment and facility would be repeated for every validation report. The third approach would combine the other two approaches, namely that the facility IQ would remain generic and the equipment IQ would be a part of the process/product validation document. Whatever approach is followed, the overall validation report must provide an effective QA tool. Thus, QA will strive to get the entire validation program documented to order to achieve its short- and long-term needs.

The process validation of a new facility [19] must be documented in a way to ensure that the facility's design and operations within it are fully covered. An outline of such activities is listed in Table 4. For example, the validation of a new facility makes it necessary to document the equipment performance under relevant conditions. All process (or facility) equipment will undergo IQ testing to make sure that each piece of equipment operates as it was designed to do. The technologist will determine how the equipment's performance will vary without the influence of the process material (operation qualification, OQ). This information will form the basis for the remainder of the validation report. From a quality assurance viewpoint, it should also be noted that this information will be useful if it is compared against the parameter measurements under load conditions. However, since this information is more properly included in the performance qualification (as process optimization), it should not become a part of the validation protocol.

On the other hand, if the process must be validated in an existing facility, existing IQ and OQ information may be adequate. In this case, the validation protocol would merely refer to the data rather than require its regeneration, especially when a credible calibration/audit program had been performed for the

Table 4   A Typical Validation Blueprint

1.   Introduction
2.   Installation qualification
     A.   Facilities
     B.   Utilities
     C.   Equipment
3.   Operation qualification
     Testing Protocols for Utilities and Equipment
4.   Validation
     Testing Protocols for Products and Cleaning Systems
5.   Documentation
6.   Validation of the QA Testing laboratory
7.   SOPs
8.   Training of personnel
9.   Organization charts
10. Schedule of events

facility and equipment after the IQ and OQ were performed. Thus, this part of the validation work would merely be referenced in the validation document.

2.   The next concern raised by the question is the determination of whether prospective, concurrent, or retrospective validation is appropriate. This decision shouldn't be considered lightly. For a new facility, there is only one possible decision, namely prospective validation. However, when significant process changes are made, it may be appropriate to choose the concurrent validation approach. For example, when the initial data indicate that a process improvement does not adversely affect the statistics associated with process capability but does warrant a change in the tolerance range, it is important for QA to ensure that the change in tolerance range does not adversely affect the overall product quality. It must also know that the newly proposed range will not float as new data are gathered. Thus, concurrent validation would be an appropriate choice, and this would indicate how PV should be used as a quality assurance tool. I refer the reader to the definition [25] of concurrent validation, which establishes "documented evidence . . . generated during actual implementation of the process."

2.   Why Should the Process Be Validated?

Personnel involved in the validation function will determine not only what will be in the validation protocol but also why the process will be validated. If a validation committee is responsible for the function, it will include personnel having varied backgrounds, such as production, engineering, process development, quality assurance, and regulatory affairs. Likewise, the process validation function would include personnel with these backgrounds or those who interact well with such individuals. When the technical details of the protocol require certain technical specialists (e.g., computer programmer), then such an individual should be added to the group to fit the need. This multidisciplinary approach will help to develop a sound rationale for undertaking the validation program in the first place. In other words, the function is strongest when no one discipline dominates the effort; rather it is the melding of each discipline's input that gives the program strength.

It is important to avoid using a routine predetermined menu when planning a validation protocol. In the ideal situation, the process development activities would dictate what tests would be included in the protocol and what ought to be the specification limits of the test results. Such activities form the basis for the data gathering because the large number of development batches, including the qualification and optimization trials, would clearly indicate why the specific parameters are being measured and why they indicate that the process is under control. Thus, when the validation protocol is the product of a multidisciplined team, it should not become a self-serving exercise of any single function.

For example, the quality assurance function might accept the principles of testing for content uniformity, but then it might also introduce the concept that it wants all the test data to be within the product's release limits, so that the product's shelf life stability would be ensured. Thus, this would give the group a broader reason for proceeding with this validation test, rather than merely looking for conformance to the USP content uniformity testing [20].

3. How Will the Process Be Validated?

The answer to this question determines the detailed activities of the validation protocol. It will state what tests will be used to determine if the process is under control. Furthermore, it will answer other questions, such as: How precise must the test results be before the specification limits will indicate when the process is reliable? Should the worse-case scenario, e.g., a deliberate failure such as being at a level of 20% over equipment's working capacity, be included to ensure the validation of the process? How many batches must be manufactured before the committee will consider the process validated? Will the initial production batch be considered the final optimization batch or the initial validation batch?

In addition to the data gathering, QA will want the validation batches made entirely by the production department. When this stipulation is satisfied, it will be demonstrated that the process control is independent of the technical background of the operating personnel. This kind of approach demonstrates that the manufacturing process will support the soon to be marketed product's volume demands. This approach also allows QA to have a baseline activity with which it can compare future audit activities.

C. Qualification/Calibration Activities

Qualification activities are usually undertaken in order to characterize a facility's services and utilities as well as the equipment that would be used as part of a manufacturing process. As indicated earlier, these activities will include installation and operational activities as part of the validation function. Most companies will issue a report that documents the features of the facility's processing rooms, such as the electrical, water, gas, and HVAC services, for the installation qualification. Table 5 is a generic outline of the items that would be found in the IQ report. Whenever the process equipment is permanently fixed in these rooms, the report will also list the equipment as well as its operating requirements and features. See Table 6 for an outline of questions that would be used to complete a report, which includes equipment qualification. It is preferred that qualification occur as soon as the equipment or facility is ready for routine operation so that any unexpected results will be corrected by the equipment vendor and/or construction contractor.

The OQ report may also contain quantitative data generated from the testing of the facility and equipment. These activities are normally performed before the facilities or equipment are put into service.

The qualification reports are normally standalone documents and become a reference for many manufacturing processes and process validation reports. They also serve as the basis for predetermined periodic calibration activities on the equipment. The existence of qualification reports and ongoing calibration logs enables QA to audit the upkeep of the facilities and equipment in a manner similar to the way it audits the validated process. Thus, both documents not only support the PV effort but also help PV serve as a QA tool. The general sections of the qualification report include [19] an equipment description, a checklist of all critical items that need to be reviewed at the outset, vendor-supplied installation and operating manuals, as-built drawings of the facility and its design features, requalification guide, required preventive maintenance program, and specific instructions (optional) for operators within production.

With the emphasis I've given to planning throughout this chapter, the qualification protocol should be written in the same way. Table 5 lists certain information that would be included, and it shows the same kind of checklist approach that was listed for the validation protocol.

The approach to the qualification work of drying equipment indicates an alternative approach to that described in Table 5. Although the type of equipment would determine the exact program, the discussion below generally indicates the qualification needs for most drying equipment. The first step is to determine the heat distribution of an unloaded hot-air drying oven. For situations in which the granulation's residual moisture must be closely controlled, this information will become the basis for determining whether the oven can uniformly dry the material by applying a uniform heating environment over all the beds. If the oven cannot provide that uniform heating environment, it is improbable that the powder will be uniformly dried. This information would be determined by measuring the heat and air flow at various points of the chamber and then calculating the variability of these conditions in it. Since this kind of information on heat distribution provides assurance that the process equipment is properly designed for

Table 5 Generic Outline for a Qualification Protocol

I. Room or facility
   1. Description: Includes a statement of the wall, ceiling and floor finishes, as they complement the process to be validated, e.g., listing of a nonporous wall finish (if wall must be chemically sanitized or sterilized) for sterile dosage form area.
   2. Utility services
      A. Electricity: general description, including available amperage/volts services.
      B. Gas supplies
         a. Compressed air: description of supply equipment and pretreatment of air (e.g., filtration), range of pressure, standard of air quality to be routinely supplied.
         b. Other gases (e.g., nitrogen): description of its source, level of purity required, method of using it to achieve the desired performance, etc.
      C. Water supplies
         a. Potable water supply, including a statement of its quality, as supplied, and its treatment, if applicable, in house before use.
         b. Purified water, USP: list the method of generation and include the equipment used to prepare and supply it; description of the system, including the piping composition and finish; filtration equipment, storage containers; circulation standards; action limits for standards deviations (chemical and microbiological).
II. Equipment
   1. Description: name and appropriate identifier numbers.
      A. Complementary equipment, e.g., process controllers or process monitoring equipment.
      B. Working capacity
   2. Service utility requirements
      A. Electricity
         a. Supply
         b. Code status, e.g., explosion-proof requirements
      B. Steam/hot water
         a. Required heat range
         b. Heating/cooling efficiency rate
         c. Pressure requirements
      C. Compressed air/nitrogen requirements
         a. Pressure range
         b. Pretreatment needs, if any
         c. Delivery needs, such as flow rate and volume for peak equipment efficiency.

Table 6 Critical Items for Inclusion in a Qualification Protocol

A. Mixing/blending equipment
The equipment's capability to blend material would be determined by asking the following questions:
  a. What is the rotating speed, expressed in revolutions per minute?
  b. What is the maximum weight that the equipment will be able to hold and process? How much volume will that load occupy?
  c. What is the required tip speed of the equipment to effect the optimal blending conditions?

B. The parameters for measurement of wet granulation equipment would include the following. Some would occur when the equipment is loaded, whereas other tests might occur when it is unloaded.
  a. What is the tip speed of the main impeller blade?
  b. What is the tip speed of the chopper blade?
  c. How much "work" do both blades perform? For example, whether the driving force is measured by a wattmeter, an ammeter, or a motor slip analyzer, it is important to determine how much work is expended in the process.
  d. What is the shape of the equipment's process curve on a graph of work vs. time? Does it indicate the work end point when the electrical force (work) required for effecting the granulation reaches a plateau after a given time? Or does the electrical force suddenly increase logarithmically in a short period of time to signal the end point?
  e. Does the shape of the work curve vary with the load? Is it dependent on the volume of granulating fluid? Or is it dependent on the rate of addition of the fluid? These parameters must be stabilized before the equipment's performance can be satisfactorily measured.

C. The following questions should be posed to develop a protocol for qualifying milling equipment:
  a. What type of mill is being evaluated? Does it have a fixed wheel, belt-driven operation? Does it have a vari-drive gear operation?
  b. How many operating speeds must be evaluated to determine the mill's process capability? Does the mill operate linearly, on the basis of mill speed vs. electrical input?
  c. Through what kind of mechanism does the mill control the granulation's feed rate? Does the equipment have a process controller to coordinate the feed (input) rate with the mill speed? How does it work? How can the operation be monitored?
  d. What test method will be employed to evaluate the equipment performance during the loaded and unloaded stages? Should a second method be employed to confirm the test data from the first method?

the required process, it will be the focus of future QA audits. Furthermore, this knowledge is also essential when a very specific drying temperature is needed for thermally labile materials. Thus, the qualification not only becomes an integral part of the validation program but also demonstrates how the information may be used.

Once the baseline data for heat distribution are established, the combination of in-process moisture analysis (of the load being dried) and heat or air flow distribution (for a loaded oven) will help the technologist understand the drying process for a product and also know whether the moisture level in the dried granulation can be controlled without exposing the material to excess heat. This relationship will help QA evaluate the process during validation as well as audit the process, if process deviations should be encountered.

The qualification of the sterilizing (aseptic processing) filter is another example of the requirements that are applicable for process equipment used in the production of sterile dosage forms. However, this kind of qualification requires frequent repetition. Thus, it may prompt the reaction that the sample questions are not indicative of a qualification activity. Herein lies the element of quality assurance in the qualification activity. While quality assurance is a part of every qualification, the nature of the process performed may require that the equipment be requalified wholly, or in part, each time it will be used. The qualification questions that must be asked for these kinds of filters are listed in Table 7, but I leave to the technologist's judgment how frequently each must be answered. The literature has ample guidance for the validation of aseptic processing (i.e., sterile filtration), and a few examples are given in the references [21–23].

The value of qualification data, that is, as validation data and QA tool, shouldn't be underestimated. In a recent issue of the Federal Register [24], the FDA issued a proposal "to require manufacturers to use a terminal sterilization

Table 7 Questions for the Qualification of Sterilizing Filters

1. What composition and porosity must the filter medium have to effect aseptic processing?
2. How must the filtering apparatus be sterilized to carry out the aseptic processing effectively?
3. What kind of microbial challenge must be used to demonstrate that the equipment will work properly? Must the anticipated bioburden of the surrounding environment be considered?
4. What kind of product(s) will be processed by the equipment? What kind of retention testing is needed to prevent compromising the process?
5. How will the bubble point test be run? What will be the conditions of the pressure hold test?

process . . . unless such a process adversely affects the drug product." The monograph clearly indicates what evidence is needed to support the manufacturer's position that it cannot use terminal sterilization, and it implies that the rationalization for using aseptic processing be clearly stated and supported. Thus, it should be recognized that the QA utility of the qualification data may also be extended to FDA review and agreement.

D. Process Validation Activities

There are three basic types of process validation. They are generally called [25] prospective, concurrent, and retrospective validation. Each type represents a different pathway to concluding that a manufacturing process is in a state of control, yet it would be short-sighted to think that each type must be used only in a given prescribed way. For example, if the protocol established for a prospective validation program states that three batches will be manufactured and tested, the data generated may not "provide . . . evidence needed to establish confidence that the quality function was performed adequately" (Juran definition [2]). Indeed, the resulting product may meet its release specifications, but the validation data may not be tight enough for good statistical treatment. Then the validation committee may withhold its approval until additional validation testing, i.e., concurrent testing for a given number of batches, is completed to establish the needed confidence. Thus, the final validation report will include data from the prospective and concurrent phases of the program in order to demonstrate that the process will do what it purports to do.

Using the concurrent validation technique to back up prospective validation data would be a proactive quality assurance tool. Herein lies the challenge for the validation function in general and QA in particular: do you use the tool? When an organization follows the precepts of total quality management (TQM), the concept of continuous improvement would routinely be used. The validation function would ask: What is the expense of producing more than the originally planned number of batches? What validation effort is required to support the commitment to FDA that only a validated process will be used to supply product to the marketplace? Should TQM become the basis for concurrent validation? It would appear that concurrent validation is the logical answer.

The main point of this example is that when process validation is used as a quality assurance tool instead of a final examination, an organization's operations will improve or stay at the highest quality level possible. The effort will be properly documented, and the overall attitudes of all the affected personnel will be positive. Finally, a more logical approach to preapproval inspections and other FDA technical interactions will be effected. How then can the quality assurance approach become part of process validation?

1. Prospective Validation

This approach to validation is normally undertaken whenever a new formula, process, and/or facility must be validated before routine pharmaceutical production commences. In fact, validation of a process by this approach often leads to transfer of the manufacturing process from the development function to production. Thus, this approach allows process validation to become the climax of a carefully planned developmental program. Recently, the FDA guidelines on preapproval inspections, associated with NDA/ANDA submissions, added a new dimension to this type of validation. FDA is seeking evidence that the manufacturing process is validated before it will allow a product to enter the marketplace [26]. I refer the reader to the article on prospective validation [9] for a more in-depth understanding of the technique.

The effort required for prospective validation makes it necessary that quality assurance principles are satisfied. The effort should bring together all the technical functions: engineering documents and qualifies the process equipment, the facility, and the systems; production checks that its operating systems are working properly; QA builds on the data base that had been accumulated during the development phase; development certifies that its process performed as designed. In short, the objective of the work is to show that the product may be routinely produced with confidence.

It is necessary for QA to know what process conditions must be controlled and what variables must be monitored to show that the manufacturing process is controlled. These variables may be caused by the facility, the equipment, the process, the product characteristics, or a combination of them. For example, in a case history [27] it was reported that a validated process had to be relocated in a production facility. The equipment used was rearranged so that the process would be more efficiently performed. Instead of operating the entire process on one floor, the tablet compression was performed on a lower level from the rest of the operation. The materials flow pattern required that totebins of the blended powder be located on the floor directly above the tablet press. This occurred by directing a tube from the totebins through the floor to the hoppers of the tablet press. The content uniformity data for the finished tablets indicated a greater variability than that experienced in the original facility (see Table 8). Furthermore, the potency of tablets ejected from one side of the tablet press was routinely lower (Table 9) than that of tablets ejected from the other side.

QA wanted more than just being satisfied, that is, having the data meet all specifications or have the relative standard deviation be below 6%. It was not confident that tablets in the batch with lower potency would be adequate to allow the normal expiration date for the product. Thus, QA did not agree that the process in the new area should be approved, i.e., validated, especially when data from the earlier blending process indicated a more uniform product.

Table 8 Content Uniformity Data from Old Facility

Drug Content (mg/Tab)			Drug Content (mg/Tab)		
Box	Left	Right	Box	Left	Right
1	49.5		19	49.7	
2		49.9	20		49.3
3	49.2		21	48.6	
4		48.9	22		48.8
5	49.5		23	49.3	
6		48.4	24		49.5
7	50.0		25	49.2	
8		48.9	26		50.2
9	49.4		27	48.7	
10		49.1	28		49.6
11	49.1		29	49.5	
12		49.9	30		49.6
13	49.5		31	49.4	
14		48.9	32		49.7
15	48.7		33	49.5	
16		48.8	34		49.4
17	49.9				
18		49.5			

Average: Left, 49.3 mg; right, 49.3 mg
Total average: 49.3 mg
Standard deviation (total): 0.43; relative SD: 0.87%

Process development diagnosed the problem through a series of tests. It was determined that, because the granulation was so potent when compared with the materials introduced during blending (approximately 90% vs. 0%, respectively), the drug distribution in the coarse particles was much higher than in the fines. The drug distribution was no longer considered optimal in the new setting. The solution was that the milling should be slightly modified, and this yielded a more uniform drug distribution in the final powder blend (Table 9). This improved uniformity then yielded tablets that were equally good physically, yet more uniform than the product made in the original facility, and the process was validated. It was validated because multiple batches, using the modified process, yielded the same data. It was also a clear case where the science (i.e., technology) was used to support the position.

As I indicated earlier, prospective validation is used when a new chapter in manufacturing is about to be established. As such, it requires a sound game plan to

Table 9   Content Uniformity Data from New Facility

Drug Content (mg/Tab)			Drug Content (mg/Tab)		
Box	Left	Right	Box	Left	Right
1	50.8		17	50.9	
2		49.8	18		49.1
3	51.4		19	51.8	
4		49.6	20		49.5
5	51.5		21	51.7	
6		48.9	22		48.4
7	50.9		23	50.2	
8		49.1	24		48.5
9	51.8		25	49.6	
10		48.7	26		48.6
11	51.9		27	49.8	
12		47.8	28		49.1
13	52.9		29	51.0	
14		49.9	30		48.7
15	50.5		31	50.4	
16		48.6	32		49.8

Average: Left, 51.0 mg; right, 49.0 mg
Total average: 50.0 mg
Standard deviation (total): 1.46; relative SD: 2.92%

document the transition from one stage to another, i.e., process development to full-scale production, the inclusion of new equipment, or the inclusion of a modified or new facility. The generated data must support the fact that the new process or facility ought to be used routinely in production. The successful validation documents that the developmental quality standards for the procedures and operations are adequate to manufacture a quality product in production. Finally, it becomes the basis for the quality standards which must be maintained throughout the product's lifetime.

These benefits make prospective validation a quality assurance tool. Quality assurance is not a stagnant activity. It consists of snapshots of distinct activities; yet, when all the snapshots are put together, a kaleidoscope of the life of a process and/or of a series of changes results. It may also include the investigative process, when a deviation occurs, and the corrections implemented to reestablish the validated state. To support such an effort, the trends shown by the data for each batch are documented. Thus, prospective validation should be viewed as the anchor for the quality assurance effort.

2. Concurrent Validation

This approach was first proposed in a public forum by Reisch and Chapman [12]. It was defined as "establishing documented evidence that a process does what it purports to do based on information generated during actual implementation of the process." Potential applications of the approach are discussed later, and they are included because they demonstrate the need to use good pragmatic science and creativity when designing a validation protocol. They show that the protocol will very frequently consist of a series of validated in-process tests to monitor the process and product release testing to assure compliance with the product's specifications. But the examples also indicate that the protocol will require the kind of intensive testing that is normally associated with optimization and development. Thus, this approach should also be considered a quality assurance tool, if the activities are carried out in this fashion.

In a number of meetings, FDA representatives have discussed the issues behind preapproval inspections [26] and the recently published Guideline on the Preparation of Investigational New Drug Products [11]. It is unclear, however, how extensively concurrent validation will be used in the future. On the one hand, it has been stated that NDA and ANDA products must be validated before their shipment into commercial channels will be allowed by FDA. Furthermore, in previous years FDA personnel had personal opposition to the concept of concurrent validation, saying that it was not a true validation activity. However, the guideline for IND products does allow the collection of "data obtained from extensive in-process controls and intensive product testing [which] may be used to demonstrate that the instant [i.e., particular] run yielded a finished product meeting all of its specifications and quality characteristics." Thus, FDA now appears to recognize that, since the development stages do occur concurrently with clinical production, each stage must be validated either as a single batch or as a combination of batches. This position seems to have resulted, because many clinical programs do not consist of three batches of the same size. Yet, it is still necessary to demonstrate that the process, which yields a product for human consumption, is under control.

Concurrent validation is especially useful as a quality assurance tool. This approach to validation is useful to QA because it enables QA to set its own objectives as criteria for process validation. For example, QA seeks to have every process validated. Most pharmaceutical products contain one or two active ingredients. PV is very straightforward for them; however, a whole new situation exists for a multivitamin multimineral product. Thus, innovative techniques are needed to achieve adequate validation.

It is intuitively recognized that with a multicomponent product the various active ingredients have to be mixed by a variety of techniques. There are no optimal blending conditions for all the ingredients which can be tested to show unequivocally that the process step is under control. However, it is possible to state that the process is under control if the various mixing steps preceding the final blend are shown to yield uniform premixes. Thus, the validation activity must demonstrate that uniform premixes exist to yield a uniform final blend.

In our example, QA's objective is to feel confident that the manufacturing process will do what it is purported to do. It follows that the validation protocol should reflect the rationale for the chosen process. The recommended technique would be first to show how uniform the content of each active ingredient is after its incorporation in its own initial premix. The process of a typical vitamin-mineral product would include the separate wet granulation of the minerals, water-soluble vitamins, and fat-soluble vitamins. Alternatively, if granular forms of the water-soluble vitamins were available, they would be mixed as a premix. Inert carriers are often used to disperse the fat-soluble vitamins. The uniformity of the mixes would be demonstrated by testing (with content uniformity tests) for the ingredients which have the lowest potencies in the respective premixes. The same ingredients would be the objectives for the content uniformity testing of the final blend. From the QA perspective, this approach utilizes markers to demonstrate not only that the premixes are uniform but also that they are also blended together uniformly before tablet compression.

After tablet compression, content uniformity testing of each active ingredient, taken from at least three samples of the batch, is recommended. If coating is included as a process step, the coated tablet would then be tested according to the normal product release testing. In effect, uniformity would not be an issue for the coated core, but it would be important to know that the final product meets its specifications.

This kind of test program admittedly is very intensive, but the nature of the testing makes it appropriate for validation testing. Furthermore, if the analytical tests themselves and the testing of so many ingredients don't give a clear analytical understanding of the validation status with three batches, the program can always be expanded to six or more batches. The point is that concurrent validation would be appropriate for this kind of situation because it would provide assurances that each batch meets not only its release criteria but also its validation criteria. Thus, such a program would allow QA to release each batch on its own merits, rather than wait for a group of batches to demonstrate the validated state.

Another case for concurrent validation is that effort which requires statistical (and possibly trend) analysis. It is appropriate to digress and explain what is meant by trend analysis. This activity really consists of product auditing, which is described in more detail elsewhere [28]. Product auditing is a quality assurance (management) technique in which each batch's analytical data provide "a running scoreboard of product performance." The quality standards would be measured periodically (monthly, quarterly, or semiannually), which would depend entirely on the number of batches made per time interval. At least six batches would be made in the same manner per chosen time interval. The data would be measured, and then it would be determined (through charting the data) if the data fell between predetermined specification limits. Each new period's data would be compared with the data trend that developed before it. Deviations, which led to a change in the trend, would be investigated. If the deviation was not caused by a change in process, further investigation and troubleshooting activity would be required.

Figure 2 demonstrates how trend analysis would be used. The standard deviation of data for a series of batches is plotted against their control (or batch) number. The graph resulting from the dotted points indicates a trend toward the upper specification limit for the test parameter, but the trend later returns to the mean level. If one merely looked at the tabular form of the data, one would not necessarily conclude that there is a problem. It is only when the data are graphically represented that the trend is seen. This would lead to an investigation into the possible causes of the trend.

There is another very helpful application to trend analysis. The approach may be useful when a series of minor process changes are implemented, while gathering the validation data for approval of the final process. In this program, it is necessary to identify all the changes in process characteristics with the data generated. This effort may demonstrate that a change in process step controls the overall process. But, if it doesn't, the ability to produce data to show statistically that the process is under control makes the approach worthwhile. It should be noted that this technique again enables QA to release each batch after its data are

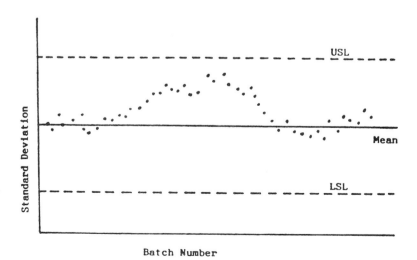

Figure 2 Simulated data representing the trend analysis technique.

analyzed, yet it is flexible enough to allow the evaluation of data from more than one batch, whenever necessary.

These examples demonstrate that, when process validation is treated as a quality assurance tool, good management is a necessity and a reality. In each of the situations described, data generation is the key. Other requirements include the need for routine data analysis and sound project management and the need for immediate decisions on change control procedures, supplemental NDAs/ANDAs, and preparations associated with preapproval inspections.

Other examples which show that concurrent validation is a viable option include the validation of a process in which a step is modified, the vendor of an inactive ingredient is changed, or the product is made infrequently.

The first type of validation is the effort to validate a process when a coating process or coating solution formula undergoes major changes. A second example is the introduction of new tooling for a tablet product. In this program, tablet appearance or weight variation might be affected, and this testing would be all that is needed to demonstrate that the process is under control.

The second type of validation is the effort needed when a new raw material (active ingredient) must be introduced. First, this raw material would have to meet all the existing specifications for its established counterpart. If earlier experiences with the original material had shown a cause-effect relationship between the process and the material, it would be appropriate to do concurrent testing to show that the use of the new material is validated. In this type of validation, QA would require that the product undergo a limited stability program before it is released for marketing. For example, this objective of the program may be achieved by a 3-month accelerated stability program or a 6-month ambient room temperature program. After the data are reviewed, the decision to release the product would be made and the normal stability program would continue until the product's expiration date is reached.

The third type of validation involves the use of a normal validation test program on a limited number of batches. Certain products may have limited batching requirements over a 6–12-month period. In this case, the original batch would be kept from the marketplace for an inordinate period of time. The important thing to remember is that the batch be tested using a preplanned written protocol and that the test data be reviewed and approved immediately after each of the batches is made.

When the concept of concurrent validation is embraced by an organization, it is important for everyone to support QA's use of it as a quality assurance tool. The quality standards of each discipline are normally stressed because of the normal commercial pressures, but it is essential that overall quality assurance not be relaxed. The validation format, in general, and concurrent validation, in particular, will allow the flexibility needed for the situation; yet, it also provides the vehicle for a disciplined approach to ensure that no unacceptable product will be released.

3. Retrospective Validation

Retrospective validation has become synonymous with achieving validation by documenting all the historical information, e.g., release data, for existing products and using that data to support the position that the process is under control. It was originally discussed in a public forum by Meyer [15] and Simms [16]. I also refer the reader to articles in the first edition of *Pharmaceutical Process Validation* [17].

This approach to validation is the clearest example of validation being a QA tool. The generated data already exist, but they need to be documented in a manner which clearly demonstrates that the existing process is under control. However, QA must first outline a plan for the validation effort, which would include the following items:

1. A quality audit of the process as it relates to the resulting product. It is necessary to categorize the process history chronologically. Then the change control history must be superimposed on the historical information.
2. A collation of the in-process control and product-release data according to batch number.
3. Pairing of these data with the change control history. It has been pointed out by many individuals that it is not sufficient merely to collect the data. First, one should identify and document the major changes in the product and/or process over the lifetime of the product. Once the data of each process phase are identified, the data may be used to show the overall integrity of the specific process.
4. Determining which changes are significant. Many types of changes would qualify, including a change in specification limits for the process change, a formula change involving the active ingredient or a critical excipient, a facility or equipment change, and a change in the limits of criteria for process control. The data associated with each process change must support the fact that the process is under control.
5. Grouping the data and statistically analyzing them. For example, trend analysis or some other acceptable statistical approach may be used to evaluate whether process control has been demonstrated.
6. Determining whether data associated with earlier significant changes also demonstrate a controlled process. This effort assumes that enough data are available for each stage. In effect, the effort establishes the documentation to declare a continued validated state for the various processes used during the product's lifetime. The approach may be similar to the one taken for concurrent validation, except that the analysis occurs with data that are on hand. It is preferred that a large number of batches (10–20) be included, but the historical data may not be adequate to do this. I have since learned that as few as six batches may be used to represent each process change.

A second application of retrospective validation would be the effort to validate a process having a minor change. For example, purchasing requests that a second vendor be established for a given raw material. This material is an excipient, it meets all of the existing specifications for the established raw material, and there is nothing that singles out the new material as being different. In this situation, it would be prudent to plan to qualify the material through a monitoring system. Classifying this effort as retrospective validation is not clear-cut. However, it is amenable to trend analysis treatment, which is effective as a proactive or passive technique.

4. Revalidation

It may appear that some of the aforementioned approaches to validation should be viewed as revalidation activities. Allow me to digress so that I can share my views and that of others [29] on revalidation. Revalidation indicates that the process must be validated once again. However, it may not necessarily mean that the original program must be repeated. In fact, if process validation is viewed as a quality assurance tool, the requirements for quality assurance will dictate how revalidation is carried out.

First, revalidation may mean that the original validation program, e.g., a prospective program, should be repeated at a predetermined frequency. Second, the retrospective validation approach may be used for a manufacturing process even though it was originally validated in a prospective manner. For this to happen, sufficient data would have been generated for the mature process to allow treatment in the retrospective manner. In a third situation, there may merely be movement of equipment to improve materials handling, which might require that the concurrent approach to validation be undertaken. I believe that the concept of quality assurance is satisfied in every one of these situations, especially when it is integrated into a TQM program.

Process validation will be seen as a quality assurance tool because it fits into the functions that QA performs. However, process validation also benefits from the quality assurance efforts of the other technical units in the company. Gershon [30] discussed Deming's concept of total quality management (TQM) and indicated that it consists of three phases. First, a cultural environment must be developed within an organization. Second, statistical process control (SPC) fundamentals must be put into place. Third, statistics must be used to develop process controls and to assist management in running complex processes in an optimal manner. Thus, revalidation fits very well in the company's TQM program.

In other words, the quality assurance benefits of a sound process validation program include the following:

1. Sound data are developed by process development to determine the process capability and optimize the overall process.
2. This becomes the basis for ongoing data development from routine batching activity and process controls.

3. It serves as the reference for comparison when investigations of process deviations are needed and corrective action must be justified.
4. It will also serve as the basis of audit activities, such as trend analysis and change control procedures.

Many statistical tools are available to quality assurance to analyze the process data. The quality of analysis is improved when the data base adequately represents the controlled process. For example, trend analysis is useful in determining whether a process change or deviation has occurred. If a good data history exists for the developmental, clinical, and early production stages, QA will have some basis for evaluating changes that might occur subsequent to scale-up activities. When the data from these stages do not show a perceivable change, it may be possible to discount batch size as a cause of the perceived problem in production. Thus, a sound data base will be useful for problem solving as long as enough data are collected on a routine basis.

Data collected for each process phase may also be evaluated statistically to evaluate objectively whether a process change was better or worse than the preceding one. For example, through analysis of variance, it would be possible to determine whether each process phase had demonstrated continued process control or clear improvement. Thus, the revalidation approach would allow the quality assurance (or production technical services) group to proactively manage their responsibilities for production support, troubleshoot a process, and/or set up a plan for more revalidation activities.

In my earlier comments on revalidation, I gave examples which might occur because of quality assurance concerns. However, there are other instances in which quality assurance would require revalidation. In one case, an investigation would be requested if product release data showed a significant shift from the population's mean. The recommended corrective action might then result in a revalidation program. A second QA tool might also be recommended, namely a short-term stability study to check for any changes in that profile. In another case, the QA audit might indicate that its confidence in a process is shaken, because newly acquired data suggest that the process is out of control. Again, the recommended corrective action might be that revalidation of the process will occur because of any one of a number of circumstances. Thus, quality control results from the quality assurance effort. In other words, quality control rests on the effort to implement action procedures when "trigger events" occur.

E. Miscellaneous Issues

Earlier, I discussed a method of planning for process validation, in particular, the overall development function leading up to it. It appears that the development group has a number of avenues which will lead to the appropriate validation approach it takes. In one approach, the critical process parameters would be identified. This search enables the technologist to determine what should be measured to monitor the process and document the fact that the process is validated.

A second approach would be to look at the worse-case challenge. An example of this approach is the challenge involving the termination sterilization of products. The widely accepted technique [31], commonly called the "overkill approach," is used for products that can tolerate heat. Such a technique avoids the need to test the product for bioburden and for the minimum lethal conditions for that microbial load. The rationale for the approach is: when a process can be demonstrated as effective even for the most challenging conditions that will be encountered during normal processing, then the process will be considered validated for routine use. Thus, the technique enables the technologist to know how effective the process is (for each batch of product processed) just by knowing how much heat was applied to the product and how long the heat exposure was.

It should be noted that bioburden testing (or viable counts) is an integral part of environmental testing, and it is very useful information to complement the effort to validate heat sterilization. The FDA position on terminal sterilization [23] supports the correctness of this statement.

On the other hand, the worst-case challenge for solid dosage forms is more difficult to define, especially if the process in question is very robust. An example of applying the worst-case challenge to the validation of a blending operation is studying the effect of increasing the batch volume by 20%. In one case, the increase might exceed the total working capacity of the equipment; in another case, both batch sizes would fit within the equipment's working capacity. In the former instance, it would be very likely that a rejectable batch would be produced, but in the latter, it would be likely that two acceptable batches would be made when the same process conditions are employed.

The quality of the development effort would be enhanced if the routine scientific activity looked at the worst-case situation. First, the process characteristics would be better understood. Second, the specification limits for the in-process tests would be based on hard data. Third, it would be easier to evaluate the process capability of two different-sized pieces of equipment performing the process activity under the same conditions. Finally, it might be possible to validate the same production-sized process of multiple batch sizes with one program in the plant.

The inherent value of process validation to the production department is based on quality assurance. From the time when the validation protocol is accepted to the time when the process is judged to be validated, the resulting value increases, and this is due entirely to quality assurance. With the availability of validation data, production has a basis of comparison, whenever the quality standard of the process must be checked. First, it represents an opportunity to utilize the principles [31] of TQM, which seek to prevent crises rather than react to them. Second, it allows production to become totally involved rather than consider quality someone else's concern. Third, it emphasizes an attitude for continuous improvement throughout the department by focusing on the process rather than the end product. Fourth, an environment is cultivated for managing with facts, not intuition. Finally, it assists personnel to seek excellence rather than settling for something that is just good enough.

Quality assurance prevails when the data generated in the validation program provide a good basis for SPC in production. If the concept of SPC becomes a part of personnel training, personnel will not only learn what in-process tests are run but why they are being run and why the desired corrective action must take place. It also encourages the personnel to report suspected problems early and seek assistance to correct the unusual problems when they are occurring. It is frustrating to investigate data from a number of batches and then learn that the same problem was occurring in every one of them. What is done cannot be undone; that is, why try to build quality into a batch after all the production effort is completed?

Another aspect of quality assurance is seen whenever process validation data may also be used as the basis for problem solving. It may be necessary to design a series of experiments to learn which control parameters are contributing to the problem. If the study enables the validation group to understand the causes better, then the decision to requalify and/or revalidate the process will be based on sound statistical principles. Thus, effective problem solving will require effective validation and a good investigative follow-up.

The final benefit of validation activity (or quality assurance) requires that production's facilities and equipment be qualified to certify their ability to perform as expected for the validation batches and the routine production. Qualification procedures form the basis of production's ongoing calibration program. Documentation of the periodic calibration activities will provide an adequate record if the information must be used to explain any changes in process. When this information is coupled with other equipment log books, a proper history is available for QA audits.

IV. SUMMARY

This chapter has shown how process validation and quality assurance are related. Process validation is a quality assurance tool because it is used by quality assurance to document the validation activities but it is also a part of the entire organization's effort to maintain quality assurance. When the validation activity becomes the focal point of an organizational unit's effort to carry out its own technical responsibilities, quality standards will be maintained for the product and manufacturing process from the design and development stages and throughout the commercial life of the product.

For example, the need for quality assurance in development work makes it possible to make process validation a goal of that work. It assures that process validation will be the basis for the periodic quality auditing of the manufacturing process throughout its existence. It requires that structured change control procedures must be closely followed by every organizational unit. It allows PV to be used as the basis for the investigation of abnormal occurrences and for the corrective action taken. Finally, it assures that all the organizational functions will undertake revalidation activities for prescribed situations rather than react to crisis situations. This chapter has demonstrated how such benefits may be realized.

An attempt was made to show how process validation is a quality assurance tool in the sense that it enables the technical departments to manage the quality function in their disciplines. For example, the development group may use it to challenge its understanding of the developing process. It may also use it to gauge the quality of the individual contributor's work. The production unit may use it as a basis for accepting the process as well as continually evaluating the existing process over time, which makes it a part of production's quality plan.

REFERENCES

1. Loftus, B. T., The regulatory basis for process validation. In *Pharmaceutical Process Validation*, Vol 23, Loftus, B. T., and Nash, R. A. (eds.), Marcel Dekker, New York, pp. 1–7 (1984).
2. Juran, J. M., Section 2: Basic concepts. In *Quality Control Handbook*, 3rd ed., Juran, J. M., Gryna, F. M., Jr., and Bingham, R. S., Jr. (eds.), McGraw-Hill, New York (1974).
3. Juran, J. M., Section 3: Quality policies and objectives. In *Quality Control Handbook*, 3rd ed., Juran, J. M., Gryna, F. M., Jr., and Bingham, R. S., Jr. (eds.), McGraw-Hill, New York (1974).
4. Nash, R. A., The essentials of process validation. In *Pharmaceutical Dosage Forms*, 2nd ed., Vol. 3, Lieberman, M. A., Lachman, L., and Schwartz, J. B. (eds.), Marcel Dekker, New York, pp. 417–453, 1990.
5. Bader, M. E., Quality assurance and quality control (in four parts), *Chem. Eng.* (1980). See Nash, ref. 4.
6. Jeater, J. P., Cullen, L. F., and Papariello, G. J., Organizing for validation. In *Pharmaceutical Process Validation*, Vol. 23, Loftus, B. T., and Nash, R. A. (eds.), Marcel Dekker, New York, pp. 11–27 (1984).
7. Rudolph, J. S., Validation of solid dosage forms. In *Pharmaceutical Process Validation*, Vol. 23, Loftus, B. T., and Nash, R. A. (eds.), Marcel Dekker, New York, pp. 99–123 (1984).
8. Rifino, C. B., "Validation of New Products and New Processes: A View from Process Development," PMA Seminar on Validation of Solid Dosage Form Processes, Atlanta, GA (1980).

9. Chao, A. Y., St. John Forbes, F., Johnson, R. F., and von Doehren, P., Prospective process validation. In *Pharmaceutical Process Validation*, Vol. 23, Loftus, B. T., and Nash, R. A. (eds.), Marcel Dekker, New York, pp. 125–148 (1984).

10. Rifino, C. B., "A Philosophical View of Certain Personnel Considerations in Validation," Purdue University Management Conference for the Pharmaceutical Industry: Regulation, Legislation, Economics and the Drug Industry, Part II (1979).

11. Food and Drug Administration, *Guidelines on the Preparation of Investigational New Drug Products (Human and Animal)*, U.S. Dept. of Health & Human Services, Washington, DC, March 1991.

12. Reisch, R. G., and Chapman, K. G., "Process Validation—Industry's Viewpoint," *Pharmaceutical Technology Conference '84 Proceedings*, Aster Publishing, Springfield, OH, pp. 92–101 (1984).

13. Ekvall, D. N., and Juran, J. M., Section 9: Manufacturing planning. In *Quality Control Handbook*, 3rd ed., Juran, J. M., Gryna, F. M., Jr., and Bingham, R. S., Jr. (eds.), McGraw-Hill, New York (1974).

14. Howe, D., in-house communication.

15. Meyer, R. J., "Validation of Products and Processes from a production, Quality Control Viewpoint," PMA Seminar on Validation of Solid Dosage Form Process, Atlanta, GA (May 1980).

16. Simms, L., Validation of Existing Products by Statistical Evaluation. PMA Seminar on Validation of Solid Dosage Form Process, Atlanta, GA (May 1980).

17. Trubinski, C. J., and Majeed, M., Retrospective process validation. In *Pharmaceutical Process Validation*, Vol. 23, Loftus, B. T., and Nash, R. A. (eds.), Marcel Dekker, New York, pp. 149–179 (1984).

18. Steinborn, L., *GMP Quality Audit Manual*, Interpharm Press, Buffalo Grove, IL, chapter 2, 1991.

19. Falkow, M., "Overview of a New Facility Validation Effort," The Eighth Annual ISPE/FDA Joint Conference, Case Studies in Validation (March 14–16, 1989).

20. *U.S. Pharmacopoeia* XXII/NFXVII, USP Convention, Rockville, MD, p. 1618 (1990).

21. Levy, R. V., Souza, K. S., and Neville, C. B., The matrix approach: Microbial retention testing of sterilizing-grade filters with final parenteral products, Part I, *Pharmaceut. Technol. 14*, 161–173 (1990).

22. Levy, R. V., Souza, K. S., Hyde, D. L., Gambale, S. M., and Neville, C. B., Part II, *Pharmaceut. Technol. 15*, 58–68 (1991).

23. Hardwidge, E. A., Chrai, S. S., Dawson, F. W., Radowitz, C., Meltzer, T. H., and Zeronsa, W. P., Validation of Filtration Processes for Sterilization of Liquids, *J. Parenteral Sci. Technol. 38*(1), 37–43, (1984).

24. *Federal Register 56*(198), 51354 (October 11, 1991). See 21CFR Part 211 et al.

25. Chapman, K. G., Validation terminology. In *Pharmaceutical Process Validation*, Vol. 23, Loftus, B. T., and Nash, R. A. (eds.), Marcel Dekker, New York, pp. 267–277 (1984).

26. Phillips, J., "Headquarters Perspective of the New Inspection Program," Proceedings, Fifteenth International GMP Conference, University of Georgia (March 18–21, 1991).

27. Rifino, C. B., "Process Validation of Solid Dosage Forms," Interphex '86: Session 7 (Validation of Production Methods for Solid Dosage Forms), New York (1986).
28. Juran, J. M., Section 21: Upper management and quality. In *Quality Control Handbook*, 3rd ed., Juran, J. M., Gryna, F. M., Jr., and Bingham, R. S., Jr. (eds.), McGraw-Hill, New York (1974).
29. Jeater, J. P., & Cullen, L. F., "Revalidation: How, when and why," Pharmaceutical Technology Conference '82, New York, Sept. 21–23, 1982, pp. 126–138.
30. Gershon, M., Statistical process control, *J. Parenteral Sci. Technol. 45*, 41–50 (1991).
31. Parenteral Drug Association, Validation of Steam Sterilization Cycles, Technical Monograph No. 1.
32. Benson, T. E., The gestalt of total quality management, *Industry Week*, pp. 30–32 (July 1, 1991).

7

Prospective Process Validation

Allen Y. Chao,* F. St. John Forbes,† Reginald F. Johnson,‡
and Paul von Doehren   G. D. Searle & Co., Inc., Skokie, Illinois

I. INTRODUCTION

Validation is an essential procedure that demonstrates that a manufacturing process, operating under defined standard conditions, is capable of consistently producing a product that meets the established product specifications.

Many individuals tend to think of validation as a stand-alone item or an afterthought at the end of the entire product/process development sequence. Some believe that the process can be considered validated if the first two or three batches of product satisfy specifications.

Prospective validation is a more reasonable approach, which makes validation an integral part of a carefully planned, logical product/process developmental program. An outline of the development sequence and requirements relevant to process validation is presented in Fig. 1. After briefly discussing organizational aspects and documentation, the integration of validation into the product development sequence is discussed. At the end of the chapter there is a discussion of specific ways in which experimental programs can be defined to ensure that critical process development and validation objectives are met.

Current affiliations:
*Watson Laboratories, Inc., Corona, California
†American Cyanamid, Pearl River, New York
‡Quality Systems and Technology, Naperville, Illinois

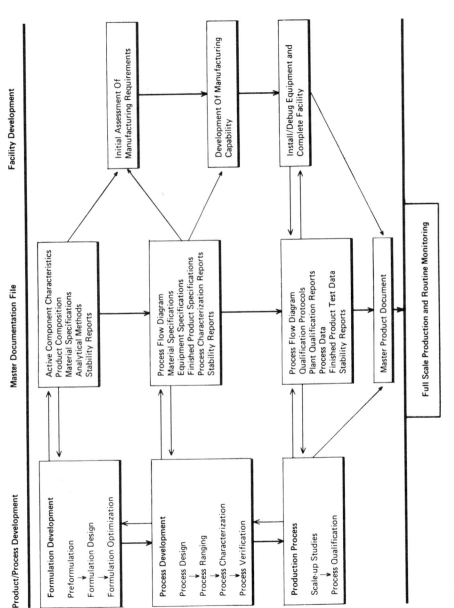

Figure 1 Prospective validation.

II. ORGANIZATION

Prospective validation requires a planned program and organization to carry it to successful completion. The organization must have clearly defined areas of responsibility and authority. The structure must be tailored to meet the requirements in the specific organization, and these will vary from company to company. The important point is that a defined structure exists, is accepted, and is in operation. An effective project management structure will have to be established in order to plan, execute, and control the program.

Without clearly defined responsibilities, there can be many portions of prospective validation programs that are not completed because it is thought that this is someone else's responsibility. The reverse can also occur; two or more individuals or groups unilaterally assume responsibility, resulting in a major duplication of effort and waste of time and money. Problems such as this can be minimized only by suitable organizational planning.

III. DOCUMENTATION

An effective prospective validation program must be supported by documentation extending from product initiation to full-scale production. The complete documentation package can be referred to as the Master Documentation File.

It will accumulate as a product concept progresses to the point of being placed in full-scale production, providing as complete a product history as possible. The final package will be the work of many individuals. It will consist of reports, procedures, protocols, specifications, analytical methods, and any other critical documents pertaining to the formulation and process. The package may contain the actual reports, or it may utilize cross-references to formal documentation, both internal and external to the organization.

The ideal documentation package will contain a complete history of the final product that is being manufactured. In retrospect, it would be possible to trace the justification or rationale behind all aspects of the final product/process.

The complete Master Documentation File becomes the reference source for all questions relating to the manufacture of a product at any plant location; however, this should not be confused with the concept of Master Product Document, which is essential for routine manufacturing of the product and is described later in the chapter. The Master Documentation File should contain all information that was generated during the entire product development sequence relevant to a validated process.

IV. PRODUCT DEVELOPMENT

Product development usually begins when an active chemical entity has been shown to possess the necessary attributes for a commercial product. The product development activities for the active chemical entity, formulation, and process form the foundation upon which the subsequent validation data are built.

Generally, product development activities can be subdivided into formulation development and process development.

A. Formulation Development

Formulation development provides the basic information on the active chemical, the formula, and the impact of raw materials or excipients on the product. Typical supportive data generated during these activities may include:

1. Preformulation profile, which includes all the basic physical or chemical information about the chemical entity
2. Formulation profile, which consists of physical and chemical characteristics required for the product, drug-excipient compatibility studies, and effect of formulation on in vitro dissolution
3. Effect of formulation variables on the bioavailability of the product
4. Specific test methods
5. Key product attributes and/or specifications
6. Optimum formulation

Formulation development should not be considered complete until all those factors which could significantly alter the formulation have been studied. Subsequent minor changes to the formulation, however, may be acceptable, provided they are thoroughly tested and are shown to have no adverse effect on product characteristics.

B. Process Development

Process development activities begin after the formulation has been developed. The process development program should meet the following objectives:

1. Develop a suitable process to produce a product which meets all:
   a. Product specifications.
   b. Economic constraints.
   c. Current good manufacturing practices (CGMPs).
2. Identify the key process parameters that affect the product attributes.
3. Identify in-process specifications and test methods.
4. Identify generic and/or specific equipment that may be required.

Process development can be divided into several stages:

Design
Ranging
Characterization
Verification

Typical activities in these areas are illustrated in Fig. 2.

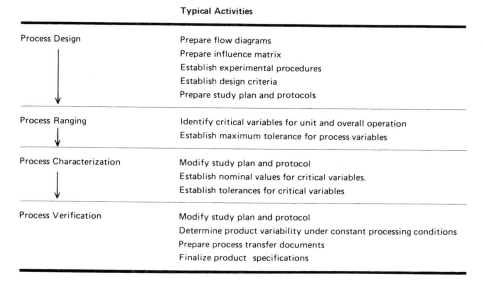

Figure 2 Product development flow.

1. Design

This is the initial planning stage of process development. During this stage, technical operations in both the manufacturing and quality control departments should be consulted. The practicality and the reality of the manufacturing operation should be kept in perspective.

Key documents for the technical definition of the process are the flow diagram, the cause-and-effect diagram, and the influence matrix. The details of the cause-and-effect diagram and the influence matrix will be discussed under experimental approach in a later section.

The flow diagram identifies all the unit operations, the equipment used, and the stages at which the various raw materials are added. The flow diagram in Fig. 3 outlines the sequence of process steps and specific equipment to be used during development for a typical granulated solid dosage form product. The flow diagram provides a convenient basis on which to develop a detailed list of variables and responses.

Preliminary working documents are critical, but they should never be "cast in stone," since new experimental data may drastically alter them. The final version will eventually be an essential part of the process characterization and technical transfer documents.

Regardless of the stage of formulation/process development being considered, a detailed identification of variables and responses is necessary for early program planning. Typical variables and responses that could be expected in a

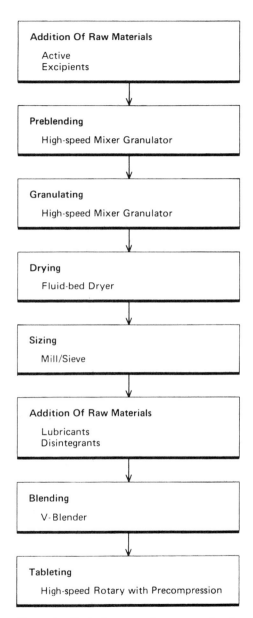

Figure 3 Typical process flow—granulated product.

granulated solid dosage form are illustrated in Fig. 4. This list is by no means complete and is intended only as an example.

As the developmental program progresses, new discoveries will provide an update of the variables and responses. It is important that current knowledge be adequately summarized for the particular process being considered. It should be pointed out, however, that common sense and experience must be used in evaluating the variables during process design and development.

Process Step	Control Variables	Measured Responses
Preblending	Blending Time rpm Load Size Order Of Addition	Blend Uniformity
Granulating	Load Size Amount Of Granulating Agent Solvent Addition Rate rpm Granulation Time	Density Yield
Drying	Initial Temperature Load Size Drying Temperature Program Air Flow Program Drying Time Cooling Time	Density Moisture Content Yield
Sizing	Screen Type Screen Size Feed Rate	Granule Size Distribution Loose Density Packed Density
Blending	Load Size rpm Blending Time	Blend Uniformity Flow Characteristics
Tableting	Compression Rate Granule Feed Rate Precompression Force Compression Force	Weight Variation Friability Hardness Thickness Disintegration Time Dissolution Dosage Form Uniformity

Figure 4 Typical variables and responses—granulated product.

An early transfer of the preliminary documentation to the manufacturing and quality control departments is essential, so that they can begin to prepare for any new equipment or facilities that may be required.

2. Ranging

Process-ranging studies will test whether identified parameters are critical to the product and process being developed. These studies determine the:

Feasibility of the designed process
Criticality of the parameters
Failure limits for each of the critical variables
Validity of the test methods

This is usually a transition stage between the laboratory and the projected final process. Figure 4 also shows typical responses that may have to be evaluated during the ranging studies on a tableted product.

3. Characterization

Process characterization provides a systematic examination of critical variables found during process ranging. The objectives of these studies are:

Confirm key process control variables and quantify their effects on product attributes.
Establish process conditions for each unit operation.
Determine in-process operating limits to guarantee acceptable finished product and yield.

A carefully planned and coordinated experimental program is essential in order to achieve these objectives. Techniques to assist in defining experimental programs are described later in the chapter.

The information summarized in the process characterization report provides a basis for defining the full-scale process.

4. Verification

Before a process is scaled up and transferred to production, verification is required. This ensures that it behaves as designed under simulated production conditions and determines its reproducibility. Key elements of the process verification runs should be evaluated using a well-designed in-process sampling procedure. These should be focused on potentially critical unit operations. Validated in-process and final-product analytical procedures should always be used. Sufficient replicate batches should be produced to determine between- and within-batch variations.

Testing during these verification runs will be more frequent and cover more variables than would be typical during routine production. The typical process verification analysis of a tableted product includes:

Unit operation	Analysis
Preblending	None required
Granulation	None required
Sizing	Granule size distribution
Blending	Uniformity
	Potency
Tableting	Weight
	Hardness
	Thickness
	Disintegration
	Dissolution
	Friability

For maximum information, the process should not be altered during the verification trials.

5. Development Documentation

The developmental documentation to support the validation of the process may contain the following:

Process ranging and characterization reports which contain a full description of the studies performed
Development batch record
Raw material specifications
Equipment list
Process flow diagram
Process variable tolerances
Operating instructions for equipment (where necessary)
In-process quality control program including:
    Sampling intervals
    Test methods
    Critical unit operations
Final product specifications
Hazards
    Chemical
    Process
Special production facility requirements
Stability profile of the product
    Produced during formulation development
    Produced during process development
Primary packaging specifications

IV. DEVELOPMENT OF MANUFACTURING CAPABILITY

There must be a suitable production facility for every manufacturing process that is developed. This facility includes buildings, equipment, staff, and supporting functions.

As development activities progress and the process becomes more clearly defined, there must be a parallel assessment of the capability to manufacture the product. The scope and timing of the development of manufacturing capability will be dependent on the process and the need to utilize or modify existing facilities or establish new ones.

VI. FULL-SCALE PRODUCT/PROCESS DEVELOPMENT

The development of the final full-scale production process proceeds through the following steps:

Process scale-up studies
Qualification trials
Process qualification

A. Scale-Up Studies

The transition from a successful pilot-scale process to a full-scale process requires careful planning and implementation. Although a large amount of information has been gathered during the development of the process, i.e., process characterization and process verification studies, it does not necessarily follow that the full-scale process can be completely predicted.

Many scale-up parameters are nonlinear. In fact, scale-up factors can be quite complex and difficult to predict based only on experience with smaller-scale equipment. In general, the more complex the process, the more complex the scale-up effect.

For some processes, the transition from pilot scale to full scale is relatively easy and orderly. For others the transition is less predictable. More often than not there will be no serious surprises, but this cannot be guaranteed. Individuals conducting the transfer into production should be thoroughly qualified on both small- and large-scale equipment.

The planning for scale-up should follow the same general outline followed for process characterization and verification. It usually begins when process development studies in the laboratory have successfully shown that a product can be produced within specification limits for defined ranges of process parameters.

Frequently, because of economic constraints, a carefully selected inert chemical may be used as a substitute for the expensive active chemical in conducting initial scale-up studies. Eventually, the active chemical will have to be used to complete the scale-up studies, however.

It is good common sense that every effort will be made to conduct the final scale-up studies under CGMP conditions. Thus, any product produced within specifications can be considered for release as a finished salable product.

B. Qualification Trials

After the scale-up studies have been completed, the protocol for the full-scale process qualification and production acceptance runs can be written. The complete qualification protocol is usually the joint effort of the following groups:

Research and development
Pharmaceutical technology or technical services
Quality control
Manufacturing
Process engineering

One of these groups usually coordinates the activities.

A complete qualification protocol will contain specific sections; however, there can be considerable variation in individual protocol section content. A typical qualification protocol may consist of the following:

Safety instructions
Environmental restrictions
   Gas or liquid discharge limitations
   Solid or scrap disposal instructions
Equipment
   Description
   Operation
   Cleaning
Raw materials
   Pertinent characteristics
   Acceptance limits
   Analytical methods
   Packaging and storage
   Handling precautions
   Sampling
Formulation
   Master batch components (percent by weight)
   Production batch component (by weight)
Process batch record
   Process sequence
   Process instructions
   Material usage
   In-process data
   In-process sampling

Qualification sampling and testing
  In-process
  Finished product
Definition of qualification criteria
  Lower and upper acceptance limits
  Acceptable variation

It is expected that acceptable, salable products will be produced, since all qualification batches will be produced using a defined process under CGMP conditions with production personnel.

A question that always arises is: "How many replicate batches or lots must be produced for a qualification protocol to be valid or correct?" There is no absolute answer. Obviously, a single batch will provide the minimum amount of data. As the number of replicated batches increases, the information increases.

The number of batch replicates will depend on:

Information gathered during process development and scale-up trials.
Finished product specification range: tight specifications may require more finished product replicate batches.
Complexity of process: a more complex process will most likely require additional replicate batches.

The technical requirements for an adequate replication of batches in the qualification protocol may be offset by:

Economics
Time constraints
Need for finished products

In general, three batches is the accepted minimum for qualification. Additional batches may be needed for added assurance, however.

C. Master Product Document

At each stage of the development and qualification of the final production process, an extensive quantity of documents is generated. Some of these documents will be directly related to the manufacture of the final product. Others may provide the basis for decisions that ultimately result in the final process.

The documents that are required for manufacturing the product then become the Master Product Document. This document must be capable of providing all of the information necessary to set up the process to produce a product consistently, and one that meets specifications in any location.

Items that will normally be included in the Master Product Document are:

Batch manufacturing record
Master formulation
Process flow diagram

Master manufacturing instructions
Master packaging instructions
Specifications
Sampling (location and frequency)
Test methods
Process qualification data

Each of the above items must contain sufficient detailed information to permit the complete Master Product Document to become an independent, single package that will provide all information necessary to set up and produce a product.

VII. DEFINING EXPERIMENTAL PROGRAMS

The objective in this section is to examine experiments or combinations of related experiments that make up development programs. The emphasis will be on techniques to increase developmental program effectiveness.

A logical and systematic approach to each experimental situation is essential. Any experiment that is performed without first defining a logical approach is certain to waste resources. The right balance between overplanning and underplanning should always be sought.

It is usually impossible to define a substantial experimental effort at the beginning and then execute it in every detail without modification. To overcome this, it is convenient to split the program into a number of stages.

Each stage will normally consist of several specific experiments. The earlier experiments tend to supply initial data concerning the process and define preliminary operating ranges for important variables. As results become available from each stage, they can be used to assist in defining subsequent stages in the experimental program. In some cases, it may be necessary to redefine completely the remainder of the experimental program on the basis of earlier results.

The following discussion describes some techniques to help improve experimental program effectiveness. A logical and systematic approach coupled with effective communication among individuals associated with the program is emphasized. Topics to be discussed include:

Defining program scope
Process Summary
Experimental design and analysis
Experiment documentation
Program organization

A. Program Scope

Defining a clear and detailed set of objectives is a necessary first step in any experimental program. Some similarity exists between objectives for different products and processes using similar existing technology. For products and processes at the forefront of technology, the definition of specific experimental objectives can be a continuing activity throughout product development.

Constraints on planning experimental programs can be classified according to their impact on time, resources, and budget. The effect and impact of these should be incorporated into the experimental program early to avoid compromising critical program objectives.

B. Process Summary

An initial clear understanding of the formulation and/or process is important. The following techniques can assist in summarizing current process knowledge.

1. Flow Diagram

A process flow diagram (Fig. 3) can often provide a focal point of early program planning activities. This diagram outlines the sequence of process steps and specific equipment to be used during development for a typical granulated product. Flow diagram complexity will depend on the particular product and process. The flow diagram provides a convenient basis on which to develop a detailed list of variables and responses.

2. Variables and Responses

For processes using existing technology, many of the potential variables and responses may have already been identified in previous product-development studies or in the pharmaceutical literature. Once properly identified, the list of variables and responses for the process is not likely to change appreciably. Typical variables and responses that could be expected in a granulated solid dosage form are illustrated in Fig. 4.

Processes at the forefront of technology present a more difficult problem. Not all of the important variables or responses will be identified in earlier development activities. As the experimental program progresses, new discoveries will provide a continuing need to update both the process itself and the summary of variables and responses. In addition, the relative importance of variables and responses already identified will likely shift during development activities.

The greatest concern is directed toward potential critical variables and responses; however, attention should also be devoted to identifying all potential process control and product variables and responses so that critical aspects, not yet identified as such, will be included in the process summary.

3. Cause-and-Effect Diagram

An efficient representation of complex relationships between many process and formulation variables (causes), and a single response (effect) can be shown by using a cause-and-effect diagram [1]. Figure 5 is a simple example.

A central arrow in Fig. 5 points to a particular single effect. Branches off the central arrow lead to boxes representing specific process steps. Next, principle

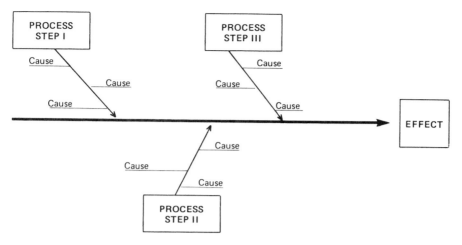

Figure 5   Simple cause-and-effect diagram.

factors of each process step that can cause or influence the effect are drawn as subbranches off each branch, until a complete cause-and-effect diagram is developed which should be as detailed a summary as possible. An example of a more complex cause-and-effect diagram is illustrated in Fig. 6. A separate summary for each critical product characteristic (e.g., weight variation, dissolution, friability) should be made.

There is no single best way to draw or arrange a cause-and-effect diagram. The important point to remember is that identifying and summarizing the various factors that might possibly cause each process or product effect are the primary objectives.

4.   Influence Matrix

Once the variables and responses have been identified, it is useful to summarize their relationships in an influence matrix format as shown in Fig. 7. Each process variable is evaluated, based on the available knowledge, for its potential effects on each of the process responses or product characteristics. The strength of the relationship between variables and responses can be indicated by some appropriate notation, such as strong (S), moderate (M), weak (W), or none (N), together with special classifications such as unknown (?).

Construction of the influence matrix assists in identifying those variables with the greatest influence on key process or product characteristics. These variables are potentially the most critical for maintaining process control and should be included in the earliest experiments. Some may continue to be investigated during development and scale-up.

As the experimental program progresses, the influence matrix can be updated

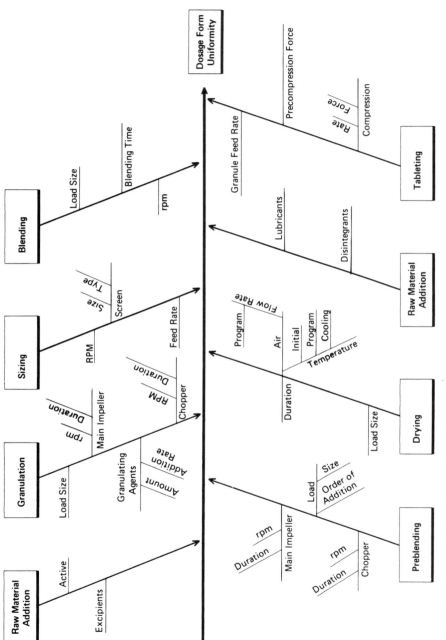

Figure 6 Cause-and-effect diagram (granulated product).

In-process/Final Product Characteristics

Process Variables		Preblend Uniformity	Power Load	Moisture Content	Granule Size Distribution	Blend Uniformity	Hardness	Friability	Dosage Form Uniformity
Preblending	rpm	S	/	/	N	W	N	N	W
	Time	S	/	/	N	W	N	N	W
Granulating	rpm	/	S	N	W	W	W	N	W
	Amount Of Solvent	/	M	W	M	W	W	W	W
	Time	/	M	N	M	W	W	W	W
Drying	Temperature Program	/	/	S	/	N	N	N	N
	Time	/	/	S	M	N	N	N	N
Sizing	Screen Size	/	/	/	S	W	N	M	W
Blending	Time	/	/	/	/	S	M	N	S
Tableting	Compression Rate	/	/	/	/	/	W	W	W
	Compression Force	/	/	/	/	/	S	S	W

Figure 7   Influence matrix for variables and responses (simplified).

to include the latest knowledge. Thus, the results of each experiment in the sequence can be used to assist in designing subsequent experiments. It can also assist in identifying variable-response relationships within isolated parts of the process and provide opportunities for conducting experiments in parallel rather than in sequence.

VIII.   EXPERIMENTAL DESIGN AND ANALYSIS

Many different experimental designs and analysis methods can be used in development activities. Indeed, the possibilities could fill several books. Fortunately, in any given situation, it is not necessary to search for that single design or analysis method that absolutely must be used. There are usually many possibilities. In general, designs that are usable offer different levels of efficiency, complexity, and effectiveness in achieving experimental objectives.

A. Types of Design

It is not possible to list specific designs that will always be appropriate for general occasions. Any attempt to do so would be sure to be ineffective and the uniqueness of individual experimental programs would be ignored. The best course of action is to examine the experimental situation carefully, including:

Specific objectives
Available resources
Availability of previous theoretical and experimental results
Relevant variables and responses
Qualifications and experience of research team members
Cost of experimentation

and determine which design is appropriate. A statistician who is experienced in development applications can assist in suggesting and evaluating candidate designs. In some cases, the statistician should be a full-time member of the research team.

A number of sources are available that give experimental designs for a wide range of applications [2–8]. A simple example of a 2^3 factorial experimental design applied to process characterization is illustrated in Fig. 8. Three granulating variables are studied to determine the magnitude of their effects on various in-process and final-product responses. Each variable appears in the design at two different levels which already have been determined from the results of earlier ranging studies. Granulation from each of the experimental conditions is carried through standardized conditions (determined from previous experiments) of subsequent process steps to produce a final product blend. Each blend is then tableted using several [3–5] levels of compression force.

B. Data Analysis

The appropriate analysis of the experimental results will depend on the experimental objectives, the design used, and the characteristics of the data collected during the experiment. In many cases, a simple examination of a tabular or graphical presentation of the data will be sufficient. In other cases, a formal statistical analysis may be required in order to draw any conclusions at all. It depends on the particular experimental situation. No rules of thumb are available. In general, the simplest analysis consistent with experimental objectives and conditions is the most appropriate.

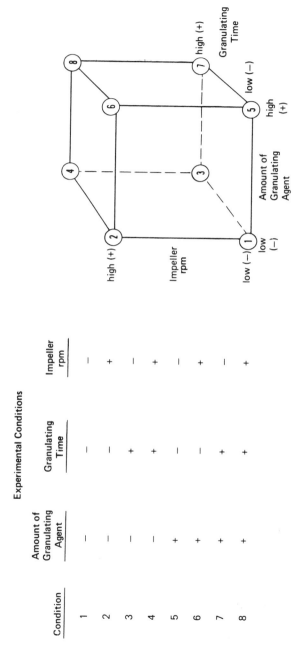

Figure 8 Experimental design example.

In the example design discussed previously, it is often sufficient to plot the final product responses (e.g., weight variation, friability, hardness, thickness, or disintegration) as a function of compression force. Visual comparisons of the resulting plots, identified by experimental condition, can illustrate important effects caused by experimental variables. If tablet hardness or other measurements are used as process-control variables, plots of the other measurements as a function of the control variables may also be useful. More formal analyses of the data are also possible when called for by the experimental objectives.

As an experimental program progresses, the amount of data increases until it becomes difficult to comprehend when presented as multiple tables or graphs. The search for an effective way of summarizing experimental results and presenting major experimental findings is usually worth the effort. A summary of major results in a graph or outline form will often be more effective than binding the results together as individual plots and tables along with wordy explanations.

C. Experiment Documentation

Documentation is essential to program planning and coordination, in addition to the obvious use for the summary of activities and results. Written communication becomes important for larger complex programs, especially when conducted under severe constraints on time and resources. Documentation can consist of some or all of the following items:

1. Objectives
    An exact statement of quantifiable results expected from the experiment
2. Experimental design
    A detailed list of the experimental conditions to be studied and the order of investigation
3. Proposed/alternate test methods
    a. A list of test methods consistent with the type of experiment being performed
    b. A detailed description of the steps necessary to obtain a valid measurement
    c. Documentation supporting the accuracy, precision, sensitivity, etc., of the test methods
4. Equipment procedures
    Documentation of safety precautions and step-by-step methods for equipment setup, operation, and cleanup
5. Sampling plans
    The type, number, location, and purpose of samples to be taken during the experiment; in addition, the type and number of all measurements to be performed on each sample

6. Protocol
   A formal written experimental plan that presents the aforementioned experimental documentation in a manner suitable for review
7. Data records
   a. Experiment log: details of events in the experiment noting process adjustments and any unusual occurrences
   b. In-process measurements: records of the magnitude of critical process parameters during the experimental sequence
      Sample measurements: recorded values of particular measurements on each sample
8. Report
   Documentation of experiment implementation, exceptions/modifications to the protocol, results, and conclusions

D. Program Organization

Throughout the experimental phases of prospective validation, it is essential to maintain effective communication among various team members. This is facilitated by having one individual with the necessary technical and managerial skills assume responsibility for the experimental program, including procuring resources and informing management of progress.

In a large experimental program, the responsible individual may serve as a project leader or manager with little or no technical involvement.

IX. SUMMARY

Prospective validation of a production process utilizes information generated during the entire development sequence that produced the final process.

Validation begins at the first indication that a final production process will evolve from a potential product concept.

As a potential product moves through the various developmental stages, information is continually generated and incorporated into a master documentation file. When the qualification runs are planned for the final process, they will be based on the master documentation file contents. The information generated during the qualification runs is usually the last major item to go into the Master Documentation File.

An abstract of the Master Documentation File is the Master Product Document. The master product document is the source of all information required to set up the process at any location.

Validation is not a stand-alone item. It is an integral portion of the entire process/product development sequence.

REFERENCES

1. Ishikawa, K., *Guide to Quality Control*, Asian Productivity Organization, Tokyo (1982).
2. Box, G. E. P., Hunter, W. G., and Hunter, J. S., *Statistics for Experimenters: An Introduction to Design, Data Analysis, and Model Building*, John Wiley & Sons, New York (1978).
3. Box, G. E. P., and Draper, N. R., *Evolutionary Operation: A Statistical Method for Process Improvement*, John Wiley & Sons, New York (1969).
4. Cornell, J. A., *Experiments with Mixtures: Design, Models and the Analysis of Mixture Data*, John Wiley & Sons, New York (1981).
5. Daniel, C., *Applications of Statistics to Industrial Experiments*, John Wiley & Sons, New York (1976).
6. Davies, O. L. (ed.), *The Design and Analysis of Industrial Experiments*, Longman Group Limited, New York (1978).
7. Diamond, W. J., *Practical Experiment Designs for Engineers and Scientists*, Lifetime Learning Publications, Belmont, California (1981).
8. Ott, E. R., *Process Quality Control: Troubleshooting and Interpretation of Data*, McGraw-Hill, New York (1975).
9. Anderson, N. R., Banker, G. S., and Peck, G. E., *Pharmaceutical Dosage Forms: Tablets*, Vol. III, Marcel Dekker, New York (1981).

8

Retrospective Process Validation

Chester J. Trubinski   *Carter-Wallace, Inc., Cranbury, New Jersey*

I. INTRODUCTION

In the present-day pharmaceutical industry the Food and Drug Administration (FDA) expects firms to have validated manufacturing processes. Process validation has been defined as a documented program which provides a high degree of assurance that a specific process will consistently produce a product meeting predetermined specifications [1]. For new products or existing products which have recently undergone reformulation, validation is usually an integral part of the process development effort. No such opportunity exists for older established products, however. Of the 200 most frequently dispensed brand and generic name drugs in the United States, about 16% were introduced in 1970 or earlier [2]. Thus, the product line of many firms is likely to contain one or more products for which the manufacturing processes have not been validated, at least not to the extent that is now expected.

II. PROCESS VALIDATION STRATEGIES

Pharmaceutical firms that do not have their product lines validated will come under increasing regulatory pressure. Indeed, the FDA already has taken the initiative by publishing a guideline for use by industry which outlines general principles considered acceptable parts of process validation [1]. To satisfy the requirement for validated processes, a firm can adopt one of the following approaches:

1. Undertake a developmental research program with the goal that all nonvalidated processes will be reassessed. Financial constraints, however, probably will intervene to preclude unilateral application of this strategy. This is especially true for many marginally profitable products that cannot support the additional charges that would be incurred. Furthermore, such an approach will shortly overwhelm the scientific resources of most companies, to say nothing of its impact on new product research.

2. Alternatively, the manufacturer can capitalize on already available information to demonstrate process validity. Let us call this second program retrospective validation. As the prefix "retro" implies, this type of validation is carried out through the use of information that already exists, the most abundant source of which is the product's production and control records. Other sources of valuable information can be found in the appropriate complaint files, equipment installation and maintenance logs, and raw material acceptance reports. The objective is to demonstrate that the process has performed satisfactorily and consistently over time and, therefore, can be counted on to deliver products of the same quality in the future.

A. Product Selection Criteria for Retrospective Validation

For a product to be considered for retrospective validation, it must have a relatively stable process, that is, one in which the method of manufacture has remained essentially unchanged for a period of time.

Therefore, the first step in the product selection process is to obtain for each product a summary of changes in the method of manufacture. In most companies, such information is part of the master batch record file. Using an estimate of annual production volume, select a time interval that represents the last 20 batches. Products for which there is no record of a change in the method of manufacture or control during this period can be regarded as candidates for validation. The 20-batch rule is quite arbitrary actually, as there is no one number that is correct for every product. The ideal number of batches required to study a product is theoretically the number that permits all process variables to come into play. By process variables, we mean raw materials from different but approved vendors, introduction of different pieces of equipment and personnel, seasonal changes, and the like. This is a rather unwieldy situation, especially where many products are under consideration. A more manageable approach would be to select a fixed number of batches, say 20, which will allow many of the variables to be represented. Individual judgment will still be required in instances of very low- and very high-volume products, however.

The second step in the product selection process addresses the situation where a change in the method of manufacture or control was implemented during the last 20 production batches. The fact that a change has occurred does not automatically disqualify the product for retrospective validation. One must first know whether the particular modification has caused an expected result to be different to the extent that it is no longer comparable to previous batches. An example may be helpful. Suppose the method of granulating was changed midway through the series of 20 batches selected for the validation study. The number of batches representing the new process would be significantly reduced and could be insufficient to capture some of the interactions which can affect process reproducibility. In general, a history of any one of the following changes to the method of manufacture and control should be fully investigated before any decision is made to validate retrospectively:

1. Formulation changes involving one or more of the active ingredients or key excipients
2. Introduction of new equipment not equivalent in every respect to that previously in use
3. Changes in the method by which the product is tested
4. Changes in the method of manufacture

Products that are found to be unsuitable can be held aside until a sufficient number of batches, 20 for example, has been produced using the most current procedure. This strategy assumes the firm has a certain amount of leeway as to when the study must be completed.

We are now in a position to compile a list of the products that can be validated retrospectively; however, before doing so, it is advisable to determine some additional information about these products.

The third and last step in our selection process is to identify which products are likely to be discontinued because of a lack of marketing interest or regulatory consideration, to be sold, or to be reformulated. The timing of these events will dictate whether the product in question remains a viable candidate for retrospective validation.

The foremost discussion on developing a list of suitable products for study is summarized in Fig. 1.

B. Organizing for Retrospective Validation

To this point, we have produced a list of products that may be validated retrospectively; that is, their manufacturing processes are relatively stable, and so adequate historical data exist on which to base an opinion. The next consideration is the formal mechanism for validating the individual products. Appropriate organizational structures for effectively validating processes have been put forth, but mostly in conjunction with validation of new product introductions. Still, these recommendations can serve as models [3]. Because the products being studied are marketed products, the quality assurance and production departments can be

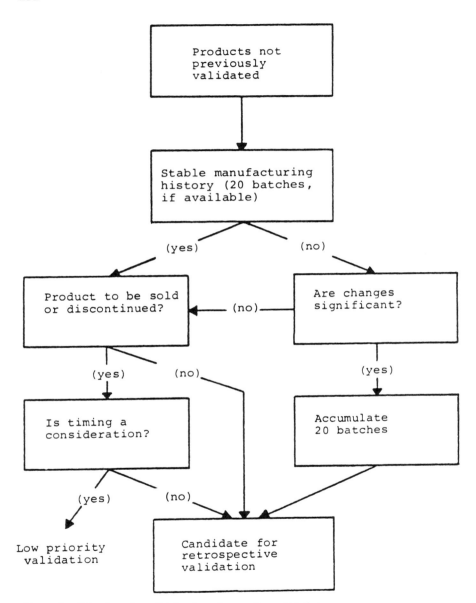

Figure 1 Selection of candidates for retrospective validation.

expected to make major contributions. In fact, as far as retrospective validation is concerned, it may be more appropriate for one of these departments to coordinate the project. The research and engineering departments, of course, will be needed, especially where recent process changes have been encountered or equipment design is at issue.

The previously discussed disciplines, operating as a team, will determine which data should be collected for each product and from how many batches; subsequently, they will evaluate the information and report their findings. Personnel resources beyond this committee are necessary to accomplish the tasks of data collection and analysis. The time requirements dictate that such work be assigned to a function with a good deal of discretionary time, possibly a technical services group or quality assurance. Management must have an appreciation at the outset of the expected duration of the project and cost in personnel. Management commitment is especially crucial if disruptive influences are to be minimized. The loss of a committee member to another project is such an example.

C. Written Operating Procedures

The various activities and responsibilities associated with retrospectively validating a product must be put in writing. All too often this simple but crucial step is omitted for the sake of expediency only to find, at a later date, that initial assumptions cannot be recalled. Aside from maintaining consistency, a written procedure to describe the work being performed satisfies the intent of the current good manufacturing practice (CGMP) regulations.

In general, the written operating procedure should delineate in reasonable detail how the validation organization will function. Not every situation can be anticipated, and this should not be the goal. There should be sufficient detail, however, to ensure consistency of performance in an undertaking that may continue for many months or even longer. In the preparation of such a document, the following questions should be answered.

1. Which organizational functions will be represented on the validation committee?
2. Have all of the products that require validation been identified and listed in priority order?
3. What mechanism exists for validation protocol preparation and approval?
4. What criteria are used to select critical process control steps and quality control tests?
5. How often will the committee meet to ensure prompt evaluation of study data?
6. Who has responsibility for documenting committee decisions? For report preparation?
7. Is there a provision for follow-up in the event of unexpected findings?
8. Where will original study data and reports be archived?

In the preceding discussion of areas of interest to the validation organization, two concepts were introduced which deserve further clarification: (1) critical process steps and quality control tests which characterize the operation and (2) validation protocol.

1. Critical Process Steps and Control Tests

Critical process steps are operations performed during dosage form manufacture which can contribute to variability of the end product if not controlled. Since each type of dosage form requires different machinery and unit operations to produce the end product, the critical process steps will also differ. For each product considered suitable for retrospective validation, a list of these steps must be compiled following careful analysis of the process by technically competent persons. In a similar manner, in-process and finished-product tests should be screened to identify those which may be of some value. As a rule, tests in which the outcome is quantitative will be of greatest interest.

A flow diagram of the entire operation, but particularly the manufacturing process, may be helpful in identifying critical steps, especially where the process involves many steps. Such a diagram is also a useful addition to the validation report prepared at the conclusion of the study.

2. Validation Protocol

A written protocol should be prepared which describes what is to be accomplished [4]. It should specify the data to be collected, the number of batches to be included in the study, and how the data, once assembled, will be treated for relevance. The date of approval of the protocol by the validation organization should also be noted. The value of a protocol is to control the direction of the study, as well as provide a baseline in the event unanticipated developments necessitate a change in strategy. A written protocol is also a FDA requirement [1].

D. Other Considerations

Comprehensive records of complaints received either directly from the customer or through a drug problem reporting program should be reviewed. Furthermore, a record of any follow-up investigation of such complaints is mandatory [5] and should be part of this file. Review of customer complaint records can furnish a useful overview of process performance and possibly hint at product problems. Therefore, complaint analysis should be viewed as a meaningful adjunct to the critical process step and control test selection process.

Batch yield reflects efficiency of the operation. Because yield figures are the sum of numerous interactions, they fail in most cases to provide specific information about process performance and therefore must be used, with caution, in retrospective validation. In any event, this information should be collected, as it can contribute to further refinement of the yield limits which appear in the batch record.

Lot-to-lot differences in the purity of the therapeutic agent must be considered when evaluating in-process and finished-product test results. In addition to potency, particle size distribution and source of the material will be of interest. Such information should be available from the raw material test reports prepared by the quality control laboratory for each lot of material received.

There is value in examining logs of equipment and physical plant maintenance. These documents can provide a chronological profile of the operating environment and reveal recent alterations to the process equipment that may have enough impact to disqualify the product from retrospective validation consideration. For this reason, it is always prudent to contemplate equipment status early in the information-gathering stage. The availability of such information should be ascertained for yet another reason: rarely is equipment dedicated to one product. More often than not, each blender, comminutor, tablet press, and so forth is used for several operations. Therefore, information gathered initially can be incorporated into subsequent studies.

Retrospective validation is directed primarily toward examining the records of past performance. But what if one of these documents is not a true reflection of the operation performed? Let us suppose that changes have crept into the processing operation over time and have gone unreported. This condition would result in the validation of a process which, in reality, does not exist. It is, therefore, essential to audit the existing operation against the written instructions. There is obvious advantage to undertaking this audit before commencing data acquisition. Ideally, the manufacture of more than one batch should be witnessed, especially where multiple-shift operations are involved. The same logic would apply to the testing performed in-process and at the finished stage. If any deviation from written directions is noted, an effort must be made to measure its impact. In this regard, the previously described validation organization is a logical forum for discussion and evaluation.

Batches which are rejected or reworked, as a rule, are not suitable for inclusion in a retrospective validation study [6]. Indeed, a processing failure which is not fully explainable should be cause to rethink the application of retrospective validation. Nonconformance to specification which is attributable to a unique event—operator error, for example—may be justifiably disregarded. In such cases, the batch is not considered when the historical data are assembled.

Raw materials, both actives and excipients, can be a source of product variability. To limit this risk, there should be meaningful acceptance specifications, and purchases must be limited to previously qualified suppliers. The 20-batch strategy takes into account multiple-supplier sourcing; nevertheless, it would be prudent to determine the existence of these controls as part of any retrospective validation effort.

III. SELECTION AND EVALUATION OF PROCESSING DATA

The following discussion will focus on how to apply the previously discussed concepts to the validation of marketed products. To provide a fuller understanding of this procedure, the manufacture of several dosage forms designed for different routes of administration will be examined. For each dosage form, critical process steps and quality control tests will be identified. Useful statistical techniques for examining the assembled data will be illustrated. A review of the application of statistical methods to historical data evaluation can be found in the presentation by Simms [7]. It is also important to note that not all of the collected information for a product lends itself to this type of analysis. This will become more apparent as we proceed with the evaluation of the five drugs under consideration.

A. Compressed Tablet (Drug A)

Drug A is a compressed tablet containing a single active ingredient. Inspection of the batch record reveals that the following operations are involved in the manufacture of the dosage unit: the active ingredient is combined with several excipients in a twin-shell blender. The premix just prepared is granulated using a purified water-binder solution. The resulting wet mix is milled using a specified screen and machine setting, then dried using either an oven tray dryer or fluid bed dryer. When dry, the blend is oscillated, combined with previously sized lubricant, and blended. The granulation is then compressed. Refer to Fig. 2 for a flow diagram of the manufacturing process.

At the premix blending step, the batch record provides two pieces of information: recommended blending time and blender load. The latter will be of little interest, as only one size batch is produced for this product. Blender speed is not specified in the batch record because it is fixed. Because mixing time has been recognized as influencing blend uniformity, this operation will become the first of the critical process steps for which we will want to collect historical information [8].

The second major step is granulation. The process is controlled by the operator, whose judgment is relied on for the appropriate end point. As no information useful for process validation is available, we will move on to the next step, comminution.

The batch record calls for passing the wet mix through a comminutor using a No. 5 or 7 drilled stainless steel screen. Knife position and rotational speed are two other factors which influence particle size; however, the step instruction is quite specific about machine setup. Therefore, only screen size is a source of variability for this step. We will want to know the frequency of use of each screen.

Next, the granulation is dried to a target moisture of 1%. Either a tray or fluid bed dryer may be used, at the discretion of area supervision. Regardless of the method, drying time will be of interest. In addition, the final moisture content

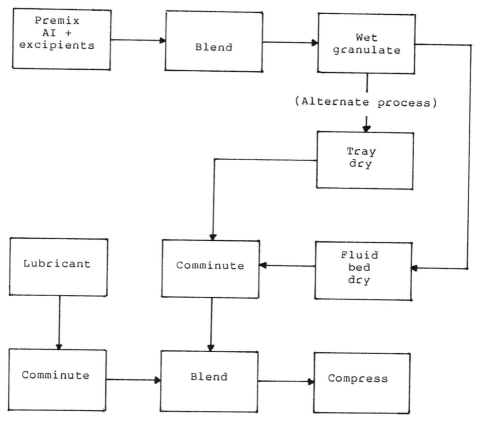

Figure 2 Drug A, flow diagram of manufacturing process.

should be ascertained for each batch. The dried granulation and lubricant are then oscillated using a No. 10 or 12 wire screen. This is the last sizing operation of the process; it will determine the particle size distribution of the final blend. Thus, it is important to know the history of use of each screen size.

The lubricant and granulation are blended for several minutes. The elapsed mixing time is of interest because of its impact on drug distribution and the generally deleterious effect of the lubricant on dissolution.

Because excess moisture is thought to have a negative effect on the dosage form, loss on drying (LOD) is determined on the final blend.

Blending is followed by tableting. During compression, on-line measurements such as tablet weight, hardness, and disintegration are made by the process operator in order to ensure uniformity of the tablets. The weight of the tablets is not measured individually; rather the average weight of 10 tablets is recorded. Although these data are good indicators of operation and machine performance, we would prefer to have the more precise picture provided by individual tablet weight.

Disintegration time and tablet hardness data could be collected from the manufacturing batch records; however, for ease of administration these figures will be obtained from the quality control test results which also contain individual tablet weighings.

Disintegration time was selected as a critical variable because for a drug substance to be absorbed it must first disintegrate and then dissolve. The resistance of a tablet to breakage, chipping, and so forth depends on its hardness. Disintegration, too, can be influenced by hardness of the tablet. For these reasons, hardness testing results also will be examined.

Specifications used by quality control to release drug A are found in a laboratory procedure. In addition to the previously discussed hardness and disintegration time requirements, the procedure calls for determining the average tablet weight by the USP procedure. That is, 20 individual tablets are weighed.

The control procedure also requires assay of individual tablets. Of all the information available, these data will be the most useful in reaching an opinion of the adequacy of the process to distribute the therapeutic agent uniformly.

In addition, the laboratory checks moisture content of the bulk tablets. It will be interesting to compare these results to the LOD of the final blend to measure the contribution of material handling.

Critical manufacturing steps and quality control tests for drug A, identified as a result of the review, are summarized in Table 1.

1. Evaluation of Historical Data

Earlier in the discussion of process validation strategies, 20 production batches were suggested as a reasonable number upon which to draw conclusions about the

Table 1 Drug A, Selected Critical Manufacturing Steps and Quality Control Tests

Processing steps	Quality control tests
Premix blending time	Disintegration time
Comminutor screen size	Hardness
Drying time and method	Average tablet weight (ATW)
Loss on drying (LOD)—granulation	Assay
Oscillator screen size	Water content—bulk tablet
Final mix blending time	
LOD—final blend	

validity of the process. In this particular example, however, two distinct methods of drying are provided. In order to have sufficient history on each operation, the number of batches examined was increased to 30.

The batches were selected so that the same number was dried by each process. For the other critical manufacturing steps and release tests listed in Table 1, data were collected for all 30 batches.

The first manufacturing step, premix blending time, was consistently reported as 10 min with but one exception. In this instance, the powders were tumbled for 20 min, which is still within the limits (10–20 min) prescribed by the batch record. It would be interesting to know if this source of variability can materially affect attributes of the final product. Unfortunately, having but one batch produced by the 20-min process does not permit statistically valid comparisons. At best, test results for the single 20-min batch can be screened using summary data from the remainder of the study. Under different circumstances, batches would have been grouped by mixing time and compared by dosage form attributes. More than likely, subsequent manipulation of the blend would have negated any contribution, allowing us to conclude that a mixing time of 10 to 20 min is not unreasonable.

At the wet milling step we encounter a situation similar to preblending. That is, only 2 of the 30 study batches are prepared using the No. 5 drilled screen. The No. 7 is obviously the screen of choice. The purpose of this step is to produce particles of reasonably uniform size, which, in turn, will improve drying. From the records, we also know that the No. 5 screen was used only with batches that were tray dried. Elapsed drying time and residual moisture were compared for the two batches from the No. 5 screen process and the other 13 batches that were tray dried. No important differences were detected. Still, in light of the limited use of the No. 5 screen, it would not be inappropriate to recommend this option be eliminated from the processing instructions.

Mean drying time for the oven tray process is 19.2 hr. All 15 batches were dried within the specified time of 16–20 hr. No seasonal influences was apparent. Average moisture content of these batches is 1.2%; the standard deviation is 0.3%. The 15 batches dried using the fluid bed dryer had a residual moisture of 0.8% (SD = 0.1%). Drying time is mechanically controlled and not recorded. The statistics favor the fluid bed process; it is more efficient and uniform. There is nothing in these data to disqualify the oven tray dryer from further use, however.

Oscillation of the dried granulation and lubricant was accomplished, in every instance, using a No. 10 wire screen. Reference to the No. 12 screen, the alternative method for pulverizing the batch, must be deleted from the manufacturing instructions for the process to be validated retrospectively.

Final mix blending time was reported as either 10 or 15 min. Twenty-one of the 30 batches were tumbled for 10 min and the remainder were mixed for 15 min. The mixing time is not mechanically controlled or automatically recorded; it is left to the operator to interpret elapsed time. Because of the importance of the step to distribution of the therapeutic agent, a comparison was made between the distribution of percent relative tablet potency [(tablet assay/tablet weight) × 100] for the two mixing times. The frequency distributions of the two populations are shown in Fig. 3.

The two histograms are visually different, with the 15-min process exhibiting more dispersion. Despite this difference both populations are tightly grouped, which is a reflection of the uniformity of the blend.

The processes may be studied quantitatively by comparing the means and standard deviations of the two populations. The effect of final blend time on lubricant distribution was examined by comparing disintegration time statistics for the grouped data. None was noted.

Moisture content of the 15 tray-dried batches following final mix remained essentially unchanged from the drying step. The batches from the fluid bed process gained moisture. This is probably attributable to handling very dry material in a relatively humid environment. Both groups are still below the target for this step of 1.5%, however.

Refer to Table 2 for a comparison of the moisture contents following the drying and tumbling steps. The sizable increase in mean moisture content of the fluid bed-dried batches deserves further study. To determine whether all batches were uniformly affected, an $\bar{x}$-control chart was plotted. Whereas the plot for the tray-dried batches is unremarkable, the fluid bed process chart (Fig. 4) depicts an unnatural pattern. Further investigation discloses that HVAC problems were experienced by the area in which a number of these batches were finally blended.

During compression, 1000 tablets were randomly selected for use by quality control. Inspection of the batch records revealed that all 30 batches were compressed on the same model press operating at approximately the same speed. All presses were fed by an overhead delivery system. Thus, tabletting equipment will not be a source of variability from batch to batch.

The test for disintegration is performed as described in the USP, and results are rounded to the nearest half-minute. Disintegration time varied over a narrow range for all batches studied. The 15-batch average for the tray dryer process (2.7 min) is well below the specification (10 min) for this test. Hardness of tablets from the tray dryer process averaged 15 SCU. All batches exceeded the minimum specification (9 SCU); there is no upper limit. Hardness and disintegration time are not well correlated, probably due to rounding of test results and the need to compare averages.

Tablets from the fluid bed process, on average, were slightly harder. Also, the individual batches had a greater range of hardness than did batches from the alternative drying process. Disintegration time for the fluid bed process averaged 3.0 min. Individual batches ranged from 2.0 to 4.5 min. As with the tray process, no correlation was found between hardness and disintegration time. In summary, tablets from the fluid bed dryer process were somewhat harder and took slightly

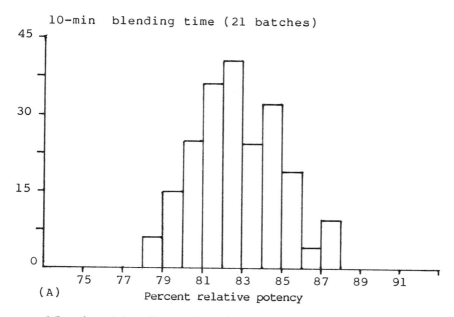

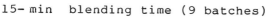

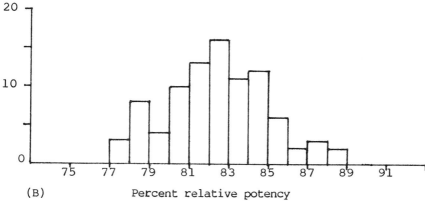

Figure 3 Histogram of drug A granulation uniformity resulting from different blending times. Percent relative potency = (tablet assay/tablet weight) × 100.

Table 2 Drug A, Comparison of Oven Tray Dryer and Fluid Bed Dryer Processes

Test	Oven tray process ($\bar{x}$)	Fluid bed process ($\bar{x}$)
% moisture dried granulation	1.20	0.80
% moisture final mix	1.10	1.30
% moisture bulk tablet	1.26	1.50
Hardness (SCU)	15.00	16.70
Disintegration (min)	2.70	3.00

longer to disintegrate. Refer to Table 2. These differences are considered insignificant, however. If any recommendations were made, it would be to lower the disintegration time specification or establish an internal action limit closer to the historical upper range of the process.

Control charts were plotted for hardness and average tablet weight (ATW) to evaluate process performance over time. Separate charts were prepared for the tray dryer and fluid bed processes. Hardness values are an average of 10 individual measurements. ATW subgroups are the result of weighing 20 tablets individually. The control charts were inspected for trends and evidence of instability using well-established methods [9]. Only the control chart for hardness of tablets from the fluid bed process responded to one of the tests for pattern instability (Fig. 5). That is, two of three consecutive points exceeded the 2 sigma limit. From the chart it is obvious the general trend toward greater tablet hardness (from 11 to 25 SCU) is the underlying cause of the instability. The trend to greater hardness was subsequently

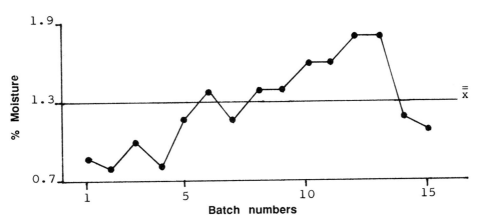

Figure 4 $\bar{x}$-control chart for drug A percent moisture at final blend step (fluid bed process).

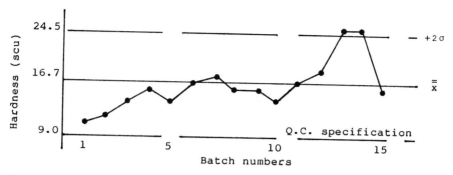

Figure 5 $\bar{x}$-control chart for drug A tablet hardness (fluid bed process).

arrested and may have to do with attempts to regulate another tablet variable—thickness, for example—though the records are vague in this regard.

Water content of the bulk tablets irrespective of the drying process was higher than at the final mix stage (Table 2). This is probably due to the compression room environment and the low initial moisture of the powder. Still, the specification limit of 2% is easily met.

Tablet weight should bear a direct relationship to milligrams of active ingredient available where the final blend is homogeneous, and handling of the granulation preparatory to tabletting does not contribute to segregation. To measure the likelihood that controlling tablet weight assures dosage uniformity, 50 tablet assays selected at random (from 300 tablet assays) were compared to tablet weight using regression analysis. Because the same tablet press and blender were employed for every batch, assay results from all 30 batches were pooled. Mean purity of the 25 receipts of active ingredients used to manufacture the 30 batches in the validation study was 99.7% or 0.3% below target. Individual lots ranged from 98.8 to 102%. Because of these lot-to-lot differences, active ingredient raw material potency was also included in the regression analysis.

The general model from the regression analysis is [10]:

$$y = b_0 + b_1X_1 + b_2X_2$$

where

y = tablet potency
b_0 = constant
X_1 = raw material purity
X_2 = tablet weight

Tablet potency was found to be related to raw material purity and tablet weight as follows:

$$y = -414.6 + 6.6050X_1 + 0.4303X_2$$

We would expect the regression plane to have a significant positive slope; that is, as purity of the active ingredient and tablet weight increase, so will tablet potency, and this was found to be the case. Both slopes are statistically significantly different from 0 at $\alpha = 0.025$. When the above equation is used to predict tablet potency given the ideal tablet weight (600 mg) for the product and mean raw material purity of 99.7%, the resulting value is only 2.1 mg different from the theoretical value of 500 mg.

In conclusion, drug A production was shown to be within established specifications, and there is no reason to believe this will not be the case for future production as long as all practices are continued in their present form. Furthermore, there is no significant difference between batches produced by the tray dryer process and the fluid bed process.

B. Coated Tablet (Drug B)

Let's now turn our attention to a different dosage form, applying some of the strategies developed during the examination of drug A. Again, we want to identify the process steps that are responsible for distributing the active ingredient as well as the tests that measure the effectiveness of those actions. Drug B is a sugar-coated tablet prepared in the traditional manner; that is, layers are slowly built up around a core by applying a coat of shellac and then subcoating, grossing, and smoothing coats until specifications are met at each stage. In the case of drug B, the core contains two active ingredients; the coating, on the other hand, has no medicinal value and is intended solely to enhance the aesthetic appearance of the product. Consequently, less attention will be given to the manufacturing operations intended to enhance product appearance solely for purposes of commercial acceptance. An unremarkable product complaint history for defects associated with the operations to be omitted could suffice to justify this decision. The manufacturing process is shown in Fig. 6.

Table 3 summarizes the selected critical steps for the manufacture of the core tablet of drug B. The core is prepared by dry-blending the first active ingredient, i.e., B1, with several excipients. Blend time is of interest for its impact on distribution of the therapeutic agent. The premix just prepared is granulated using an alcohol-binder solution. The process directions allow the operator some latitude in use of additional alcohol to ensure that the batch is uniformly wet. It will be necessary to know whether additional alcohol is routinely required and, if so, how much is used. Besides measuring operator technique, the wetting step affects particle size distribution. The oven tray dryer is identified for drying the wet mix. Granulation drying time is of interest, because loss on drying is not measured. Once dry, the granulation is milled using a specified screen size and machine setting. Alternate equipment is not provided for in the aforementioned steps.

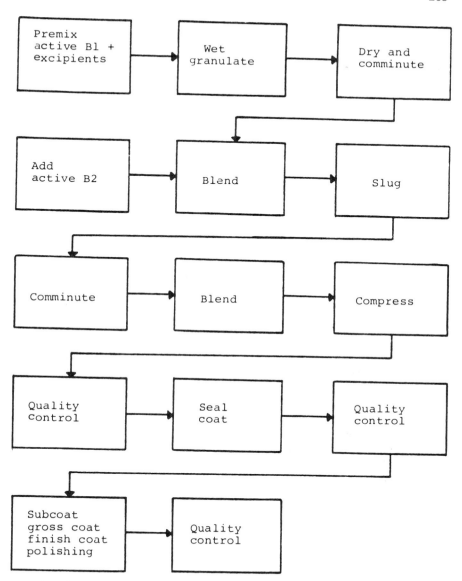

Figure 6 Drug B, flow diagram of manufacturing process.

Table 3 Drug B, Selected Critical Manufacturing Steps and
Control Tests

Processing steps
  Premix blending time
  Quantity of additional alcohol used
  Granulation drying time
  Blending time to combine active ingredients B1 and B2
  Final blending time
  Number of shellac coats
Quality control tests
  Average tablet weight (core and coated tablet)
  Hardness
  Disintegration time (core, shellacked core, and coated tablet)
  Assay for active ingredients B1 and B2

    The powder produced in the prior operation is combined with the second active ingredient (B2) as well as several other excipients in a twin-shell blender and mixed for several minutes. For reasons previously discussed, mix time is of interest, and thus it is listed as a critical process step.

    The blend of the two active ingredients (B1 and B2) is slugged and then the slugs are oscillated. Slugger model and tooling are listed in the batch instructions. No information is recorded on the slugging operation, as control of this procedure is left to the experience of the press operator. The batch record permits the use of only one screen size. Therefore, no variability can be expected for this step from batch to batch.

    Next, lubricant and oscillated granulation are blended for several minutes. The elapsed mixing time is of interest because of its impact on drug distribution and the effect of the lubricant on dissolution. During compression, 1000 randomly selected cores are accumulated for quality control evaluation.

    ATW, hardness, and disintegration time are determined by the press operator during compression. As in the case of drug A, we will not rely on these results for our study but, rather, on the test data from quality control.

    Following approval of the bulk cores by quality control, they are shellac coated. According to the manufacturing directions, one or two coats may be applied based on the process operator's judgment. A third coat is permissible but only in response to directions from the supervisor. In any event, the actual number of coats applied is recorded in the batch record. Because of its potential impact on drug availability, this information is listed as a critical parameter in Table 3.

    Once the shellacking stage has been completed, the cores are built up through a series of coating operations. However, because these steps are not considered critical, they are not included as part of our retrospective validation study. This is consistent with the previously discussed philosophy, which called for avoiding steps intended solely to improve appearance; however, we will want to be certain to select a control test that supports this position. Final product disintegration is one such parameter.

The quality control tests selected after review of in-process and finished-product specifications are listed in Table 3. The rationale for selection has been addressed in general terms during the review for drug A.

1. Evaluation of Historical Data

Inspection of assembled data for 19 batches of drug B confirmed that premix blending was consistently performed for 15 min as specified in the manufacturing directions.

On average, 11.5 kg of additional alcohol was needed to wet the premix adequately. Actual quantity used range from 6 to 16 kg, and in no instance was a batch produced without the use of extra alcohol. These data support an increase in the minimum quantity of alcohol that is specified in the manufacturing directions.

Granulation drying time was unremarkable. All 19 batches were dried within the specified time of 12 to 16 hr; the mean time was 13.4 hr, and no trends, seasonal or otherwise, were detected.

The operator is instructed to combine the premix containing active ingredient B1 with active ingredient B2 and blend for 30 min. All 19 batches were handled as directed in the batch record. Oscillation of the slugs back to powder was accomplished, in every case, using the screen listed in the batch record. For final granulation, we found that each batch was blended for 30 min, as directed.

From one to three sealing coats may be applied by the process operator. The third coat was never required, however. All 19 batches were completed with two coats of shellac.

Our historical review thus far has revealed little batch-to-batch variability. We will next direct our attention to the quality control release tests selected earlier.

ATW at the core stage is based on the results from weighing 20 randomly selected tablets. The control chart in Fig. 7 depicts a process with no single value outside the upper control limit (UCL) and the lower control limit (LCL). Other tests for instability show the process to be operating normally. All 19 batches were compressed on the same model press, according to the batch record. ATW for the coated tablet is shown for comparison; however, no great importance is attached to batch-to-batch variability, as coating weight has no bearing on efficacy. Correlation between changes in core weight and finished tablet weight is poor. Such fluctuations would be expected of a manual coating operation intended solely to enhance pharmaceutical elegance. Nevertheless, the control chart did not respond to our tests for patterns of instability (Fig. 7).

Disintegration time is measured at three steps in the process: at compression, after application of the second shellac coat, and at finished product release. Table 4

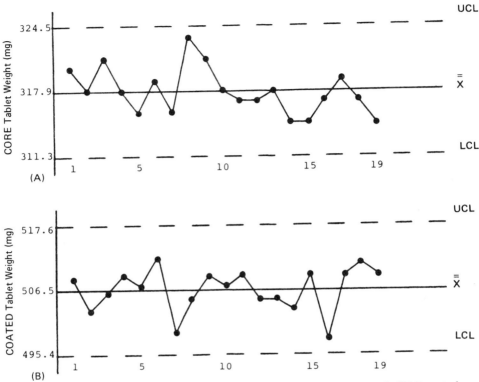

Figure 7 (A) $\bar{x}$-control chart of drug B average tablet weight (core stage). (B) $\bar{x}$-control chart of average coated tablet weight for drug B.

compares the values of mean hardness obtained for 10 individual cores to the disintegration times for core, shellacked core, and coated tablets. No relationship was found between core hardness and uncoated core disintegration time or among the three groups of disintegration times. Noteworthy is the increase in dispersion of disintegration times (measured by the standard deviation) from uncoated core to finished tablet. It appears that the coating steps, shellac in particular, contribute more to process variability than does compression. This is understandable in light of the subjective nature of sugar coating.

Receipts of active ingredient raw materials B1 and B2 are accepted by quality control based on standard tests for potency, chemical attributes, and particle size. Particle size is determined by sieve analysis. Unfortunately, this is a limit test where 99% of the sample must pass through a certain mesh screen. Therefore, any

Table 4 Drug B, Comparison of Mean Hardness and Disintegration Times

Batch number	Hardness (SC units)	Disintegration time (min)		
		Core tablets	Shellacked cores	Coated tablets
01	11	8	15	22
02	10	9	20	25
03	10	8	19	21
04	11	9	16	22
05	8	8	13	17
06	8	8	14	18
07	8	7	14	21
08	9	8	14	20
09	8	8	15	20
10	10	8	17	19
11	12	9	13	20
12	12	8	13	20
13	8	7	14	17
14	8	7	13	18
15	12	8	13	18
16	10	11	17	23
17	11	9	20	26
18	10	8	18	20
19	9	7	14	19
$\bar{x} =$	9.74	8.16	15.37	20.32
$\bar{s} =$	1.49	0.96	2.43	2.47

influence particle size distribution might have on dosage form potency cannot be examined.

Figure 8 is a plot of mean assay results for active ingredient B1. Drug potency (100 mg per tablet) is measured in duplicate from samples obtained by grinding a composite of 20 randomly selected tablets. Figure 8 is also influenced by variability of the purity of the raw material, which ranged from 97.6 to 99.5%. Nevertheless, the pattern was unresponsive to our standard tests for process instability, and individual batch results were well within established control limits for this product (90–110 mg). The grand mean of 99.0% is 1.00 mg below the theoretical tablet potency, probably because of below-target purity of the active ingredient raw material. Regression analysis was not attempted because individual tablet assays and weights were not available.

Another method of showing how well the process is suited to produce tablets

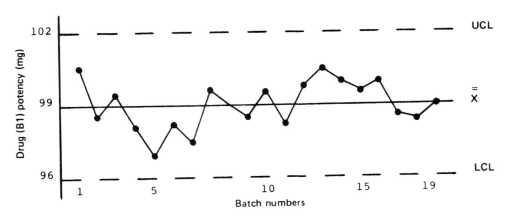

Figure 8 $\bar{x}$-control chart for drug B tablet assay (ingredient B1).

within specification is to calculate the process capability ratio (Cp), which is defined as [11]

$$Cp = \frac{USL - LSL}{6\,SD}$$

where

   USL = upper specification limit
   LSL = lower specification limit
   SD = standard deviation

For active ingredient B1 the Cp is 3.3 (Cp = 90–110 mg/6 mg), which implies that the process is exceedingly reliable. Although the distribution of active ingredient B1 is undoubtedly good, the Cp is likely overstated because individual batch assays are based on a 20-tablet composite, which conceals tablet-to-tablet differences. Individual tablet assay would have been better for this purpose.

   Two additional indices are available to measure capability. Unlike the capability ratio, the capability index (Cpk) provides a measure of how well the process is centered over the target. The Cpk is calculated as follows:

$$Cpk = \left| \frac{\text{nearest spec limit} - \bar{x}}{3\,SD} \right|$$

A variation of the Cpk is the Taguchi capability index (Cpt), which should prove valuable for monitoring performance of a stable process, that is, one for which the Cp $\geqslant$ 2 [12]. Taguchi's calculation defines a new function to be used in place of the standard deviation:

$$Cpt = \frac{USL - LSL}{6\,MSD}$$

where

$$MSD = \left[\frac{\Sigma\,(target - x_i)^2}{n - 1} \right]^{1/2}$$

Taguchi computes the sum of the squares of deviations from the target rather than the mean to provide a better measure of where the process is relative to the desired value.

Active ingredient B2 (25 mg per tablet) is measured on 10 individual tablets per batch. We randomly selected 50 tablets from the 19 batches for use in regression analysis. Because purity of the raw material varied from 98.4 to 99.7%, it was included as the second variable. Our predictor equation for tablet potency (y) is

$$y = -51.10 + 0.5342X_1 + 0.0752X_2$$

where

X_1 = raw material purity
X_2 = tablet weight

The slope of the regression plane was found to be positive for both tablet weight and raw material purity, as we would expect. The slope for tablet weight was statistically significantly different from 0 at $\alpha = 0.01$, while the slope for purity was significant at $\alpha = 0.05$.

Substituting the ideal tablet weight (at the core stage) of 320 mg and mean raw material purity of 99% in the above equation yielded a tablet potency of 25.85, or 0.85 mg greater than theoretical. Although predicted tablet potency is close to the ideal and well within specification limits (22.5–27.5 mg), it is possible this outcome was influenced by differences arising from the method of determining the purity of the raw material and potency of the dosage form. The former is a wet chemistry analysis, whereas the potency of the drug in the finished tablet is determined by use of an automated procedure. Unfortunately, we were unable to quantify this difference.

The process for drug B has been shown to operate within narrow limits and yield finished dosage forms which are therapeutically equivalent, as measured by standard product release criteria. There is no reason to believe subsequent batches will perform differently as long as all conditions remain static.

C. Softgels (Soft Gelatin Capsules), Drug C

This dosage form consists of a solution of active ingredient encased within a spherical, plasticized gelatin shell. Unlike hard gelatin capsules, for which several discrete operations are required to produce the final product, the softgel is formed, filled, and hermetically sealed in one continuous operation [13]. Molten gelatin mass is formed into two sheets or ribbons, each of which passes over a die of the desired size and shape. At the point at which the two rotating dies meet, the hemispheres are sealed and simultaneously filled with the solution of active ingredient. Next, the capsules are cleaned by immersion in an organic solvent, dried, and inspected. Refer to Fig. 9.

According to the process instructions, the active ingredient powder is dissolved in vegetable oil with the aid of a solubilizer. Blend time is stated as 25–30 min. This is an elapsed time. Because of the inherent variability, this step is one for which historical data will be sought (Table 5). The purity of each active ingredient raw material receipt is also of interest for reasons previously stated.

The instructions for gelatin mass preparation direct that gelatin powder be blended with water, a plasticizer, and colorant until a uniform consistency is achieved, then heated until molten. The recommended blend time is 20 min at a temperature of 60°C ± 5. Temperature of the molten gelatin just prior to formation into a ribbon is critical. Too high a temperature causes the gelatin to deteriorate, and a low temperature affects flow rate. Both conditions are to be avoided for their deleterious effect on capsule formation. For these reasons, gelatin mass temperature is given in Table 5. Blend time is of interest too as a measure of process and raw material performance.

An important specification for gelatin is bloom strength, a quality of the raw

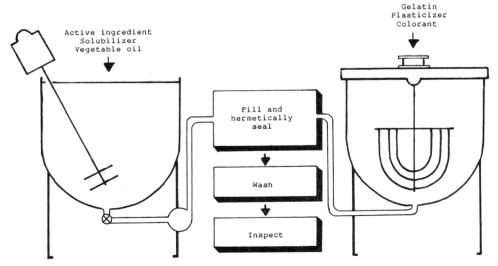

Figure 9 Drug C, flow diagram of manufacturing process.

Table 5 Drug C, Selected Critical Manufacturing Conditions and Quality Control Tests

Critical manufacturing conditions	Quality control tests
Blend time to solubilize active ingredient	Dissolution
Gelatin mass mix time and temperature	Average fill weight
Die rotation speed	Assay
Gelatin ribbon thickness	Microbial content
Relative humidity of encapsulation room	

material that determines whether a capsule can be formed and sealed. As with active ingredient purity, we will want to know this value for each lot of gelatin used in the validation study.

Speed of die rotation and gelatin ribbon thickness are two important machine conditions which are included in Table 5. The rationale of their selection is as follows: die rotation speed controls dwell time. If there is insufficient contact time, the capsule halves will not properly seal. Subpotent softgels may result from loss of liquid fill through a poorly developed seam. Gelatin ribbon thickness determines capsule wall and seam thickness. Insufficient thickness will contribute to poorly formed capsules and leakers. An overly thick ribbon results in shell sealing problems. Ribbon condition is influenced by the temperature of the gelatin mass, as previously noted. Relative humidity in the encapsulation room is important to efficient drying. Minimally, we will want to know the room condition during the time when the 20 batches in this study were manufactured. It would be best to examine environmental conditions over a longer time period, say 1 year, to capture seasonal trends should they exist.

The batch record instructs the encapsulation machine operator to measure and record seam and wall thickness every 45 min. Softgel weight is also checked periodically by this operator. This information could be useful in demonstrating process control. But seam and wall thickness, to a large extent, are controlled by manufacturing conditions for which historical data are already being sought. For this reason, results of these in-process monitors need not be pursued initially. Consistent with the approach taken for other dosage forms previously discussed, finished softgel weight data can be obtained from quality control reports when dissolution and assay results are collected.

1. Evaluation of Historical Data

The first step in the production sequence is solubilizing the active ingredient in an appropriate volume of vehicle. For drug C, this blend is a solution, and the activity was routinely accomplished in the prescribed time (25–30 min). The nine receipts of active ingredient raw material used to prepare the 20 batches under review had a mean potency of 99.5%. Individual receipts ranged from 98.7 to 102%. No trends were noted when these receipts were examined graphically.

Gelatin mass preparation time was recorded as between 17 and 23 min. Such small differences were not thought to be worthy of further consideration. Gelatin mass temperature is critical for reasons previously noted. The temperature range achieved during compounding was examined by means of the recorder charts for evidence of equipment problems and lack of operator attention. The degree of variability within a batch and batch to batch was considered reasonable for an operator-controlled process of this type. Mass temperature at the end of compounding, just before the start of encapsulation, averaged 60.5°C. Individually, all batches met the specifications of 60°C ± 5. Control over gelatin mass temperature for the duration of the filling operation was generally unremarkable, although larger fluctuations were present for 4 of the 20 batches in the latter stages of filling. The cause of these fluctuations was not apparent, however.

A bloom strength determination is part of the acceptance criteria for each receipt of gelatin raw material. The bloom gelometer number range from 125 to 195 for the 12 lots, with a mean of 147. This number was compared to gelatin ribbon thickness and die rotation speed during encapsulation to ascertain whether lot-to-lot differences had to be compensated for. No relationship was found.

Encapsulation machine setup specifications were considered for their impact on softgel seam and wall formation. Die speed is given as 4.0 rpm ± 0.2. Gelatin ribbon thickness is to be controlled at 0.032 in. ± 0.003. More than one machine was used to produce the 20 batches; however, they were all the same make and model. Machine settings during encapsulation are summarized in Table 6. Slight machine-to-machine differences are present, but all three operations are easily within suggested settings for this product. Gelatin mass temperature, on average, was the same for each encapsulation machine.

The influence of gelatin mass temperature, gelatin ribbon thickness, and die speed on softgel formation, and the interactions of these variables were explored by regression analysis, as follows:

Table 6   Drug C, Encapsulation Machines Settings—Die Speed and Ribbon Thickness

Machine number/batches	Die speed ($\bar{x}$) (rpm)	Ribbon thickness ($\bar{x}$) (in.)
All machines ($N = 20$)	4.01	0.032
Machine 1 ($N = 7$)	3.93	0.032
Machine 2 ($N = 7$)	4.07	0.031
Machine 3 ($N = 6$)	4.02	0.033

Finished softgel weight = gelatin mass temperature + die speed + gelatin ribbon thickness

The outcome was inconclusive, probably due in part to use of data which did not take into consideration variability in fill volume.

Quality control release testing was performed on a sample of 1000 softgels randomly selected at the conclusion of processing. The outcome of dissolution, assay, and average fill weight tests is reported in Table 7 along with the corresponding specification. These data were analyzed using methods previously illustrated. In addition, all batches passed the microbial limits test.

Dissolution and average fill weight results are not remarkable. Active ingredient assays averaged 16 mg above specification, which is not assignable to raw material purity where the mean potency is 99.5%. Examination of in-process checks of wall thickness showed this parameter to be under control at all times, effectively ruling out fill volume as a factor. A review of laboratory methodology provided no useful information. One explanation could be the manner in which the active ingredient solution is prepared. It is noteworthy that all 20 batches exceed the midpoint of the specification. Individual batches range from 509 to 523 mg. This distribution suggests that a condition common to all the batches is part of the explanation.

Available information reveals a process that is consistently reproducible and can be considered validated on that basis. Before doing so, however, the assay results should be justified.

D. Solution Dosage Form (Drug D)

The solution dosage form to be discussed is an elixir. A review of the batch record shows that it contains two active ingredients (D1 and D2). The different steps in preparing the dosage form are outlined in Fig. 10.

Drug D may be produced in both 1000- and 2000-gallon batches to meet inventory requirements. Major equipment and operator instructions are the same regardless of batch size. The only difference is amount of each ingredient charged to the make tank. With a formulation such as this, there is little likelihood that

Table 7 Drug C, Quality Control Release
Specifications and Results

Test	Specification	Result ($\bar{x}$)
Dissolution (%)	NLT 75%	89.1
Average fill weight (mg)	855–945	901.7
Assay (mg)	475–525	516.2

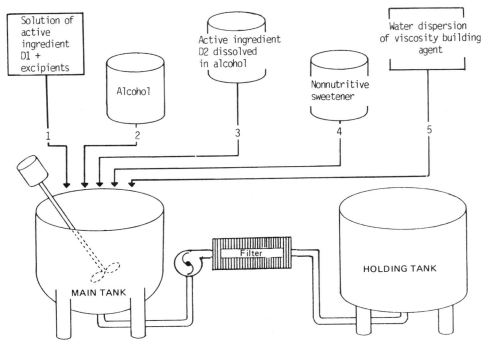

Figure 10 Drug D manufacture: Flow diagram showing major sequences of steps as described in Manufacturing Batch Record. The numbers indicate the order in which the process is carried out.

batch size is an important process variable. Nevertheless, we will be conservative and treat each size batch as a unique process. An alternative strategy would be to validate the 2000-gallon process and demonstrate for the 1000-gallon batch adequacy of mixing, using, for instance, assay data.

The batch is prepared using a single tank. Large-volume liquid excipients and deionized water are metered into the main tank. The other materials are pre-weighed. Final yield is calculated from a freeboard measure of the bulk liquid in the holding tank. Variable-speed agitation is available; however, the batch instructions do not require the rate of mixing to be adjusted from step to step. Nor are temperature adjustments needed to get the solid raw materials into solution. A standard filter press is employed to clarify the batch just prior to transfer to the holding tank. Thus, the only variable information available from the batch record is the time required to accomplish such steps as addition, mixing, and dissolution of raw material active ingredients in vehicles. Although elapsed time to perform these steps is identified in Table 8 as a process variable to be considered, this information is useful only as a crude measure of operator performance.

Table 8 Drug D, Selected Critical Manufacturing Steps and Quality Control Tests

Processing steps	Quality control tests
Elapsed time to complete steps A, B, and C	Appearance
	pH
Batch yield	Specific gravity
	Viscosity
	Alcohol (% v/v)
	Assay of active ingredients D1 and D2

Yield at conclusion of processing is available from the batch record and is identified in Table 8 as an important step. Yield data are potentially useful in explaining atypical quality control test results; they also provide a rough measure of equipment condition and operator technique.

The quality control test results for each batch are relied on almost exclusively for the critical information used in this study. The rationale for selecting the finished dosage form parameters listed in Table 8 is as follows:

Physical appearance of the finished product is a good indicator of the adequacy of the filtration step. Although it is only a subjective test, it does provide information on equipment performance. The pH of the finished dosage form is critical for the stability of active ingredient D1, hence its measurement is warranted. Specific gravity reflects the quantities of ingredients charged as well as adequacy of the mixer to distribute them uniformly. A viscosity check is performed to ensure that no untoward viscosity buildup has occurred that could affect pourability. Viscosity of the end product can also indirectly indicate quality of the dispersion of the viscosity-building agent. Determination of the quantity of alcohol in the end product is critical as well, because the solubility of one of the active ingredients, D2, depends on the concentration of alcohol. Also, because alcohol can easily be lost during processing, any values below established limit would be evidence of a problem associated with the process. Finally, concentration of the active ingredients is measured. These data attest to the adequacy of both the dissolution of each ingredient and the subsequent mixing during phase combination. Any major deviation from established limits would indicate problems in manufacturing. Because raw material active ingredient purity is known to vary from one receipt to the next, it too should be included in any review of dosage form potency.

1. Evaluation of Historical Data

The time required to accomplish mixing and addition steps is summarized in Table 9. The differences in elapsed time were thought to reflect those typically encountered in manual operations. Batch yield is also shown in the table for future reference.

Table 9 Available Process Information Gathered
from Batch Records for the Manufacture of Solution
(Drug D) Dosage Form

Batch number	Time required for the completion of the step (in hr and min)			Batch yield (%)
	Step A[a]	Step B[b]	Step C[c]	
01	5:00	1:05	1:30	99.10
02	5:00	0:40	1:10	99.20
03	6:00	0:40	1:00	100.10
04	5:00	1:10	1:20	98.50
05	4:30	0:50	1:15	99.20
06	5:00	1:05	1:10	98.90
07	6:00	1:15	1:40	98.95
08	5:30	0:45	1:30	98.50
09	6:00	1:00	1:35	98.60
10	4:30	0:45	1:20	98.87
11	5:30	1:00	1:25	98.81
12	5:45	0:50	1:25	98.70
13	5:00	1:00	1:30	99.20
14	5:00	1:10	1:40	98.95
15	6:00	1:15	1:20	99.02
16	5:00	0:45	1:00	99.40
17	5:00	1:00	1:05	99.50
18	6:00	0:50	1:30	99.10
19	5:00	0:40	1:10	99.48
20	5:00	1:05	1:25	99.30
				$\bar{x} = 99.07$

[a]Step A: Time required for the dispersion of viscosity building
agent in water
[b]Step B: Time required to dissolve water-soluble formulation
ingredients in water
[c]Step C: Time required to dissolve alcohol-soluble formulation
ingredients in alcohol

Product appearance was unremarkable. pH was examined using a control
chart. Because this is a single point observation, the moving range method was
employed [9]. The chart disclosed that the process operates within the calculated
control limits. No trends were apparent. Individual batch results all met specification, and the process average (4.07) is close to the target value of 4.10. Refer to
Figure 11.

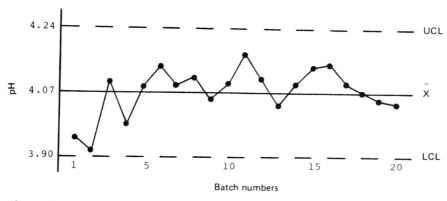

Figure 11 $\bar{x}$-control chart of pH using moving range method for drug D.

Mean specific gravity for this 20-batch study is 1.091, the midpoint of the specification range. The control chart for this variable was prepared by the moving range method (Fig. 12). The calculated upper and lower control limits (1.0914 and 1.0888, respectively) are within the product's specification limits. Individually, all batches met specification. The specific gravity of batch 3 is at the lower control limit. A plausible explanation for this can be found in the bulk yield (Table 9), which is 0.1% greater than theory and 1.03% in excess of the average for this study. Hence, "overdiluting" the batch during manufacture is a possible explanation. The alcohol concentration of batch 3 should be compared to the 20-batch mean to determine whether this step was the cause.

Alcohol content averaged 15.09%, or 0.09% above target. Individual batches met specification in every instance. The control chart (Fig. 12) was unremarkable in terms of trends or tests for pattern instability. Batch 3 is slightly below the process average, effectively ruling out overaddition of alcohol as a factor in the low specific gravity previously observed.

The concentration of active ingredient D1 batch to batch is shown in Fig. 13. Mean potency of all batches is 0.1 mg/5 mL above target. The control chart did not respond to tests for unnatural patterns and trends. It is noteworthy that the calculated upper control limit (16.7 mg/5 mL) for the 20 batches in this study exceeds the release specification for the product (15.5–16.5 mg/5 mL). Thus, a probability exists that a batch may eventually fail to meet the release criteria. Raw material purity is not a factor in the potency of an individual batch because it is taken into consideration at the time of manufacture. A possible explanation for the wide historical control limits is the assay methodology for D1. As a starting point, the next 20 production batches could be monitored for this variable to see whether the condition persists.

Assay results for active ingredient D2 individually met specification. The 20-

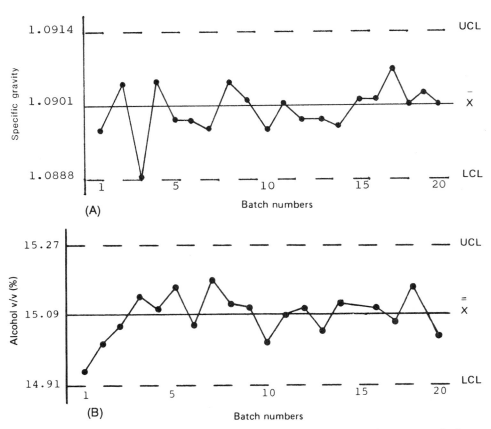

Figure 12 (A) $\bar{x}$-control chart for drug D specific gravity using moving range method. (B) $\bar{x}$-control chart of drug D alcohol percent (v/v).

batch average was 126.3 mg/5 mL, or 1.3 mg/5 mL in excess of target. Inspection of the $\bar{x}$ control chart for this variable (Fig. 13) discloses an atypical pattern. That is, batches 1–6 have distinctly greater potency than batches 7–20 with the exception of batch 14. The biomodality of the data is readily apparent when batch 14 is disregarded. The phenomenon can be explained by a change in assay method from ultraviolet to high performance liquid chromatography commencing with batch 7. Further investigation revealed that the UV procedure was used for batch 14 as well, in this instance because the HPLC instrument was out of service. With the two populations properly grouped, consistency of the HPLC method to detect ingredient D2 becomes apparent. Refer to Table 10.

Eleven receipts of active ingredient D2 were used to compound the batches

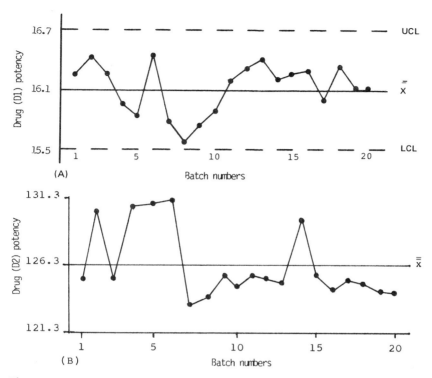

Figure 13 (A) $\bar{x}$-control chart for drug D1 potency. (B) $\bar{x}$-control chart for drug D2 potency.

included in the study. Lot purity ranged from 99.5 to 101.1%; the average was 100.4%. Purity of the raw material receipt was not seen to have an affect on potency of the batch(es) in which it was used. This is probably due to the occasional need to use more than one receipt to compound a batch.

In summary, the study demonstrates the wisdom of switching to an HPLC method for finished bulk approval. It also raises questions about reproducibility of the assay for drug D1, which should be investigated. Otherwise, no recommendation for change in the method of operation can be made based on historical results from selected manufacturing steps and control tests. Furthermore, with a better understanding of the cause of drug D1 potency variability it is not unreasonable to conclude future production will continue to meet specifications.

E. Semisolid Dosage Form (Drug E)

The product we have selected for examination is an emulsion cream of the oil-in-water type. We will refer to this product as drug E. The directions for manufacture

Table 10   Drug D, Comparison
of UV and HPLC Assay for
Active Ingredient D2

| Statistic | Test Method | |
	UV	HPLC
N	7	13
$\bar{x}$	129.07	124.79
$\bar{s}$	2.44	0.70

call for addition of the active ingredient to a methyl cellulose solution, followed by addition of an humectant.

Heat is applied, with continued mixing, until a specified temperature is reached. Consistency is then increased through the introduction of several viscosity-building agents. Occlusives and preservatives are then incorporated. The batch is held with agitation at this temperature for several minutes and then cooled with varying rates of agitation to prevent air entrapment.

Table 11 lists the critical process steps that should be considered for evaluating batch-to-batch uniformity [14]. Although other information such as melting time for waxes is available from the batch record, those were not thought to be critical.

Also included in Table 11 are six tests routinely performed by the quality control department on a sample of the bulk. Appearance of the product was selected as an indicator of filter performance. A stable pH, within specification, is essential to preclude degradation of active ingredient and obviate dermal irrita-

Table 11   Drug E, Selected Critical Manufacturing Steps and Quality Control Tests

Process steps
    Rotational speed of the inner and outer sweep blades during processing
    Total time required to increase the batch temperature to 65°C
    Time required to achieve batch cool-down (65 to 35°C)
Quality control tests
    Appearance
    pH
    Assay
    Specific gravity
    Penetrometer reading
    Microbial contents

tion. Specific gravity, which is a measure of the amount of suspended solids, indicates that all formulation ingredients have been incorporated. Penetrometer readings measure the consistency of the cream, which may affect ability to package the product as well as acceptance by the patients. Microbial content is determined routinely in the interest of safety of patients as well as product efficacy. Finally, the assay of the active ingredient is selected as a measure of the efficiency of the process to distribute the drug uniformly.

1. Evaluation of Historical Data

A review of the records for 20 batches shows that the rotational speed of the inner and outer sweep blades in the manufacturing vessel is always set at 24 to 20 rpm, respectively, during the heating cycle. Therefore, statistical treatment was considered inappropriate. During the cool-down cycle, the batch record specifies rotational speeds of inner and outer sweep blades. It also allows the operator to change the agitator speeds to prevent aeration and instructs the operator to record any such changes. The review shows that no adjustments were necessary. Because of the consistency of the operation from batch to batch, no statistical treatment of available data was deemed necessary.

Time required to increase the batch temperature to 65°C was studied. Of the 20 batches, 18 required 35 min, while the other 2 batches attained the desired temperature in about 30 min. Such small differences were not thought important enough for further evaluation. Time required for the cool-down cycle was found to be 65 min for 16 batches, while 4 batches took 60 min. Final product characteristics, such as appearance and penetrometer readings, were compared for batches with cooling times of 60 and 65 min, and no difference was found in the end product.

Data collected from the quality control tests were next evaluated. The assay for active ingredient varied from 19.60 to 19.90%, indicating a yield of 98 to 99.5% of the original quantity added. These assay values also indicate that the drug is well distributed in the cream and manufacturing losses of the drug during the various processing steps are negligible. Specific gravity of the batch varied from 1.120 to 1.126, a good indication that the level of solids from batch to batch is consistent. The pH of the end product varied from 5.4 to 5.9. This variability may be partly attributed to the difference in pH of excipients and/or deionized water used. Unfortunately, pH of purified water was not always available for the date on which a batch of drug E was compounded. Similarly, pH is not a routine quality control test for several of the excipients; thus, further investigation was not possible.

Data from the quality control tests for the various parameters selected were used to prepare control charts. These control charts were then analyzed for any evidence of instability or unnatural pattern. None was detected.

A microbial limit test was performed on a routine basis and the 20 consecutive batches each showed conformance to specifications.

One recommendation arises from the review of this product. The rotational speeds of the agitator were remarkably constant during the heating cycle and therefore should be included in the written instructions for future batches. Otherwise, the process is considered validated.

IV.   COMPUTER-AIDED ANALYSIS OF DATA

Once the mechanics of retrospective validation are mastered, a decision is required as to how data analysis will be handled. The illustrated calculations may be performed manually with the help of a programmable calculator and the control charts may be hand-drawn, but computer systems are available which can shorten the task. If the computer route is chosen, commercially available software (such as SAS from SAS Institute and RSI from BBN Software Products Corporation) should be considered as a starting point. The validation team should plan to enlist the services of a programmer to make changes to the program as the need arises. In his article on the subject, Agallaco notes that although basic available programs will allow rapid preparation of control charts, needed program refinements such as addition of details, deletion of extraneous data, and data manipulation in general will require the skills of a competent programmer [15].

Computer analysis of historical data requires a certain amount of planning to avoid potential pitfalls. Before beginning data entry, the following issues should be addressed:

1.   The amount of data should be limited to that needed to reach a sound conclusion. The computer's facility for processing large data bases easily can prove disadvantageous. For instance, too many data points on an axis can obscure trends or interfere with readability of the chart.
2.   The vertical scale has to be chosen carefully to accommodate both control and specification limits. The latter may have to be entered manually to avoid unreasonable compression of the chart.
3.   Care must be taken that tables and graphics are fully identified as to product name and variable(s) under review.
4.   Manual examination of some information should be anticipated. Output will have to be interpreted and related to other factors which may not be part of the data base. Nonnumerical information is an example.

Figure 14 illustrates the construction of a table containing the results of end-product testing of 22 batches of a tablet dosage form. For simplicity, let's refer to the product as drug F. There are 22 rows and 14 columns, for a total of 308 data points. Each column has an abbreviated heading which describes the information

0	1 Batch	2 Form	3 LOD	4 $\bar{x}$ Diss AI 1	5 $\bar{x}$ Diss AI 2	6 ATW	7 Hardness
	Laboratory Results			Drug F			1988-89
1	8B10	M210	0.3	97.1	91.5	455.6	12.9
2	8B11	M210	0.4	97.2	96.8	457.0	10.3
3	8D10	M210	0.4	98.3	96.4	456.0	18.7
4	8D11	M210	0.3	98.2	97.3	457.4	18.7
5	8E10	M210	0.5	96.4	94.6	456.0	14.6
6	8E11	M210	0.3	98.0	89.0	455.7	14.3
7	8G10	M210	0.5	99.5	91.4	458.0	12.9
8	8G11	M210	0.4	98.1	90.3	454.4	12.9
9	8H10	M210	0.5	100.3	86.3	456.9	15.1
10	8H11	M210	0.5	100.3	99.3	459.8	15.3
11	8H12	M210	0.7	99.5	100.0	457.7	14.8
12	8K10	M210	0.7	101.2	101.6	458.5	13.8
13	8L10	M210	0.5	101.3	99.8	457.1	15.6
14	8L11	M210	0.3	101.6	99.1	457.1	12.9
15	8L12	M210	0.2	97.7	97.5	457.8	11.3
16	9D10	M210	0.3	96.2	95.9	458.4	14.1
17	9D11	M210	0.3	98.7	96.8	456.6	12.2
18	9E10	M211	0.5	97.3	90.6	457.1	15.3
19	9I10	M211	0.6	97.1	92.5	456.6	13.7
20	9J10	M211	0.4	98.7	91.1	456.6	18.0
21	9J11	M211	0.7	87.1	88.3	456.2	10.5
22	9K10	M211	0.4	98.9	95.2	457.6	11.3

0	8 %FRIAB	9 $\bar{x}$ Asy AI 1	10 $\bar{x}$ Asy AI 2	11 Method AI 2	12 DU AI 1	13 DU AI 2	14 Bulk Capped
1	0.8	224.5	102.9	1	1.7	1.3	0
2	0.9	220.9	102.7	1	1.3	1.6	0
3	0.7	226.5	104.5	1	2.1	1.2	1
4	0.8	225.2	104.8	1	1.6	1.1	0
5	1.0	221.0	106.8	2	2.2	2.0	0
6	0.7	220.6	101.4	2	1.6	1.4	1
7	0.7	220.8	99.6	2	1.3	2.0	0
8	6.5	219.4	102.1	1	1.8	2.1	2
9	0.9	219.5	102.9	1	1.8	2.1	0
10	0.8	221.4	100.7	1	1.4	1.5	0
11	0.7	221.7	98.4	1	1.3	1.0	0
12	0.8	227.8	105.8	1	1.7	1.6	0
13	5.8	226.5	101.4	1	1.1	1.7	0
14	5.9	228.5	103.3	2	2.0	1.2	1
15	7.5	230.7	107.4	2	1.6	1.3	2
16	0.7	219.7	103.7	2	1.1	1.0	0
17	0.7	220.6	104.1	2	1.5	1.3	0
18	0.8	222.1	106.3	2	2.1	1.5	0
19	1.9	217.6	103.7	2	2.7	2.4	0
20	0.7	222.3	99.2	2	1.3	1.2	0
21	0.8	220.3	97.4	2	1.7	2.3	3
22	0.9	223.5	98.7	2	2.1	0.8	0

Figure 14 Drug F, product release test results organized for computer analysis.

contained therein. The headings are not needed for computer analysis but make manual review possible. The 22 batches, one per row, have been assigned a reference number (1 to 22) to simplify control chart preparation. The batch and formula numbers are listed next for information only, in the event further manual investigation of a conclusion is deemed appropriate. Columns 3 through 12 (except 11) contain mean results for tests performed by the laboratory: % LOD, dissolution (for two active ingredients), ATW, hardness, % friability, assay, and dose uniformity (DU). Column 11 describes the assay method employed for active ingredient 2. The number 1 was assigned to the UV assay procedure; the number 2 refers to the HPLC method. This is one solution for including nonnumerical information in the data base. Column 14 lists results of the inspection for capped tablets. The numbers shown reflect the actual number of capped tablets recovered from a random sample of a given size. The table in Fig. 14 could easily be expanded to incorporate other variable information, such as observations about critical process steps, which might be needed for the validation.

Data analysis would normally commence with the calculation of means and standard deviations for each column of numbers where this was appropriate. Next, tests would be performed to establish whether the data were normally distributed. The data could then be grouped according to a particular variable—for example, year of manufacture, oscillator screen size, or assay method—and compared statistically for differences between means and standard deviations. For ease of review by the validation team, a table should be printed summarizing statistics calculated and conclusions reached as a result of these data manipulations.

Graphical methods are powerful tools for extracting the information contained in data sets and making statistical conclusions easier to understand. In recent years, a variety of techniques have been developed. An excellent overview of these methods is given by James and Polhemus [16].

Figure 15 is a scatter plot of ATW vs. assay using data from columns 6 and 9 of the table (Fig. 14). It was prepared using RSI software on an IBM personal computer. The scatter plot enables the reviewer to visualize the relationships among two or more product characteristics.

Control charts similar to the hand-drawn ones used earlier to illustrate evaluation of processing data are also easily prepared using the RSI software. Figure 16 is an $\bar{x}$ chart of tablet assay for active ingredient 2. Note that minimum-maximum specification limits have been included. Figure 17 depicts a traditional $\bar{x}$ control chart for dissolution, to which error bars have been added to denote individual tablet assays for each batch.

Regression analysis requires that a new table be constructed listing individual tablet weight (column 1), corresponding assay (column 2), and % purity of the raw material used to compound the tablet (column 3). From these data, regression lines and confidence intervals can be plotted to complement the usual statistics.

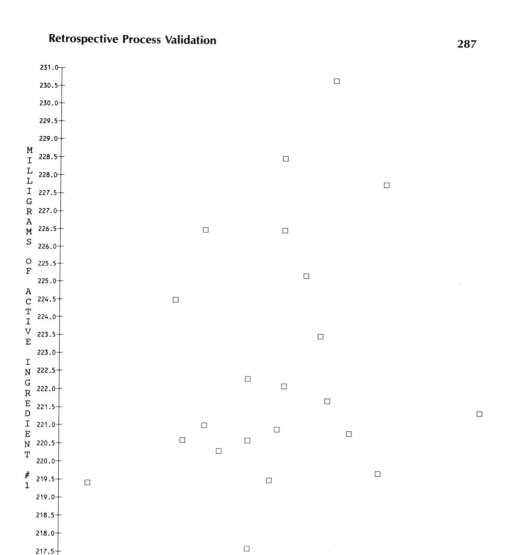

Figure 15 Drug F, computer-generated scatter plot of ATW vs. assay (AI 1).

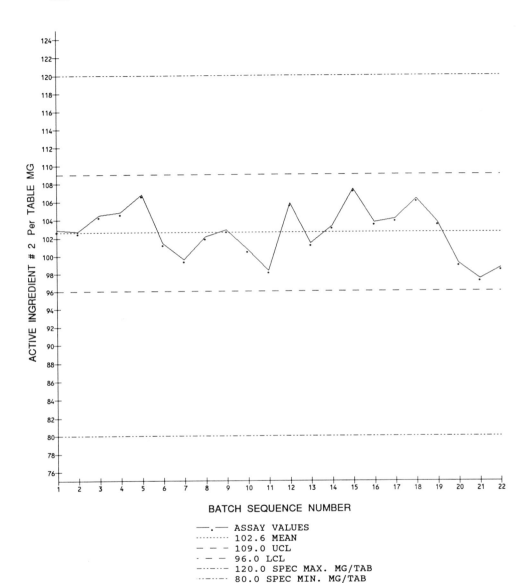

Figure 16 Drug F, computer-generated $\bar{x}$-control chart of tablet assay (AI 1).

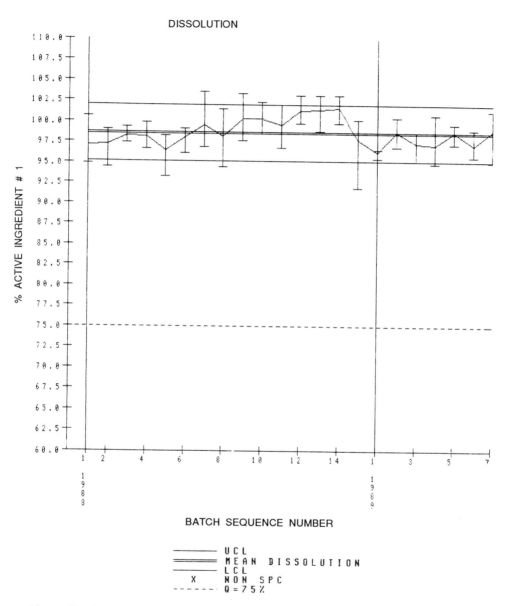

Figure 17 Drug F, computer-generated $\bar{x}$-control chart of tablet dissolution (AI 1) with tablet assay error bars.

V. USING VALIDATION EXPERIENCE TO SET PRODUCT ALERT LIMITS

Experience gained during validation can be used to fine-tune the process for greater reliability. Several examples where change was recommended based on study findings may be found in the section of this chapter devoted to evaluation of processing data. Another application of the information gathered during validation is in setting alert limits to be incorporated into the mechanism for product release. The alert limits would be the control limits (UCL and LCL) calculated as part of the review process for each analytical test; they could be made part of the written specifications for product release.

The recommendation to use control limits calculated as part of validation as alert limits is based on the expectation that test results from future production should normally fall within these limits. Indeed, this is the essence of retrospective validation. Furthermore, for a stable, centered process the control limits would fall within the release specification for the test. Exceeding an alert limit, therefore, would not necessarily delay product release but could precipitate an investigation into the cause.

Requiring quality control to use validation experience to release product achieves two objectives: it monitors conclusions reached during validation for ongoing reliability and identifies a trend early before a rejection occurs. For quality control laboratories using a laboratory information management system (LIMS) or having access to a personal computer, routine performance of test result–alert limit comparisons can be automated. An $\bar{x}$ plot depicting the process in relation to the alert and specification limits should be considered for monitoring trends. Refer to Fig. 18 for an example of such a plot.

VI. RELIABILITY OF THE VALIDATED PROCESS

Once the process has been validated, controls must be put into place to make certain that operations continue to be performed as originally described. It is unreasonable to assume that machines, instruments, plant services, and personnel will remain static indefinitely. The FDA recognized the need for revalidation when it issued the process validation guidelines [1]. A number of systems can be used for this purpose. The quality assurance department can perform periodic audits of manufacturing and laboratory practices against official procedures, review equipment maintenance records including calibration history, and examine personnel training programs. Any departures from original assumptions must be brought to the attention of the validation team for evaluation of their impact on the process.

CGMPs require the manufacturer of a product to conduct an annual review of written records to evaluate product quality [5]. A number of authors have

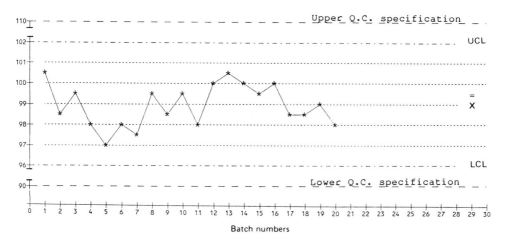

Figure 18 Computer-generated $\bar{x}$-control chart showing relationship of historical control limits (UCL and LCL) and quality control release specifications.

suggested that, when done properly, the review can highlight trends that might otherwise go unnoticed. Lee discusses how analytical and production data, as well as product complaint experience, can be arranged or collated for this purpose [17]. The annual review would be an expedient means of monitoring conclusions reached during validation.

When planned changes are made to the process, equipment, or immediate operating environment, the validation team should have input in deciding whether or not the change is of sufficient magnitude to warrant revalidation [4]. To ensure that this review occurs, a formal change control system must be in place. It would also be appropriate to have in place a written procedure describing the circumstances under which revalidation should be considered, as well as the company functions that have responsibility for monitoring the process.

VII. SELECTION AND EVALUATION OF PACKAGING DATA

To this point, retrospective validation has been discussed in the context of dosage form manufacture. Some of the same concepts may be applied to validating a packaging operation. Consider the following: Packaging lines are typically controlled by making spot observations to confirm machinery performance and component usage. The frequency of the inspections and the number of samples examined during each cycle are normally defined in a written procedure. Furthermore, the results of each monitor are generally documented in an inspection report, which becomes part of the packaging record for that lot of product. Also available from the packaging record is the number of units produced. Thus, information needed to allow inferences about reliability of a particular operation is readily accessible.

If we can show that over an extended period of time an operation had a certain reliability, it is not unreasonable to expect the same level of performance for the future as long as the equipment is reasonably maintained. Conversely, any conclusion reached by such a study would be invalidated by substantial change to the equipment or its method of operation.

How many packaging runs must be examined to draw a sound conclusion about reliability of the operation? Unfortunately, no one answer is appropriate for every situation. But there are some rules which will aid the decision process: The sample size should be large enough to capture all variables normally experienced, for instance, routine machine problems, shift and personnel changes, component vendor differences, and seasonal conditions. Furthermore, the sample must be of sufficient size to provide a high degree of confidence in the conclusion. Ten thousand observations made over 6 to 12 months of continuous production generally satisfy these requirements. For high-speed, multiple-shift operations the 10,000-observation figure is likely to be reached well before sufficient time has elapsed to include all avenues of variability. In these cases, time rather than units produced should be the first consideration.

To validate an aspect of the packaging operation retrospectively the following information must be tabulated:

1. The total number of observations made for the quality attribute under review.
2. The total number of non-conformances detected by the inspection process.

Figure 19 summarizes the retrospective validation strategy for a packaging operation. It also takes into consideration an opportunity for process improvement. For example, we may learn from the study that a particular operation has a defect rate which in our judgment is unreasonably high. The effectiveness of remedial action could be evaluated after a suitable period of time has elapsed by repeating that phrase of the validation study. In addition, the information provided by the study about machine and operator dependability permits informed replies to inquiries by customers or the FDA about alleged package defects.

A. Sources of Historical Information

A specific example can serve to illustrate how validation may be accomplished. A typical high-speed packaging line for solid dosage form products consists of several pieces of specialized machinery, usually in series, connected by a moving belt. Refer to Fig. 20. When the line is operational, there is a roving inspection designed to evaluate performance of each piece of equipment. For example, at the labeler the inspector would be asked to confirm that the serial number on the label

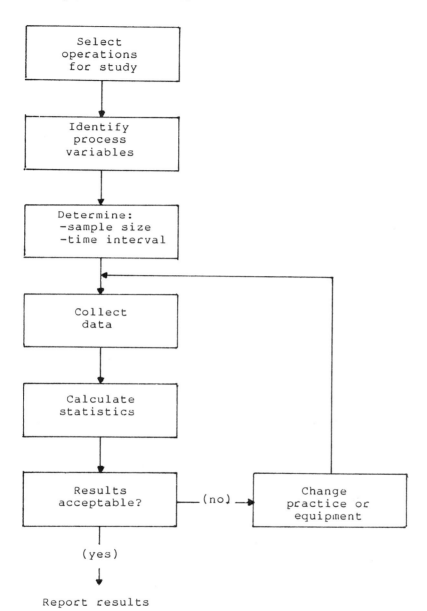

Figure 19 Packaging operation validation strategy.

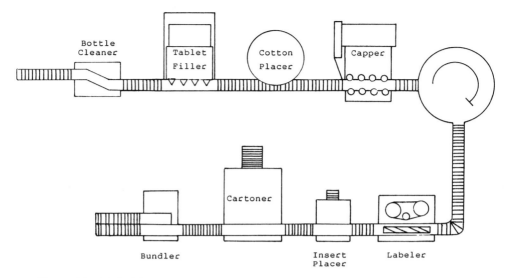

Figure 20   Typical layout for high-speed solid dosage form packaging line.

matches the work order, that the correct lot number and expiration date appear on the label, and that the label is properly adhered to the bottle. The outcome of each inspection is recorded. In the event nonconformance is observed, packaging supervision is notified. Remedial action may take the form of a machine adjustment and/or isolation and removal of nonconforming production. These roving inspections have the effect of limiting the number of defectives that reach the finished goods stage.

In addition to the roving inspection, a finished piece inspection is performed each half-hour. That is, the inspector randomly selects for examination one finished unit from the end of the line. In our example, the finished unit is a unitized bundle of 12 bottles of 100 tablets each. Each finished piece is torn down into its component parts, which are examined for specific attributes and conformance to the work order. Table 12 summarizes the tests made by the inspector as well as the number of pieces examined at each half-hour interval. When nonconformance is detected, a notation is made in the inspection record. With 13 finished product audits performed on each shift, a considerable pool of information is readily amassed.

Because we are interested in line machinery and package attributes and not the drug product being packaged, inspection results for all 100-tablet bottle runs may be pooled. One could even argue convincingly that the type and number of doses in the bottle are of no import as long as the line configuration remains

Table 12 Finished Product Audit: Package Attributes and Number Examined[a]

Attribute	Number examined		
	Each audit	Each shift	Each year
Intact bundle	1	13	1,300
Carton	12	156	15,600
Outsert	12	156	15,600
Bottle	12	156	15,600
Label	12	156	15,600
Lot number			
Expiration date			
Adhesion			
Cap	12	156	15,600
Seal			
Tablet Count	4	52	5,200

[a]Because of the high labor content, tablet count is performed on only four bottles. Annual figure is based on 100 shifts.

constant. In any event, the pooling of production volume as well as inspectional observations substantially accelerates data accumulation. This may be an important consideration where a particular packaging line is used for multiple products and sizes.

Let's say the line to be studied runs 100 shifts per annum of a particular package size at the rate of 50,000 bottles per shift; thus, in 1 year 5 million bottles are produced. During the same period, between 1300 and 15,600 inspectional observations are made, depending on the attribute (Table 12).

B. Estimating Outgoing Product Quality

It remains to count the number of defects for each attribute as reported by the inspector during the course of the year following the finished piece inspection. This task is more time consuming than difficult, assuming line inspection documents are well organized. The outcome is reported in Table 13. With this information available, the maximum fraction defective at a preselected confidence level may easily be estimated. The figures in Table 13 are derived from the Poisson approximation rather than the normal approximation to the binomial, which is quite adequate for this purpose [18].

According to Table 13, the cap was present for each bottle sampled; however, the lip seal was not fully adhered in 16 instances. The proportion of defectives is estimated to be 16/15,600 or 0.001 (0.1% or 1/1000). To extend the sample

Table 13 Inspectional Results and Fraction Defective

Attribute	Number of samples examined	Number of observed defects	Maximum fraction defective at 99% confidence limit
Intact bundle	1,300	11	16.5/1000
Carton	15,600	0	0.3/1000
Outsert	15,600	7	1.0/1000
Bottle	15,600	0	0.3/1000
Label	15,600	0	0.3/1000
Lot number		1	0.4/1000
Expiration date		2	0.5/1000
Adhesion		5	0.8/1000
Cap	15,600	0	0.3/1000
Seal		16	1.8/1000
Tablet count	5,200	3	1.9/1000

experience to the population (production lot) the upper 99% confidence limit for the expected value of a Poisson variable, in this instance 28.03, is derived by the sample size (28.03/15,600) to obtain the fraction defective. The fraction defective for incomplete lip seal is 0.0018 (0.18% or 1.8/1000). Stated another way, there is 99% assurance that the number of bottles with an incompletely adhered seal will not exceed 2 units for every 1000 produced. The value has been calculated for the other quality attributes to illustrate the impact of sample size and different levels of machine performance on lot defectives.

Calculating the maximum fraction defective for important package attributes provides a clear picture of the quality of goods sent to the customer as well as machine capability. If the defect rate is uncomfortably high, an investigation can be made to identify the cause. Possibly the solution is to modify a practice or replace a particular item of equipment.

VIII. CONCLUSION

Under certain conditions, a firm may rely on existing production, quality control, and facilities maintenance information as well as consumer input to validate retrospectively the processes of marketed products. The end result of this effort is the ability to predict with a greater degree of confidence the quality of subsequent batches. Furthermore, familiarity with the product acquired through such in-depth study can lead to process improvement, which in turn enhances overall control. The knowledge acquired and data amassed during retrospective process validation provide a performance profile against which daily release testing can be compared, to say nothing of their value as a guide when resolving production and control problems. A point not to be taken lightly is that process validation has become a CGMP requirement and, therefore, an area of interest to the FDA. The program just discussed is one approach to satisfying this obligation. The chapter also extends the concept of using historical data to predict future performance of packaging operations.

REFERENCES

1. Food and Drug Administration, *Guidelines on General Principles of Process Validation* (1987).
2. Top 200 prescription drugs dispensed in U.S. community pharmacies, new and refill prescriptions—all strengths, *American Druggist* February, pp. 28–32 (1990).
3. Willemotean, J. G., "Validation of Solid Dosage Forms: An Organization within the Manufacturing Division," presented at the PMA Seminar on Process Validation of Solid Dosage Form Processes, pp. 36–46 (1980).
4. Estes, G. K., and Luttsell, G. H., An approach to process validation in a multiproduct pharmaceutical plant, *Pharmaceut. Technol.* April, pp. 76–77 (1983).
5. Current Good Manufacturing Practices in Manufacture, Processing, Packaging and Holding of Human and Veterinary Drugs, F. R. 43 (190) (1978).
6. Avallone, H. E., "Retrospective Validation," presented at the NAPM Meeting, Port Chester, NY, p. 8 (September 1983).
7. Simms, L. L., "Validation of Existing Products by Statistical Evaluation," presented at the PM Seminar on Process Validation of Solid Dosage Form Processes, pp. 81–99 (1980).
8. Sadek, H. M., Considerations for achieving content uniformity in solid/solid blending, *Pharmaceut. Manuf.* March, pp. 18–21 (1985).
9. *Statistical Quality Control Handbook*, 6th printing, Western Electric Company (1982).
10. Juran, J. M. (ed), *Juran's Quality Control Handbook*, 4th ed., Sec. 23, McGraw-Hill, New York (1988).
11. Heidenreich, P., Designing for manufacturability, *Quality Progress* May, pp. 41–44 (1988).
12. Spat, M., On-line Tagushi methods, *Quality* May, p. 67 (1990).
13. Berry, I. R., Process validation for soft gelatin capsules, *Drug and Cosmetic Industry* April, pp. 26–30 (1984).
14. Goldfarb, A., "Validation of Procedures, the Manufacture of Ointments and Creams," presented at the NAPM Meeting, Port Chester, NY, pp. 12–14 (September 1983).
15. Agallaco, J. P., Practical considerations in retrospective validation, *Pharmaceut. Technol.* June, pp. 88–90 (1983).
16. James, P. D., and Polhemus, N. W., "Graphical Methods for Quality Achievement," presented at the ASQC Quality Congress, San Francisco (1990).
17. Lee, J., Product annual review, *Pharmaceut. Technol.* April, pp. 86–92 (1990).
18. Pearson, E. S., and Hartley, H. O., *Biometrika Tables for Statisticians*, Vol. 1, Table 40, Cambridge University Press, London (1962).

9

Validation of Water Systems for Sterile and Nonsterile Products

Ward M. Johnson   *CIBA-GEICY Corporation, Summit, New Jersey*

I.   PURPOSE OF VALIDATION

A.   The Raw Material Attributes of Water

Water is the most commonly used raw material in pharmaceutical manufacturing. It is used in the manufacture of all dosage forms (for cleaning manufacturing equipment, at the very minimum) and is a component of most of them. It is the one raw material that must be processed by the pharmaceutical manufacturer prior to use because it cannot be used as supplied by the vendor. The quality attributes of this raw material can vary seasonally without warning.

The USP identifies several grades of this raw material, all with somewhat different quality attributes. Water must be continuously tested for these quality attributes, and in some instances the results are not available for days after the sample was obtained. Meanwhile, the water is being used to batch very expensive pharmaceutical products.

Water treatment systems are highly dynamic and unreliable to some degree. Consequently, they must be validated and then closely monitored and controlled.

B.   The Importance of Validation

The purpose of validation is to demonstrate the capability of the water treatment system to continuously supply the required quantity of water with the specified quality attributes [1]. "Demonstrate" means to provide documented evidence. Validation provides the system owner with the means of assessing when a water treatment system is operating outside established control parameter limits and provides a means for bringing the system back into a state of control. It results in written operating and maintenance procedures for personnel to follow, which, in turn, help ensure consistent system performance. Validation also results in properly trained and qualified personnel using and maintaining the system, thereby improving its reliability.

II. BASIC VALIDATION STRATEGY

Regardless of the engineering design of the water treatment system and the desired quality attributes of the treated water, the basic validation strategy remains the same. The basic strategy is to prove the performance of the water treatment system under all conditions expected to be encountered during future operations. To prove the performance, you must demonstrate (document) that the water treatment system consistently produces the specified quantity and quality of water when operated and maintained according to specific, written operating and maintenance procedures. In other words, validation involves proving:

Engineering design
Operating procedures and acceptable ranges for control parameters
Maintenance procedures

To accomplish this, the system must be sampled and tested extensively over a prolonged period of time under all operating conditions.

Variations in daily, weekly, and annual system usage patterns must be validated. For example, water may be drawn from the system for manufacturing use only during normal working hours; there may be no demands on the system at other times during the 24-hour cycle. The system may be idle on weekends and on holidays, which could extend for as long as 4 days. In addition, many firms have annual plant maintenance shutdowns, typically in the summer, and systems must be sanitized and restarted prior to use. And, of course, emergency shutdowns can occur at any time and the system must be brought back on line. Systems with ion exchange resins (deionizers) must be at least partially shut down to regenerate the resins when the chemical quality of the treated water drops below a specified level (this could be a matter of a few days or even a few months, depending on the quantity of water processed through the system and other factors). Water treatment systems must be validated under all of these normal operating conditions in order to prove the adequacy of the engineering design and the effectiveness of the operating, control, and maintenance procedures.

III. WHAT TO VALIDATE

A. Engineering Design and Equipment

Water treatment systems must be designed to consistently produce the required quantity of water that meets the user's predetermined quality standards. A number of design choices have to be made by the project engineer and materials of construction must be selected (see Fig. 1 for a diagram of a typical water treatment system that will produce USP purified water).

1. Piping

Stainless steel (304L, 316, and 321) is normally the material of choice because of its chemical inertness after passivation, ease of sanitization, and use over a wide range of temperatures. Glass or polycarbonate resins are used where transparency is required. Polyvinyl chloride (PVC) may be used in ambient temperature systems but not when ozone is used as a sterilant [2]. Stainless steel is the only acceptable piping material for water for injection (WFI) systems.

Stainless steel piping must be butt welded and each weld either visually inspected or boroscoped and documented. Before the start of welding each day, a sample weld should be made by each previously qualified welder and approved and the welding machine settings should be recorded. Should the welding machine settings be changed during the day, this procedure should be repeated.

Regardless of the choice of piping material, the bottom of the pipe (BOP) elevations must be measured and documented in order to verify the slope to drain (this ensures that the piping can be completely drained).

2. Valves

Gate, ball, butterfly, and diaphragm-type valves are commonly used in water treatment systems. However, only diaphragm valves should be used downstream from the unit that removes dissolved solids (reverse osmosis unit or deionizer) because of its inherent ease of sanitization. Only ozone-inert polymers such as

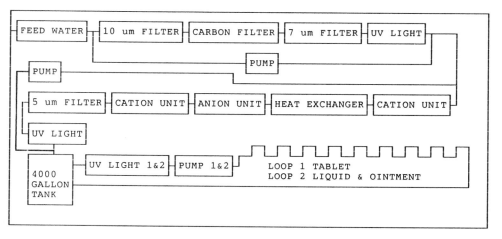

Figure 1 Diagram of a typical USP purified water system.

Teflon should be used as valve seats in ozone process water systems [2]. The same restrictions on choice of piping material apply to valves as well.

3. Storage Tanks

Stainless steel is the usual material of choice for water storage tanks, although certain types of resins are used in ambient temperature systems. Resistance to chemical sanitizers must be verified, however.

Storage tanks must be sized properly, depending on the projected peak demand on the system; 2,000–4,000 gallons are the most common sizes. Suitable insulation is necessary on storage tanks used in high-temperature systems in order to conserve energy and meet safety requirements. The tanks also may need to be jacketed in order to heat (or cool) the contents.

Storage tanks must be vented to allow for fluctuations in water levels in order to prevent collapse. The vent must be fitted with a sterilizing air filter to prevent the air entering the tank from microbiologically contaminating the stored water.

4. Filters

As noted above, the water storage tank vent must be equipped with a sterilizing air filter in order to prevent the air, which displaces water drawn from the tank, from microbiologically contaminating the water. The filter must be hydrophobic in order to prevent condensation from blinding the filter and preventing air entry or escape from the tank, and it must have a mean porosity of less than 1 micron.

Water filters are used in various locations in water treatment systems for two basic purposes: removal of undissolved solids, some of which are added to the water by various components of the water treatment system, and removal of bacterial contaminants. Filters are commonly used downstream from carbon beds and resin beds and on the incoming water supply line, and they are typically in the order of 10–50 micron mean porosity. Membrane filters of 0.2 micron are used to remove bacteria. Sand filters are a type of depth filter which may be used to pretreat the incoming feed water in order to remove undissolved solids.

Filters must be properly maintained in order to keep the water treatment system operating efficiently and to prevent them from becoming a source of bacterial and endotoxin contamination. Bacteria are not destroyed by these filters but rather become concentrated in and on them. Certain bacteria have the capability of growing through a membrane filter. Also, filters can become damaged by frequent or sudden changes in water pressure (water hammer).

5. Carbon Beds

These are commonly employed by the project engineer to remove organic compounds dissolved in the feed water. One of the most important organics is the chlorine added by the municipal water company to control bacterial proliferation. It is important to understand that once the chlorine (preservative) is removed from the feed water, strict controls must be observed in order to control bacterial growth.

Just as is the case with filters, carbon beds are a source of bacterial and endotoxin contamination when improperly maintained. Organic material necessary for growth of bacteria is concentrated in the carbon bed, which then becomes a breeding ground for bacteria that can contaminate the entire water treatment system. To kill microorganisms, carbon beds are periodically heat treated using steam or hot water.

6. Deionizers and Reverse Osmosis (RO) Units

These devices are used to remove dissolved solids from the feed water.

Deionizers use ion exchange resins to remove charged particles. Cation resin beds remove negatively charged particles; anion resins remove positively charged particles. Mixed bed deionizers (containing both cation and anion exchange resins) are commonly used to give the water a final "polishing" treatment. Resins lose their ability to remove charged particles and must be periodically regenerated using strong caustic and acid solutions. This treatment also sanitizes the resin beds, which, like carbon beds, are a fertile breeding ground for bacteria when improperly maintained.

RO units use high pressure and membranes to remove dissolved solids. They too require periodic chemical sanitization treatments in order to control bacterial growth.

7. Distillation Stills

Distillation equipment is used to produce USP WFI quality water. The distillation process kills bacteria, deactivates bacterial endotoxins, and removes dissolved solids not otherwise removed by deionizers or RO units. The chemical quality of the steam supplied to the still must be controlled to prevent recontamination of the distillate. Also, the condenser must be of a double-tube design to prevent condenser coolant from coming into direct contact with the distillate, thereby causing recontamination.

8. Ultraviolet (UV) Lights

These have two uses in water treatment systems. The most frequent application is as a surface disinfectant. They are also used to remove ozone from ozone process water systems.

The most effective biocidal wavelength is 2537 angstroms (255 nanometers). Usually, mercury vapor lamps are used as the UV light source. To be effective, the absorbed ultraviolet dose must be sufficient to kill bacteria. The intensity of a UV lamp decreases with the square of the distance from the light source. Consequently, UV lights must be sized properly for the required water flow. The amount of light at 255 nanometers emitted by a UV light decreases with time, so lamps have to be monitored and replaced when necessary. Also, "shadowing" by undissolved particles in the water neutralizes the effectiveness of UV light. As a result, UV lights are most effectively employed in water treatment systems after undissolved particles have been removed from the water. UV light will not penetrate biofilm and kill embedded bacteria.

UV lights are often used in recirculating loops in order to keep bacterial counts low at times when no water is being drawn from the system (see Section 10 below).

9. Ozone and Heat Sterilants

Heat and, less frequently, ozone are used to control microbial growth in water treatment systems.

Ozone has been shown to be an effective biocidal agent in water treatment systems for pharmaceutical and electronics manufacturing plants [2]. It removes bacterial endotoxins as well as destroying viruses. Ozone is an effective oxidizing agent at extremely low concentrations (0.05–0.1 ppm) and is easily removed from water by exposure to UV light.

More commonly, heat is used to control microbial growth in water treatment systems. Typically, treated water is heated to 80°C in the storage tank and kept at that temperature while circulating through the distribution loops. A heat exchanger is used to cool the water at the point where it is drawn from the system for use in batching or equipment rinsing. USP WFI systems are often kept at 80°C at all times, whereas water systems not required to produce water of that quality are periodically heated to that temperature (usually daily) in order to sanitize the storage tank, distribution piping, and valves.

10. Continuous Flow, Absence of Dead Legs, and Biofilm

Experience has shown that water flow must be continuous in water treatment systems. No-flow or low-flow conditions are conducive to microbial proliferation and the development of biofilm, particularly in water distribution piping. (Biofilm is a mucus-like material that coats the interior surfaces of pipes, valves, etc. Microorganisms become embedded in the biofilm, which increases their resistance to chemical sanitizers and UV light. Biofilm is the usual source of random, periodic, high microbial counts which occur and disappear spontaneously in water treatment systems. A quick, inexpensive test for the presence of biofilm is to soak the distribution piping overnight in 250–350 ppm chlorine solution. If the solution turns cloudy, biofilm is present and should be promptly removed.) Dead legs in distribution piping can cause no-flow conditions, thereby providing a place for microbial growth. (A dead leg is any length of pipe or valving more than six diameters away from circulating water.)

Recirculating loops enable water to stay in motion during low- or no-demand times. They are commonly used to keep water circulating through carbon filters, resin beds, RO units, and storage tanks and often contain UV lights to help keep the microbial counts low.

11. Hoses and Other Attachments to the Distribution Piping

Treated water must be transferred from the water treatment system to the point of use by some means. Rubber or Tygon hoses are often used for this purpose. Heat exchangers, water meters, and other devices may also be periodically attached to the distribution piping. These devices are usually the "weakest link" in the water treatment system. When not drained after use and sanitized properly before use, they contaminate the water during the transfer process.

B.   Operating Procedures and Key Control Parameters

The validation program for a water treatment system must include verification of the procedures used to operate the system and to keep it in a state of control. Examples of these procedures are:

1.   Start-up and flushing prior to daily use
2.   Daily monitoring of key control parameters
3.   Actions taken to bring the system back on line after an unscheduled shutdown
4.   Start-up after prolonged shutdown (such as a maintenance shutdown)
5.   Start-up after routine maintenance such as resin regenerations, filter changes, and system sanitizations
6.   Cleaning, storage, and sanitization of hoses and other equipment not permanently attached to the water treatment system

These procedures must be consistently followed during the validation study so that adequate experimental data are obtained to support their effectiveness. The procedures must be written (at least in draft form, which can be later modified based on the outcome of the validation study) to help ensure that they are understood and followed by the personnel responsible for operating the water treatment system. Personnel must be trained to used these procedures and supervisory personnel must be vigilant to ensure that the procedures are consistently followed.

The validation program must also establish the operating ranges for the system's key control parameters. These key parameters may include temperature, flow rates, resistivity or conductivity, UV light wavelength intensity, pH, and quantity of water processed. These are the key operating parameters that will be monitored daily when the system is in use to ensure that it is maintained in a state of control.

C.   Maintenance Procedures

Water treatment systems require considerable maintenance to ensure consistent delivery of the desired quantity and quality of treated water. Maintenance procedures include:

1.   Resin regeneration procedure (if a deionizer is a component of the system)
2.   RO membrane sanitization procedure (if a RO unit is a system component)
3.   Filter sanitization and change procedure (including filter specifications)

4. UV light monitoring and replacement procedure
5. Storage tank and distribution piping sanitization procedure
6. Instrument calibration program and calibration procedures
7. Carbon bed sanitization and change procedure
8. Oxygen and ozone generator maintenance procedures (for ozone process water systems)

As with the operating procedures previously listed, these maintenance procedures must be in writing and consistently followed. Data gathered during the validation study will demonstrate the effectiveness and appropriateness of these procedures.

IV. HOW TO VALIDATE A WATER TREATMENT SYSTEM

The validation of a water treatment system follows the same basic sequence as does the validation of other pharmaceutical manufacturing equipment. Equipment installation and operational qualification are done first and referred to as prevalidation activities. Next, the water treatment process is validated.

An installation qualification (IQ) must be performed on the newly installed equipment to verify that the equipment was installed according to the manufacturer's and user's written specifications. All process controlling/monitoring instruments are calibrated at this time. The IQ is followed by an operational qualification (OQ), during which the system is put on line and verified to operate in conformance with the manufacturer's specifications and the user's requirements. The process validation phase, during which the water treatment system is operated under the full range of anticipated conditions, is now ready to begin and may require a year or more to complete.

Conceptually, these three phases are distinct, but in practice they overlap to a degree. For example, it is often hard to determine when the OQ concludes and the process validation begins. The important point to keep in mind is that all the activities specified in the protocol be completed and that all documentation be attached to the final IQ, OQ, and process validation reports.

A. The Validation Protocol

The validation protocol is a detailed plan for conducting a validation study. It is drafted by the individual or task group responsible for the project, reviewed for content and completeness following the firm's protocol review procedure, and approved by designated individuals. It describes the responsibilities of each individual or unit involved in the project.

All protocols, whether for IQ/OQ of new equipment or for validating a new process, have the same basic format. They start with an *Objective* section in which the reasons for conducting the validation study are described as well as the results to be achieved. Next, there is a *Scope* section. Here, what is to be included and excluded from the study is specified, effectively establishing the boundaries for the study.

Following the Objective and Scope sections is a *Detailed Description of the Process/Equipment* to be validated. Here, block diagrams of equipment, batch formula and master manufacturing records, process flow diagrams, and other documents which will help with the descriptive process are essential and should be attached to the protocol. The protocol should contain a detailed description of the sampling and testing schedule and procedures and clearly state the acceptance criteria for each test. References to official procedures such as those of the USP are acceptable. The number of times that specific trials will be repeated in order to demonstrate reproducibility of results must be specified.

The protocol should be endorsed by designated representatives of each unit that will participate in the validation study. This is essential because it documents mutual acceptance of the protocol and ensures that each unit understands and agrees to fulfill their responsibilities as stated in the protocol. Subsequent changes to the protocol, should they be necessary, must be endorsed by the same individuals. Protocol addenda are sometimes necessary because circumstances later arise which were impossible to anticipate when the study was planned and the protocol drafted.

B. The Validation Report

Validation reports are written at the conclusion of the equipment installation and operational qualification and when process validation is completed. The reports should be "stand-alone" documents containing all pertinent information because they will serve as primary documentation for later FDA regulatory inspections and as reference documents when changes to the system are planned and the need for revalidation is under consideration.

The validation report, like the validation protocol, has a standard format. It begins with a brief *Executive Summary* section in which the major findings and recommendations are presented. All protocol deviations are identified here along with a brief explanation of the reason for the deviation and its impact, if any, on the outcome of the validation. Next is a *Discussion* section, in which all findings, conclusions, and recommendations noted in the *Executive Summary* are explained in detail. Topics should be presented in the order in which they appear in the protocol. Protocol deviations are fully explained, justified, and a judgment made by a competent individual(s) regarding their impact on the validation study. Data tables and attachments should be referenced as needed.

Conclusions and Recommendations is the next section. Here, a statement is made regarding the validation status of the water treatment system and the possible need for additional validation studies focusing on some aspect or component of the system.

The last section of the report is a listing of *Attachments*. Because the report will be the official, complete file on the water treatment system validation, it must contain all raw data, drawings, manuals, tables, instrument calibration reports, and a copy of the validation protocol along with any protocol addenda. The report is then endorsed and dated by designated representatives of each unit involved in the water treatment system validation.

C. Prevalidation

These are the activities which precede the process validation phase. During prevalidation, equipment is installed, verified, and then started up.

1. Installation Qualification of the Water Treatment System Equipment

Verification that the new equipment was installed according to the manufacturer's specifications; collecting manuals, reports, and other documentation; calibrating instrumentation; and establishing a preventive maintenance program are the basic objectives of the IQ phase. The IQ protocol specifies the scope of the project and defines the responsibilities of each unit.

These are the key elements of the IQ of a newly installed water treatment system:

1. Verify that the plant utilities to which the new equipment is attached meet the equipment manufacturer's specifications. Electricity, compressed air, steam, and feed water are the utilities requiring verification. Each should be tested at point of attachment to the water treatment system equipment. Stainless steel piping is degreased and passivated to prevent pitting.

2. Calibrate all *process-controlling* instruments according to written calibration procedures and certify that they conform to specified tolerance limits for accuracy and precision. These instruments include such things as conductivity or resistivity meters, total organic carbon (TOC) monitors, temperature recorders/controllers, UV light intensity meters, and pressure gauges. A calibration program should be written which specifies the frequency of calibration, the limits of accuracy/precision, and corrective action to be taken when instruments are found not to conform to these limits. A listing of test instruments and their traceability back to the National Bureau of Standards (NBS) must be part of the documentation. Provision for recording and archiving calibration results must be made.

3. Obtain all necessary documentation from the equipment manufacturers so that a preventive maintenance program can be established and maintenance

mechanics trained. This includes "as-installed" drawings, service and operator's manuals, recommended spare parts lists, etc. Then train the maintenance personnel to service the equipment properly and document the training.

2. Operational Qualification of the Water Treatment System Equipment

The new water treatment system is now ready to be started up and the proper operation of each component verified. The OQ protocol specifies the scope of the project and defines the responsibilities of each unit. These are some of the key OQ activities:

1. The system is filled with water and any leaks repaired and defective valves or seals replaced.
2. Pumps are checked to make certain they are running in the specified direction.
3. Heat exchangers and stills are tested at the low and high ends of the ranges for key operating parameters.
4. The proper operation of valves and controllers is verified.
5. The water storage and distribution part of the system is sanitized.
6. Resin beads are regenerated.
7. Flow rates are verified against design specifications.
8. SOPs are written to describe start-up, shutdown, and sanitization procedures.

Test procedures are described in the OQ protocol along with acceptance criteria. The number of times each test will be repeated in order to show reproducibility of results is also specified in the OQ protocol.

D. Validation

Now that each major component of the water treatment system has been operationally verified against the manufacturer's specifications, validation of the system is ready to start. Full validation of the system could require as long as a year because of the operating problems, equipment failures, and maintenance errors, which should be expected to occur during the validation period. Also, it takes a full year to determine the seasonal variation in the microbiology of the feed water and water treatment system and to demonstrate the effectiveness of the system sanitization procedures against these resident organisms.

The basic validation strategy is first to maintain the system under normal operating conditions during which frequent and extensive sampling and testing are performed in order to "profile" the system. During this time, the effectiveness of each major system component is determined. Next, the system is operated under "stress conditions," such as start-up after emergency shutdowns of various durations, and more frequently encountered normal maintenance situations, such as start-up after resin regenerations, filter changes, etc. This first phase of testing should take 4–6 months to complete.

During the second phase of testing, the frequency of sampling, number of samples taken, and number of sampling locations are reduced from phase I levels. Basically, this is phase I confirmatory testing and should take another 6 months to complete. Based on management's satisfaction with the system, it could be turned over for production use before completion of phase II, however.

One additional element is included in the validation program for water treatment systems using ozone as a sterilizing agent. One or more batches of your product most sensitive to oxidation should be made using water from this system and placed on accelerated stability testing. These data are necessary to show that any residual ozone in the water will not adversely affect product stability.

The validation protocol is very specific regarding the sampling schedule, sampling points, tests to be performed, test methods employed, and acceptance criteria. A sampling point diagram of the system is helpful, with the sampling points numbered to correspond to the diagram (Fig. 2). The protocol must also specify the water treatment system operating parameters, which must be recorded.

A permanent record of the operating condition of the water treatment system must be created during the validation period. Daily readings are taken of key control parameters such as temperature, flow rate, pressure, conductivity or resistivity, quantity of feed water processed, and UV light wavelength intensity. These data are essential to show that the water treatment system was maintained within the specified ranges for the key control parameters and will validate those ranges. When and for how long out-of-limit conditions were encountered, their subsequent effect on the chemical and microbial quality of the process water, and the start-up procedure followed to put the system back into operation are documented. This information is essential to support the effectiveness of the start-up procedure.

1. Phase I Testing

As noted previously, the performance of each major system component will be verified during phase I testing. This will be accomplished by intensively sampling the system at numerous points for 4–6 months or longer, if necessary, and performing chemical analyses and microbiological evaluations on these samples.

The sampling program must provide data regarding the chemical and microbiological quality of the water at the point at which it is used in the process. Consequently, point-of-use samples are taken from the distribution loop(s). This means that samples must be taken from the rubber or Tygon hoses (if hoses are used to transfer water from the loop to the use point), or from takedown stainless steel piping, heat exchangers, water meters, or whatever other device is periodically attached to the distribution loop. Experience has shown that devices attachable to the distribution loops are the most difficult to control and therefore the weakest link in most water treatment systems. The validation program must

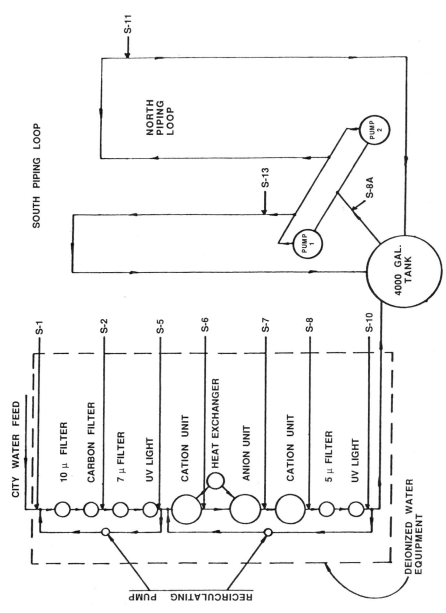

Figure 2 Water treatment system sampling point diagram.

demonstrate the effectiveness of the sanitization procedures for attachable equipment, and this is accomplished by point-of-use sampling.

Daily sampling of the feed water (Fig. 2, sampling point S-1) for chemical analysis and microbiological testing is essential, as previously explained. It is the chemical and microbiological baseline against which the treated water is compared.

Samples for *chemical analysis* should be removed before and after each process device in the system (carbon bed, resin bed, filter, etc.) in order to evaluate the device's effectiveness compared to its design specifications. Referring to Fig. 2, samples should be taken at S-2, S-6, S-7, and S-8 daily and when the carbon bed is changed or the resin beds regenerated. Distribution loop samples S-11 and S-13 for chemical analysis do not require daily collection but should be taken at the use point farthest from the storage tank.

Samples for *microbial evaluation* are collected daily from system sampling points S-2, S-5, S-6, S-7, S-8, S-10, S-8A, and S-11, and S-13 (point of use). The S-11 and S-13 sampling points from the distribution loops should be rotated among the use points to ensure that all use points are sampled weekly. The sample size actually tested should be no less than 100 mL of purified water and 250 mL of WFI.

The water treatment system must be validated under the full range of operating conditions expected to be encountered during future operations. Some of these conditions will have to be created artificially during later phase I testing. For example, an electrical failure should be simulated, as well as a steam pressure failure. If the water treatment system uses ozone, a failure of the ozone and oxygen generators should be simulated. The chemical and microbiological data collected during these "stress conditions" will validate the start-up procedures for putting the system back on line.

2. Phase II Testing

Phase II is a continuation of phase I but with reduced sampling frequency. Phase II should be initiated only after the requirements stipulated in the protocol for phase I testing have been satisfied.

Referring back to Fig. 2, a typical phase II sampling schedule should include assessing the quality of the treated water entering the storage tank (S-10) and at points of use in the distribution loops (S-11 and S-13). Samples should be taken every day that water is drawn from the system, and complete chemical and microbiological analyses should be performed. Be prepared to increase the sampling frequency and number of sampling locations at any time the ranges for key operating parameters are exceeded or when any undesirable trend in the test data is observed.

Data should be presented graphically whenever possible. There are excellent computer software packages for this purpose. Graphic presentation of data aids in the recognition of relationships between variables and helps analysts spot trends. Figure 3 is a simple chart showing the results of the microbial total plate count in the distribution loops in an ozone process water system between February and October. Just a glance at the chart reveals that the plate counts (expressed as colony forming units/mL of water) are usually zero but that an occasional "spike" is observed. For example, on one day in March, one of the loops exceeded the action limit (100 cfu/mL) while no growth was detected in the other loop, an implausible result if the entire system was contaminated. This pattern of results should have an explanation (our microbiologist later determined that the periodic high counts were coming from improperly maintained Tygon transfer hoses. The sanitizing and storage procedures for these hoses were subsequently revised).

When personnel responsible for validating the water treatment system are satisfied with the data and confident in the reliability of the system, a decision could be made to turn over the system to production use even though phase II

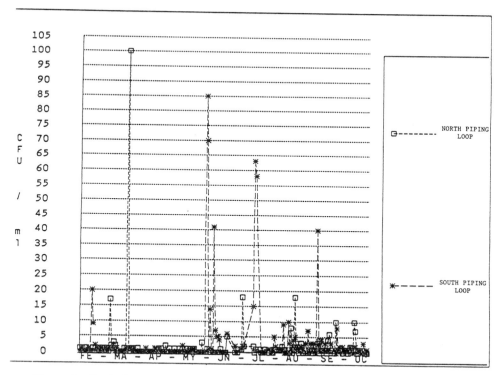

Figure 3 Total plate count in the north and south distribution loops from February to October.

testing has not been completed. This is a judgment call and could pose some risks; in extreme cases, product rejection could result. However, if the validation project team is satisfied with the performance of the system, putting the system into production should be considered. Regardless of when the system is put into production, the water quality alert and action limits must be finalized, all necessary SOPs must be written, and all operating and maintenance personnel must be trained to do their jobs correctly.

The equipment installation and operational qualification report(s) and the system validation report must be written, reviewed, and approved according to your firm's procedures. The validation project cannot be considered complete until the final reports are approved.

V. POSTVALIDATION MONITORING AND CHANGE CONTROL

A. Periodic Sampling and Testing

Once validation is completed, the water treatment system is maintained in a state of control by keeping the system within the acceptable ranges for the key control parameters established during the validation program and by adhering to the validated operating and maintenance procedures. Typically, these key control parameters are flow rate, temperature, resistivity or conductivity, pH, and, for ozone systems, ozone concentration in the distribution loops. Data from the periodic sampling and testing of water from the distribution loops merely confirms that the system is being kept in a state of control.

Point-of-use sampling frequency and the tests to be performed on the samples should be mutually agreed to by quality control/quality assurance and production personnel and put into written operating procedures. Any less frequent sampling than once a week with complete USP testing is not likely to be considered acceptable by FDA personnel, however. Another consideration is the response to a sample exceeding the action limit; all product made since the last satisfactory sample was taken would be subject to quarantine pending the outcome of your investigation.

B. Change Control

Subsequent changes to a validated water treatment system can be expected to occur for a variety of reasons. For example, a filter, resin, activated carbon, or RO membrane manufacturer may discontinue supplying a component of your system, making it necessary for you to find and validate a suitable replacement. You may need to expand the water treatment capacity of the system or add an additional distribution loop.

Your firm should write a change control procedure if one does not already exist. The procedure specifies a method for documenting proposed changes and for routing the proposals to specific individuals or groups delegated the responsibility for assessing their impact on the validated system (the change control quality control unit). When judged significant, a revalidation plan is made and the validation protocol distributed for the specified approval signatures. In all instances, the system users must be made aware of proposed changes.

The extent of the revalidation effort is determined by the change control quality control unit. There are no easy rules to follow here, but a change, for example, in the sanitization procedure or frequency is a significant change requiring fairly extensive microbiological revalidation. A change in the process technology employed, for example, replacement of the deionizer with an RO unit, is a major change requiring complete revalidation. The important thing here is that a change control procedure is established and followed.

VI. WATER TESTING PROCEDURES AND SPECIFICATIONS

The USP defines the various grades of water suitable for pharmaceutical use, establishes the specifications, and details the *analytical* test procedures to be used in determining conformance to these specifications. To claim that a water treatment system produces water of a particular USP grade, the system owner must have data to show conformance with the USP specifications, using the USP analytical test procedures (or other procedures, providing the user has adequate data to show that equivalent results are obtained).

The USP is not as helpful regarding *microbiological* specifications and test procedures suitable for use on water samples. It states only that the USP microbial limit test is not a suitable test procedure and that purified water and WFI must meet the Environmental Protection Agency's (EPA's) Part 141, National Interim Primary Drinking Water Regulations. WFI has an additional USP endotoxin specification. The EPA standard for drinking water is primarily concerned with coliform bacteria and, when they cannot be reliably measured, imposes a total plate count limit of 500 cfu/mL. However, the USP action limit guideline (not a specification) for USP purified water is 100 cfu/mL; the action limit guideline for WFI is 50 cfu/mL. FDA recommends tighter limits: 50 cfu/mL for purified water and 10 cfu/100 mL for WFI.

Each firm must establish microbiological *alert* and *action* limits based not only on USP and FDA recommendations but also on their knowledge of the organisms found in their water treatment system and those potentially deleterious to their products. For example, solid oral dosage form products with moisture levels below 5% do not ordinarily provide suitable growth media. Consequently, a water treatment system specifically for these products will tolerate higher alert and action levels. Conversely, products such as antacids and other water-based products will support growth and must be manufactured using water with lower microbial levels. In addition, certain types of organisms are objectionable in specific pharmaceutical dosage forms. For examples, *Pseudomonas cepacia* survives in the preservative commonly used in nasal preparations (benzalkonium chloride). Manufacturers of nasal solutions should use water test procedures that will detect this particular organism.

The most widely recognized source of microbiological test procedures for water is published by the American Public Health Association [3]. R2A medium incubated for 5–7 days at 25–28°C is recommended for the test procedure. When organisms are recovered on this medium, they should be speciated on selective medium until a positive identification is obtained. In this way, isolates can be identified and documented and seasonal variations in the resident organisms can be determined.

As previously noted, alert and action levels should be established for microbial tests that, when exceeded, require that specified corrective action be taken. An alert level should be set well below the action level so that line management can react to lower the counts as quickly as possible. Typical corrective action when an alert level is exceeded is system resanitization. In any event, an investigation should be initiated into the possible cause of the elevated count. When an action level is exceeded, use of the system should be discontinued and actions taken both against the water treatment system and the product made using the water. Batches manufactured since the last acceptable test result should be quarantined pending the outcome of the investigation. The investigation should include testing of the product for the presence of the objectionable organisms using validated procedures. The system should be sampled and tested daily until satisfactory conditions are once again restored. The results of the investigation and corrective action must be clearly documented.

The current state of pharmaceutical water nomenclature, specifications, and test procedures is far from satisfactory. Some analytical test procedures are antiquated, others are far too analyst dependent (for example, the total dissolved solids test), and others are probably irrelevant and should be deleted (for example, the heavy metals test). Microbial testing is more of an art than a science. At the time this chapter was written, the Pharmaceutical Manufacturers Association (PMA) has established a Water Quality Committee with responsibility for reviewing test procedures and specifications. During the next few years, they plan to make proposals to the USP aimed at rationalizing water testing.

VII. SUMMARY AND RECOMMENDATION

In this brief chapter, the purpose of validating water treatment systems was described and a basic validation strategy presented. How to go about validating a water treatment system was described. The need for and contents of a typical validation protocol and validation report were presented. The need for a change control procedure was explained. Analytical and microbiological test procedures were discussed. The need to establish microbial alert and action limits and to document investigations and corrective action when these limits are exceeded was presented.

In conclusion, these recommendations are offered to the individuals responsible for validating a water treatment system:

1. Design the system to exceed your present water quality specifications. Water treatment systems have a long life expectancy and water quality specifications can be expected to become tighter, not looser, in the future. Design the system to treat the lowest-quality feed water ever provided by your municipal water company or your on-site wells.

2. Be extremely selective when choosing your contractor. Make certain the contractor has experience installing the type of system you want. Visit sites where the contractor has made similar installations and talk with plant and maintenance management about their experiences with the contractor and the system. Make certain the contractor will have the necessary resources to support your project on your time schedule.

3. Hoses, meters, heat exchangers, and other equipment attachable to the water distribution loop tend to be the weak link in a water treatment system. If not drained properly and dried after use and sanitized, when necessary, prior to reuse, they have pockets of stagnant water where microorganisms proliferate and contaminate the process water. These attachables must be cleaned, sanitized, and stored properly in order to avoid contaminating the process water during transfer.

4. Maintenance and operating personnel must be trained to do their jobs correctly and be required to demonstrate proficiency. When inadequately trained personnel are allowed to work on or draw water from the system, errors will be made which could result in unscheduled system shutdowns and, in extreme cases, product loss.

REFERENCES

1. PMA Deionized Water Committee, Validation and control concepts for water treatment systems, *Pharmaceut. Technol.* 9(11):50–56, November (1985).
2. Nebel, C., and Nebel, T., Ozone, the process water sterilant, *Pharmaceut. Manuf.* 4(2):16–23, April (1984).
3. American Public Health Association, American Water Works Association, and Water Pollution Control Federation, *Standard Methods for the Examination of Water and Waste Water*, 16th ed. (1985).

10

Cleaning Validation

Paul Y. McCormick *Wyeth-Ayerst Research Laboratories, West Chester, Pennsylvania*

Leo F. Cullen *Wyeth-Ayerst Research Laboratories, Radnor, Pennsylvania*

I. INTRODUCTION

This chapter will address issues related to the validation of equipment cleaning procedures used in the pharmaceutical industry to prevent cross-contamination or adulteration of drug products. Although the information presented here may prove useful in conducting related studies, such as packaging component cleaning validation, the scope of this chapter will be limited to validation of the cleaning of nondedicated equipment. Both general conceptual information and practical "how-to" examples will be presented, to assist the reader in establishing a cleaning validation strategy and in conducting studies to evaluate the effectiveness of existing, new, or modified equipment cleaning procedures.

The primary benefit usually attributed to a cleaning validation is ensuring compliance with federal regulations. However, a more important benefit from conducting cleaning validation work is the identification and correction of potential problems, previously unsuspected, which could compromise the safety, efficacy, or quality of subsequent batches of drug product produced with the equipment. It is important to keep the true purpose of cleaning validation studies in mind throughout the planning and execution stages of the project in order to utilize the valuable resources dedicated to the effort as efficiently as possible.

Several serious problems can be prevented through the use of a reasonable cleaning validation program. All are related to adulteration, therapeutic safety and efficacy, or overall quality of the product over its shelf life:

Cross-contamination with active ingredients: By definition, contamination of one batch of product with significant levels of residual active ingredients from a previous batch cannot be tolerated. In addition to the obvious problems posed by subjecting consumers or patients to unintended contaminants, potential clinically significant synergistic interactions between pharmacologically active chemicals are a real concern.

Contamination with unintended materials or compounds: While inert ingredients used in drug products are generally recognized as safe or have been shown to be safe for human consumption, the routine use, maintenance, and cleaning of equipment provide the potential for contamination with such items as equipment parts and lubricants, chemical cleaning agents, and pieces of cleaning tools such as brushes or rags. Contamination with such items can cause problems ranging from poor pharmaceutical elegance, to exceeding acceptable levels of particulate matter in parenteral products, to inadvertent inclusion of toxic compounds in the product. In addition, some actives are adversely affected by trace contaminants and may exhibit changes in stability or bioavailability if exposed to such contaminants.

Microbiological contamination: Maintenance, cleaning, and storage conditions may provide adventitious microorganisms with the opportunity to proliferate within processing equipment. This could pose obvious problems for sterile product manufacture (generation of high levels of pyrogens, decreasing the assurance of sterility achieved by equipment sterilization procedures, etc.). It can also be a serious problem for the manufacture of nonsterile dosage forms, particularly unpreserved products which support microbial growth.

We will endeavor to provide some general information about cleaning procedures and systems required to ensure that routine operations are under control and to help the reader think about the appropriate goals of cleaning validation and some practical ways to achieve them. The major objective of the cleaning validation program should be to provide an adequate level of assurance that the problems described above will not occur during routine manufacturing operations.

As with any such program, the benefits gained increase with the amount of time, money, and effort expended, but *not* in a linear fashion. A relatively modest commitment to cleaning validation can provide fairly high levels of assurance of product safety, purity, and efficacy. Conversely, no reasonable level of support granted to a cleaning validation program will result in an absolute guarantee that contamination cannot occur. It is the task of the validation specialists and their management to determine what constitutes adequate assurance and to secure the required technical, monetary, and organizational support required to achieve this goal. It is imperative that this difficult compromise be made in a responsible and conscientious manner in order to avoid future difficulties, both technical and regulatory. This chapter will benefit the individuals charged with making such decisions, as well as those charged with carrying out the program.

II. GENERAL CLEANING METHODS AND CONCEPTS

It is first necessary to understand the general concepts and specific practices commonly used in the industry for the cleaning of processing equipment. Customary methods used for cleaning equipment can be divided into *manual* cleaning procedures, *semiautomated* procedures, and *fully automated* systems (such as clean-in-place, or CIP systems). Regardless of the method used, each cleaning procedure must be fully documented and controlled, usually through the use of *standard operating procedures* or manufacturing instructions. This documentation should include a clear and unambiguous definition of its intended scope and applicability. This includes definition of the processing equipment and products to which it applies and the circumstances under which it may be used.

For example, a clear distinction must be made between an abbreviated cleaning procedure designed for use between batches of the same product (sometimes called "serial" cleaning) and a rigorous cleaning procedure designed for use between batches of different products. Similarly, in some cases it is best to dedicate the use of some equipment to certain products. For example, dust collection bags used on Trost mills or in fluid bed dryers are sometimes very difficult to clean. One way to avoid problems in this regard is to purchase separate bags for each product made using this equipment. Under these circumstances, cross-contamination is not a concern, but the dedicated equipment should be cleaned routinely anyway to minimize batch-to-batch contamination and to prevent any problems with microbial contamination. Obviously, the scope and applicability of such a cleaning procedure will differ significantly from those of other procedures, and this should be explained in its documentation.

A. Manual Cleaning Procedures

Manual cleaning procedures, by definition, are operator dependent. This is not meant to imply that they are not effective. On the contrary, well-thought-out and well-written manual cleaning procedures, when performed by qualified and properly trained operators, can often be superior to automated methods. However, they must be clearly defined and operators must be well trained (not only *what* must be done, but *why* it is done) to minimize variability in their execution.

It is not possible to list all possible cleaning sequences which may be used, but the vast majority of cleaning procedures follow the same basic format, in one form or another, as described below. Throughout this description, the use of an aqueous cleaning system is assumed. When organic solvents are required, the conditions of their use should be specified with the same detail as shown below for water-based washing.

1. Equipment Disassembly (If Required)

Most equipment should be disassembled to some extent prior to cleaning to ensure that it can be thoroughly cleaned. In determining how far to go in disassembling equipment, particular attention should be paid to areas where shafts penetrate a shell and to gaskets. Problems with residual contamination have been traced to such areas with some regularity. The disassembly instructions should be clear and complete and written so that the operator does not have to interpret unfamiliar terminology. Diagrams and drawings can be extremely beneficial as part of disassembly instructions.

2. Prewash/Inspection

This is perhaps the most important step in any cleaning procedure and is usually one of the most operator-dependent ones. The purpose of the prewash step is to eliminate gross accumulations of residual materials. It therefore serves to improve the reproducibility of the subsequent steps by ensuring that the equipment is in roughly the same state of dirtiness prior to the wash step each time the procedure is executed.

Potable water is usually sufficient for this step, which may entail filling the equipment with the water to a predetermined level and circulating it (e.g., tumble blenders, tanks, and other enclosed vessels), or using a hose or hand-held spray gun to remove the material (e.g., comminuting mills, filling machine change parts). Since this step usually relies on the physical motion and impingement of the water to remove materials, it may not be necessary to specify the temperature of the water to be used. In any case, the critical part of this step is inspection by the operator and repetition of the prewash step if required. The criteria to be used by the operator in making such a determination should be defined as clearly as possible (e.g., "Continue spraying all areas of the machine until no residual granulation can be seen. In particular, check the underside of the rotor mounting plate and . . .").

3. Wash

Having removed most visible material, the next step is usually to perform the actual washing of the parts or equipment. If chemical cleaning agents are required, this step is where they will be used. In order to minimize variation, the approved cleaning agents must be defined and the proper concentration to be used must be spelled out. The method to be used to achieve this concentration should be provided. For example, "Add 1 gallon of [specified detergent] to the water in the tank [approximate quantity previously specified]. This provides a detergent concentration of approximately 1 part detergent to 99 parts water . . ." is much less likely to cause errors than "Add detergent. Use a concentration of approximately 1%. . . ."

Since this step usually relies on dissolution of residual materials, the temperature of the water or detergent mixture may be important. If so, a suitable temperature range should be specified and a means of measuring the temperature must be available to the operator.

Multiple wash steps in cleaning procedures are not uncommon, especially when sequential use of both acidic and alkaline cleaning agents is desired. For obvious reasons, such a sequence should include a rinse step between the two wash steps.

4. Initial Rinses

The wash step usually dissolves most of the residual material, but the washing liquid must still be removed from the equipment. This residual liquid contains water, cleaning agent(s), and residual material from previous usage of the equipment. A single rinse of the equipment sometimes provides a sufficient reduction in the levels of these items, but a series of rinses is generally more effective. All cleaning procedures result in serial reductions in residual contaminant levels because dilution effects and equilibrium conditions prevent an instantaneous abolition of all undesirable compounds in a single step.

As one proceeds through the cleaning procedure, and especially through the rinsing stages, the quality of water used should be increased. For the initial rinses, it may be desirable to use purified water, distilled water, or water for injection (WFI) to ensure that the final rinse is effective in providing the cleanliness required. However, the use of potable or municipal water is also acceptable, providing that adequate cleanliness is demonstrated at the conclusion of the final rinse and drying. If the temperature of the rinse water used is important, it should be specified.

5. Final Rinse

The final rinse is used to reduce the quantities of any residuals to their final level without introducing any more potential contaminants than necessary. For this reason, the final rinse is generally performed using the highest-quality water available (purified water, USP, or water for injection). The temperature of the water used for this step is usually not important except to speed the drying process, since the main purpose of this step is usually simply to remove already-dissolved residuals (at a very low level) and to provide a final liquid residue of the highest quality possible (minimum dissolved solids, microorganisms, etc.), since this residual water will be evaporated from the surfaces of the equipment.

6. Reassembly (If Required)

Instructions for reassembly should include all items listed above for disassembly. In addition, care must be taken to avoid recontamination of the parts during the reassembly process.

B. Semiautomated Cleaning Procedures

Portable clean-in-place (CIP) systems, cabinet-type cleaning equipment (i.e., "dishwasher"-type equipment), and similar systems are considered semiautomated systems. These have many features of fully automated systems but require more extensive operator intervention in order to function properly.

Portable CIP systems are typically tank and pump assemblies on wheels and are installed temporarily to the equipment to be cleaned and to the various utilities and detergents required. Their sequencing may be controlled automatically or by the operator. They are most commonly used for cleaning closed vessels such as blenders and tanks.

Cabinet-type cleaning equipment is usually a stationary machine with hard-plumbed utilities. The operation is usually automatic, but it must be loaded and unloaded manually. If detergents are required, they can be added by the operator at the time of use or a constant supply may be provided (as with a separate tank). These machines are usually used to clean containers (e.g., drums, transport bins), glassware (e.g., biologicals manufacturing), or machine parts. Loading is critical to ensure that all surfaces are cleaned by the jets and that the items drain readily to facilitate drying.

C. Automated Cleaning Procedures

Automated cleaning procedures offer the distinct advantage of improved reproducibility as compared to manual procedures. The reduced operator involvement, however, also reduces his or her ability to intercede during the procedure to inspect the equipment at various stages and to repeat steps if necessary. Thus, automated procedures must be designed to handle a wide variety of equipment conditions in order to be effective (e.g., incomplete discharge of granulation can put a much greater demand on the cleaning procedure than normal operations, in which the granulation is completely discharged).

The most common fully automated cleaning procedures are CIP systems designed to clean large, stationary pieces of equipment. The same basic sequence of events described above for manual procedures is often used with such CIP systems, except that the operations are controlled automatically. A typical CIP system is designed to circulate cleaning and rinsing fluids through the equipment at controlled flow rates for predetermined periods of time.

The use of automated systems requires careful consideration during the preparation of validation protocols due to some inherent difficulties:

Control system qualification: Aside from the normal concerns of cleaning validation studies, the reproducibility of the automated system must be verified. For example, if a minimum temperature is required, the system should have a mechanism in place to check the water temperature before continuing. If the temperature is too low and the process is suspended, will the abnormal delay in the sequence adversely affect the results?

Sampling considerations: CIP systems are usually closed systems—i.e., they cannot easily be observed and sampled without upsetting the programmed sequence of events. Therefore, equipment modifications, such as the addition of a sampling port, may be required to allow sampling of the wash or rinse fluids. Alternatively, pause capabilities may have to be changed or added to the program to allow inspection and/or sampling.

Material supply: Fully automated systems usually require separate, hard-plumbed supply lines and tanks for water, cleaning agents, acids or bases, etc. In addition to checking the various volume and dispensing controls, the potential impact of long storage periods must be considered. For example, if a detergent supports microbial growth, the system must include some means of preventing proliferation of microorganisms prior to use of the detergent. If a suspension is used, the holding vessel must have sufficient mixing capabilities to prevent sedimentation and to supply a reasonably uniform content throughout the expected holding time.

III. GENERAL CLEANING PROCEDURES AND SYSTEMS (PREVALIDATION VERIFICATION)

Before launching a cleaning validation program, it is important to do some background work to ensure that the cleaning procedures, controls, and documentation systems used are logical, controlled, and properly documented. Without such controls, validation work will be pointless. It is also important to review the basic practices being used to clean processing equipment and to verify the completion of basic qualification work on utilities and equipment involved.

A. Documentation and Traceability

In order to have a coherent and functional cleaning system, some basic controls and documentation procedures must be in place. These systems ensure reliable and reproducible operations and enable proper tracking and troubleshooting when required. The systems currently used should be evaluated, and corrected if needed, before beginning any cleaning validation studies.

Equipment identification: All major pieces of equipment should be assigned unique identification numbers to prevent any confusion as to which cleaning procedure is to be used for a particular piece of equipment and to allow clear documentation of usage and cleaning activities.

Equipment use, maintenance, and cleaning records: A functional system should be in place to record equipment usage, maintenance, and cleaning. Such records may be compiled into a single equipment-specific logbook or card system, or may be retrievable through several documentation systems (e.g., batch records, maintenance logbooks, and cleaning logbooks). Computerized systems for such record-keeping tasks are beginning to gain acceptance in the pharmaceutical industry and are entirely appropriate when properly designed and qualified. In any case, it should be possible to identify the sequence of events before and after the manufacture of any specific batch of product in each piece of equipment. This allows efficient troubleshooting and can identify other batches which may be in jeopardy should a batch made in the same equipment be rejected for some reason.

Labeling: The state of cleanliness should be readily apparent for each piece of equipment at all times. This can be accomplished by labeling (e.g., "Cleaned—Ready for Use," "To Be Cleaned," "Hold for Maintenance Work") or by physically placing portable machinery into appropriate, clearly identified locations set up for the purpose (e.g., Quarantine [to be cleaned] or Ready for Use [clean] areas).

Cleaning equipment maintenance and calibration: Systems should be in place to ensure that all equipment and instrumentation used for cleaning is in proper working condition and suitably calibrated.

Utilities used: Water for injection, purified water, steam, and compressed air systems used during cleaning and drying operations should be properly qualified and operated in a state of control.

Standard operation procedures: As described previously, all cleaning procedures should be documented, usually as standard operating procedures. These documents are the foundation on which reproducibility is built (through equipment design and qualification and personnel training), and, as such, must be complete and unambiguous if cleaning validation efforts are to be meaningful. They should include a clear statement of scope and applicability; specification of all solvents, cleaning agents, cleaning tools, and equipment to be used; and detailed step-by-step instructions. Additional information on these items is included throughout this chapter.

B. Control of Cleaning Materials

As defined here, these include all materials which are used and consumed during the cleaning operation—solvents, cleaning agents, ancillary utilities (such as steam and compressed air), and scrubbing agents. Their production or purchase, testing, and use should be adequately controlled to ensure reproducibility in the cleaning operations.

1. Solvents

The primary solvent required for most cleaning operations is water. The quality of water required will vary depending on the intended purpose of the particular operation. For prewash operations, and usually for the actual wash steps, municipal or potable water is normally sufficient. For rinse steps, especially final rinsing, Purified Water, USP, or Water for Injection is often specified. The minimum water quality required for a given step should be clearly specified. The water systems supplying the cleaning operations should be qualified (validated) and operated in a state of control.

When nonaqueous solvents such as alcohols or other organic solvents are required, the source and quality should be controlled. The usual raw material controls (approved suppliers and incoming testing requirements) are generally sufficient in this regard. Nonaqueous solvents should be used only if absolutely necessary due to their inherent problems of safety, cost, and environmental considerations.

2. Cleaning Agents

Various cleaning agents, added to the cleaning solvent, are often required to remove residual product effectively. These may be acidic or alkaline and are usually commercial preparations containing surfactants, sequestering agents, dispersants, buffering agents, and/or other ingredients.

As with organic solvents, the use of cleaning agents should be considered only if simpler systems (e.g., water rinses) are ineffective, because use of such agents introduces another potential contaminant that must be removed by the cleaning procedure. Furthermore, control of the composition of cleaning agents is often difficult, since commercial formulations are usually considered proprietary and are sometimes changed without the user's knowledge.

When cleaning agents are used, the qualified type, brand, and/or grade should be specified. When a known formulation change occurs, the potential impact on the affected cleaning procedures should be evaluated.

3. Ancillary Utilities

Steam is sometimes required for cleaning procedures, and compressed air is often permitted to speed drying after cleaning. The quality required for the utility used should be assessed in light of the application. For example, plant steam may be appropriate for a washing step which is followed by a purified water rinse, whereas clean steam should be used for final rinse/sterilization steps. Compressed air used for drying should be essentially free of oil and other potential contaminants.

4. Scrubbing Agents

When traditional cleaning methods are found to be only marginally effective in removing residuals, a step may be included to the cleaning procedure in which an inert solid material is processed through the equipment to scrub or abrade residuals from the product contact surfaces. For example, compression of placebo tablets has been shown to be an effective method of reducing residual actives from punches and dies when normal aqueous and/or organic solvent wash/rinse procedures did not achieve acceptable levels of cleanliness. Similar results have been seen for blenders (removal of dyes) and encapsulation machines (removal of residual actives).

When such procedures are specified, the precise placebo formulation to be used must be clearly identified. The quality of the raw materials used should be adequately controlled, usually through the use of normal raw material controls (approved suppliers and incoming raw material testing).

C. Control of Ancillary Tools and Equipment Used for Cleaning

The use of ancillary tools and equipment is often specified for cleaning operations. These may be as simple as cleaning tools (e.g., brushes and rags), or as complex as a portable CIP system. Their purpose and suitability for the task should be understood and verified. A basic principle to keep in mind is that unnecessary complications should be avoided at all cost. This not only helps ensure consistent and reproducible operations but also reduces difficulty of the validation effort. Where superfluous or unnecessary steps are discovered, they should be deleted.

1. Cleaning Tools

The use of brushes, rags, sponges, and other cleaning tools is common. To minimize variation, a standard set of such items should be available to the operator. Restrictions as to which items may be used for a given procedure are usually not required, since such manual scrubbing operations are usually controlled by use of a reasonably objective end point (i.e., absence of visual contamination).

Tools provided should be selected to avoid contamination (e.g., brushes should not easily drop bristles, rags should not readily shed fibers). Formal validation of these characteristics by experimental testing is generally not required, however, since such operations are always followed by additional washing and/or rinsing steps. In some cases, the use of cleaning tools could be a potential source of additional chemical contamination, and appropriate cleaning methods for the tools themselves must be used. The potential for problems caused by the use of cleaning tools should be evaluated based on the methods of use, the overall cleaning procedure, and the compounds likely to be contacted.

2. Equipment Used for Cleaning

A wide variety of cleaning equipment is used routinely to assist cleaning operations. The kinds of equipment range from the simple thermometer monitoring the temperature of the water being used to complex CIP systems consisting of tanks, metering pumps, circulating pumps, heat exchangers, spray nozzles, and attendant instrumentation and control systems. This equipment should be maintained, calibrated, and controlled as carefully as the processing equipment. It should be subject to routine maintenance and calibration and should be carefully evaluated in the course of the cleaning validation studies.

D. Frequency of Cleaning

The frequency with which cleaning must be performed depends on the manufacturing operations being used, the products involved and the use and maintenance of the equipment. Situations requiring cleaning of the equipment can be categorized as follows:

Cleaning between batches of the same product: Abbreviated cleaning procedures are often specified for use between batches of the same product or between different strengths of the same product when the formulations used are qualitatively identical (i.e., identical actives and excipients are used and the formulations vary only in the quantities of ingredients specified). Such cleaning procedures are designed to achieve visual cleanliness only, and do not usually require comprehensive validation studies. As described by Harder [1], the main focus in evaluating these abbreviated procedures should be evaluation of the potential for problems caused by microbial contamination.

Cleaning between batches of different products: More rigorous cleaning procedures are required for cleaning between batches of different products, or between batches of products that contain the same active but different excipients and are therefore judged likely to exhibit different behavior during the cleaning process.

Cleaning after maintenance: Almost all required maintenance activities have at least the potential for contaminating the equipment. Therefore, they should be followed by rigorous cleaning procedures.

Cleaning after accidental contamination: The need for rigorous cleaning after known incidents of contamination is obvious. Since the removal of all possible contaminants cannot be validated in advance, it is prudent to sample and test for the particular contaminant involved in these unique situations, on a case-by-case basis, when they occur.

Appropriate corporate policies stating when cleaning is required and the thoroughness needed for each circumstance should be documented. Specific instructions on this subject should be included in plant operating procedures.

IV. METHODS OF VALIDATION AND PROTOCOL DEVELOPMENT

This section will address the steps required to develop an overall validation plan, to determine project scope and objectives, to decide on general methods of evaluation, and to arrive at a practical yet meaningful set of specifications.

A. The Validation Protocol

There is nothing unusual about the preparation of a protocol for cleaning validation as opposed to the preparation of a protocol for any other type of validation. The following information should be included:

Scope and objectives: These two items are intimately related and may be presented together or separately. In either case, they should be unambiguous and should represent the culmination of significant thought and consideration. Additional information on this subject is included in the following section.

Introductory information and background: No validation study is designed in a void. Historical data, previous developmental studies, and related validation studies should all be used to full advantage—making the planned validation studies as useful and efficient as possible. Some description of this background information should be included in the protocol. This is also the appropriate place to include basic conceptual information, such as a description of the overall validation approach being used (e.g., placebo or rinse sampling, equipment train concepts) and how the current studies fit into the overall plan.

Procedure: A complete and detailed description of the experimental plan is mandatory. This should include material and equipment to be used, required calibration checks, step-by-step instructions for carrying out the studies, full and detailed sampling information, and appropriate controls related to sampling (e.g., special sample containers required, storage conditions and maximum storage times before testing, if needed).

Acceptance criteria: Complete, explicit, and meaningful acceptance criteria for each test must be included. Specific testing methods to be utilized may be included, or a statement of the method's required specificity and accuracy may be substituted. This is often necessary when method development work has not yet been completed. Part of the final validation documentation should include reference to the method validation work completed for any new or different testing methodology developed for the study.

Additional information on each of these parts of the protocol is provided in the following sections.

B. General Considerations

When a cleaning validation program is initially undertaken, some general concepts and an overall philosophy must first be established. This planning stage is of paramount importance to set realistic and sound objectives for the program, establish a reasonable and meaningful overall scope, prevent inefficient use of resources, and ensure that the results of the program will meet the stated objectives.

The objectives of the program are to provide reasonable assurance that routine equipment cleaning procedures are adequate to prevent problems which could result from contamination of drug products. The definition of "reasonable assurance" is intimately related to the overall scope of the program and requires careful consideration.

1. Scope of the Program

The list of the possible contaminants from normal usage of equipment is endless, including all ingredients and processing aids previously used, cleaning agents, compounds produced by unanticipated reactions between ingredients, processing aids, cleaning agents or equipment components, degradation products from the previous batch, lubricants and materials leaked or abraded from the equipment during processing, chemicals or materials mistakenly added to the previous batch during processing, cleaning tools such as brush bristles, textiles, or shredded paper, foreign objects such as ink from pens, ground metal or plastic, etc.

It is clearly not possible to evaluate all possible sources of contamination. For this reason, there is no substitute for careful evaluation and good judgment in determining the objectives of the cleaning validation program. As with any such study, careful, reasoned compromise between anticipated benefits and associated risks/costs must be made.

Reasonable assurance that lubricants and machine parts will not contaminate drug products can usually be achieved by proper evaluation of the equipment design and verification that proper procedures are in place for inspection and maintenance of the equipment. Contamination from unusual sources such as accidental spillage, unusual equipment or facility degeneration, and the like cannot reasonably be anticipated and prevented. Protection from such contamination is best accomplished through the use of well-designed cleaning and inspection procedures and should be addressed at the time that they occur (on a case-by-case basis).

Thus, the core of the cleaning validation program should be aimed at demonstrating acceptable reduction in the levels of the known potentially dangerous contaminants and the primary non-product-related contaminants to which the equipment has been exposed—specifically, residual actives and cleaning agents. However, if there are other areas of particular concern, such as historical problems with lubricant contamination or known interactions of an ingredient with trace levels of a particular contaminant, these should also be specifically addressed in the program.

2. Making the Validation Program Manageable

All of the individual projects within the validation program will be interrelated. Many different products are manufactured using the same equipment. Multiple cleaning procedures are used, depending on the product(s) manufactured. Many products are sold in a variety of strengths and dosage forms. The list of possible contaminants which could find their way into processing equipment is endless.

One of the first tasks, then, is to make the cleaning validation program manageable. It is in no one's best interest to scrutinize randomly every product, in every piece of equipment, using every possible cleaning procedure, and looking for every possible contaminant. The cost of such an approach, in terms of both resources and time, would be unacceptably extravagant and would unjustifiably drive up the cost of products. Fortunately, it is possible to get meaningful information and to provide reasonable levels of assurance with a more rational program. Some of the ways to consolidate the work follow.

Product families: In the simplest case, multiple product strengths will be formulated using identical ingredients and will be manufactured using the same equipment. Under normal circumstances, the greatest cleaning challenge among such a family of product strengths will be that which contains the highest concentration of the active ingredient. Thus, validation of the highest concentration of active can be used to cover all product strengths. While the highest-strength product usually contains the highest concentration of active, this is not always the case, and care must be taken to select the highest-*concentration* product for study.

When products contain different excipients and different or multiple active ingredients, it is sometimes still possible to group them into categories and use successful cleaning validation on the "worst-case" product to cover all products in the group. In these cases, the use of different excipients or even additional actives may be judged not to have any significant effect on the ability to clean the equipment. Such a judgment must be very carefully considered and based on sound scientific reasoning (e.g., solubilities and rates of solution, wettability). It is prudent to confirm such theoretical conclusions with actual scientific experimentation, at a bench or pilot scale.

Equipment families: Products are manufactured in a variety of batch sizes. Often the only difference between batch sizes is the capacity of the equipment used. If the product contact surfaces are fairly simple, such as tanks or tumble blenders, it is reasonable to assume that ease of cleaning is similar between sizes. Again such a conclusion must be considered very carefully, taking into account such factors as surface area-to-volume ratios, equipment complexity, differences in cleaning procedures required to accommodate the different sizes, etc. If there is any doubt, the safest course is to validate all sizes used.

For example, a product may be manufactured in either a 150-ft^3 or a 75-ft^3 twin-shell blender, both of which use a manual cleaning procedure for this example. To justify qualification of the 75-ft^3 blender being extrapolated to cover the 150-ft^3 blender, one must begin by evaluating the configuration, surface area, and volume of the two pieces of equipment.

The configuration includes port covers on each leg and a discharge valve at the bottom of the V. It may also include an agitator/intensifier bar along with the mounting trunions. These are the more difficult areas to clean, since they include gaskets, packing (if a bar is included), and crevices which may collect material. The trunions can prevent good contact with cleaning solvents. The agitator bar should be cleaned separately, since it includes many parts which may be difficult to clean in place. The gaskets on the ports and valve may need to be removed for cleaning.

If all of these portions of the cleaning procedure are examined and found to be adequate, then the overall cleaning procedure must be evaluated for adequacy based on the blender size (volume of solvent used, contact times, etc.). A twin-shell blender is basically a cylinder, cut on a diagonal, and welded into a V shape. Thus, its approximate volume and surface area can be estimated using a cylinder of the same diameter as one leg of the blender and as long as the long (outer) leg length and short (inner) leg length combined. The volume calculation should, of course, agree within reason with the theoretical capacity (nominal working capacity × approx. 1.6). These calculations can then be used to evaluate the quantity of wash and rinse water specified for each cleaning procedure. Based on this theoretical evaluation, it may be concluded that the two blenders are essentially the same in terms of ease of cleaning. To be safe it would be wise to verify this conclusion by testing both several times using a product which is difficult to clean. Once this is done, future work for products which may be made using either blender can be reasonably limited to examination of one blender only, or (more conservatively), to full validation in one blender with a single confirmatory run in the other.

Equipment trains: Another technique which can be used to limit the number of sample analyses required is the equipment train approach. Rather than a separate evaluation of each piece of equipment used to manufacture a product, the entire equipment train can be studied at once. This technique lends itself to the placebo method of evaluation (see below) extremely well.

Challenging the cleaning procedure: To evaluate the effectiveness of a cleaning procedure, the equipment to be cleaned must be contaminated. This can be accomplished either by deliberately contaminating the equipment in some way or by conducting the cleaning studies after normal use of the equipment. Deliberate contamination can be designed to try to simulate worst-case conditions (high concentrations of the compound to be cleaned, methods of application, etc.) but does not duplicate actual production conditions and therefore cannot be assumed to match subtleties of contamination encountered in actual production. It is therefore recommended that cleaning studies follow actual production runs.

The selection of production runs to be followed by cleaning validation studies should take into account the concentration of active and the batch size. As previously stated, the most challenging contamination generally can be expected to result from production of the product in a product family which contains the highest concentration of active, as described above. The greatest surface area will be contaminated by the largest batch size made in a particular piece of equipment. Thus, the largest batch size of the product having the highest concentration of active should be used as the model for cleaning validation studies.

Conversely, the highest concentration of contamination in a subsequent batch of any particular product will result from the production of the smallest batch size normally made in the equipment being evaluated (i.e., fixed total quantity of contamination distributed into the smallest quantity of product). Therefore, minimum testing sensitivity and specifications for residuals should be set based on the minimum batch size for that equipment. This can be accomplished by simulating a subsequent batch using this minimum batch size and testing to a level equivalent to the desired maximum concentration in an actual batch of product or by using a larger batch size (e.g., to ensure complete contact with all surfaces), and testing to a level below that required for a subsequent batch of product. For example, if a 1000-liter tank is used to produce bulk solutions for injection at batch sizes ranging from 500 to 1000 liters and a maximum concentration of 1 ppm of residual active is specified for a subsequent batch of product, then the cleaning validation studies can be conducted using a batch size of 1000 liters (to ensure contact with all internal surfaces in the tank) and the resulting rinse or placebo samples should be tested using a minimum sensitivity of 0.5 ppm.

C. Active Ingredients

The most obvious area for evaluation in cleaning validation is removal of active ingredients from the equipment. This evaluation can be carried out by a number of methods, but all have in common the need for adequate analytical methodology and the establishment of practical yet meaningful acceptance criteria for residuals. Wherever visual inspection of the equipment is practical, in-process acceptance criteria should require visual cleanliness upon thorough inspection. While this is an important requirement and should not be overlooked, it clearly must be supported by appropriate sampling and chemical testing for residuals, as discussed below.

1. Analytical Methods Requirements

It is important to develop and qualify sensitive analytical methodology to detect residual actives. Whereas conducting generic testing (such as USP WFI testing) can provide some information about equipment cleanliness, current state-of-the art cleaning validation work is developed around the detection of the actual ingredient being studied. This is the only way to achieve good assurance that the cleaning procedure is effective for the removal of the active in question.

The methodology developed must be able to detect the active ingredient itself and perhaps some of its major degradation products in the appropriate diluent. The diluent used will depend on the particular cleaning validation method chosen. Typical diluents are water, organic solvents, solid placebo, and liquid placebo. The required sensitivity of the method will depend on the acceptance criterion chosen. The final analytical method should be challenged and validated to be meaningful.

2. Acceptance Criteria

Selection of a practical but meaningful acceptance criterion is one of the most challenging and most important facets of a cleaning validation study. A simple specification of "none detected" is not meaningful without specifying the sensitivity of the method used. It is likewise unreasonable to require samples to demonstrate absence by the most sensitive method currently available. Analytical sensitivities vary widely from one compound to another, the cost of the analytical equipment required to run the "most sensitive" method currently available can be prohibitive, and all studies would have to be repeated each time a more sensitive method is developed. There is thus no easy way around the question of "how clean is clean." A number of approaches to answering this question have been used, ranging from basing the requirements on published specifications for highly toxic or poisonous compounds to use of quantitative pharmacological and toxicological information. Some reasonable approaches follow:

Use of a single, blanket specification: This approach usually uses a poison/toxin analogy and is based on the assumption that the active ingredients used in pharmaceutical products are no more dangerous to humans than such items as arsenic, DDT, hydrogen cyanide, and the like. EPA limits for pesticides in food products allow from about 0.5 to 200 ppm, depending on the hazardous material and the food product involved [2]. All else being equal, contaminants in food products represent a greater threat to consumers than contaminants in drug products, simply because of the differences in quantities ingested. USP and NF limits for heavy metals in such items as acetaminophen, aspirin, microcrystalline cellulose, lactose, and sucrose (among others) allow levels in the range of 5 to 10 ppm [3]. Similarly, USP/NF specifications for arsenic in such items as propylene glycol and liquid glucose range from about 1 to 3 ppm [3]. These examples are chosen simply because they are ingredients which often make up a large proportion of some drug products, and many other examples exist. From these examples, conservative specifications can be set. A typical specification selected for cleaning validation work is not more than 1 ppm calculated as contamination in a subsequent batch of product. This is an important point—specifications should be set using a meaningful basis. To set a specification requiring "not more than (X) parts per million in the sample tested" is meaningless, unless the result can be extrapolated to a quantity to which a patient or consumer would be exposed. The simplest basis is contamination in ppm in a subsequent batch of product.

Acceptance criteria based on pharmacological and/or toxicological data: Another approach, often used to avoid the need for the sometimes excessively conservative limits resulting from the above approach, is to base specifications on known pharmacological and/or toxicological data for the drug compound in question. This approach requires quantitative data, particularly on possible effects from chronic exposure to very low levels of the compound. When such information is available, it can be used effectively to establish acceptance criteria which will generally be more lenient than those which would be established using the poison/toxin analogy. (For further information, see Note Added in Proof.)

Acceptance criteria based on assay limitations: Some compounds do not lend themselves to accurate analysis at very low concentrations. In other cases, the analytical methodology to detect very low levels exists but requires expensive equipment not currently available within the company. In these cases, the maximum sensitivity readily attainable should be determined and evaluated in light of the product's characteristics and normal dosage level. As an example, during the method development work for residual meprobamate, a sensitivity below 10 ppm could not be achieved (the target sensitivity was 1 ppm). Meprobamate is a minor tranquilizer, and the usual dose is about 400 mg. The lowest strength marketed is 150 mg (in a combination product). A worst-case situation in terms of contamination of a subsequent product with residual material from the equipment would be a large tablet or capsule. Using the dosage form weight of the heaviest product which could be made using the same equipment (approx. 1 gram), 150 mg of meprobamate is equivalent to about 150,000 ppm. Thus, a 10-ppm detection limit was judged to include a sufficient safety factor.

3. Methods of Evaluation

There are several reasonable ways to evaluate the effectiveness of cleaning procedures. Each has certain advantages and disadvantages associated with it, and the choice of one over the others should be based on the unique characteristics of the equipment and product(s) involved.

A. Swab Samples

After cleaning the equipment, product contact surfaces can be swabbed to evaluate surface cleanliness. Swabs used should be compatible with the active, in that they should not interfere with the assay, should not cause degradation of the compound, and should allow extraction of the compound for analysis. The solvent used for swabbing should provide good solubility for the compound and should likewise not encourage degradation.

Sampling considerations: The area to be sampled should be in its final condition, as it would be when ready to use. In some cases, it is reasonable to swab the entire product contact surface. However, when this is not reasonable, a known surface area should be tested, and the approximate overall surface area which is represented by the swab(s) should be known. This is necessary in order to convert analysis results from the swab(s) into meaningful information about the total amount of contamination present in the equipment. The area to be sampled should be selected using judgment about which areas are most difficult to clean. Swabs should be contacted with the surface in as reproducible a manner as possible (force used, number of strokes over the same area, etc.). Swabs should be changed regularly to avoid saturation or physical disintegration of the swab. Between sampling and testing, the swabs should be protected from contamination and should be stored in a stable condition to prevent degradation of the residuals. For example, immediately after sampling the swabs could be immersed in a container of the solvent and transported as quickly as possible to the testing laboratory for analysis, or the swab could be carefully dried and stored in the dried state until it is analyzed. In any case, the suitability of the sample storage conditions and allowable storage times should be carefully considered and, as appropriate, demonstrated through suitable experimentation. Control samples should also be provided (unused swabs and solvent). To ensure accuracy of the overall procedure, it can be applied to a surface which has been deliberately contaminated with a known, low level of the active. Obviously, the surface used for this challenge must be made of the same material as the equipment to be tested. To assess the possible reduction in accuracy caused by degradation of the compound during handling and storage, the challenge swab/solvent can be held for various lengths of time (at various temperatures if needed) prior to testing.

Advantages: This method has the advantage of being a direct sampling of the surface and allows the use of solvents which could not be used in bulk to rinse the equipment. This can help ensure the most complete extraction possible from the areas sampled. It is also relatively inexpensive in terms of material required. Finally, the development of appropriate analytical methodology may be facilitated by the use of an appropriate solvent.

Disadvantages: In practice, this method has proved to be subject to wide variations in results. This is explained by the number of variables inherent to the method. Selection of sites to be sampled must be based on somewhat arbitrary judgment, and will vary from person-to-person and with the type of equipment being evaluated. Sampling technique is difficult to standardize. The rubbing force used varies from one person to another, as does the thoroughness with which the surface is contacted. Sampling errors can be frequent. Most solvents continually evaporate while the surface is being swabbed, and the extent of this evaporation can dramatically influence results. The swabs themselves (usually just cotton-tipped swabs) can shed a significant portion of their fibers if the sampler is not careful. In addition, many types of equipment cannot be swab-tested because of their configuration. Any equipment with inaccessible surfaces such as pipes or tubing, hoses, cavities, and the like must be tested by some other means.

Finally, swab testing does not accurately simulate the manufacture of a subsequent batch of product in the equipment. For example, a granulation passed through a grinding mill may well extract more residual material than a swabbing process simply due to abrasion from the impact and shear forces involved. Conversely, swabbing or other pieces of equipment may extract significantly more residual material than would be extracted by its normal operation (e.g., tumble blenders, granulation hoppers), and cleaning sufficiently to meet the acceptance criterion may demand heroic measures which would otherwise be unnecessary.

In a recent article on the subject, Smith [4] proposes an interesting alternative to traditional swabs. Although the work reported in this article involved residual detergent sampling (discussed later in this chapter), the method and results can be applied generally. In Smith's technique, filter paper "swabs" are saturated with an extraction solvent (in this case, water), placed onto the surface to be sampled, and rubbed with light pressure to ensure contact with the surface. This method allows for very accurate determination of the surface area sampled and would seem to provide improved reproducibility in terms of technique. However, its utility may be limited to those residuals with very good solubility in the extraction solvent, since the method sacrifices the ability to improve extraction by physically "scouring" the surface of the equipment.

B.   Rinse Samples

Sampling and testing rinse samples for residual active ingredient is a commonly used method to evaluate cleanliness. This is a fairly convenient method in many cases and requires only control over the solvent used for rinsing and the contact time/mixing involved. The solvent used should be selected based on the solubility of the active ingredient and should either simulate a subsequent batch of product (see Placebo Samples, below) or at least provide adequate solubility. Since the volume of rinse solvent is almost always many orders of magnitude larger than the permitted amount of residual, the solubility of the material in the solvent does not have to be excellent. However, the material's overall solubility and rate of solution, if applicable, should be considered when developing the sampling method to ensure that they exceed the expected needs. As with the swab samples, the potential for degradation of the active in the solvent should be considered. If degradation is a potential problem, either the sample holding time prior to analysis must be reduced to an acceptable level or the assay method developed must be capable of detecting the degradation products.

Sampling considerations: If possible, steps should be taken to ensure the uniformity of the residual material in the rinse prior to sampling. For example, a liquids mixing vessel which is rinsed by filling and subsequently discharging should have the mixer activated for a short time prior to discharging so that any concentration gradients within the rinse are eliminated. Alternatively, a sufficient holding time to ensure uniformity due to diffusion should be used. If the compound in question is insoluble and is therefore present as a suspension, either the rinse must be well mixed prior to sampling or samples must be taken from different levels within the vessel to allow estimation of the total quantity of residual present.

It is also critical that the volume of rinse solvent used be controlled. For equipment designed to hold liquids, either the volume of rinse solvent used should be sufficient to ensure contact with all product contact surfaces, or the method of introducing the rinse solvent should ensure adequate contact with all surfaces. As previously stated, maximum concentration specifications for these rinse samples should be adjusted based on the maximum allowable concentration in a subsequent batch of product, produced at the minimum batch size for that equipment. For equipment not designed to contain liquids, care must be taken to ensure that all product contact surfaces are contacted by the rinse solvent for a period of time sufficient to allow dissolution of any residual material which may be present. In cases such as this, the best way to determine the quantity of rinse solvent used and to ensure uniformity of the sample taken is to collect all of the solvent used for the rinse in a suitable container and to mix the solvent well before sampling. Again, the quantity of solvent used must be known to allow computation of meaningful results. As always, analytical control samples (uncontaminated rinse solvent) should be taken to ensure accurate analysis.

Advantages: This testing method theoretically provides data for the entire product contact surface area of the equipment—something which is rarely possible with the swab method. If the compound being studied is highly soluble in the solvent used and the contact time is sufficient, essentially complete extraction of the compound from the surfaces is likely. Also, when properly executed, the uniformity of the material being sampled should preclude the occurrence of assay variations due to poor sampling technique.

In some cases, the rinse sampling method can make it relatively easy to evaluate the approximate margin of safety achieved by the cleaning procedure. For several water-soluble parenteral products, a simple WFI rinsing procedure using a spray ball has been shown to be adequate for cleaning. This was accomplished by taking timed samples during the rinsing of equipment and plotting the residual active assay results vs. time or amount of water used. The results were as expected—a rapid reduction from relatively high levels initially, then asymptotically approaching a final level below 1 ppm. By extrapolation of the curve obtained, good assurance of routinely reducing residual levels below 1 ppm could be achieved.

Disadvantages: In most cases, only relatively innocuous solvents (most commonly water) can be used with this method for safety and environmental reasons. Should solubility of the active suffer because of this, most of the prime advantages of this method are lost.

As with swab sampling, many equipment designs do not lend themselves to rinse sampling methods. The method applies well to tanks, blenders, filter housings, liquid circulation systems, and similar equipment—all of which are designed to contain liquids. The method is less suitable for fluid bed dryers, granulation milling equipment, powder filling equipment and the like and is unsuitable for tablet presses, most encapsulation equipment, and other equipment which cannot be completely rinsed without risking damage to electrical components and instrumentation.

When nonaqueous solvents must be used for this rinse sampling scheme, the potential for corrosive damage and the cost of acquisition and reclamation of the solvent may be prohibitive.

Finally, the method does not accurately simulate the production of a subsequent batch of product where solids are being studied. This presents the same problems described above for the swab sampling method.

C. Placebo Samples

The placebo sampling method provides the best simulation of actual production of a subsequent batch of product. To use this technique, a suitable placebo formulation must first be chosen. Factors to consider in making this selection include placebo manufacturability, solubility of the compound being studied (liquids), and accurate simulation of actual production conditions. For liquid products, either sterile or nonsterile, water is often the best placebo formulation. For sterile liquids, WFI is usually selected, whereas purified water, USP is generally best for nonsterile liquids. Some actives have only limited solubility in water and are therefore formulated using alternative bases such as a glycol base. If the solubility limitation precludes the use of water, a placebo formulation based on the actual product formulation can be used. This allows meaningful data to be generated—glycol-based products are accurately simulated, whereas products using a straightforward aqueous base would have an additional safety factor built in, above that achieved for the glycol-based products (due to the solubility differences).

For solid products, extraction of residual material from the equipment is usually accomplished through abrasion and physical entrapment or incorporation. Therefore, solubility is not normally an important consideration.

Although it may be desirable to use a generic solid placebo for all applications, this can present some problems. The placebo formulation chosen must be capable of being processed through the appropriate equipment under realistic conditions. For example, a fluid bed agglomeration process must be delicately controlled to be successful. To avoid extensive process development work, which may be required using an arbitrary placebo formulation, use of a formulation based on that of the actual product may be used. This is particularly advantageous when using the equipment train approach, since multiple processing steps are then required, and a placebo formulation based on the active formulation is more likely to behave properly through all steps than a generic formulation.

Sampling considerations This sampling method is well suited to the equipment train approach. If a single placebo batch can be processed through most or all of the processing steps, it will have been exposed sequentially to all possible sources of contamination from residuals. This allows direct testing of cumulative contamination exactly as would be the case when processing a subsequent batch of product. While samples should be taken after each major processing step, only the final end-of-processing samples (e.g., tablets, capsules, filled vials or syringes) need to be tested. Should these samples fail to meet the acceptance criteria, the other (secondary) samples would be tested to identify the source of the contamination. The cleaning procedure for that piece of equipment can then be corrected or improved and the test repeated.

Whether or not the equipment train approach is used, some basic sampling strategies need to be established for each type of process. Process steps designed to provide uniform blends (mixers, blenders, liquid tanks, fluid bed equipment, etc.) should be sampled from various portions of the material, as one would do for content uniformity testing. Conversely, semicontinuous processes (e.g., granulation milling equipment, sluggers, extruders, tablet and capsule machines, vial and syringe fillers) are likely to contaminate the initial material processed more than material which follows. This should be reflected in the sample scheme by taking frequent samples at the beginning of the process and less frequent samples thereafter.

As an example, the sampling scheme specified for sluggers or tablet presses should include samples of the first slugs or tablets produced and then timed samples every 1 or 2 minutes for 10 to 15 minutes and perhaps a sample after 20 and 30 minutes. The first several samples should be tested for residual material, with the other samples only being tested if the initial samples fail to meet the acceptance criteria. When this occurs, data can be analyzed in a manner similar to that described above for rinse samples to plot the reduction in residuals vs. amount of placebo processed. Such an analysis has been used successfully to add a routine placebo scrub step to tablet press cleaning procedures, since this proved to be more reproducibly effective than more traditional cleaning methods (solvent rinses) for cleaning tablet press die tables and tooling.

Advantages: As previously stated, the major advantage of this method of testing is its more accurate simulation of the process which we are trying to protect—production of a subsequent batch of product. It can also allow direct assessment of the effect of cumulative processing steps on levels of residuals when used with the equipment train approach. The use of this approach also reduces the amount of analytical testing required, assuming the end-of-processing samples meet acceptance criteria.

This is also the only method which is applicable to all processing equipment, since the method requires only that the equipment handle the type of material which it was designed to handle (solids, semisolids or liquids). The use of this method with liquid processing is very similar to the rinse sampling method but also allows the use of the equipment train concept with all of the advantages inherent in that approach (described previously).

Disadvantages: The use of full-scale placebo processing to conduct cleaning validation studies can be quite expensive. Except in rare cases, the resulting material is not useful for anything and must be discarded.

The extraction of residuals in solids processing by this method may not be as complete as that achieved by swab or rinse methods, which use dissolution of the residuals more than physical extraction. However, there have been several specific applications in which the use of a placebo was more effective than solvent rinses (cleaning of tablet presses and tooling, encapsulation equipment, and related processes). Also, the extraction achieved is most likely to be similar to that which could be expected when actually processing another batch of product.

Finally, for solid products, questions about uniformity and the resulting validity of the samples are more acute than they would be with rinse samples. This potential disadvantage can be ameliorated by designing the study to include a combination of rinse and placebo samples.

Some examples of processing equipment for which each of the aforementioned sampling schemes would be appropriate are shown in Table 1.

D. Cleaning Agents

A second important focus of cleaning validation is the removal of cleaning agents. These are known equipment contaminants which are added, ironically, to assist in the cleaning operation itself. In most cases, more than one cleaning agent is approved for use. The removal of each one may have to be investigated to ensure that no problems will be encountered with their use. For this reason, it is prudent to limit the number of approved cleaning agents to the minimum required for effective cleaning in various situations. Change control systems at the plant site should cover cleaning agents so that the need for revalidation can be assessed whenever cleaning agents are changed.

Table 1 Applications of Sampling Methods

Sampling method	Common applications (processing equipment)		
	Solids	Liquids	Semisolids
Swab samples	Metal detection devices and magnets Tabletting and excapsulation change parts Film coating equipment Tumble blenders Comminuting mills Wet mixing equipment Intensifier or agitator bars	Filling machine parts Vessels and tanks Agitators and mixers	Emulsification equipment Suppository filling molds and machine parts Kettles Homogenizer parts Agitators and mixers
Rinse samples	Tumble blenders Wet mixing equipment Coating pans	Vessels and tanks (including agitators) Filter housings	Recirculation lines and hoses Kettles and mixers Pumps
Placebo samples	All equipment	All equipment	All equipment

1. Analytical Methods Requirements

Most cleaning agents consist of several different ingredients, each intended to serve a particular function (e.g., surfactants, sequestering agents). In addition, most are designed to be relatively safe for use in food and drug applications. Accordingly, a wide variety of analysis techniques can be considered acceptable. Some common approaches to analysis for residual cleaning agents are:

Simple visual inspection: This method would be suitable only in rare circumstances, such as for checking for removal of cleaning agents which have been proved to be totally inert and harmless.

Physical testing or nonspecific chemical testing: Examples of tests which fall into this category include pH, surface tension, conductivity, and/or standard USP tests for purified water or water for injection. If these non-compound-specific tests are employed, some work should be done to evaluate their relative sensitivity for this application. For example, pH can be a relatively sensitive test in the unbuffered solutions likely to be used for rinsing equipment. By testing the pH of known dilutions of the cleaning agent in question, some idea of the level detectable by the method can be determined. For standard USP water tests to be meaningful, it should be demonstrated that the presence of the cleaning agent will in fact change one or more of the test results.

Single-component assay: When one of the known components of the cleaning agent can be easily assayed, this assay often can be used to estimate the total amount of residual cleaning agent present. Assuming a true solution, the removal of one component of the cleaning agent can be assumed also to demonstrate adequate removal of the other components. In cases where a cleaning agent is known to contain a relatively hazardous ingredient, an assay method for that ingredient should be developed.

Multiple-component assay: The most thorough assay method would be one which quantitatively assays all components of the cleaning agent. As a general rule, such a sophisticated analysis is probably unnecessary. The selection of an appropriate method should be based on evaluation of the relative risk involved (safety or toxicity of the cleaning agent involved, history of problem-free operations, etc.) and the cost (analytical equipment availability, unwieldy methodology, etc.). Even if one had reason to be concerned about varying rates of removal and wished to evaluate all components of the cleaning agent quantitatively, adequate assurance could probably be gained through experimentally evaluating the rinsability of the detergent in laboratory experiments. If these studies showed that all components are removed at roughly the same rate during rinsing, then a single component assay would be formally proven to be justified.

2. Acceptance Criteria

The establishment of an appropriate acceptance criterion is inextricably intertwined with the selection of the analytical methodology to be used, and the foregoing discussion applies. As with residual actives, a conservative specification can be developed using the poison/toxin analogy described previously. As always, any specification should reflect actual implications in product (e.g., "Not more than 1 ppm in a subsequent batch of product" as opposed to "Not more than 1 ppm").

3. Methods of Evaluation

The same methods of evaluation described for residual actives can be applied to cleaning agents. However, the rinse sampling method is predominantly used, due to its simplicity. For solids processing equipment, the placebo approach is generally unsuitable due to sampling and analysis difficulties. Swab samples are usually not needed since the cleaning agents used must be soluble in the rinse solvent if they are to be effectively removed. To rinse and dry the equipment and then swab the surfaces with the same solvent would be redundant (sampling the rinse would be simpler and more representative). For liquids processing equipment, where water can be used for the placebo technique, this is basically just an extension of the rinse method. However, it has the advantage of providing true and direct simulation of cumulative effects when applied to an equipment train.

Studies to demonstrate adequate removal of cleaning agents can be executed in conjunction with those evaluating removal of active residuals. However, each study on actives need not include sampling and testing for residual cleaning agents. Once a sufficient amount of acceptable data has been generated for a particular piece of equipment, using a particular cleaning procedure, validation for that cleaning agent can be considered complete. This is based on the assumption that the removal of cleaning agents is essentially unaffected by the original material processed in the equipment [5]. This is a reasonable assumption, in that any significant deterioration in the ability to remove cleaning agents because of the presence of residual product previously processed indicates an unsatisfactory cleaning procedure which will not meet residual actives acceptance criteria and will have to be corrected anyway. Once the procedure has been made effective for removing the residual product, removal of the cleaning agent should no longer be problematic.

E. Microbiological Contamination and Particulate Matter

Two final areas of potential importance to a cleaning validation program are microbiological contamination and particulate matter contamination. The former may be applicable to both sterile and nonsterile products, while the latter is predominantly a concern for parenteral and ophthalmic sterile products (although gross particulate matter contamination is obviously objectionable in any dosage form).

1. Microbiological Contamination

Equipment may be subjected to sanitization or sterilization processes after completion of cleaning. Where sterile products (or nonsterile products which are at risk from microbial proliferation) are to be produced using the equipment, failure to employ additional treatment after cleaning would be foolhardy. Sanitization and sterilization procedures themselves are beyond the scope of this chapter, but the impact of cleaning procedures on gross microbial contamination and on subsequent equipment processing should be mentioned.

In addition to the obvious potential problems caused by microbial contamination, the associated contamination with pyrogens is of concern. For sterile products, both bioburden and pyroburden increases caused by poor cleaning and storage techniques can have serious deleterious effects on the subsequent processing of the equipment. Any increase in bioburden lowers the assurance of sterility achieved by an ensuing sterilization procedure. Although this may not be significant due to the ability to use overkill sterilization processes for most equipment, these sterilization processes often are not designed to achieve significant inactivation or removal of pyrogens (e.g., steam sterilization). Even dry-heat sterilization procedures designed to deactivate pyrogens may be compromised by a significant increase in pyroburden.

A certain amount of endotoxin removal can be demonstrated for most cleaning procedures, by virtue of the fact that endotoxin can be physically removed along with other contaminants (they are not deactivated by cleaning) [6]. However, this is not usually an objective of cleaning procedures, and further discussion of the subject is beyond the scope of this chapter.

The storage conditions of the cleaned equipment are as important as the cleaning procedures themselves in preventing serious microbial contamination. Cleaned equipment should be adequately dried before storage, and under no circumstances should pooled, stagnant water be allowed to remain in equipment. The use of good judgment is important when it comes to specifying equipment storage conditions.

Methods of evaluation: Unlike residual actives and cleaning agents, control of microbial contamination is more a matter of prevention than one of removal. Evaluation of the effectiveness of a cleaning procedure in removing existing microbial contamination would require challenge testing by deliberately contaminating the equipment or using spore strips. Such studies are conducted for sterilization validation and are inappropriate for cleaning validation work. If active measures to reduce microbial contamination levels are required, reliance on normal cleaning is not reasonable and true sterilization methods must be employed.

However, some evidence that the routine cleaning and storage of the equipment does not allow microbial proliferation may be prudent, depending on the type of product involved and the likelihood of difficulties with the particular cleaning method, storage conditions, and environment. Such evidence should be gathered, when appropriate, by subjecting the equipment to worst-case treatment within the bounds of control employed in the procedure. The proper conditions for such a study can be determined only by a thorough and careful review of the particular procedure(s) involved but should include sampling over time while the equipment is stored under the worst conditions allowed. Proper design and control of procedures and systems is likely to be a better safeguard than such anecdotal evidence, however.

The potential sources of microbial contamination should be considered in its evaluation. These include the water or solvent used for cleaning, the cleaning tools and/or equipment employed, any cleaning agents used, and the environment in which the equipment is cleaned and stored. Adequacy of the water source should be ensured during qualification of the water system. Avoidance of wet storage conditions for cleaning tools and equipment should provide reasonable assurance that they will not be a major source of microbial contamination. Selection of proper cleaning agents and proper storage and use thereof should remove this potential source of contamination. Finally, environmental conditions should be addressed in facility qualification studies.

2. Particulate Matter Contamination

Contamination with gross particulate matter (e.g., brush bristles, large fibers, and other easily visible material) is of concern for all products. Its control, however, is usually a simple matter of proper rinsing (sufficient quantity and/or velocity for removal) and control of the quality of cleaning tools used. Physical inspection of the equipment during or after routine cleaning should also be standard practice to avoid problems with such contamination.

Smaller, visible particles and microscopic particles are of concern for parenteral and ophthalmic preparations. To prevent the processing equipment from being a significant source of such contamination, the quality of the rinse water should be carefully controlled.

Validation of the adequacy of the overall cleaning procedure with respect to particulate matter can be accomplished by sampling and testing the rinse water. While the use of placebo testing methods is feasible, it is generally too cumbersome to consider in a serious way. This is especially true for solid products, in which the placebo would have to be dissolved prior to testing. When taking rinse samples, care should be taken to ensure that all surfaces have been adequately contacted by the rinse water and that the samples removed are representative (e.g., ultraclean sample containers should be used, and the rinse water should be mixed to prevent settling of any particles present). In all cases, sample evaluation should be done in comparison to control samples (e.g., a sample of the rinse solvent before use).

Standard testing procedures should be used (e.g., microscopic evaluation, electronic particle counters). Acceptance criteria should again be based on potential for contamination of a subsequent batch of product and can be extrapolated from current product requirement and USP specifications (section <788>, USP XXII, pp. 1596–8) [3], incorporating suitable safety factors.

V. REVALIDATION

The need for revalidation of cleaning procedures can arise for several reasons. An initial, simple approach to revalidation might be to require routine revalidation, based on the length of time since the original or last validation studies were performed. Although this is certainly possible, it represents a very conservative philosophy and requires an extraordinary commitment of resources to validation. Periodic revalidation of all processes, sterilization procedures, analytical methods, cleaning procedures, facilities, utilities, and equipment is difficult to justify unless changes have been made. A more practical and pragmatic approach is to revalidate for cause. This links revalidation to change control in an important way. Responsible individuals must approve the implementation of changes in materials, equipment, and procedures, and the potential impact of these changes on the original validation work and conclusions must be assessed. With such a system in place, the risk of problems arising from compromising previous validation work can be minimized. It can also be argued that such a system allocates resources in the most efficient way possible.

Assuming proper and sound validation studies were conducted initially, it is reasonable to limit revalidation studies to situations in which something about the materials, equipment, or procedures originally validated has changed in such a way as to put the validity of the original work in significant jeopardy. The key here is evaluation of the potential effects of any change in the materials or procedures used. Depending on the conclusions of this evaluation, no revalidation, full revalidation, or partial revalidation may be judged necessary. "Partial re-validation" in this context, denotes reduced-scale validation studies designed to verify the acceptability of a procedure or portion of a procedure after a change has been made. Some general categories and specific examples follow:

Processing equipment changes: A major change in the equipment used to make a product, such as the use of a fluid bed dryer rather than tray drying, would obviously require revalidation. More minor changes, such as a batch size change in which the capacity of some of the equipment used has been changed, might require only limited work to verify that the cleaning procedures are still effective.

Cleaning equipment changes: Similarly, a significant change in the equipment used to clean the processing equipment (e.g., new spray ball designs which provide different spray patterns) would require at least some revalidation to verify the equivalence or improvement in results. More minor changes, such as the use of different cleaning tools, may require no revalidation at all.

Changes in cleaning agent(s) used: When cleaning agent formulations are changed, revalidation may or may not be warranted. If only minor changes are made, it may be sufficient to compare the effectiveness of the new and old formulations under simulated conditions, using selected products which are known to be difficult to clean. Some evaluation of the ease of removal of residual cleaning agent should also be performed. A major change in the cleaning agent such as use of an entirely new product, normally would require full revalidation.

Changes in cleaning procedures: Again, the significance of the change must be carefully evaluated. Minor changes, such as use of distilled water rather than municipal water or using an additional rinse step, are not likely to affect the overall procedure adversely and probably do not require revalidation work. Major changes, such as cleaning a piece of equipment intact rather than disassembling it, should be fully evaluated by conducting comprehensive validation studies on that piece of equipment. A change in the cleaning procedure used for only one piece of processing equipment would require revalidation of the cleaning of that piece of equipment only.

A multitude of similar examples exists, and the responsible individuals must use sound judgment and reasoned analysis of the potential effects of any change. This analysis, in turn, is used to determine the extent of revalidation required in order to provide adequate assurance that the new procedure can effectively perform its purported function. This analysis and the conclusions drawn may be documented using the existing change control procedures.

VI. CONCLUSIONS

Formal cleaning validation programs are relatively new to the industry and are evolving rapidly. A sound cleaning validation strategy, like other forms of validation, is basically just a blend of common sense, clear analysis, and documentation. There is no one recipe for carrying out cleaning validation studies, but it is possible to provide common concepts and examples to permit one to develop a sound program that applies to the situation at any particular manufacturing facility. This chapter has been prepared to provide such basic concepts and examples, but also to initiate additional deliberation on the subject by others. As with other forms of validation, cleaning validation will evolve as time passes and more and more people develop systems for their companies. This presentation, in conjunction with the articles written on the subject, hopefully provides a reasonably clear depiction of the current state of the art in cleaning validation which should serve as a firm foundation for future development.

NOTE ADDED IN PROOF

Using the estimated maximum allowable mg/kg/day dose, and a reasonable safety factor, a maximum ppm specification can be set for residuals. An exhaustive approach to setting cleaning validation specifications using pharmacological/ toxicological data would have to take into consideration all aspects of the drug products which could be subject to cross-contamination with the drug in question (i.e., those made in the same equipment). This evaluation should include all variables which would affect actual exposure of a patient to the residual contaminant. These include dosage form size (larger dosage forms would contain more of the residual contaminant), dosing schedule (more frequent dosing exposes the patient to more of the residual contaminant), and typical patient population (drug products intended for children and infants present a worse case situation in terms of mg/kg exposure).

Working backward from the maximum allowable mg/kg/day, and applying these considerations to the range of products which could be subject to this cross-contamination results in a series of maximum ppm specifications. These can then be used to determine the maximum total amount of residual permitted in the equipment by taking into account the smallest batch size of each product made in the equipment (the smallest batch size resulting in the highest concentration of residual contamination). However, in order to avoid having to repeat this entire exercise in the event of a future batch size reduction, it may be prudent to simply use the lowest value for maximum ppm of residual in any of the dosage forms, and to calculate the maximum allowable amount of residual in the equipment by assuming that the smallest batch size which would ever be made in the equipment may be used to make that product. Finally, this maximum allowable amount of residual in the equipment can be used to calculate a final maximum cleaning validation sample ppm by taking into account the appropriate factors inherent to the cleaning validation sampling method being used (e.g., quantity of rinse water used or ratio of surface area swabbed to total surface area).

The above approach includes may inherent assumptions and suppositions and requires a considerable amount of analysis including many variables, each with its own uncertainty, which reduces the precision of the overall conclusion. This approach may therefore have the appearance of being a more comprehensive analysis than it really can be, and it should be reasonable to perform a less exhaustive analysis in setting cleaning validation specifications by including larger safety factors, as demonstrated in the example that continues on p. 335.

REFERENCES

1. Harder, S. W., The validation of cleaning procedures, *Pharmaceut. Technol.* May (1984).
2. Code of Federal Regulations, 21 CFR, Part 193.
3. *The United States Pharmacopeia*, XXII Revision, and *The National Formulary*, XVII Revision (official from 1/1/90), United States Pharmacopeial Convention, Mack Printing Co., Easton, PA.
4. Smith, J. M., A Modified Swabbing Technique for Validation of Detergent Residues in Clean-in-Place Systems, *Pharmaceut. Technol.* January (1992).
5. Blackmon, M. L., "Cleaning Validation of Existing Products in Solid Dosage Processes," Proceedings of the PMA Seminar Program on Validation of Solid Dosage Form Processes, May 11–13, Atlanta, Georgia, Pharmaceutical Manufacturers Association, pp. 100–104 (1980).
6. Smith, J. C., "Component and Equipment Preparation Validation," Proceedings of the Second PMA Seminar Program on Validation of Sterile Manufacturing Processes: Aseptic Processing, March 1–2, Atlanta, Pharmaceutical Manufacturers Association, pp. 97–125 (1979).

11

Equipment Validation

Bohdan M. Ferenc, Luanne Kot, and Rodney
Thomas   *Sandoz Pharmaceuticals Corporation, Inc., East Hanover, New Jersey*

I. INTRODUCTION

Commonly accepted equipment validation standards have evolved over recent years through the interpretation of Food and Drug Administration (FDA) guidelines and from various papers at industry conferences and periodicals.

Each chapter in this text contributes a theme to the overall validation picture. We in the pharmaceutical industry have addressed the quality theme in our product, process, personnel, and company through validation.

A validation program encompasses various components within a pharmaceutical organization. It is important to grasp this concept in order to have a successful validation program. This chapter will deal with the equipment validation program, which is only a part of the overall picture toward the goal of a high quality standard.

The other interrelated programs, such as product validation, annual product quality review, change control, standard operating procedures (SOPs), and training have just as important a role as equipment validation. Without the other pieces of the validation puzzle, there would be a fragmented validation program.

Departments such as engineering, quality assurance, compliance, manufacturing, research and development, and technical services are considered integral areas which should understand and contribute to the big validation picture. This team approach program fosters better communication and validation role definition when dealing with various validation projects. Of course, a commitment from management to pursue validation in this manner is a prerequisite.

The validation department, group, or person has various responsibilities within an organization. The individual must be a catalyst to ensure clear validation understanding and philosophy to foster team play, to coordinate various functions between departments, and to contribute to a validation master plan.

FDA is also a key player in the industry. The role of FDA within your organization depends once again on the validation programs and philosophy you have established. If you accept the philosophy mentioned above, FDA could become another team player in your organization.

The following topics will be discussed to establish an overall scheme toward satisfying equipment validation requirements. It is intended to follow a project time line and reference the various personnel involved in its successful completion.

II. PROJECT SCOPE

Usually an operating department will require the purchase of a piece of equipment such as a blender or a system such as a HVAC unit to either replace or complement an existing unit or introduce it as a new investment. The operating department should establish those requirement definitions in order to initiate the project.

The requirements are presented to a team, which is represented by at least the engineering, validation, and operating departments. Preliminary discussions will focus on the actions to pursue the various units that are available on the market. Also, the size and commitment of the investment are focused here to establish the extent of resources (internal and external) and funds to accomplish this task. If the investment is a major project (i.e. facility construction), it might be worth considering the early involvement of FDA as a team player.

Field work or vendor evaluations should always be stressed to identify properly the pros and cons of an investment and how those attributes affect validation requirements.

Assuming that preliminary discussions and field work have been accomplished, it is reasonable to expect assignment of responsibilities to the project at this point. An engineer should be assigned as the technical project manager and an individual representing the customer or operating department should be assigned the role of project coordinator.

The technical project manager is responsible for gathering all the technical information in a file which will eventually be housed in the operating department and also be used as the equipment validation reference file. The organization of such a file, which could be called a technical master file, will include all project definitions, the technical information and specifications about the equipment, various communications and correspondences, the project time line, purchase orders, capital expense requests, a validation plan, etc.

The validation representative ensures that such an equipment file is clearly understood by the project manager and project coordinator. The project manager is a key player in fulfilling equipment validation requirements. The concepts of equipment qualification forms are introduced here also. This will allow the entire team to understand the equipment validation program theory before the actual purchase and implementation.

Once this understanding is achieved, it is an easy task to incorporate the equipment validation time line with the engineering project time line and scope (see Fig. 1).

III. PREQUALIFICATION

An equipment validation program can be described in four sequential phases:

1. Prequalification (vendor specification, design, and operation checkout)
2. Qualification (installation and operational checkout)
3. Process qualification
4. Ongoing evaluation or process validation

Once the decision to purchase a piece of equipment has been narrowed to a few vendors, the project team is assembled to develop an overall implementation plan. Here are a number of important common considerations:

The vendor's previous experience in implementing similar projects
The vendor's financial stability
The vendor's guarantee of installation, training, and start-up support
The client's degree of confidence in the vendor's ability
The level of training offered by the vendor
Performance testing at the vendor site
The vendor documentation and support for testing
Definition of user needs and environment
Experience of current users
Vendor delivery
Cost analysis
Vendor's familiarity with current good manufacturing practices (CGMPs)

Although technical and economic factors have a major bearing on the selection of a vendor, no final decision should be made before analyzing each prospective vendor's capabilities in each of these areas.

Once chosen, the vendor can be considered a team player. The vendor should offer time to assist in establishing the equipment validation plan or protocol with the project team. Of course, the vendor will have normal operational checks and demonstrations, and these should be incorporated into the prequalification protocol with any additional agreed upon testing criteria for equipment prequalification. This initial draft and subsequent performance bond will be the cornerstone of the actual equipment qualification program at the manufacturer's or operating department's site. This protocol should be reviewed and approved by the project team and a sign-off committee (i.e., quality, engineering, validation, and technical services). Acceptability criteria and operational limitation will be clearly understood by the vendor and project team.

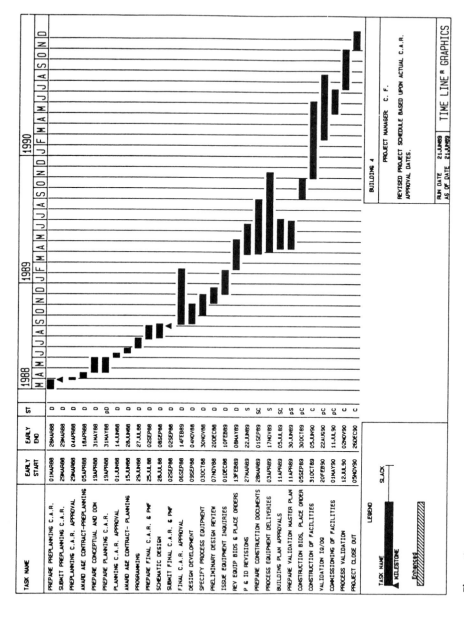

Figure 1

By utilizing this structured evaluation and selection process, the manufacturer is making a relatively minor investment up front to ensure that the major effort of implementation of the new equipment will be minimized.

IV. INSTALLATION QUALIFICATION

The equipment installation is the qualification of equipment as it is to be installed. This qualification involves the coordinated efforts of the vendor (equipment manufacturer), the operating department (owner/purchaser of the equipment), and the project team that will provide input into the purchase, installation, operation, and maintenance of the equipment. Each of these groups is responsible or will contribute to areas of its expertise during the qualification. In most cases this group is established early on during the project scope and definitions phase of the project.

The project team may be organized differently from company to company, and certain team players may wear two hats. The operating department is the department which will own, operate, and be responsible for any GMP issues involved with the equipment. As mentioned earlier, it is in this department that the project scope and definitions began.

At the installation qualification stage, the following support groups should be concerned with the following areas:

Plant engineering is usually responsible for providing an adequate working environment. Issues that should concern this representative are equipment operation space, equipment utilities, and utility capacities.

The equipment management group will be responsible for the maintenance of the equipment. Some of the areas that should concern this representative are the amount of personnel that will be needed to maintain the equipment, filter programs, lubrication programs, drawings, manuals, change parts, spare parts, etc.

It is the responsibility of the validation representative to coordinate the input and effort of all the supporting groups and to ensure compliance with federal and in-house guidelines. The validation group will coordinate all of the documentation; this includes SOPs and operating manuals. It is advantageous for the validation representative to maintain close contact with the operating and engineering departments.

As discussed previously, it is a good practice to begin the equipment installation qualification (see Fig. 2) with a factory installation qualification or prequalification at the vendor's plant. However, this might not be practical for each project or company. If a factory prequalification phase is utilized, it will provide an opportunity to change discrepancies before the equipment reaches the owner's plant. It is a good practice to have representatives of all groups present at this factory installation qualification. The vendor should have representatives from the

A. UTILITIES AND BUILDING SERVICES
    1. Compressed Air
    2. Electrical
    3. Electrical Back-Up System
    4. Lighting
    5. Plumbing
        a. Water
        b. Drains
    6. Steam
    7. Vacuum
        a. Cleaning
        b. Dust Collecting
    8. Ventilation, air filtration, air heating and cooling
    9. Pest Control
    10. Cleaning
B. EQUIPMENT FEATURES
    1. Description
    2. Manufacturers Specifications/Operating Manual
    3. Purchase Order
    4. Materials in Product/Commodity Contact
    5. Instrumentation
        a. Critical
        b. Non-critical (convenience)
C. AUXILIARY EQUIPMENT FEATURES
    1. Description
    2. Manufacturers Specifications/Operating Manual
    3. Purchase Order
    4. Materials in Product/Commodity Contact
    5. Instrumentation
        a. Critical
        b. Non-critical (convenience)
D. SPARE PARTS
E. S.O.P.'s
    1. Operating
    2. Set-Up
    3. Sanitation
F. LOG BOOKS
    1. Preventative Maintenance Program
    2. Cleaning and Use
G. FILTERS
H. LUBRICANTS
I. INSTALLATION DRAWINGS

Figure 2   Equipment installation qualification contents.

various groups that took part in manufacturing the equipment present at the factory installation qualification to provide assistance if questions should arise. A similar detail should be considered if a prequalification program is not utilized. That is, the equipment installation qualification at the owner's site should incorporate those common practices.

Once the prequalification is completed, the efforts move to the owner's plant. The installation area should be reviewed to verify that it is in accordance with the specifications. Again, special emphasis should be placed on the utilities and physical working area. At this point it would be wise to coordinate all documentation in a validation documentation file. This file could be broken down into areas that include installation, operation, and performance qualification, operating manuals, manufacturing and design specification, instrumentation, spare parts, preventative maintenance, lubrication, purchase order, filter program, change control program, engineering drawings, test and inspection reports, standard operating procedures, and cleaning and use log books. These are areas which are important to the use of the equipment.

Once the equipment reaches the owner's plant, a parts list should be reviewed. This is to verify that all parts have been delivered and found acceptable. After the parts list has been verified, the equipment is ready to be installed. Once the equipment is installed, the owner should go through a thorough equipment installation qualification. Beginning with the utilities, it should be documented that each is provided in the necessary capacity. All critical gauges, recorders, sensors, etc. should be calibrated and set up on a calibration schedule. This is part of the instrument installation qualification. Each critical instrument is tagged with an identification number which is used for tracking purposes. The instrument information is also placed in a file (see Fig. 3).

This file should include information such as the instrument type, the manufacturer, the purpose of the instrument, its location and serial number, and its description. Some other information that should be entered into this file is the instrument's calibration frequency, the calibration limits and scale, the utilization range, and the SOP used to calibrate the instrument. This should be in place prior to the validation runs. After the equipment has been properly installed and all critical instruments documented and calibrated (see Fig. 4), the documentation for the equipment IQ can be completed. This document contains information such as equipment description, identification number, model number, serial number, location, and manufacturing operation. This information is used for identification purposes (see Fig. 5).

Other information to consider would be utilities and building services, equipment features, auxiliary equipment, spare parts, standard operating procedures, log books, filter programs, lubrication programs, and installation drawings. This information is used for the purposes of maintenance and equipment operation.

The utilities and building services section should cover the following areas: electricity, air, lighting, plumbing, steam, vacuum, HVAC, pest control, and cleaning (see Fig. 6). The equipment features section should be concerned with the

Instrument Features:
  Description:
  a.   Identification Number:
  b.   Model #/Serial #:
  c.   Capacity:
  d.   Location:
  e.   Utilization:

Calibration Information:
  1.   Calibration Frequency:
  2.   Calibration Number:
  3.   Calibration SOP #:
              Title: _____
  4.   Calibration Limits:
  5.   Minimum Scale Graduation:
  6.   Utilization Range: Minimum:
                           Maximum:

Data Sheet Compiled By: _____ Date: _____

Figure 3   Instrument data sheet.

equipment's description, manufacturer's specifications, operating manuals, purchase orders, materials in product contact, and instrumentation.

The auxiliary equipment features section is for items that may be considered as part to the main piece of equipment but can function as a separate piece of equipment. An example would be a weighing system on an encapsulator. It is important to give a description of the equipment, manufacturer's specifications, operating manuals, purchase orders, materials in product contact, and instrumentation.

The spare parts section should reference a list of spare parts and their location. When parts must be ordered, a purchase order should also be listed.

The section for standard operating procedures should include procedures for operation, setup, and sanitization.

The section for log books should include sign-off books for preventive maintenance programs, as well as sign-off books for equipment cleaning and use.

The filter section should include information on all filters that are part of the main piece of equipment. It should include manuals on the filter type, a list of the spare parts and cartridges associated with the filter, and a preventive maintenance program. A similar section for lubricants associated with the main equipment should be included.

The final section of this document would be one for the drawings that are associated with the piece of equipment. This section should include a reference to the engineering drawings.

```
┌─────────────────────────────────────────────┬──────────────────────┐
│  ▵ ▵ ▲ ▲                                     │                      │
│                                              │   Certificate        │
│                                              │      Of              │
│                                              │   Calibration        │
├─────────────────────────────────────────────┴──────────────────────┤
```

Date Calibrated _____ Time: _____ Equipment No. _____

Last Calibration _____ Due Next: _____ Equipment Name _____

Type _____

Calibration Limits _____ Equipment Location _____

Was Instrument in Calibration: _____ Calibrated Range _____

Instrument Range _____

Calibrated By: _____ Operating Range _____

Minimum Scale Graduation _____

TEST EQUIPMENT USED FOR THIS CALIBRATION:

Name _____ Calib. # _____ Last Calib. Date _____

Name _____ Calib. # _____ Last Calib. Date _____

Name _____ Calib. # _____ Last Calib. Date _____

Name _____ Calib. # _____ Last Calib. Date _____

Name _____ Calib. # _____ Last Calib. Date _____

Name _____ Calib. # _____ Last Calib. Date _____

Scheduled: _____ Non-Scheduled: _____ Reason _____

RECORD READING BEFORE ADJUSTMENTS:

Standard		Equipment Being Calibrated	
_____	_____	_____	_____
_____	_____	_____	_____
_____	_____	_____	_____
_____	_____	_____	_____
_____	_____	_____	_____
_____	_____	_____	_____

RECORD READING AFTER ADJUSTMENTS:

_____	_____	_____	_____
_____	_____	_____	_____
_____	_____	_____	_____
_____	_____	_____	_____
_____	_____	_____	_____
_____	_____	_____	_____

RECORD ADJUSTMENTS/REPAIRS MADE: _____

No. of Charts _____

Document Approved By:
(Plant Operations) _____ Date: _____

Equipment Checked By:
(Operating Dept.) _____ Date: _____

82530/80 (Rev. 4)

Figure 4 Certificate of calibration.

B.   EQUIPMENT FEATURES

    1. Description:

        a.   Identification Number:

        b.   Model Number:

        c.   Serial Number:

        d.   Dimensions:

        e.   Capacity:

        f.   Location:

        g.   Purpose:

        h.   Work Center Number:

    2. A. Manufacturer's Specifications / B. Operating Manual

    A.   Copy Available?
        Location
    B.   Copy Available?
        Location

    3. Purchase Order (If Available)

    a. P.O. #:
    b. Location:

    4. Materials in Product/Commodity Contact
        (Parts -- Material)

    a.   --
    b.   --
    c.   --
    d.   --
    e.
    f.
    g.

Compiled By:_____Date:_____

Page___of___

Figure 5   Equipment installation qualification.

PHARMACEUTICALS CORPORATION Plant Operations	**STANDARD OPERATING PROCEDURE**	
	DEPT. Plant Operations	
	S.O.P. NO. 415-021, Rev. 2	
DESCRIPTION AIR HANDLING SYSTEM 415B-ACAH-01 CONDITIONS AND PROCEDURES COVERING THE OPERATION AND PREVENTIVE MAINTENANCE	ISSUE DATE: 6/30/87	
	PREVIOUS ISSUE 6/19/85	
	PREPARED BY	

1.0 PURPOSE:

To define the Standard Operating Conditions and the
Standard Operating Procedures for the air handling system
415B-ACAH-01.

2.0 GENERAL INFORMATION:

    2.1 Supply Air Fan

2.1.1	Fan	:	Manufacturer	:	Trane
2.1.2			Model #	:	35
2.1.3			Capacity	:	20,130 CFM
2.1.4	Motor	:	Manufacturer	:	General Electric Co.
2.1.5			Serial #	:	K3B229134
2.1.6			HP	:	40
2.1.7			RPM	:	1770
2.1.8			Power	:	460V, 3 Phase, 60 cycle
2.1.9			Power Source	:	415B-MCC-01 in 415B Mezz.
2.1.10	Roll Filters	:	Manufacturer	:	Drico
2.1.11			Size	:	68" x 124"
2.1.12			Efficiency	:	40%

OPERATING DEPARTMENT		COMPLIANCE			
NAME	DATE	NAME	DATE	NAME	DATE

89789/82A (Rev. 2)   Page 1 of 9

Figure 6 Utility operating procedure.

V. OPERATION QUALIFICATION

On completion of the installation of the equipment at its final processing site and of the installation qualification document, a complete equipment operation qualification (see Fig. 7) must be performed. This should be accomplished via an established and accepted protocol which will give adequate assurance that the equipment to be validated performs within the assigned limits when operated by approved standard operating procedures. The proper operation will be verified by performing the test functions specified in the protocol. A conclusion will be drawn after the test functions are checked and all data are analyzed.

The equipment operation qualification protocol should describe all aspects of the testing of the equipment in detail. This protocol should be similar to the pre-qualification testing performed at the vendor's site. The equipment should be identified by physical description as well as by model number, serial number, and location. The vendor should help in supplying the necessary information. All standard operating procedures that pertain to the unit should be listed by number, title, and location for ready reference. A utilization list should be completed and should include any and all applications for which the equipment will be used. For instance, it should detail the exact products or raw materials to be processed by the equipment. This information will prove useful especially in the case of portable equipment, which may be used for several different applications or in different locations.

A process description should also be included which explains exactly how the equipment is to be used to process or package a product. The actual performance and documentation of the physical testing will be of ultimate importance in completing the operation qualification. Testing previously performed at the vendor's site may be necessarily duplicated at the processing site to ensure quality of performance.

At this stage of development, decisions should be finalized as to which parameters will be deemed critical operating parameters. These decisions will be based on the combined expertise of the validation, operating, technical services, compliance, or other responsible department. A critical operating parameter is one which has significant impact on the equipment's ability to operate and meet process specifications satisfactorily and is challenged through the use of an

    I.   Application S.O.P.'s
   II.   Utilization List
  III. Process Description
  IV. Test Instruments Utilized to Conduct Test
   V. Test Instrument Calibration
  VI. Critical Parameters
 VII. Test Functions (List)
VIII. Test Function Summaries

Figure 7 Equipment operation qualification contents.

appropriate test function (see Fig. 8). Several critical operating parameters for a mixer, for example, would be speed, rotation, and time. The operation qualification should clearly list all critical operating parameters and their corresponding test functions. It should also list all test instruments utilized to conduct the test functions prescribed by the protocol. All applicable test instruments used in the qualification should be calibrated both before and after the test is performed. The only deviation from this procedure occurs in the case of an instrument requiring factory calibration, in which case the most recent factory NBS traceable calibration certificate will be used. All documentation to support test instrument calibration should be included in the qualification report.

As test functions are performed, a test function summary sheet should be completed detailing the testing. Here, the actual test is described and accompanied by a statement of purpose and the procedure used to implement the testing. Test instrumentation or equipment is listed, if applicable, as well as determination of acceptability, results, and conclusions. A separate summary should be drawn up for each different test function performed.

Much of the qualification testing may entail working with placebo batches. Placebo testing would be required for the validation of parenteral filling machines, tablet compressors, encapsulators, sugar or film tablet-coating systems, granulators, branding machines, lyophilizers, packaging fillers, and other types of equipment intended for the processing or packaging of drug products. Consideration should be given to the scheduling of placebo batches to be manufactured, and advance notice should be given to the responsible department. An appropriate sampling plan should be devised and approved in order to properly monitor the processing of the placebo batch. Quality assurance support will also need to be scheduled carefully in order to accommodate any testing.

VIII. Test Function Summary
      EQUIPMENT DESCRIPTION
      IDENTIFICATION NUMBER
      MODEL NUMBER   SERIAL NUMBER
      TEST FUNCTION NUMBER
TEST DESCRIPTION
TEST INSTRUMENTATION/EQUIPMENT NEEDED
TEST PROCEDURE
ACCEPTABILITY DETERMINED BY
RESULTS
CONCLUSIONS
Compiled by: _____ Date: _____
                    Page ____ of ____

Figure 8 Equipment operation qualification.

Upon satisfactory completion of the qualification testing and documentation, process qualification work may commence.

VI. PROCESS QUALIFICATION

This stage could be considered a transitional stage for the roles of the individual team players. The project engineer or manager had a significant role prior to this phase to ensure proper delivery, installation, and operation as prescribed by the vendor's purchase order and equipment validation protocol. The Validation representative was the member who assured clear definitions of equipment validation, performed various tests as prescribed by the equipment validation protocol, and was the bridge between the engineering and operating department functions of the project. The operating department supported the engineering function with resources for mechanical requirements, schedules to allow implementation of the project in the particular area, and programs such as SOPs and training.

This phase will see the engineering function coming to a close with the various engineering and validation sign-offs. The validation function will allow the project to move closer to final close-out and transfer of the entire project to the project coordinator or operating department.

There are usually several additional steps to be addressed at this point. If the project involves equipment in the sterile area, the process qualification program will follow a plan of additional testing to prove lethality, particulate reduction, bioburden reduction, etc. This area is clearly explained in the chapter on validation of sterile products. If the project involves equipment in the solids area, involvement with technical services testing may be included with the equipment validation program.

There might be an issue with product dependency with the new equipment, and actual product runs under the direction of technical services might be necessary. The work could generate equipment operating limitations with particular products. This in turn could lead to involvement of a group to establish statistical process control limits of operation.

The quality assurance and compliance departments have a role throughout the process. However, at this stage there are decisions to be made from a small amount of data as to acceptable means of operation. The decisions made here do not end, because the next program of ongoing evaluation or process validation will continually examine the product characteristics. This data base of information will allow quality assurance and the operating department to make a better judgment of product runability in relation to the equipment operating parameters.

VII. EQUIPMENT APPROVAL

The validation team has now successfully demonstrated equipment validation. They have worked together and across various departmental responsibilities to allow the transfer and completion of the project.

The validation individual constantly works closely with each of the team members to bridge the communications gap of engineer and operating department. The project manager at this point is anxious to transfer the project to the customer or project coordinator/owner. This is accomplished with the role of the validation individual and the coordination and summarization of all work to the sign-off personnel. The validation individual will circulate the completed installation, operation, and process qualification documents for final comments and approvals (see Fig. 9).

The final documents and project should be understood by the sign-off group. It is imperative that the validation individual spend as much time as necessary to explain and educate those personnel about the project results. Those personnel should include representatives from the following areas: quality, engineering, manufacturing, technical services, and validation.

Any comments or corrections by the sign-off committee will be followed up by the validation individual.

Once the documents are signed off, the validation individual will transfer the documents and all engineering files to the operating department (owner) for retention. The project at this point is considered complete. The owner is responsible for organizing those files properly for controlled access. It is also recommended that all files be microfilmed as an added security measure.

VIII. CHANGE CONTROL

The preceding discussions elaborated on the validation of a piece of equipment and the roles of various individuals until project completion. The operating department has a final ongoing responsibility for maintaining the validated equipment or system during its entire operating life.

Change control is a monitoring system which ensures that a validated system remains validated by recognizing and addressing the potential impact of a change to the system.

Implementing change control requires a number of decisions regarding scope, responsible disciplines, documentation practices, review procedures, etc. The user has the ultimate responsibility for change control; however, approval by the quality department and technical areas such as engineering and validation is suggested.

The initial qualification of the equipment is the foundation for change control systems for the physical portions of the equipment, be they process equipment or control hardware. Sufficient detailed documentation is necessary for each critical change (impact to the process) in order to maintain control over the system with the passage of time (see Fig. 10).

Various changes can be categorized by multiple, planned, or emergency changes. Multiple changes require a broad awareness of the potential effect a change will have elsewhere in the equipment system. A multidisciplinary review provides greater assurance that the effects of change on the entire equipment system will be properly assessed. Planned changes, their impact on the entire

EQUIPMENT DESCRIPTION:

		Signature	Date
COMPLIANCE	O Acceptable		
	O Unacceptable	_____	____
QUALITY ASSURANCE	O Acceptable		
	O Unacceptable	_____	____
TECHNOLOGY	O Acceptable		
	O Unacceptable	_____	____
OPERATING DEPARTMENT	O Acceptable		
	O Unacceptable	_____	____
EQUIPMENT MANAGEMENT	O Acceptable		
	O Unacceptable	_____	____
BUILDING ENGINEERING	O Acceptable		
	O Unacceptable	_____	____
VALIDATION	O Acceptable		
	O Unacceptable	_____	____

Remarks: _____
_____
_____
_____
_____
_____
_____
_____
_____
_____
_____
_____
_____
_____
_____

Prepared by:_____Date:_____

Figure 9   Acceptance of equipment validation.

ORIGINATING DEPT.

Equipment/System No._____ Location_____
Title/Name_____

Description of Change and Purpose_____
_____
_____
_____

Originator:_____Date:_____

- -

Validation, Engineering, Technology or Operating Dept.

Results to be Accomplished:_____
_____
_____
_____

Description of Tests and Requirements:_____
_____
_____
_____
_____
_____
_____
_____

Signature:_____Date:_____

Certification Documents Updated:

1.____Installation Qualification   3.____Validation   5.____None
2.____Operation Qualification   4.____Calibration

APPROVED BY:

Operating Dept.   Quality Assurance

_____,_____   _____,_____

Compliance   Other

_____,_____   _____,_____

Figure 10 Change control form.

equipment system, and the criteria for equipment evaluation after implementation should be agreed to before the change is made. Time should be allotted for consideration, design, development, and execution. Emergency changes are often the result of an equipment malfunction (either process or control). These problems can be remedied by having the necessary spare parts, installation, and performance checking and documentation.

The operating and validation departments will work closely together to follow through with assessing any change impact and its corresponding testing, documentation, review, and approval.

IX. SUMMARY

This chapter discussed equipment validation through the normal responsibilities of various individuals within a pharmaceutical plant. It should be clear that although those individuals have their separate responsibilities, a project team approach toward any equipment validation requirements is the most practical. The engineering, operating, and validation department individuals must understand validation definitions and how they can best interact among themselves and with any support groups through a project time line. An approved test plan or protocol from the prequalification to process qualification phases of the validation requirements is the heart of the documentation that will satisfy CGMP requirements. The remaining engineering, validation, and operating department files, such as communications, drawings, and specifications, are the documents that will complete an equipment validation file. Each pharmaceutical company will be organized differently, but a commitment to an equipment validation program as described above or one designed to achieve similar results will set forth a standard of quality excellence for our processes, products, and industry.

REFERENCES

1. Agalloco, J. P., and Carleton, F. J., *Validation of Asceptic Pharmaceutical Processes*, Decker, N.Y., 1986.
2. Avallone, H. L., CGMP inspection of new drug products, *Pharmaceut. Technol.* *13*(October):60–68 (1989).
3. Byers, T. E., "Validation: A Systematic Approach to Quality Assurance," Pharmaceutical Technology Conference, New York, September (1981).
4. Chapman, K. G., Validation; a way of thinking, *Pharmaceut. Eng. 7*:15–16 (1987).
5. Food and Drug Administration, *General Principles of Process Validation*, Current Good Manufacturing Practice Guideline, March (1987).
6. Federal Register, Department of Health, Education and Welfare, Food and Drug Administration, Human and Veterinary Drugs, *Current Good Manufacturing Practices*, Rockville, MD (1978).
7. Fry, E. M., General principles of process validation, *Pharmaceut. Eng. 4*:33–36 (1984).
8. George, A., Validation considerations in pharmaceutical processes and plant design, *Pharmaceut. Eng. 4*:15–20 (1984).

12

Process Validation of Raw Materials

Ira R. Berry *Banner Pharmacaps, Elizabeth, New Jersey*

I. INTRODUCTION

Validation of pharmaceutical raw materials (sometimes referred to as components) is an important exercise in process control. Before validating a specific process or raw material, all phases of the basic manufacturing operation must be evaluated to assure that the basic operation is under control. It does not make good business sense to validate the part of a manufacturing operation concerned with a specific process or raw material while there may be basics that are out of control.

This concept is important and will be elaborated upon. Hence, the following material is presented on validating the manufacturing process for a specific pharmaceutical product with one active ingredient. Much time, effort, and expense are devoted to generating data to validate the raw material to be used and to identify any potential pitfalls. For example, raw material sampling plans, specifications, test procedures, and stability data will be developed and validated. Criteria will be developed to assure that uniform and reproducible product batches will be manufactured. There will be no assurance, however, if there are not operating procedures and controls to prevent cross-contamination of product batches, use of raw materials before they are approved, and manufacture of product batches by untrained personnel. These are but a few of the basic phases of a manufacturing operation that must be studied and validated first; they must be shown to be under control before validating a specific process or raw material. If this exercise is not done first, process validation will be meaningless and without foundation.

A. Why Validate a Process?

In order to perform process validation properly, it is important to understand why it is done. The explanation has two essential parts.

First, process validation of a finished pharmaceutical product is required by the current good manufacturing practice (CGMP) regulations promulgated by the U.S. Food and Drug Administration (FDA). Section 211.110 of these regulations states "to monitor the output and to validate the performance of those manufacturing processes that may be responsible for causing variability in the characteristics of in-process material and the drug product" [1]. This means that we must establish in-process and finished product controls—such as physical checks and chemical and microbiological tests—so that we will be able to identify any undesirable change that may occur during batch manufacture and to generate data to support batch approval. Testing of the finished product is not adequate for batch approval and, in some cases, in-process checks are more meaningful. In the case of a sterile product, for example, sterility testing of a finished product is based on testing a statistical number of samples that have been selected as representative of the batch. The results generated by such testing will indicate the probability that a given production unit is sterile. It would not be economically feasible to assure 100% sterility, so this testing is by no means a guarantee of absolute sterility. In-process controls—such as in steam sterilization, the use of temperature probes placed throughout the chamber with temperature readout and recording—can be used to verify that the desired temperature for sterilization has been reached and the operation has been performed successfully. Such controls may provide more assurance than finished-product testing.

The other part of Section 211.110 quoted requires that we identify and study all parts of the manufacturing process that may cause variation in the in-process material or finished product. Then we must validate the manufacturing process that is established to assure that if this process is followed variations will not occur in the finished product. In other words, any variation in a product batch manufactured from a validated process would be caused by a deviation from the established manufacturing process. Such variation should be detected by the in-process controls or finished-product testing. Validation of a process is based on challenge and testing, and is performed once as a study, as contrasted to in-process testing, which is performed on every batch.

Second, process validation should be performed because it is in accord with good business judgment. The requirements to evaluate a process, provide challenge, and accumulate and interpret the resulting data all provide a greater understanding of the process and the product. If a problem should occur at some time in the future during production of a batch, there will be a base of knowledge and familiarity with the product to draw on for cause and solution. The net result will be a reduced number of batch rejects and problems that may result in product recalls. The integrity of the manufacturer will be strengthened, as higher-quality products will be distributed commercially. Financial losses that occur through batch rejects, product returns, and complaints and recalls will be reduced and less likely to occur. All factors being considered, process validation is appropriate not only for pharmaceuticals, but it should be considered for any other manufactured product including foods, chemicals, cosmetics, and diagnostic agents.

II. WHAT TO VALIDATE

A. Recordkeeping

The first step toward process validation is to establish a recordkeeping system that considers all aspects of the manufacturing process, which includes controls (or testing). A recordkeeping system must be established, if it does not exist already, to provide written records for the validation operations to be conducted. In order to duplicate a favorable result and prevent duplication of an unfavorable result, we must document the operations performed so that we have records that we can review, interpret, and pass judgment on. We cannot rely on memory and word of mouth. The system of recordkeeping has multiple facets.

1. *Standard operating procedures* (SOPs) are written procedures that describe how to perform basic operations in a plant. They explain certain minimum requirements to assure that there is a level of control which is necessary to operate the process and as a foundation for validation. These procedures should be written in language that is simple enough for an untrained nonprofessional to understand. Also, any new personnel with minimal experience should be able to understand and follow these procedures. They are applicable to many different phases of a manufacturing operation.

a. *Facilities.* One type of SOP applies to the physical facilities of the plant. Procedures must be written that include frequency, a listing by steps of what must be done, and how it is to be accomplished. Often, it is important to keep a log that indicates the dates on which certain operations are done and the individuals who perform the operations. Every plant is different, and the types of products manufactured in each facility may be totally different. Written SOPs must cover all operations performed within a plant with emphasis given to preventing potential problems in a specific plant based on knowledge of the physical facility, the nature of the products and materials used, and the personnel employed.

There must be *cleaning procedures*, first, for cleaning the walls, floors, and ceilings. They must include frequency of cleaning, the different steps that are required, and the cleaning agents acceptable for use. Different areas within a plant will require different SOPs. For example, a sterile filling room will require more elaborate cleaning than a warehouse. A prototype SOP is illustrated in Fig. 1.

Another SOP category related to the physical facility is *environmental*

XYZ CORPORATION

STANDARD OPERATING PROCEDURE

TITLE: CLEANING PROCEDURE	*DATE APPROVED: 6-11-80*
FOR PROCESSING DEPARTMENT	*PAGE 1 OF 1*

DAILY (or as needed)

1. *Mop floor in the morning and end of day, or as needed, with an approved detergent. Replace cleaning solution as needed when it becomes dirty. Floor must be clean when the department is shut down.*

2. *Sanitize the floor at least once daily with an approved disinfectant. The mop used for sanitizing should be placed in a pail of water and steam bubbled through for 15 minutes first.*

3. *Empty waste containers.*

4. *Wash countertops with a solvent such as isopropyl alcohol.*

5. *Inspect bulk drums and tanks - top and exterior walls - and wipe with a solvent.*

6. *All spills must be wiped up immediately.*

7. *All waste should be deposited in the proper trash receptacles provided.*

WEEKLY

1. *Wash plastic entrance curtains with an approved detergent.*

2. *Sanitize sink with an approved disinfectant.*

Record checks in the attached log.

ISSUED BY:	*APPROVED BY*
JJ	*EM*
AL	*LS*

Figure 1   Facility cleaning procedure.

control. All plants must be kept free of rodents and insects. Such an SOP will indicate acceptable materials to be used, precautions to prevent product and personnel contamination, frequency, and area monitoring procedure. In some operations such as an area to manufacture sterile products, there are requirements for control of air temperature, humidity, flow rates and patterns, and particulate matter. These SOPs require steps such as checks to be performed including temperature reading and frequency, maintenance to be performed such as changing air filters and frequency, recording instrument checks, and calibration such as for temperature and frequency. A prototype SOP is illustrated in Fig. 2.

A third SOP category relating to the physical facility covers the plant *maintenance* function. The key consideration in these SOPs for manufacture of the highest-quality products most efficiently is preventive maintenance. Correcting a breakdown in a plant support system such as a motor burned out because it was never oiled is not maintenance but rather repairs, which generally are more costly. Preventive maintenance SOPs in a plant should cover the basic air-handling systems, water systems, physical structures as walls and ceilings, waste removal system, and the heating and cooling systems. They should include replacement of worn parts, lubrication, replacement of filters, cleaning traps, checking for leaks. A prototype SOP is illustrated in Fig. 3.

Safety represents the fourth type of SOP related to the general facility. When unsafe conditions are present in a plant, the probability that an accident will occur increases. Besides the fact that personnel will be affected detrimentally, an accident may occur and unknowingly affect a product batch. For example, a person carrying a container of waste material may slip and fall and simultaneously spill some waste into an open container of a product batch without being aware that this contamination has occurred. It is prudent to establish SOPs to include safety concerns such as cleaning spills, importance of dry floors, proper storage of hazardous materials such as flammable solvents, personnel practices such as running, emergency evacuation of the plant, and plant safety inspections. A program of SOPs such as these will aid also in increasing employee morale, as the employer shows that he is concerned about the personal well-being of the plant employees. High morale is a very important factor in producing quality products.

Housekeeping is the fifth category of SOP that relates to the basic facility. Housekeeping is concerned with keeping materials, especially those in storage, neat and orderly and always identifiable. Proper housekeeping provides better efficiency and minimizes mix-ups. A warehouse that is organized with pallets properly aligned and not tipped, with adequate aisle space to move materials and properly segregate different items will be less apt to use unauthorized material or ship a customer the wrong product. In a label storage room that segregates labels well and in a neat and orderly manner, there will be small risk of the wrong label being issued. If the wrong label should be issued for a product batch, after an investment of a good deal of expense in validating a process to produce the highest

XYZ CORPORATION

STANDARD OPERATING PROCEDURE

TITLE: ENVIRONMENTAL CONTROL PROCEDURE	*DATE APPROVED: 8-15-79*
FOR PEST CONTROL	*PAGE 1 OF 1*

A program will be followed to control pests such as insects and rodents. Twice per month the plant will be inspected. Cracks and crevices will be sprayed with a liquid stream of an approved chemical for insects. If there is an opening where a roach nest is suspected, a fogging aerosol will be used - nontoxic for use in drug establishments. Bait in enclosed stations will be used for rodents.

The following materials only are acceptable for use in pest control:

> *Cracks and Crevices (insects) - Chemical A*
> *Opening (roaches) - Chemical B*
> *Rodent bait - Chemical C*

The attached log and this SOP are to be posted and operations noted after each semimonthly inspection.

Each inspection is to include the following:

1. Bait boxes should be in place and checked for rodent bodies.
2. Management should be notified of any rodent body found. Location of box must be included in notice.
3. A map is attached listing bait box locations. If a box is crushed, it must be repaired and reported. Employees must protect against product contamination from pesticide.
4. The following areas shall be checked and treated as explained above:

A. All offices	*D. Shipping and Receiving areas*
B. Cafeteria	*E. Warehouse area*
C. Quality Control Laboratory	*F. Rest Rooms*

5. All production areas are to be inspected and any evidence of insects or rodents reported to management immediately.

ISSUED BY:	*APPROVED BY:*
KB	*EM*
SB	*LS*

Figure 2 Environmental control procedure.

TITLE: MAINTENANCE PROCEDURE *TO BLOW DOWN WATER LINES*	*DATE APPROVED: 10-20-81* *PAGE 1 OF 1*

DAILY

1. *Blow down tank T1 and T2 ball valves in the compressor room.*

2. *At deionizer unit, clean the screen in "Y" connection with tap water and replace.*

3. *Blow down the boiler make-up water tank using the ball valve.*

4. *Record all work done, and any other maintenance or repairs, in the attached log.*

5. *Report any damage to the Maintenance Supervisor.*

ISSUED BY:
  BR
  WT
	APPROVED BY
	EM
	LS

Figure 3   Facility maintenance procedure.

quality product, this is a very unfortunate problem and a not uncommon one. Housekeeping is important to all the operations conducted in a plant.

   b.   *Equipment.* A second type of SOP relates to the equipment used to manufacture product batches. Equipment includes tanks; mixers; utensils; scales; pumps; measurement devices for temperature, pressure, and speed of movement; lyophilizers; tableting machines; ovens; mills; sterilizing chambers; encapsulators; filling machines; labelers; conveyor systems; laboratory instruments such as pH meters, spectrophotometers, gas chromatographs, and HPLC systems.

   One category of these SOPs describes equipment cleaning. The same type of information is required as in facility cleaning except as relating directly to the equipment involved. SOPs must describe step by step what is to be done, disassembly and assembly, frequency, and acceptable cleaning agents. A typical SOP is illustrated in Fig. 4.

   Sterilization SOPs can be included with cleaning procedures for the corresponding equipment or can be treated separately. In either case, when sterile equipment is required, there must be a written procedure for the sterilization operation. Details of the procedure include step-by-step instructions for sterilization using a medium such as steam, ethylene oxide, or radiation.

XYZ CORPORATION
STANDARD OPERATING PROCEDURE

| *TITLE: CLEANING PROCEDURE* | *DATE APPROVED: 10-15-72* |
| *FOR PROCESSING EQUIPMENT* | *PAGE 1 OF 1* |

1. *All equipment is maintained in a clean and sanitary manner.*

2. *All equipment is checked for cleanliness before use.*

3. *After equipment is cleaned it is tagged "Clean." Used equipment is
    tagged "To Be Cleaned." This equipment includes tanks and mixers.
    Batch identification labels are not removed from the tanks until the
    tanks are cleaned.*

4. *Records are maintained in log books for cleaning the tanks and mixers.
    The records include: date, product, lot number, equipment number,
    cleaned by, checked by.*

5. *After a batch is processed, the empty tank is cleaned with hot water,
    then with deionized water and air dried completely. Tanks with valves
    are then disassembled, steam-cleaned and reassembled dry.*

6. *All mixers are cleaned after use. The mixing blade is removed and
    cleaned with hot water, then with deionized water and dried completely
    with a clean and lint-free absorbant.*

7. *Utensils are cleaned with hot water, then deionized water. and dried
    with a clean and lint-free absorbant or air dried.*

8. *All clean equipment and utensils are protected from accumulating dust
    in storage, either by a cover or by being placed in a drawer or cabinet.*

ISSUED BY:	*APPROVED BY:*
LR	*EM*
AT	*LS*

Figure 4 Equipment cleaning procedure.

    The third category of equipment SOPs describes *maintenance*. These SOPs
are similar in nature except that they relate specifically to equipment used in
production and testing. Highlights of these procedures include preventive maintenance by lubrication, replacement of worn parts, disassembly and cleaning,
changing oil and filters, and inspecting for problems. A typical example is shown
in Fig. 5.
    Equipment *operation* is another category of these SOPs. This type of proce-

```
XYZ CORPORATION
STANDARD OPERATING PROCEDURE
```

TITLE: MAINTENANCE PROCEDURE FOR MIXERS	DATE APPROVED: 11-19-78 PAGE 1 OF 1

MONTHLY

1. Grease all fittings.

2. Visually inspect the lugs on the base for wear and signs of cracking.

3. Start mixer and listen for any squeaks. Correct as necessary.

4. Record all operations in the attached log, for each mixer.

5. Report any problems to the Maintenance Supervisor.

ISSUED BY:
    AS
    TL
	APPROVED BY:
	    EM
	    LS

Figure 5   Equipment maintenance procedure.

dure is applicable to more complex types of equipment but not to all. Obviously, we would not need an operating procedure for a stainless steel tank but would for a lyophilizer. These SOPs provide a detailed step-by-step sequence of operations to run a piece of equipment. They begin with equipment assembly, then operation, and finally equipment disassembly.

Calibration SOPs are needed for all measuring equipment. Temperature, pressure and speed of movement, and weights are typical measurements performed on production equipment. There are many different types of instruments in the control operations that perform measurements, i.e., pH, dissolution rate, chemical assays, tablet hardness, optical rotation, and optical density. Some measurements are taken routinely with a gauge (e.g., a thermometer) and some with recording devices (e.g., a temperature recorder). In either case, the gauge or recording device must be calibrated periodically with a reliable standard such as a National Bureau of Standards traceable source. An example of this type of SOP is illustrated in Fig. 6.

c. *Personnel.* A third type of SOP relates to the personnel in a plant who are involved directly in the manufacturing and control process. We have described many different types of procedures and the steps to be performed. We have not indicated the personnel to be responsible for these operations, however. All personnel in a plant who are involved in the manufacturing process—especially production, maintenance, and control—should have specific written *job descriptions*. As part of the SOP system, these job descriptions must be very clear in

XYZ CORPORATION
STANDARD OPERATING PROCEDURE

TITLE: CALIBRATION PROCEDURE FOR   *DATE APPROVED: 1-15-76*
CONSTANT TEMPERATURE CHAMBERS   *PAGE 1 OF 1*

All constant temperature chambers - including refrigerators, incubators,
water baths, ovens,and autoclaves - will have their temperature monitored.

1.   *Once every day each chamber will be checked and the temperature*
     recorded.
     SPECIFICATIONS:
     a. $5^{\circ}C \pm 3^{\circ}C$
     b. $32^{\circ}C \pm 2^{\circ}C$
     c. $37^{\circ}C \pm 2^{\circ}C$
     d. $40^{\circ}C \pm 2^{\circ}C$
     e. $45^{\circ}C \pm 2^{\circ}C$
     f. $121^{\circ}C \pm 2^{\circ}C$

2.   *Each chamber will contain a partial immersion thermometer in a con-*
     tainer of fluid.

3.   *Each thermometer will be calibrated quarterly using an NBS thermo-*
     meter and noted in the attached log.

4.   *If temperature is outside the acceptable range, notify the supervisor*
     immediately.

5.   *Any adjustment or maintenance is to be recorded in the log.*

ISSUED BY: *APPROVED BY:*
     ST   *EM*
     RV   *LS*

Figure 6   Calibration procedure.

indicating a person's responsibilities and duties. A porter must understand very
clearly which areas are to be cleaned and how this is to be accomplished. A
production line operator must understand which lines to work on, what he or she is
responsible for, and when to call on other employees. The operator must fully
understand, for example, if a machine on the line spills product whether to clean
the spill or call a porter. In addition to knowing their duties, all individuals must
be intimately familiar with the different SOPs that are required to perform their

job. SOPs should not be written to be kept in the company's files. They should be used by personnel performing their respective functions and, at times, even posted.

Other categories of personnel SOPs include *personnel practices and cleanliness*. In a pharmaceutical plant, there must be established rules and regulations regarding proper dress, i.e., uniforms and hats, safety glasses, hard hats, jewelry, smoking, eating and drinking, storage of personal articles, and washing hands. A very important SOP is the one that describes *personnel training*. All newly hired personnel should participate in training in their job responsibilities, all related SOPs, company rules and regulations, and CGMP regulations. After initial training there should be a continued routine program to emphasize the information that employees must not forget and to update any changes. An example of this type of SOP is illustrated in Fig. 7.

d. *Control*. The last type of SOP includes procedures that are more general and not covered by the other three types. Many of these SOPs refer to basic good business principles and some relate to basic control of the manufacturing operation. These procedures include *receipt, sampling, and storage of components* to assure that every raw material and packaging component is inspected on receipt, sampled, stored on hold, tested and released, or rejected and placed in approved or reject storage; *stability testing* to assure that there are adequate data to support the stated expiry dating of a product and a continual program to assure product batch reproducibility; *rotation of stock* to assure that the oldest raw material lot is used first or the oldest product batch is shipped first; *product sampling* to assure that samples of the correct number and size are withdrawn from the appropriate number of containers with proper microbiological control.

The SOPs described by no means have mentioned all those required in a manufacturing plant. They do, however, satisfy basic requirements and should provide insight so that areas in the specific organization for which standard operating procedures are needed can be identified. It should always be remembered that more than one individual must be capable of performing a given task; at times he or she will be on vacation or absent because of sickness. In addition, an individual should not be relied on to perform tasks from memory, as there is no guarantee that such operations will be performed as reproducibly as may be required. Certainly, no two individuals performing an operation from memory will do it identically. Written SOPs are necessary to avoid these pitfalls. Also, a written record provides a history that can be read and studied if, for example, a product batch should fail and we seek to identify the cause.

2. *Specifications*, the second set of records, are parameters that describe the characteristics of a particular material. Each parameter has an acceptable range that is measurable using a given test procedure. For example , a raw material may be purchased as a free-flowing powder. There may be a specification for water content which requires that when a sample of raw material is analyzed using a

XYZ CORPORATION
STANDARD OPERATING PROCEDURE

TITLE: PERSONNEL PROCEDURE	*DATE APPROVED: 4-20-78*
FOR ROUTINE TRAINING	*PAGE 1 OF 1*

All personnel will receive training commensurate with their assigned

duties and responsibilities. The training will be on matters of GMP,

Safety, and the nature of the company's business.

All training sessions will be documented on the attached Personnel Train-

ing Report and submitted to the Director of Compliance who will maintain

a file.

ISSUED BY:	*APPROVED BY*
AR	EM
ML	LS

Figure 7   Personnel procedure.

given test procedure the water content cannot be more than 1.0%. If the assay exceeds this specified limit, the raw material lot is to be rejected. Sometimes a specification stipulates a minimum level, such as an assay of no less than 97.0%. At other times, a specification may indicate a range such as a pH of 6.5 to 7.5. Specifications must be written for each raw material, packaging component, in-process material, and finished product. They provide a yardstick by which we can analyze a material and evaluate whether it is desirable or undesirable. In the case of a component lot (raw material or packaging component), specifications enable us to judge whether or not we should use the lot to prepare a product batch. They provide a basis for comparison to previous lots received. The specifications for in-process material or finished product are a yardstick that enables us to determine whether or not the batch was manufactured properly.

Several officially recognized compendia describe specifications for components and finished product, e.g., United States Pharmacopeia, Food Chemicals Codex, British Pharmacopeia, and European Pharmacopeia. These specifications have been established by an advisory board to each compendium and represent the views of many manufacturers and government based on a history of the component or product. Such specifications are reviewed and updated as the need arises when new information becomes available. These compendia are very useful and should always be used as a guide whenever possible. In the case of the USP, for example, if a monograph exists for a component or product, U.S. drug manufacturers are required to satisfy those specifications as a minimum requirement.

Sometimes compendia do not contain a monograph for the specific item that we are interested in. We can use the compendia as guides, following the specifications established for similar items. Then we must use our judgment to establish parameters that the material should be tested for based on our knowledge of the chemistry of the material. The next step is methods development to derive a test procedure that enables us to measure each parameter. By testing different lots of the material, we can establish a specification for the parameter. This work can be done in-house if your organization has the technical expertise and instrumentation that is needed. If not, outside consultant firms are available to assist.

Specifications have been established for several raw materials, and these provide a review of how they were derived. Figure 8 illustrates the prototype specifications for a raw material that is commercially available as a solid and is found in the USP. As indicated, all compendial specifications are listed and some others are included also. The manufacturer may have had some experience with this raw material and, based on the product requirements, has identified other critical parameters to test for. Similarly, Fig. 9 illustrates an example of a raw material purchased as a liquid and found in the FCC.

Figures 10 and 11 illustrate specifications for solid and liquid raw materials that are not listed in any compendium. Some specifications are established using compendial test procedures. Other specifications are established using test procedures that have been developed in-house.

Specifications are an important tool in validating a raw material or a process. They must be written and followed, unless there is just cause to change them. Once specifications have been established for the raw materials used to manufacture a product, there is a way to screen out inferior and unacceptable materials. All too often, product batch failure is traced to the use of an unacceptable raw material. Sometimes the defect cannot be identified because it is not even considered in the raw material specifications. It is extremely important to understand well the chemistry of each raw material and to devote careful attention to setting specifications. Emphasis should be placed in a strong attempt to identify all potential problems and establish critical specifications. As a history develops from use of raw materials—continued testing of different raw material lots and subsequent product batches as finished-product and in stability studies—more data develop and information accumulates. Revision and upgrading of specifications may be called for and must be done, but carefully.

3. *Test procedures* are written procedures that provide the step-by-step details of how to perform the tests indicated in specifications or SOPs. They indicate the reagents to be used, sources of the chemicals, how the reagents are to be prepared, and shelf life of the reagents. Also described are the apparatus to be used and special handling and precautions to be followed. At times, a

XYZ CORPORATION

RAW MATERIAL SPECIFICATIONS

| *MATERIAL: ACETAMINOPHEN* | *DATE APPROVED: 10-20-80*
PAGE 1 OF 1 |

TEST	*SPECIFICATION*	*TEST METHOD*
DESCRIPTION:	*White, odorless, crystalline powder* *with a slightly bitter taste, soluble* *in boiling water and in alcohol.*	*XYZ*
IDENTIFICATION:	*A - IR absorption compared to USP RS.*	*USP*
	B - UV absorption compared to USP RS.	*USP*
	C - Positive for violet blue color.	*USP*
MELTING RANGE:	$168^\circ - 172^\circ C$	*USP*
pH:	*5.1 - 6.5*	*USP*
WATER (METHOD I):	*NMT 0.5%*	*USP*
RESIDUE ON IGNITION:	*NMT 0.1%*	*USP*
CHLORIDE:	*NMT 0.014%*	*USP*
SULFATE:	*NMT 0.02%*	*USP*
SULFIDE:	*No coloration or spotting of the test* *paper.*	*USP*
HEAVY METALS *(METHOD II):*	*NMT 0.001%*	*USP*
READILY CARBONIZABLE *SUBSTANCES:*	*NMT matching fluid A*	*USP*
FREE p-AMINOPHENOL:	*NMT 0.005%*	*USP*
p-CHLOROACETANILIDE:	*NMT 0.001%*	*USP*
ASSAY (DRY BASIS)	*98.0 - 101.0%*	*USP*
TOTAL AEROBIC MICROBIAL *COUNT:*	*NMT 1000/g*	*XYZ TEST* *PROCEDURE 16*
MOLD AND YEAST COUNT:	*NMT 500/g*	*XYZ TEST* *PROCEDURE 09*
E. COLI:	*Negative*	*XYZ TEST* *PROCEDURE 03*

ACCEPTABLE CONTAINERS: FIBER DRUM WITH PE LINER
APPROVAL EXPIRATION DATE: 1 YEAR
APPROVED SUPPLIERS: AB CHEMICAL CO., ST CORP.
REFERENCES: USP XX, pp. 11-12; XYZ CORP.

ISSUED BY:	*APPROVED BY:*
MB	*EM*
LC	*LS*

Figure 8   Raw material specifications for acetaminophen.

XYZ CORPORATION
RAW MATERIAL SPECIFICATIONS

MATERIAL: BETA-CAROTENE		*DATE APPROVED: 10-20-81*
(30% IN VEGETABLE OIL)		*PAGE 1 OF 1*

TEST	*SPECIFICATION*	*TEST METHOD*
DESCRIPTION:	*Reddish-brown oily liquid with character- istic odor.*	*XYZ*
IDENTIFICATION:	*A. Positive by TLC* *B. Positive by UV*	*FCC* *FCC*
ASSAY:	*28.5 - 31.5 beta-carotene*	*FCC*
TOTAL AEROBIC PLATE COUNT:	*NMT 1000/g*	*XYZ TEST PROCEDURE 16*
MOLD AND YEAST COUNT:	*NMT 500/g*	*XYZ TEST PROCEDURE 09*
E. COLI:	*Negative*	*XYZ TEST PROCEDURE 03*

ACCEPTABLE CONTAINERS: L-D POLYETHYLENE CONTAINERS

APPROVAL EXPIRATION DATE: 1 YEAR

APPROVED SUPPLIERS: LLD CORP.; TMX, INC.

REFERENCES: FCC III, p. 73; XYZ CORP.

ISSUED BY:	*APPROVED BY:*
TL	*EM*
RT	*LS*

Figure 9 Raw material specifications for 30% beta-carotene.

compendial test procedure is not in sufficient detail for a laboratory technician to follow exactly. In such a case, the procedure should be written in the necessary detail. A laboratory technician should not run a test without having the proper written procedure.

4. *Manufacturing formulas* are listings of raw materials, by name and quantitative (weight or volume) measure, of a unit measure of finished product. Most manufacturers assign a code number to each raw material to provide a shorter way to refer to the raw material in batch records and labels, especially if such

XYZ CORPORATION
RAW MATERIAL SPECIFICATIONS

MATERIAL: DEXTRAN   *DATE APPROVED: 7-28-72*
                                                        PAGE 1 OF 1

TEST	*SPECIFICATIONS*	*TEST METHOD*
DESCRIPTION:	*White granular powder*	*XYZ*
IDENTIFICATION:	*The IR spectrum of the KBr dispersion of the sample matches the standard.*	*XYZ TEST PROCEDURE 101*
SOLUBILITY:	*Soluble in water and in alcohol.*	*XYZ*
STARCH TEST:	*Negative*	*USP*
HEAVY METALS:	*NMT 10 ppm*	*USP*
ARSENIC:	*NMT 1 ppm*	*USP*
REDUCING SUGARS:	*Positive*	*USP*
TOTAL AEROBIC PLATE COUNT:	*NMT 1000/g*	*XYZ TEST PROCEDURE 16*
MOLD AND YEAST COUNT:	*NMT 500/g*	*XYZ TEST PROCEDURE 09*
E. COLI:	*Negative*	*XYZ TEST PROCEDURE 03*
SALMONELLA:	*Negative*	*XYZ TEST PROCEDURE 88*

ACCEPTABLE CONTAINERS: CARDBOARD BOX WITH PE LINER

APPROVAL EXPIRATION DATE: 1 YEAR

APPROVED SUPPLIERS: ACE CHEMICAL CO., SP, INC.

REFERENCES: USP XX; XYZ CORP.

ISSUED BY:	*APPROVED BY:*
JR	*EM*
VE	*LS*

Figure 10 Raw material specifications for dextran.

XYZ CORPORATION
RAW MATERIAL SPECIFICATIONS

| *MATERIAL: LINSEED OIL* | *DATE APPROVED: 9-14-79* |
| | *PAGE 1 OF 1* |

TEST	*SPECIFICATIONS*	*TEST METHOD*
DESCRIPTION:	*Yellowish liquid with characteristic odor and bland taste.*	*XYZ*
SAPONIFICATION NO.:	*187 - 195*	*USP*
UNSAPONIFIABLE MATTER:	*NMT 1.5%*	*USP*
IODINE VALUE:	*NLT 170*	*USP*
SOLUBILITY:	*Slightly soluble in alcohol; miscible with ether, petroleum ether, chloroform or carbon disulfide.*	*USP*
TOTAL AEROBIC PLATE COUNT:	*NMT 1000/g*	*XYZ PROCEDURE 16*
MOLD AND YEAST COUNT:	*NMT 500/g*	*XYZ PROCEDURE 09*
E. COLI:	*Negative*	*XYZ PROCEDURE 03*
SALMONELLA:	*Negative*	*XYZ PROCEDURE 88*

ACCEPTABLE CONTAINER: STAINLESS STEEL DRUMS

APPROVAL EXPIRATION DATE: SIX MONTHS

APPROVED SUPPLIERS: NB CHEMICAL CO., TTL INC.

REFERENCES:USP XX ; XYZ CORP.

OTHER NAMES: FLAXSEED

ISSUED BY:	*APPROVED BY:*
RT	*EM*
CL	*LS*

Figure 11 Raw material specifications for linseed oil.

systems are computerized. A master formula generally contains the manufacturing formula expressed as weight or volume of each raw material per unit of finished product (e.g., capsule or fluid once) and also weight or volume of each raw material per standard batch size (e.g., 1 million capsules or 10,000 gallons). These formulas represent the average theoretical measurements by which product batches are manufactured, including any overages. Finished-product unit assays and fill weights are designated upper and lower limits in product specifications, which are derived from manufacturing formulas.

5. *Manufacturing instructions* are the written directions that personnel follow to prepare product batches. They describe, in sufficient detail and step by step, the operations to be performed, providing blank spaces for personnel to record the operations that they perform. The instructions (or procedures) must document the equipment and materials used and specific operations performed, signed and dated. They must describe all phases of manufacture of the product which include, as applicable, preparation of the product in bulk, bulk storage, sterilization, lyophilization, drying and tableting, encapsulation, filling into finished-product containers, labeling, and cartoning finished-product containers. The records must indicate accountability and reconciliation for materials used to assure that a mix-up has not occurred during manufacturing. Also, they must indicate that materials from two product batches were not on the same line at the same time which also can cause a mix-up.

6. *The approval process* is the last and most important part of recordkeeping. All documents must be approved before they are used. If they require a change, the documents must again be approved before the change is implemented. One type of problem discussed earlier identifies the need for and importance of written records. Now we must focus attention on the dilemma created if the records are wrong or if they become obsolete. Once a document has been approved and issued, it is the responsibility of the respective personnel to use it and follow it. No change should ever be permitted without observing an established approval procedure, because that defeats the purpose for the document in the first place. If a procedure is to be changed, several designated individuals should be aware of the need for change. It does no good if one person changes a procedure and the others who use it, or those who approved it, are not made aware of the change.

A manufacturer must establish a list of approvals required for its records, a list that is not unmanageable yet provides adequate assurance that a signed document is meaningful. Theoretically, at least two signatures are required on such documents—one representing production and one quality control. Generally, there is also another signature, that of the one who either wrote the procedure or initiated the change. A manufacturing organization must designate a list of individuals appropriate to its own operation; however, it is important to remember that changing an established procedure indiscriminately in the midst of a serious product problem, without bringing the matter to the attention of the proper individuals, may do more harm than good. Effecting a short-range solution with no thought of the long-range effect can be damaging.

B. Evaluation of Sources of Variation

The second step toward process validation is to evaluate all possible sources of variation in the process [2]. In validation, it is important to identify all sources of variation that are possible from materials, machines, methods, and people. These potential problem areas then form the framework for what is to be validated. The overall objective in validation is to study these variables and the effect they will have on product batches. A product batch failure can always be traced to a deficiency in one of these four areas.

1. Materials

This includes all raw materials and packaging components utilized to prepare and package a product. A given component can differ from one supplier to another, from one lot to another from the same supplier, from one container to another of the same lot or even lack uniformity in one (nonhomogeneous) container. If the components that we purchase are listed in official compendia, there is a significantly lower likelihood that these differences will occur, because the raw material manufacturer and the drug manufacturer both are aware of the standards published as monographs; both can perform necessary testing using the stated test procedures to determine whether or not the material meets specifications. If the component is not listed in a compendium, the raw material manufacturer and drug manufacturer may use totally different acceptance and rejection criteria.

We could, for example, use a raw material with the following characteristics:

Suspension
Hygroscopic
Sensitive to light and temperature
Oxidizes readily

Fortunately, we do not find a combination of factors that presents such a high potential for variation very often. In investigating potential sources of variation, however, several checks must be done.

First, several raw material lots from at least two suppliers should be tested to assure that the material can be manufactured reproducibly and uniformly and so that we would not anticipate a problem in supply. Each lot from each supplier should meet the established specifications.

Second, in performing the checks described, it is important to demonstrate that there is no difference in the material from one lot stored in different containers. Factors to consider include the material used in the construction of the containers, adequacy of the container/closure system, protection by the container and package from temperature extremes and light transmission, use of a nitrogen gas head in the container, and supplier distribution practices to avoid storage in hot or cold depots.

Third, there should be uniformity in each container. In the case of a suspension, such as our theoretical example, this should not present a problem, as the container contents would always require thorough mixing before material is removed. If we use as an example crystalline material, in which case mixing is not routinely performed, several factors must be considered: Does the material at the top of the container show a higher water content? Does the material touching the walls of the container show evidence of instability as a result of temperature extremes or light exposure? Does the physical appearance of the material differ when sampled from various points in the container?

It is not necessary to study all these factors for every raw material. What is important is that the chemistry of each raw material is known and all the potential sources of variation are evaluated.

2. Machines

This includes all equipment, apparatus, and instruments used to prepare and test a product. Potential variations in the operating characteristics of production equipment must be evaluated carefully. Measurement of temperature, such as in processing and holding tanks; pressure, as in a lyophilizer; and speed of movement, as in a mixer are important in terms of the measurement's being accurate and the equipment being capable of performing the desired functions. Reactivity of all equipment parts that contact the product must be evaluated to be sure that there is no additive or absorptive effect.

Testing instrumentation must be reviewed carefully also. All too often, after a product batch has been rejected, it is discovered that the instrument performing the failing assay did not function properly. Each instrument manual should be studied so that those performing the test can become intimately familiar with the instrument's functions and weaknesses. Factors to consider are the laboratory ambient temperature and humidity, instrument operating temperatures, tubing that can become worn or clogged, speed of movement such as in recording charts, uniformity of power supply, effect of vibration, and rapid air movement. There are several means to prevent problems from growing, to identify them early. One is to use controls in testing periodically and the other is to submit samples to outside reference laboratories periodically and compare results. Proper calibration can prevent many variations in production and testing equipment by identifying problems such that the equipment must be calibrated, repaired, or replaced. Equipment that requires calibration often is not performing satisfactorily.

3. Methods

This pertains to all written procedures used to prepare and test a product and to establish uniformity and control over the entire manufacturing operation. Procedures must be in sufficient detail so that their use by different personnel with different techniques will enable the operations to be performed reproducibly; however, there should not be such detail that a procedure is meaningless and painful to the person using it. If the wording of a procedure is verbose, the chances are people will not use it. Language used in procedures must be clear and geared to the personnel who will use them. A procedure may be written as perfect in content and style by management yet not understood by the production worker who will use it. In this case, the objective of the procedure will not be accomplished.

4. People

This includes all personnel involved in manufacturing (including testing) a product. Personnel who are improperly trained and/or who lack certain expertise can cause serious problems in a manufacturing operation. They may believe that they are performing well yet may not be capable of following written procedures or CGMP. As time passes, their confidence will probably increase and by the time the problem is discovered and corrective measures acted upon, they will have difficulty in changing their routine. Also, their morale will certainly not have been strengthened nor will their attitude toward their employer be positive.

Personnel attitude and morale in general must be reviewed and set in a framework of positive action. Standard operating procedures and specifications can be written ad infinitum but cannot compensate for employees who are not satisfied and interested in manufacturing quality products. Personnel programs must be positive and geared to addressing problems with firm disciplinary measures.

C. In-Process Testing

The third step toward process validation is to evaluate the requirement for in-process testing and evaluation. Before the concept of process validation, in-process testing was not required by the CGMP regulations, although many drug manufacturers had internal SOPs that stipulated this testing. Currently, however, it is a requirement of CGMP.

In-process testing means that a product batch is evaluated at specified critical stages of the manufacturing process to assure that the batch is being manufactured as stipulated in the manufacturing batch records. Failure to meet an in-process specification indicates either that procedures were not followed or that some factor(s) is out of control. In-process testing, if properly established, enables easier identification of a problem. Also, from a business standpoint, it sometimes identifies a defective product batch that can be corrected by rework, whereas once the batch has been completed, this may not be possible.

In-process tests and specifications must be consistent with finished-product tests and specifications in order to be meaningful. In general, an in-process specification such as for an assay should be tighter than a finished-product specification to allow for any slight deviations that may occur in subsequent manufacturing or testing stages and still allow the batch to meet the finished-product specifications. If the finished-assay limits are ±10%, the in-process specification might be appropriate at ±5%, with an adjustment to be made if the batch exceeds these limits.

An example of an in-process evaluation or control, as contrasted to a test, might be the specifications set on an autoclave cycle to sterilize a product batch in bulk. For example, the following criteria might be established for the cycle:

Product temperature   121 ± 2°C
Chamber pressure   15 ± 1 psi
Time at proper temperature   45 ± 5 min

By reading the gauges and examining recordings of time, temperature, and pressure, identification of a failure can be facilitated. If the product temperature never exceeded 25°C for a particular batch, for example, we know that the product is not sterile and we have saved the cost of filling the batch into final containers; possibly we have saved the entire batch if it should not be feasible to rework it. It certainly would not necessitate performing sterility testing on the finished product to determine that the batch is sterile when indeed the sterilization cycle was never performed adequately. This is a perfect example of the thrust of in-process controls in the CGMP regulations; they are often more meaningful and indicative of batch success or failure than is finished-product testing.

D. Challenge

The fourth step toward process validation, and the heart of the concept, is to challenge and then evaluate the process. It is no longer adequate to develop a product, prepare pilot batches, scale up, and bring to market. Validation requires that the manufacturing and testing process be challenged by using acceptable and possibly unacceptable materials and procedures to produce product batches.

The concept that a possibly unacceptable material or procedure may be used intentionally to manufacture a product is somewhat difficult to understand at first but not after it has been thought out. Before process validation was conceived, new products were developed by writing a manufacturing procedure that could be used to prepare a product having the desired characteristics, then developing finished-product specifications to set measurable limits for different characteristics within which the product would perform properly, and then establishing raw material specifications that would lead to manufacture of acceptable product batches. There were weaknesses in this type of product development, which often was done very quickly and without much thought. Such a manufacturing procedure, for example, might have required incubation at 37°C, mixing for 30 min, and centrifugation at 1800 rpm for 20 min at 5°C. Questions relating this procedure to the real world were not asked, such as: Is incubation at 36°C or 38°C acceptable? Is mixing for 50 min acceptable? Is centrifugation at 1800 rpm a minimum and should 2000 rpm be a maximum? Is there really a difference produced by centrifugation for 20 or 40 min? Is a condition of 2° to 8° acceptable or must it always be 5°C?

Today, product development must include studies performed to challenge a process. If the example above were followed, it might be desirable to manufacture a batch with incubation at 35, 37, 45°C; with mixing for 10, 30, 120 min; with centrifugation at 1500, 1800, and 2500 rpm—for 10, 20, and 40 min—at 2, 5, and 40°C. This may seem like too much work and expense; however, we must consider the kind of information about the product and process these studies will provide for us.

Some of the batches will fail to meet in-process or finished-product specifications, or they may not perform properly in stability studies. The procedures used to prepare those batches will have been demonstrated to be unacceptable. If all batches satisfy all specifications and stability studies, which is unlikely, we will have demonstrated that any stage of the manufacturing process that should deviate but remain within those limits should still produce acceptable batches. When these challenge batches are prepared, only one variable should be introduced into one batch. Otherwise, we cannot rely on the results obtained. The information generated will be helpful in the future when product batches are prepared and deviations occur, this time unintentionally. When this happens, a batch may satisfy product specifications but we are not sure whether or not to release it because we are not sure that it will remain acceptable for the stated shelf life. The goal of process validation is to provide data on such a batch, at the product's development stage, when a product can be evaluated *without the pressure of a production schedule to meet or a customer's demand to satisfy.*

Some of the specific examples cited above need further consideration here to determine the value of this system in challenging a process. This evaluation is purely hypothetical and is not intended to refer to a specific product:

The optimal incubation temperature for the desired reaction may be 37°C; 36°C may be the minimum acceptable temperature, with 35°C producing an unacceptable product batch; 40°C may be the acceptable upper limit, with 45°C producing an unacceptable batch. Unacceptable is used to describe a batch that fails either in-process, finished-product testing, or stability testing. The written manufacturing procedure can be stated to perform the incubation at 37°C, with 36 to 40°C being recorded as acceptable in the product history; or the record can be stated to incubate at 37°C (36 to 40°C). In any case, if we know what the incubation temperature was during the incubation time period—if a thermostat in the incubator should fail and the temperature increases to 45°C—we know whether to release or reject the batch.

The mixing time required based on theoretical solubility may be 30 min, with a reasonable extended period of time to assure solution. The minimum time required for solution may be 10 min; 120 min may not produce a different solution than 30 min. The written procedure can be stated to mix for 30 min or alternatively 30 min (20 to 40 min); 120 min should not be stated because we would prefer that not happen. If someone goes to lunch and forgets to turn off the mixer until 50 min have elapsed, we know how to respond, however.

Centrifugation at 1800 rpm may be optimal for producing packing that is adequate yet not so tight that it cannot be removed from the containers. The minimum required may be 1600 rpm. 2500 rpm may cause the containers to break, and 2000 rpm may be acceptable. The written procedure can be stated to centrifuge at 1800 rpm or 1800 rpm (1600 to 2000 rpm). The limits of 1600 to 2000 should be established as providing acceptable product batches with reasonable, and without unnecessary, calibration of centrifuge tachometers. This equipment specification, or any other, should not be more stringent than is necessary. We would not require a centrifuge and tachometer to be accurate to 1790 to 1810 rpm, in this case.

Centrifugation for 20 min may be optimal; 15 min may be the minimum required, 40 min may cause occasional unacceptable batches by subjecting the in-process product to stress that is not necessary, and 30 min may be acceptable. The written procedure can be stated as 20 min or 20 min and an additional 10 min if needed or 20 min (15–30 min).

Centrifugation at 5°C may be optimum. 0° may cause the material to freeze and 2 or 10°C may be acceptable. Nonrefrigerated centrifugation such as at 40°C may be unacceptable. The written procedure may be stated as 5°C or 5°C (2 to 10°C). The temperature, or a range, should be stated and checked. The record should not state to "centrifuge under refrigeration" because the operator probably will tend not to check the temperature and may not even be aware that the refrigeration system is not working.

Challenge of a process is time-consuming and can be costly. It need not be a matter of generating meaningless data and records to satisfy FDA regulations, however. It can be geared to the practical and real world, to answer questions before they are asked in anticipating deviations from fixed procedures and critical steps where there is a high probability that something may go wrong. The best part is that the problems are solved and answers generated without dissatisfied customers, back orders, and recalls being generated.

E.   Approvals

The last step toward process validation is to document everything that is done, to follow established procedures and protocols as closely as possible, and not to make a change without proper documentation and approval. A system of written procedures and records and a cast of personnel involved in manufacturing and testing a product have been discussed here. Also discussed were possible variations that can occur in manufacturing a product, the in-process controls that are followed, and the significance of challenging a process. Whenever a master document is written—as a manufacturing procedure, specification sheet, personnel training program, or a corporate operating guideline—it should be approved by certain individuals before being implemented. Before such a document is changed, it should be approved by the same individuals to verify that it is correct and to check whether it is necessary to validate the change or revalidate the process. Changing an established procedure without proper authorization can be a deadly mistake.

During the course of writing procedures, training personnel, and investigating the manufacturing process, many ancillary supportive activities will be occurring. There will be investigations, studies, and data; lists of items to be investigated; and decisions on what should and should not be done. These phases should be documented also, and there should be more than one person who decides what should be done to validate a process. The value of a written product history will be evident when a problem arises in the manufacture of a batch, and there are written records to review so that the cause of the problem can be identified. Based on the approval system, several people would have been involved in generating the data and making decisions. This body of personnel should then be able to attack the problem in a scientific and orderly manner.

At this point, we have discussed all the basic requirements for process validation—that is, *why* it is necessary to validate a process and *what* is to be done. It is appropriate now to discuss briefly *who* in a manufacturing organization is responsible for performing this validation.

III. WHERE DOES THE RESPONSIBILITY LIE?

It is important for a manufacturer to establish which department within the organization is charged with the responsibility for process validation. Different companies have different policies, with the responsibility usually given to R&D, process development (pilot plant), or production. In order to decide which department has the responsibility, some of the basic objectives and operations in process validation should be reviewed.

Generation of a data base to describe a given product requires that the process be challenged in a rigidly controlled operation so that we are not faced with several variables at one time, some perhaps even being unknown to us. If this instance should occur, we would not be measuring the effect of the challenge to the process. Strict control relates to several areas of the operation.

A. Facilities and Environment

The physical area must be subject to certain procedures such as for cleaning, housekeeping, maintenance, and water supply. The working environment must have defined ranges of temperature and humidity, for example. Obviously, the smaller the facility and the more confined the environment, the easier it will be to control.

B. Equipment

All equipment, apparatus, and instruments used must be properly cleaned, maintained, and calibrated at all times. The fewer the number of pieces of equipment—such as mixing tanks and instruments—the more probable (and the easier) it will be to assure that everything is in order.

C. Materials

All materials used in the area must be subject to control also. They must be tested before use in the product. They must be stored under proper conditions to protect their shelf life and such as in the case of solvents, to protect the environment.

D. Personnel

People who perform the operations should be trained in the technical and compliance areas. They must be knowledgeable to handle and perform the manufacturing operations, to follow instructions, to document in sufficient detail and so that others can understand. They must be consistent in technique. The fewer people involved, the tighter the control will be. Frequent changeover, such as that associated with absenteeism, is to be avoided.

   We should also consider the basic objectives established for each department of the organization. In most companies, R&D and/or process development has the responsibility to develop a formula and manufacturing procedure. Success is measured by uniformity and reproducibility of product batches to satisfy the established product attributes. R&D and process development do not have other responsibilities that will interfere with or detract from this primary objective. The basic objective of production is to manufacture products, using established and proven procedures and specifications, of high quality, and in a timely manner, to satisfy customer demand. Production has a schedule to meet in output but must not sacrifice quality. This phase of the organization cannot be compromised because it is necessary to generate sales dollars. Development of a new product in a production department would have to assume a lesser priority and not necessarily receive the attention that it should. Also, when production is compared to R&D or process development, all facilities and equipment are on a considerably larger scale, making control more difficult and validation more difficult to achieve.

Physical facilities are larger in scale and more spread out. Numbers of pieces of equipment are larger and concentration of effort to calibrate becomes more difficult. If there is absenteeism in personnel, there may be frequent turnover while validating a process, adding greater potential for variation in the results.

Whether process validation should be performed in R&D, process development, or production is a decision that must be made by the management of a manufacturer. The last mentioned, i.e., production, may be best in some organizations. The important point is to stress the importance of validation and do it— weigh the pros and cons for each department, make a decision, and follow it. A discussion of "how" to validate a raw material follows.

IV. RAW MATERIALS VALIDATION: PART I

One very important phase of process validation requires that all potential variations in raw materials be considered [3]. As mentioned earlier in the chapter, many product batch failures are identified by use of a defective raw material. Sometimes a raw material is used in a batch with the knowledge that it failed to meet a certain specification—under the belief that the specification is not critical. At other times, there may be a defect in a raw material that is not identified because it is not tested for. This may occur because a test procedure is not available, because the test may not be considered important, or simply because the test was not even thought of. The typical reaction to this problem, however, is that from time beginning with the batch failure and henceforth the test is considered to be critical. During process validation, our objective is to anticipate problems such as these and to generate data to establish the raw material requirements to produce uniform and reproducible product batches.

A. Cost Versus Risk

In the performance of process validation, we have been discussing the investigation of all potential problems and the validation of all critical steps. Both the investigation and the validation phase can be very time-consuming, labor-intensive, and expensive. What is even worse is that we may not even anticipate or be able to predict some problems that may occur. This means that we can spend a lot of time and money in developing a product and still have problems; however, we will all probably agree that the risk of a problem will be reduced significantly, provided that validation is done properly. Also, if a problem in manufacturing should develop, we will have a significant data bank to call on toward a quick resolution of the problem.

Process validation can be more meaningful and less expensive if we consider very carefully exactly how we are to perform the necessary operations. Many decisions will be made in these evaluations, and we should establish firmly the cost versus risk for each. For example, we must establish the cost to determine the difference between mixing a bulk preparation for 10 min and also at 120 min versus the risk that this will occur and leave us without data to show that both are acceptable. We must determine how much of a chance we wish to assume. All considerations, evaluations, and decisions should be documented so that in the event a product problem arises in the future we will be able to retrace our steps easily and quickly.

Several steps are required to validate a raw material, and these are discussed below:

Step 1. *List all the raw materials needed to prepare a product batch*. This list should include all active ingredients, excipients and processing aids used in production and all chemicals, official standards, and laboratory materials used in testing. Active ingredients include all components that contribute toward the pharmacologic action of the product. Excipients include the components that form the base or vehicle in which the active ingredients are carried, such as water, polyethylene glycol, fillers, and oils. They also include additives such as colors, flavors, and preservatives. Processing aids categorize those raw materials that are used during the manufacture of a product but which are removed by the stage of finished product. Examples are filter aids and solvents used for extraction. Laboratory chemicals are those materials employed to prepare reagents that are used to test products, and they are as important as the materials used in production. Official standards are those components that a laboratory uses to convert measurements taken into results relating to a product's attributes, such as assay. This is a very critical area to consider, as very often an acceptable batch is rejected because an assay is too low, which is actually caused by a defective standard. Finally, laboratory materials are to be considered. They include items used in a laboratory in conjunction with reagents and standards and instruments, such as columns for gas chromatography and high-performance liquid chromatography.

Step 2. *Identify at least two suppliers for each raw material*. After we have a complete list of all raw materials needed, we must locate sources of these materials. It is not adequate to identify one supplier of a raw material because if a problem should develop in that organization—either a problem in satisfying demand, a technically related problem, or a business-oriented problem—we conceivably could be prevented from manufacturing our product. Therefore, it is always advisable to locate and validate at least two suppliers.

Several considerations must be evaluated in selecting a supplier. First, it is understood that the supplier can provide the raw material that we need. Second, if more than one grade of the raw material is available, the supplier must be capable of providing the grade that we want. Third, the supplier must be capable of providing the quantity that we require to satisfy our production schedule. Fourth, we should evaluate the supplier's capacity to provide increased quantities quickly in the event that demand for our product increases rapidly. Fifth, we should determine whether our supplier is a manufacturer or distributor. It is better to deal with a manufacturer in that we will have a direct line of communication with the organization in control rather than dealing with a third party. Our supplier, if a distributor, may have very little control or a limited amount of time to exercise control over the suppliers who manufacture the raw material. If we cannot determine whether our supplier is a manufacturer or distributor, we can visit the supplier's facility and the manufacturing facility, if separate, to answer the question. Sixth is consideration of the cost of the raw material. Seventh is the reputation and reliability of the supplier. This determination is based on our past history with the supplier, referrals from our contacts in the industry, and government regulatory evaluations such as recalls and plant compliance profile. It is important that we have good communication with our supplier. The supplier must be able to meet commitments without sacrificing quality. The supplier's operation must be under control following the same guidelines that we do or else we may not have the level of process control we think we do. The supplier must use written standard operating procedures and establish proper raw material storage conditions and distribution procedures. The supplier must know whether precautions must be followed in shipment to a customer in order to prevent material degradation. Certainly, our supplier should not change any established procedures or joint agreements made with us without making us aware of the change.

In considering the possibility of variation from one supplier to another, attention must be drawn to the method of manufacture of the raw material. Also, each supplier will differ in facility, methods of plant operation, distribution procedures, and control procedures. In comparing any two manufacturers, one facility may be a modern building with sufficient space to segregate materials and provide proper housekeeping and cleaning. The other facility may be old and poorly maintained, overcrowded without proper segregation of even approved and unapproved materials, disorderly, and dirty. One manufacturer may have well-trained personnel who maintain an orderly system of records, as compared to the other company in which personnel are not trained properly and use inaccurate records that require many handwritten changes. One company may transport its products by air and the other by ship. One manufacturer may have a fully equipped and modern testing laboratory and the other may send all testing requirements to an outside laboratory.

It is prudent at this point to consider the activities of our supplier, as a raw material manufacturer, in light of the discussion of process validation and its requirements—especially if the raw material is an active. Raw materials in pharmaceutical products are sometimes referred to as bulk pharmaceuticals or bulk pharmaceutical chemicals, and the question arises as to whether manufacture of the raw material should be validated [4]. The question becomes whether raw material manufacturers must comply with CGMP, which includes process validation. We can highlight some important considerations here to evaluate how our needs bear on our supplier.

It is important to recognize at the outset that a chemical manufacturer will be reluctant to comply with CGMP and plant inspections by FDA, including validation of processes. Chemical raw materials are generally supplied to industries that are not nearly as controlled as the pharmaceutical industry. For example, dextrose raw material is used mostly for food; however, it is used also as an inactive ingredient in drug products such as a sweetener and as an active ingredient in dextrose solutions for parenteral use. For economic reasons, a dextrose manufacturer will not want to be subject to the controls of the drug industry; however, all chemical manufacturers would be wise to understand drug CGMP and process validation. In order to manufacture their products uniformly and reproducibly without batch losses and rejects, many of the systems and controls that we have discussed should be used. For example, written records should be used to cover the range of documents needed in any manufacturing plant—including standard operating procedures, specifications, and manufacturing procedures. Critical stages in the manufacturing process should be investigated very carefully and consideration given to validation. This exercise often seems like much extra work and expense, but it is often cheaper in the long run than facing batch losses and rejects.

Step 3. *If a supplier is new, visit the supplier's facility.* It is important to establish a good relationship with a supplier, to meet representatives personally, and tour the facility. During the visit, it is also important to observe the housekeeping and sanitation practiced, the use of written procedures and logs, the controls exercised in manufacturing operations such as proper segregation and batch identification, the laboratory controls followed, the use of laboratory notebooks, the use of up-to-date laboratory instrumentation and production equipment, and the size of the laboratory area and staff as compared to production. A plant that is dirty or disorderly, that does not use written procedures, does not have adequate controls, does not use modern equipment, does not have an adequate laboratory and staff cannot produce a quality product.

It is important to visit a new supplier and also important to visit all suppliers periodically. When touring a facility, it is best to be critical, as though you are an inspector, to be sure that this facility meets the same standards as your own. Remember that quality cannot be tested into a product, it must be incorporated in the manufacturing process. Certainly, the manufacture and distribution of raw materials are included. We have indicated earlier that finished-product testing may be extremely sophisticated and intensive, but conceivably it may not detect a problem that occurs as a result of poor attitude and carelessness by production personnel in the drug manufacturing plant or raw material manufacturing plant. Testing does not compensate for poor production practices.

In discussing visits to suppliers, questions sometimes arise—such as who should visit and how often. Personnel generally do not seem to have the time and the visit does not seem to be important until there is a problem. Such meetings are important, and there should be an attempt to predict and prevent problems from beginning. The personnel who tour a plant may represent purchasing, planning, quality assurance, or production functions, but they must have been trained in what to look for, namely the CGMP regulations. The visit should be completed once before any material is purchased and then periodically with a frequency based on knowledge of the supplier. If the supplier's reputation is good and our confidence high, one inspection annually may be sufficient. If there is some uncertainty, perhaps two or four visits for the first year may be prudent. Judgment must be used in making this decision, as there are no hard and fast rules.

Step 4. *Obtain samples and supplier's certificates of analysis.* After the suppliers whom we believe are best able to fulfill our raw material needs have been identified, the next step is to obtain samples with certificates of analysis from each supplier. Ideally, two or three suppliers have been identified for each raw material, and samples from two or three different lots should be requested from each supplier. This will accomplish several purposes dealing with raw material lot uniformity and reproducibility. By studying the certificates of analysis provided, and any other available technical information, we begin to get an understanding of the chemistry of the raw material. We can begin to determine any characteristics that indicate stability problems by learning what other people believe to be important about the material.

We begin to determine the characteristics of the raw material that are critical to our product as we review our suppliers' performance standards. What is critical for one product may not be important to another, also depending on the manufacturing process and handling of the raw material. There may be characteristics of the product that we must examine and expand that our supplier is not even concerned about or aware of because of our product's requirements.

Last, the certificates of analysis and samples demonstrate the extent of variation from lot to lot on specific tests. It is important to measure this variation between different lots from the same supplier and then the variation between suppliers. These determinations, in conjunction with our supplier relationships and knowledge of the manufacturing process of the raw material, will provide the basic foundation for raw material specifications—the characteristics of the raw material that we will test for and measure and the range of acceptable results. The narrower this range, the more uniform and reproducible the raw material lots will be.

Step 5. *Establish specifications for each raw material.* A monograph describing a raw material, obtained from an official recognized compendium, should be used in conjunction with suppliers' certificates of analysis to establish raw material specifications. If there is a conflict of information, the monograph should be followed unless, for some reason, the specification is to be made tighter. If the raw material is not listed in a compendium, our task is considerably more difficult.

The development of specifications requires that a list of parameters that describe each raw material be prepared, differentiating those believed to be critical to the product from those that are simply descriptive of the raw material [5]. For each parameter listed, an acceptable, measurable range of activity should be established. One very important factor that is often overlooked is the determination of breakdown products which reflect the stability of the raw material. For example, if the specification for assay of the raw material activity is 95 to 105% and one lot assay is 95%, it is significant whether the 5% loss is caused by impurities normally present or by the presence of breakdown products. The latter case indicates that the raw material was not handled properly and/or is experiencing degradation and poor stability which is a continuing process and can result in unacceptable raw material.

Each testing parameter that we establish must have a measurable, acceptable range of variation established. It is not appropriate to establish a numerical value or a fixed descriptive term as a specification. For example, we should not specify that the water content be 1% or that the color be white. More often than not, allowance for some variation is appropriate, such as no more than 1% and white to pale yellow, respectively, in the examples above. The range of water content could be expressed also as 0 to 1%, or 1% maximum. The important point is that an acceptable (and unacceptable) range be established and validated based on our suppliers' capabilities and the requirements of our product.

Specification setting is more difficult for noncompendial raw materials. In this case, the research and development program must include a thorough chemical analysis of the material, investigation of its method of manufacture, and decisions reached to establish meaningful specifications. In some cases, this program may be more beneficial to us as we are forced to think, consider, and evaluate, and we cannot use a compendium as a crutch, which occurs too often. In addition, compendial monographs should represent the minimum test requirements for a raw material. As a manufacturer, we have developed our own technical expertise and base of data through our own experiences on raw materials and products that we handle. We have insight and opinion and may wish to perform tests in addition to those listed in compendia.

Specifications, when finalized for a raw material, should be considered firm; however, there must also be flexibility in accepting changes to specifications as the technological state of the art becomes updated. For example, when high-performance liquid chromatography instrumentation and techniques became available, and assay results were shown to be more accurate than results from traditional methodology, the basic state of the art underwent a change. Assay methods were developed for HPLC and then validated. Test procedures used in raw material analysis then changed in a positive manner, to provide more accurate assays.

Step 6. *Establish test procedures*. Along with the development of specifications, a test procedure must be established for each specification. For the raw materials that are compendial, test procedures are denoted along with their respective specifications.

In establishing test procedures for specifications that are noncompendial, such as an assay for a suspected impurity, or for specifications of raw materials that are not listed in official compendia, we embark into methods development. This work calls on compendial methods that exist for similar compounds and which can be modified; it also calls for methods that are found in the published literature. Expertise is required to adapt these procedures into meaningful test methods.

One of the most common pitfalls in test procedures is that not enough attention is devoted to writing them in sufficient detail and to assuring that all personnel use the written procedures. Many personnel in a control laboratory may perform the same USP test, for example, and the laboratory may have only one copy of that compendium. The tendency may be, therefore, to perform the test from memory, which should not be done. The second part of the problem is that a laboratory technician may perform an operation believing that it will provide a more accurate result, which operation may not be mentioned in the USP method or not described in adequate detail and which relies on the individual's laboratory technique. In such a case, the USP method should be made more comprehensive and turned into a more detailed written test procedure that has been discussed with all the laboratory technicians and approved by the responsible supervisory personnel. It is equally inadvisable for a technician to have a copy of a written test method with his or her own handwritten notes indicating techniques and manipulations.

Step 7. *Establish sampling procedures if special requirements are needed.* Early in the chapter the need for a written procedure to describe raw material sampling in general terms was mentioned. That procedure includes general requirements that may apply to any raw material received in the plant, such as the number of containers to sample, labeling requirements for the bulk raw material and sample containers, sample containers and closures to be used, sample size, and method of sampling.

On the other hand, individual raw materials may have certain sampling requirements based on their stability and/or intended use. For example, materials received as sterile or to be used in the manufacture of sterile products must be sampled in a manner to maintain the proper conditions. Materials that are especially sensitive to light must be protected during sampling. Materials that are oxidized easily should be restored to an inert environment, such as under a head of nitrogen, after sampling. If we anticipate that there may be lack of uniformity between different containers of the same lot number, or from bottom to middle to top in the same container, more than the usual number of samples should be taken—in the first case, a sample from each container and, in the second case, separate samples from the bottom, middle, and top of a container, and all samples should be tested separately.

Some of the precautions described above are based on theoretical predictions, and the best means to implement them may have yet to be determined. Such is the case in suspected variation between containers and within a container. Before these individual sampling procedures are instituted in routine practice, they should be evaluated as part of process validation. All special sampling stipulations should be explicit in written procedures.

Step 8. *Establish optimum storage conditions*. Raw material containers must be handled and stored under prescribed conditions in order to protect their stability over the stated shelf life. Critical characteristics of raw materials and factors affecting their stability were identified during the time that specifications were established. Now, that information must be translated into proper storage conditions. The chemistry of each raw material should be reviewed and questions should be asked concerning hygroscopicity, sensitivity to light, sensitivity to high and low temperature extremes, ability to support microbial growth, reactivity with any container or closure system, and oxidizing capability.

Once we have established the factors that critically affect a raw material, we can conduct stability studies that will indicate the optimum storage conditions and establish a shelf life for the raw material.

Step 9. *Establish shelf life*. Hand in hand with the definition of storage conditions for a raw material is the establishment of a shelf life. Expiry dating, or shelf life, of a raw material is the time period within which it must be used. Sometimes we assign an expiry date that is shorter than our data indicate, so that we will always use fresh raw materials. For example, the use of sodium chloride as a raw material may be such that if it is handled and stored properly the shelf life is 10 years. We cannot be certain it will always be handled and stored properly so we may establish 3 years as an expiry date, with the provision that any material remaining at the end of that time period can be retested and reapproved.

The shelf life of a raw material is established by testing over time in the containers and closures to be used, after storage under the anticipated optimum conditions, and also under adverse conditions. If the expected storage conditions are expected to be 2 to 8°C and 75 to 85% relative humidity (RH), we will store materials under those conditions and also adverse (or accelerated) conditions such as (approximately):

45°C and 80% RH
37°C and 80% RH
25°C and 80% RH
5°C and 80% RH
0°C and 80% RH

These conditions will also simulate the environment while a shipment is in transit from the raw material supplier. The raw materials can be stored in the container/closure of choice and also in a container with a partially open closure as well as in containers/closures of glass, polyethylene, polypropylene, polystyrene, stainless steel, or other metals.

After storage and at prescribed time intervals, the raw materials should be tested for conformance to the established specifications, which must include assays for breakdown products. At some point, the raw material will fail to meet specifications and will be unacceptable for use. By examining the data generated under adverse conditions, a projected shelf life under those conditions that we specify as optimal for storage can be established. Stability studies on material stored under those conditions to the projected shelf life and beyond must be continued until the material fails. This will verify that the projected shelf life is correct.

Step 10. *Challenge of the raw materials.* The last step required to validate a raw material is the operation in which the information that has been established concerning the raw material is challenged, to assure that it is scientifically sound and meaningful. This step will be treated separately with a specific example to illustrate theoretically how a raw material is validated.

V. RAW MATERIALS VALIDATION: PART II

In considering a hypothetical product, it is possible to validate the manufacturing process and concentrate on one active ingredient. It is not intended that this validation plan be representative of any commercially available product or that it be followed word for word in any plant, but it is merely suggestive of the degree of planning and testing that must be done to validate any process. The product is a soft gelatin capsule containing a combination of actives that are useful to provide temporary relief from the symptoms of colds. We will specify the information required in the steps enumerated above and then elaborate on how to challenge one of the raw materials [6,7].

List All the Raw Materials

1. Actives
    a. Acetaminophen
    b. Phenylpropanolamine hydrochloride
    c. Dextromethorphan hydrobromide
2. Excipients
    a. Soybean oil, as the vehicle for the actives
    b. Gelatin, for the capsule shell
    c. Glycerin, for the capsule shell
    d. Water, for the capsule shell
    e. F, D, & C Red No. 40, for the capsule shell color
3. Processing aids
    a. Mineral oil, used in the encapsulation process
    b. Naphtha, used to wash excess oil off the capsules

4. Laboratory chemicals (just a few are listed)
    a. Potassium bromide
    b. Hydrochloric acid
    c. Methanol
    d. Water
    e. Sodium carbonate
    f. Acetic acid
    g. Sodium nitrite
    h. Ferric chloride
5. Official reference standards
    a. USP acetaminophen
    b. USP phenylpropanolamine hydrochloride
    c. USP alpha-aminopropiophenone hydrochloride
    d. USP dextromethorphan hydrobromide
6. Laboratory materials
    a. Calcium chloride, as a desiccant
    b. Whatman No. 4 filter paper
    c. Silica gel, for thin-layer chromatographic plates

A. Identify at Least Two Suppliers for Each Raw Material

In addressing a source of supply for acetaminophen, it can be assumed that there are six basic manufacturers throughout the world. Two may be located in the United States and one in the United Kingdom, where we conduct much of our business and have many contacts. Also, we may purchase many of our raw materials from a distributor in the United States who deals with all six manufacturers. Our purchasing personnel may start to contact the three manufacturers and one distributor. Acetaminophen is listed in the USP, so that grade is selected. All four suppliers can satisfy our anticipated demand; however, one manufacturer in the United States may supply many companies, so it maintains a substantial inventory of the raw material. It is located 3000 miles from our plant. The other American manufacturer supplies only a few companies, has a smaller plant than the first, keeps a low inventory, and is located 50 miles from our plant. The British plant may supply most of the international market outside the United States and some companies here. Its facility and capacity is much larger than both U.S. manufacturers. The distributor may keep no inventory and has a sales office 15 miles from our plant.

Purchasing personnel will request price quotations and delivery schedules based on anticipated order quantities. They will investigate the reputation and reliability of each supplier and perhaps visit the U.S. suppliers with their quality assurance personnel. A determination will be made eventually of first, second, third, and fourth choice as suppliers based on several factors which follow, not necessarily in order of importance:

Inventory kept
Capability to supply demand on time
Capacity to supply increased demand on time
Distance from our plant
Degree of clout that we have with supplier
Reputation and reliability
Cost

B. Visit New Suppliers' Facilities

An important part of the decision-making process described above is to visit and inspect the facilities of any new suppliers. We certainly can tour the plant located 50 miles away and perhaps also the one at 3000 miles. Our contacts in Great Britain may be able to tour that plant and report to us, if we cannot justify the trip. Low raw material cost and promises to supply all the acetaminophen that we need can become a minor issue if we see a plant that is small, dirty, and poorly managed—which obviously will not be able to fill our demand and supply quality material.

C. Obtain Samples and Certificates of Analysis

We can decide to request that each supplier send us samples from three different raw material lots with the certificate of analysis for each. The samples should be large enough to perform all the testing and validation studies that will be described below, with sufficient material remaining as "retains" to perform the testing described in raw material specifications at least twice.

D. Establish Raw Materials Specifications

Because acetaminophen is a compendial material, with a monograph published in the USP, we would not have had difficulty in locating suppliers. Similarly, the development of raw material specifications will not be difficult.

Specifications that we develop were referred to previously and are illustrated in Fig. 8. Now we must consider those parameters in the specifications that are critical to our product and identify those that we wish to challenge. This decision is made by studying the list of tests that are to be performed on each lot of raw material in light of all the potential variations that may occur—such as in supply, storage, and the manufacturing process. The following parameters may be selected (in addition to breakdown products):

1. *Melting range*—a good measure of acetaminophen purity; to determine the effect of variation in levels of impurities on the finished product.
2. *Water*—to simulate long-term storage and potential absorption of moisture from the environment and determine the effect on the finished product.
3. *Free para-aminophenol*—a measure of the level of one of the reactants used to

prepare acetaminophen; to determine the effect of different levels of this reactant on the finished product

4. *Parachloroacetanilide*—a check on the quality of raw material that we are purchasing and its effect on the product

5. *Assay*—a very critical determination that must be satisfied at all times.

E. Establish Test Procedures

After the development of specifications and the decision as to which ones should be challenged, the next step is to evaluate the procedures that are utilized to perform the tests in those specifications. In the case of acetaminophen and the five specifications enumerated in the previous section, first, it is necessary to review the test procedures described in the USP and determine if they are written in adequate detail. If there are any uncertainties or ambiguities, the procedure should be rewritten in an established format to correct the deficiencies. Next, critical parameters in the test procedures should be identified and challenged. These parameters may include the following:

1. In the melting range procedure—reliability of the reference standard, reliability of the thermometer, accuracy of reading the end point by different personnel

2. In the water determination—stability of the Karl Fischer reagent over time in the laboratory and stability on exposure to light

3. In the free para-aminophenol assay—effect of the time period of storage of the test solution and standard solution; also, the incubation time of 30 min

4. In the parachloroacetanilide determination—steps in the sample preparation such as shaking for 30 min and centrifuging at 1000 rpm for 15 min; also, reliability of the standard solution and irradiation for 30 min

5. In the assay procedure—reliability of the reference standard

F. Establish Special Sampling Procedures

Acetaminophen is especially sensitive to light and moisture. Therefore, the sampling procedures must indicate that care be exercised in order to prevent deterioration caused by exposure to light and moisture, in addition to any general sampling procedure.

The requirements that we establish may include a precautionary statement to keep all containers of acetaminophen well closed at all times and to protect from light. We will want to establish a representative and statistical number of containers from which to withdraw a sample, such as the square root of the number of containers plus one, or a fixed number such as 10, per lot shipment. The procedure should describe the label information that is to be included on the bulk raw material container and the sample container—such as material name, code number, and lot number. The container and closure should be indicated and should be opaque or amber and well closed, such as an amber glass bottle with a screw cap. The sample size should be stipulated, approximately sufficient material to perform the required testing three times. The method of sampling should be described in adequate detail so that the average warehouse employee can understand it. This description should include inspection of the containers on receipt for proper labeling and no damage—if the material and lot identification are not properly indicated, or if the containers are broken, there is cause to reject the material. Also, the container should be cleaned before it is opened, appropriate clean and dry sampling utensils used, and the container resealed adequately— all of these steps explained in detail.

In considering these procedures as part of the validation of acetaminophen, several steps must be undertaken. All personnel who use the procedures should be instructed as to the necessary precautions and should be aware where the procedures are kept for their reference use. Next, the procedures should be studied to determine any critical stages at which an error may occur. One such example is the unnecessary storage of open containers for prolonged periods of time in the event that someone does not close the container properly after sampling or who forgets to close a container before leaving the premises. In such a case, material would be exposed to light and moisture. This can cause variation of the material within a container, the material at the top deteriorating faster than that in the middle and at the bottom. We may also want to check on the difference between containers of the same lot to be sure that the closures are adequate and also to be sure that the raw material manufacturer did not expose the material unduly.

G. Establish Optimum Storage Conditions

In order to establish the conditions for proper storage of acetaminophen, we must challenge those conditions that we consider ideal. We know that the material is sensitive to light and moisture. Accelerated stability studies can be performed on the raw material to determine the effect of storage under extremes of light exposure and humidity, and any other conditions that we wish to challenge, such as temperature.

H. Establish Shelf Life

If we assume that the optimum storage conditions for acetaminophen are protected from light in a sealed container at 20 to 25°C and 65 to 75% RH, the next step is to establish a shelf life. We must be concerned that containers are opened to be sampled and again to be used in production, and the closure may not be perfect. The following accelerated storage conditions may be considered in validation to establish the shelf life and they will indicate the optimum storage conditions also:

45°C and 70% RH in the dark
37°C and 70% RH in the dark
25°C and 70% RH in the dark
25°C and 90% RH in the dark
5°C and 70% RH in the dark
25°C and 70% RH exposed to light

I. Challenge of Acetaminophen

Thus far, we have discussed in detail how to validate a raw material in general and how to validate acetaminophen specifically. We have indicated factors that should be considered in challenge studies, and now we will discuss how these studies should be conducted.

Samples of three different lots of acetaminophen have been obtained from each of the four suppliers that we are considering. These lots are to be tested in accordance with the established raw material specifications—parameter, specification (range), and test procedure—to determine that they are in conformance. If any one is not, the lot should be retested until it is either accepted or rejected. If it is rejected, it may be desirable to obtain another lot from the supplier, which lot is tested and probably accepted.

The next step is to manufacture product batches, each batch using acetaminophen under challenge conditions. The only variable should be acetaminophen—all other phases of the manufacturing process should be under rigid control and kept constant, i.e., procedures, personnel, equipment, and all other material lots. We might decide to manufacture one product batch with one acetaminophen lot from each of the four acceptable suppliers and subject these batches to a stability program. If all batches are acceptable, we can say that the acetaminophen used is acceptable and we have established a baseline stability profile indicative of acceptable batches. Ideally, the four different lots of acetaminophen will cover the range of each specification. This is to say that the four lots may have a melting range respectively of 168, 169, 170, 172°C; water content of 0.0%, 0.1, 0.2, and 0.5%; free para-aminophenol content of 0.000, 0.001, 0.003, and 0.005%, parachloroacetanilide content of 0.0000, 0.0002, 0.0008, and 0.0010%; assay of 98.0, 99.0, 100.0, and 101.0%.

After the baseline has been established, product batches are manufactured. The product batches should then be placed on a stability program. Some may fail to meet the established product specifications at different stages of the stability program. Failure may occur on completion of the batch, after accelerated storage and/or after storage under optimum conditions. The fact is that we have challenged the manufacturing process and measured the effect on stability of the finished product to validate the raw material.

Some of the above testing may seem redundant. For example, if we purchase other raw materials from all four of the suppliers—and if we are satisfied that these suppliers are reliable and conform to CGMP as we would like them to—it may not be necessary to use all four lots of acetaminophen. Rather, we can select any one or more of them.

As part of this overall scheme, and before any product batches are manufactured, the acetaminophen test procedures must be validated, on any one of the raw material lots. This requires that a given test procedure be performed varying one parameter at a time as we did with the raw material specifications. We have identified five critical test procedures for acetaminophen and they can be performed exactly as they are written with the following variations introduced one at a time in a test trial:

1. Melting range.
   a. Use two or three lots of reference standard.
   b. Use two or three different thermometers.
   c. Have three different people perform the test and read the endpoint
2. Water content.
   a. Use three different lots of Karl Fischer reagent prepared fresh.
   b. Use one lot of Karl Fischer reagent stored in the dark at room temperature for 1 week.
   c. Use one lot of Karl Fischer reagent stored at room temperature exposed to light for 1 week.
3. Free para-aminophenol
   a. Store one lot of the test solution for 1 week.
   b. Store one lot of the standard solution for 1 week.
   c. Incubate for 20 min.
   d. Incubate for 40 min.
4. Parachloroacetanilide
   a. Shake for 20 min.
   b. Shake for 40 min.
   c. Centrifuge at 800 rpm.
   d. Centrifuge at 1200 rpm.
   e. Centrifuge for 10 min.
   f. Centrifuge for 20 min.
   g. Irradiate for 20 min.
   h. Irradiate for 40 min.
5. Assay
   a. Use three lots of reference standard.

Some of the variations, or challenges, will cause the test procedure to give results that are different from the established procedures. When this is done, we can say that the test procedures have been validated.

In order to validate the sampling procedures, the different challenge conditions that were discussed previously can be set up. The acetaminophen raw material is then tested following the prescribed test procedures to determine the effect of the challenge on the raw material. We can store material exposed to accelerated conditions and then test it for conformance to the established specifications. This will validate the sampling procedures and established storage conditions.

VI. FUTURE CONSIDERATIONS

At some point in the future, a change in the acetaminophen raw material may be desirable. We may want to use a new supplier for a better cost or improved availability, or an improved test procedure may become available in the USP. Before making these changes, the entire data base generated by the validation process should be reviewed by those responsible for approving it—probably the quality control, production, and development departments. It may be necessary to revalidate following the guidelines and constraints that we have discussed. Any change should be documented and subjected to the established approvals system before being implemented.

In considering the testing requirements for new raw material lots received after the validation process has been completed, the subsequent control process must be evaluated. At some point, it is acceptable to use the suppliers' certificates of analysis, and it is not necessary to perform all compendial testing on all lots of raw material received. We can use our suppliers' test results—if they are within our specifications—and routinely perform only a few critical tests such as description, identification, water content, assay, and microbiological profile. If we choose this practical route, we should periodically perform complete testing as an audit, in order to monitor our suppliers properly.

REFERENCES

1. Code of Federal Regulations, Title 21, Food and Drugs, Parts 200-299, U.S. Government Printing Office, Washington, D.C., April 1991, pp. 81–100.
2. Madan, P. L., and Komotar, A., *Drug Cosmet. Ind. 24*(4):66 (1979).
3. Berry, I.R., *Pharmaceut. Technol. 5*(2):38 (1981).
4. Fry, E. M., paper presented at the Workshop of the Bulk Chemical Committee of the PMA Production and Engineering Section, Newark, NJ (September 1980).
5. Berry, I.R., *Drug Cosmet. Ind. 129*(5):46 (1981).
6. Berry, I.R., *Manuf. Chem. 54*(1):34 (1983).
7. Berry, I.R., *Drug Dev. Ind. Pharm. 14*(2 and 3): 377 (1988).

13

Analytical Methods Validation

Louis A. Pasteelnick *Warner-Lambert Company, Morris Plains, New Jersey*

> You must not keep weights of different sizes in your bag, and you must not keep measures of different sizes in your house; you must keep a full, just weight, a full, just measure, that you have a long life in the land which the Eternal your God is giving you.
>
> Deuteronomy XXV

I. THE NEED

Validation of analytical methods is the cornerstone of process validation. In the absence of a proven measurement system, there is no way of judging whether or not the process has done what it purports to do. There are two important reasons for validating assays in the pharmaceutical industry. The first, and by far the most important, is that assay validation is an integral part of the quality control system. The second is that current good manufacturing practice (CGMP) regulations [1] require assay validation. There are also various other reasons, such as being able to carry out business transactions based on assays of materials and providing a means for scientists to communicate effectively concerning technical matters. The United States Pharmacopeia [2] has recognized the important role of analytical methods validation in the pharmaceutical industry by including a general chapter on the subject.

As part of the quality control system, assay validation plays a key role in the universal control cycle. This cycle includes the following four steps:

1. Setting standards
2. Appraising conformance to standards

3. Taking appropriate action when standards are not met
4. Planning for improvement

Without confidence in measurements taken on samples of incoming, in-process, and finished-drug product, it would be difficult to confirm that the product being manufactured is uniform and that it meets the standards set to assure fitness for use. Since the quality control cycle is an evolutionary process, the need for assay validation implies that some form of validation or verification continues throughout the period of use of the assay procedure and is not something that is done initially when the assay is developed and then forgotten.

There are good scientific and business reasons for validating assay procedures even in the absence of regulatory or compendial requirements. The nature of the differences between the analytical development laboratory and the quality control laboratory is one good reason for a validation program. Also, the basic responsibility of the manufacturer to provide product at levels of quality that fully satisfy customers' needs requires an ongoing program of assay validation, particularly in laboratories testing pharmaceutical dosage forms. Those who work in the process industries repeatedly encounter situations in which problems develop because of an inadequate validation program. Frequently, the problems develop during the introductory phase of a new product. Great care is usually taken to ensure that the product can be manufactured in the plant environment; however, when similar efforts are neglected in transferring the technology to analytical laboratories, difficulties often arise.

Consider the regulatory issue. In the 1971 CGMPs [3], there was no explicit mention of validation; however, paragraph 133.11 stated that laboratory controls shall include the establishment of scientifically sound test procedures, and in paragraph 133.11(f) the regulation mentioned accuracy and precision in relation to laboratory test procedures. The CGMPs [1] for drug products, which became effective on March 28, 1979, implied in two different sections the need for validation. In 211.165(e) the word validation was explicitly used, and in paragraph 211.194(a)(2) the regulations called for proof that each method used in testing meets proper standards of accuracy and reliability and that the suitability of all testing methods is verified under actual conditions of use. Although the word "validation" was not used specifically, the process of proving accuracy and reliability of the method and the demonstration of its applicability to a specific laboratory certainly imply the concept of validation. It is clear that the promulgators of the regulation recognized that validation is an ongoing process, since either an inexperienced, rushed, or casual analyst can usually find ways to confound the intent of an assay procedure. Paragraphs 393 and 475 of the preamble to the 1979 CGMPs refer to the two sections cited above. Although the statement is made that compendial methods need not be validated, the intent is clear that the commissioner requires all test methods to be verified under actual conditions of use. The fact that CGMPs exempt compendial assays from the requirement for validation for routine testing does not eliminate the need when the method is used for stability testing. Furthermore, the Food and Drug Administration requires all analytical methods used for stability testing as part of a new drug application (NDA) or an abbreviated NDA (ANDA) submission to be validated in order to demonstrate that they are stability indicating.

II. HISTORICAL BACKGROUND

It should be noted that the problem of transferring technology from one laboratory to another is not a new one. The literature discloses examples of the study of variability associated with intralaboratory and interlaboratory test programs using statistical analysis of the data, to have begun appearing in 1946.

Wernimont [4] dealt with problems involving the control and detection of sources of variation in a specific test method in a single laboratory. His investigations showed the effect on test results of such variables as analyst, time, equipment, and reagents. Wernimont was also the first to expand the subject to cover interlaboratory test programs [5]. These papers gave examples of balanced sampling designs and demonstrated analysis of the data utilizing statistical methods.

In addition to the early work by Wernimont, W. J. Youden of the National Bureau of Standards is probably the most significant contributor to the literature of the design and analysis of assay validation experiments. One of his many publications [6] is full of insights into the problems of the analyst in developing assay procedures and transferring the technology to other laboratories—all of which gets to the heart of the validation challenge; this work should be studied by those who have a serious interest in the subject.

Another excellent work is that of Kavanagh, who is chief editor of a book on analytical microbiology [7] published in 1963 and revised in 1972 [8]. This book is particularly timely in the 1990s—the decade of biotechnology. Many of the assay procedures applied to the new products of biotechnology are dependent on microbiological methods with their inherent large variation; Kavanagh's book provides some thoughtful insights into sources of variation and easy-to-follow statistical techniques to deal with the variability of microbiological methods.

A reference targeted for the pharmaceutical industry is *The Greenbrier Procedure* [9]. This work focuses on validation of alternative assays but could easily be adopted for use (with or without a computer for the associated statistical analysis) in an assay validation program in the quality control laboratory. *The Greenbrier Procedure* describes the objectives of validation in simple language and suggests sensible-sized experiments.

When one reflects on the process of developing an assay, it becomes evident that a key portion of assay validation should be entwined in the analytical development process. Youden, in his article on collaborative testing mentioned earlier, has a section entitled Ruggedness Test for Procedures. In this section he stresses the importance of intentional efforts to abuse an assay to determine the factors associated with the test procedure that are considered to be insignificant but in fact have significant effects on the outcome of the assay result. If the development laboratory carries out such a study and finds results are altered by minor variations in the method, it will be in a better position to warn the prospective users of the method not to depart by more than some specified quantity from the conditions indicated in the written analytical procedure. He concluded that the transfer of technology from an initiating laboratory to a prospective using laboratory should never be undertaken until the method has been subjected to an abuse procedure and satisfactory results obtained in spite of the abuse, to assure that critical parameters have been identified and controlled. The importance of ruggedness testing is evidenced by the number of articles appearing in the literature referring to Youden's work. Among these is a paper describing specific statistical procedures that could be used in carrying out a ruggedness evaluation [10].

Two additional references are noteworthy in reviewing the historical background of this subject. The first is a publication by the Chemical Division of the American Society for Quality Control entitled *Interlaboratory Testing Techniques* [11]. This is a compilation of articles written by such noteworthy authors as Wernimont, Youden, and Mandel. Included in this volume are descriptions of the design and evaluation of experiments for use in assay validation, and it also includes details of experiments for ruggedness evaluation of test procedures. The second volume is entitled *Validation of the Measurement Process* [12] and is the result of a symposium sponsored by the Division of Analytical Chemistry of the American Chemical Society. One of the six articles included in this work is The Role of Reference Materials and Reference Methods in the Measurement Process by Uriano and Coli. In that article is the following statement: "This leads to the conclusion that the establishment of a compatible measurement system is an iterative, self-consistent process, sometimes requiring several generations of validating tests." This comment concerning the iterative nature of assay validation is one which some in the pharmaceutical industry seem to have missed. There appears to be an erroneous belief that if any assay has been validated, the procedure is acceptable for use in any laboratory at any time. McGonigle and Kaminski [13] support the view that assay validation only starts in the analytical development laboratory and that, to complete the process, trials need to be carried out in the laboratory where the assay is to be used.

III. DEFINITIONS

One of the most important attributes of an assay procedure that we should like to validate or verify is the accuracy of the test method. A procedure is accurate if, on the average, the method provides the true answer. The analytical development chemist more broadly defines accuracy in terms of selectivity or specificity. A method that is selective and specific discriminates the analyte from synthesis precursors, process contaminants, and degradation products; such a method is also considered to be indicative of stability. Accuracy implies that there is no inherent systematic error in the procedure. The statistician calls a systematic error "bias"; it is the deviation from the true value. The pharmaceutical industry is fortunate to have a large number of reference standards available from the United States Pharmacopeia against which to measure the accuracy of many assay procedures and determine the extent of bias that may exist.

Another important attribute to define is the pattern of variation of single assays on a uniform sample. This is called the random error by the statistician and is generally referred to as the precision of the assay by the analyst. The standard deviation is the measure of random error or precision. This measure of precision can help us determine how many tests to run on a sample to be comfortable that the average assay result is close enough to the true value.

Three factors usually combine with the true response to determine any analytical result in the quality control laboratory. First, there is random error. Second, there is the inherent systematic error in the procedure. Third, there is the modification of the systematic errors that is a consequence of a particular laboratory's environment, equipment, and technique. When used effectively, a reference standard can help reduce or eliminate the systematic errors mentioned above. Caution must be used when working with reference standards, because random errors in dispensing these reference standards become a constant or systematic error when unknowns are compared to the standard. Other commonly used terms include repeatability and reproducibility. Repeatability is defined as the variability within a given laboratory and can be affected by such factors as the analyst, environmental conditions, or laboratory equipment—none of which is constant from time to time. Reproducibility is defined as the variation between laboratories. This difference between laboratories is a major factor in the pharmaceutical industry, as it is in most industries.

Three other analytical performance parameters merit mention before we proceed further. They are 1) the limit of detection, 2) the limit of quantitation, and 3) ruggedness. The limit of detection is the lowest concentration of an analyte that can be detected by the analytical procedure. The limit of quantitation is the lowest concentration of analyte that can be determined with suitable precision and accuracy by the analytical procedure. The ruggedness of an analytical procedure is a combination of its repeatability and reproducibility as defined above. For more detail on these definitions and methods of determining measures of these parameters, see USP XXII [2].

The situation in which many pharmaceutical companies find themselves is one in which there exist two independent laboratories. One of these laboratories has the prime function of developing analytical procedures during the investigational new drug (IND) and NDA phases. This laboratory is usually well endowed with equipment and personnel, both in skills and numbers, and may not need rapid turnaround for batch release. The principal responsibility of this laboratory is to produce a procedure for analyzing a development formulation and to carry out the first phase of analytical methods validation. More often than not, this analytical methods development unit acts as the quality control function for the product development unit, including not only the initial acceptance of the product but also release of clinical supplies and stability testing. When the drug product has been transferred to production, it becomes the responsibility of the second laboratory, in most cases the quality control laboratory, to take that method and utilize it for routine release of the drug products.

It is this transfer of technology that usually produces the most formidable obstacle to obtaining a validated assay for routine use by the quality control laboratory. Generally, one will find that the analytical methods development unit has produced an impressive scientific document that demonstrates the successful performance of the assay in the laboratory where it was developed. While the assay is being developed, the analyst will generally explore the major problem areas that have caused difficulty with similar procedures. Then in the words of the late Jack Youden [14]:

> Sooner or later, and it is usually sooner, a set of analytical conditions that does give satisfactory results appears to have been found. At this point, the investigator may freeze the procedure and proceed to accumulate some data for publication. Unfortunately, he is meticulous in adhering absolutely to this particular set of conditions, never deviating. This holds true, not only for conditions which he has specifically written into the procedure, but also for various little habits of work which are faithfully followed every time. Under such circumstances, it is little wonder that repeat results show phenomenal agreement and it is on the basis of such results . . . the new procedure is offered to the quality-control laboratory as a routine tool.

There are many factors that may cause an assay result obtained in a single laboratory to deviate from the true value, but it is widely agreed that much larger deviations are likely to occur when the assay is moved from the environment of one laboratory to the environment of a second one. Figure 1 shows the results of a typical interlaboratory study. The bottom curve represents the total variability of the method. Shown above the bottom curve are the contributions of laboratories, analysts within laboratories, different days within laboratories, and repeat tests. As is frequently the case, variation among laboratories is the largest contributor to the overall variation of the method. When the first laboratory is an analytical methods development laboratory and the second is a quality control laboratory, where the need is for people to follow procedures as written rather than develop new ones, we are more likely to find results deviating further from the true value than those obtained in the original laboratory that developed the method.

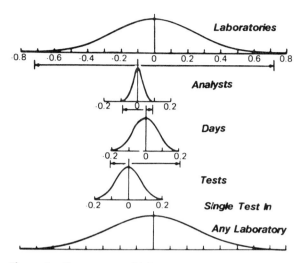

Figure 1   Components of laboratory validation.

Finally, let us define assay validation in the broad sense that any act that relates an assay value to the true value is assay validation. This definition will present some interesting opportunities for validating assay procedures on an ongoing basis for established products.

IV.   PREMARKETING ACTIVITIES IN ASSAY VALIDATION— METHODS DEVELOPMENT

Both the Food and Drug Administration (FDA) and the United States Pharmacopeia Convention (USP) have recently published articles that help publicize and define assay validation for a larger audience. In February 1987, the FDA published its *Guideline for Submitting Samples and Analytical Data for Methods Validation* [15]. Even more recently, the USP published USP XXII [2]; general information chapter 1225 is titled Validation of Compendial Methods. These two documents and their revisions will be the key references for assay validation in the pharmaceutical industry.

A.   Validation for a New Drug Application (NDA)

In their guideline for methods validation [15], FDA indicates that regulatory methods validation may be anything from a cookbook repetition of the assay to a more elaborate study of accuracy, precision, sensitivity, and ruggedness, depending on the quality of the submission. It therefore behooves an applicant to comply with the FDA guideline as a minimum and carry out other validation steps that appear to be scientifically appropriate.

The contents of the methods validation package should include a statement of composition of the drug substance, the new drug substance and drug product specifications, certificates of analysis, and a detailed description of the method of analysis from the NDA. Detailed information should also include 1) a tabular listing of all samples to be submitted, 2) a listing of all proposed regulatory specifications, 3) information supporting the integrity of the reference standard including the method of synthesis and information characterizing the reference standard, and 4) a detailed description of each method of analysis such that a competent analyst could carry out the method and obtain satisfactory results. The following characterize a typical description of a method of analysis:

1. Statement of the principle of the method
2. List of necessary reagents
3. Detailed list of instrumentation required
4. List of instrumental parameters
5. Detailed step-by-step procedure
6. Representative calculations

In addition, FDA recommends a section of information supporting the suitability of the methodology for the new drug substance that includes 1) a summary flowchart of the synthesis of the new drug substance, 2) control of polymorphs and/or isomers, 3) data demonstrating accuracy, precision, and linearity of the method as well as data that demonstrate the specificity of the method, 4) data demonstrating the determination of limits for degradation products or impurities, and 5) representative chromatographs and instrumental recordings.

Finally, FDA requires information supporting the suitability of the methodology for the dosage form. This should include:

1. Data demonstrating suitable accuracy, precision, and linearity over the range of interest (usually 80–120% of the label claim).
2. Data demonstrating the specificity of the methods and the determination of limits for degradation products and/or impurities.
3. Data demonstrating recovery from the sample matrix.
4. Data demonstrating that neither fresh nor degraded placebo interferes with the method.
5. Reproductions of representative chromatographs and instrumental recordings (where appropriate).
6. Ruggedness data; characterizing day-to-day, laboratory-to-laboratory, analyst-to-analyst, and column-to-column variability.
7. A degradation schematic for the active ingredient.

8. If the method is not stability indicating a limit test for the degradation product(s) must be submitted.

9. System suitability tests for chromatographic assays (as defined in USP XXII, p. 1566).

B. Validation for an Abbreviated New Drug Application (ANDA)

The principal difference between methods validation for ANDA and NDA submissions is that, for an ANDA, the new drug substance has usually been characterized as an official item of the United States Pharmacopeia or some other recognized source such as the British Pharmacopeia, and the applicant commits to adhering to those specifications. The remaining items outlined above should be included in the ANDA methods validation package.

C. Some Additional Comments on Validation in the Methods Development Phase

The first step in the analytical methods development procedure is to establish what is to be measured and how accurately it should be measured. Then, on the basis of a literature search and knowledge of the chemistry involved, choose from the methods available or decide that a new method is required. If a new method is required, proceed to develop the basic method. After the rudiments of the method have been determined, some stage of development is necessary to improve the repeatability and carry out ruggedness experiments of the type proposed by Youden. At this point, a reference standard should be developed, if one does not already exist. Then, finally, prepare a written procedure.

Once it appears that the procedure has been defined, it is appropriate to carry out a series of experiments to validate the procedure. These experiments should include evaluation of factors such as accuracy, precision, recovery, linearity, system suitability for chromatographic assays, and whether or not the assay is indicative of stability. An approach that has been successful is to start by preparing a placebo or a series of placebos and showing whether or not there is any interference with the active ingredient. It is equally important to demonstrate that the method discriminates between the compound for which it is designed and synthesis precursors, process contaminants, and degradation products. Then placebos could be spiked at 90, 100, and 110% of label claim and checked for recovery and precision.

Next, a check for linearity should be run at concentrations that cover the entire range of interest from 25 to 125% of label claim or higher, if large excesses are used as in vitamin products. Additional experiments should be run to check repeatability over time—within days and between days. Samples from production should be run and compared with a standard method if the new procedure is one that has been developed to replace an existing procedure. It is also appropriate to check stability samples to see if aging of the product has any impact on the assay procedure, such as interference or poor recovery. At this point, consider if any revisions should be made in the written procedure based on the results of the foregoing experiments. It would now be appropriate to try out the method utilizing an analyst not familiar with this specific procedure. Then, where appropriate, interlaboratory testing might be considered.

The sample for the experiments can come from a variety of sources. Among these, three types of samples stand out:

1.   A USP standard sample
2.   Samples that have been fabricated from available production or laboratory materials and spiked appropriately
3.   A single lot of homogeneous material that has been tested a number of times so as to have a valid estimate of the characteristics of the lot

Many forms of statistical analysis are described in the references at the end of the chapter; however, it is appropriate to mention a few key approaches at this point. First, the method of data analysis should be decided on before the experimentation is started, including levels of significance to be used in any hypothesis testing. It is always appropriate to plot the experimental data to determine whether any outstanding features can be observed [16]. These plots could take the form of a simple frequency distribution and a graph of the assay results versus time, as in a control chart. Subtracting the expected value from each assay value and plotting the residuals as a frequency distribution or versus time can be useful when various levels of analyte have been utilized in the development program. A well-designed experiment followed by an examination of a plot of the data will frequently be the only analysis necessary. During this phase, check for outliers and follow up with appropriate statistical tests if questionable values occur. Two measures of the method should come out of the experiments performed; these are measures of the precision and accuracy.

V.   ONGOING METHODS VALIDATION IN THE QUALITY CONTROL LABORATORY AND TRANSFER OF METHODS FROM ONE LABORATORY TO ANOTHER

A technique that serves the dual purpose of auditing laboratory performance and providing an ongoing validation program for a quality control laboratory is as follows. If a series of homogeneous, stable samples of known concentration are routinely submitted as unknowns to the quality control laboratory and if these results are recorded on a control chart and the assays average close to the known value and are in statistical control, the data may be used to demonstrate that the analytical method has been validated. Figure 2 is an actual example of that situation. In this example, a portion of a reference lot of vitamin B_{12} was submitted along with the routine production samples on each day the analytical method was run. By demonstrating that the results from the reference lot were in statistical control and that the average was close to the known value, the quality control laboratory demonstrated the continuing validity of the analytical method.

At the heart of any discussion of this subject is the question of how much work is needed to validate the analytical methods for all the products the company produces. When one works in a world where limited resources exist, I believe it is better to do a modest amount of validation work on as many assays as possible rather than an exhaustive job on a few assays and no work on the rest. Another factor suggesting modest-sized validation experiments is the frequency with which process and formulation changes are made in the product; this could influence the need for additional validation. Also, there is the fact that technology advances rapidly, providing new methods that, despite their improved precision and accuracy, still need to be validated.

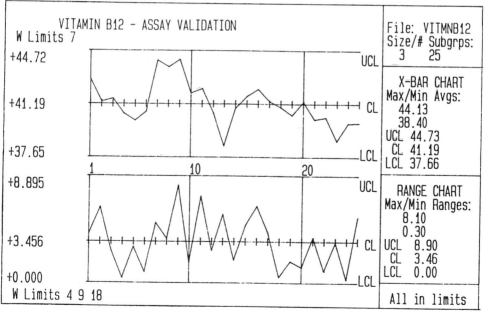

Figure 2 A control chart for a reference standard.

Building on these realities, it is proposed that relatively simple validation experiments be carried out to demonstrate a continuing state of validation and control. It has been learned, based on experience in quality control laboratories, that as many questions were raised in the initial attempt to validate an assay as were answered. Therefore, the validation procedure would appear to lend itself to an iterative process rather than one in which resolution is attempted with one grand experiment. In fact, several years ago an exhaustive study of the subject by several conscientious and competent analysts resulted in a proposal to have four analysts test 48 samples, 16 on each of 4 different days, as the standard protocol for validation. This program was designed to satisfy the most stringent FDA investigator. Several such programs were carried out and the results appeared quite satisfactory for the products tested; however, the amount of work required would be oppressive to all but the most overstaffed laboratories. When the quality control laboratory supervisor realized the implications of repeating this procedure for all the products tested in that laboratory, the program was halted.

If a thorough job of validation of the assay procedure had been carried out in the analytical methods development laboratory, the follow-up work needed in the quality control laboratory should be relatively modest. By the time the method has been offered to the quality control laboratory for routine use, problems concerning accuracy, precision, linearity, and interference should have been resolved.

Generally, three concentration levels of analyte are chosen for confirmatory testing. These are at, or slightly outside, the specification limits and at the target or label claim. Typical levels are 90, 100, and 110% of label claim or 85, 100, and 115% of label claim. For compendial assay procedures and also for situations in which extensive laboratory work has been done in an analytical methods development laboratory and the quality control laboratory is familiar with the assay or similar testing procedures, there is nothing wrong with running the validation procedure at 90 and 110% of label claim and eliminating the center point.

The number of tests we run at any of these points presents another interesting question. Some laboratories have carried out experiments in which as few as two or three tests at each of three different levels of drug potency were adequate to show that the procedure is satisfactory. *The Greenbrier Procedure* proposed duplicate tests at each of three levels on three different days; however, for assays with a relatively large standard deviation, it will probably be necessary to run considerably more tests at each level. The decision in any situation should be based on knowledge of the variability of the assay procedure and its relation to the specification limits.

Where automated sample processing is available, such as when using an autoanalyzer or chromatograph and automatic injection, increasing the number of tests to five or six should be relatively simple and will provide an extra measure of security at little extra cost. A more rigorous approach is described in International

Standard 5725 [17]. Once a decision has been made on the number of repeat tests at each level selected and one such experiment has been carried out by one analyst, you can consider whether it is necessary to run additional experiments using one or more analysts, shifts, days, or analytical instruments—if several are routinely available for the test. The number of analysts included in the validation experiment should be related in some way to the number of analysts expected to run that test in the laboratory. If one or two analysts are planned to do all the testing of a certain product, it makes sense to validate or verify each of those analysts running the assay. If many analysts are to be used, some thought should be given to having each one participate in a small experiment to verify their ability to get a known value.

A procedure currently being used as a type of methods validation in quality control laboratories is to obtain a sample that has been analyzed a number of times by the analytical methods development laboratory and have each analyst in the quality control laboratory who runs the test determine results for this known sample in duplicate on two different days.

A plan that may be used in transferring a product to people who have had no previous experience with the manufacture or assay of the product is first to provide as much information as possible to help them understand the analytical method. Along with a copy of the assay procedure and background information on the analytical method, copies of the data used to support the initial claims for the procedure are supplied. Included, when available, are the details of the difficulties encountered, suggested precautions when utilizing the method, information on techniques that were tried but did not work, and assay validation data or the analytical monograph from an NDA or ANDA submission. When possible, an analyst from the receiving laboratory is sent to observe the more experienced analyst run the test procedures and perhaps even try to have the observer run the test under the supervision of the experienced analyst. This act of faith assumes that the sending laboratory has already validated the analytical method and has a comprehensive program in place designed to assure that all calibration, standard-ization, and auditing programs are functioning effectively.

The next step in this process is to obtain for the receiving laboratory the materials needed to run the test, such as reagents, standard solutions, and reference standards. Then the analyst in the receiving laboratory would prepare the test samples, including placebos where indicated. The preparation of test samples is a crucial step in the process and should be given appropriate attention. At this point, a single analyst may run three tests on samples at each of three levels of concentration. Figure 3 shows the results of a typical trial. A second analyst might repeat the experiment, and the combined results are shown in Fig. 4. Now you could indulge in an orgy of statistics, but I submit that the most prudent scientists would agree, after examining Fig. 4, that this assay is sufficiently

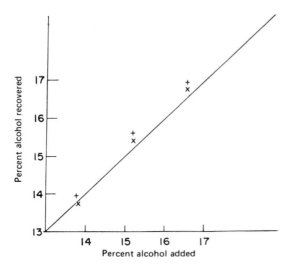

Figure 3 Prospective validation—a plot of amount added versus amount recovered based on duplicate assays by a single analyst. ×Analyst one—1 result; +Analyst two—2 results.

accurate and precise to be considered validated. Not all experiments have gone so smoothly, as can be seen in Fig. 5. The precision was quite satisfactory; however, there was clearly a problem with accuracy. An investigation revealed that the receiving laboratory was very anxious to start preliminary testing on the product and decided to substitute a piece of drying equipment for the special one specified. When the proper equipment was received and tests repeated, the results were much more satisfactory, as shown in Fig. 6. Several similar experiences have led to the belief that a program of small experiments performed by one or two analysts is the proper strategy to follow in assay validation or verification in the quality control laboratory.

VI. SOME CONSIDERATIONS OF LABORATORY COMPUTER VALIDATION

During the 1980s, the use of computers in the pharmaceutical industry grew from almost nonexistent to almost omnipresent. The FDA recognized the existence of computers in the 1979 CGMP in section 211.68 and worded their requirements in traditional terms of calibration, checking, written procedures, and change control. By 1983, FDA realized that its investigators needed more information and they issued the "Blue Book" [18], which triggered a series of articles [19,20] in

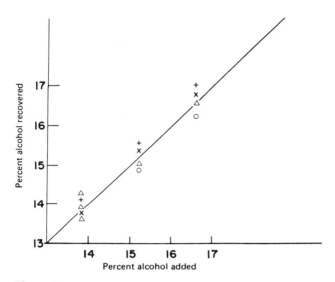

Figure 4   Prospective validation—a plot of amount added versus amount recovered based on replicate assays by two different analysts. ×Analyst one—1 result; +Analyst one—2 results; △Analyst two—1 result; ○Analyst two—2 results.

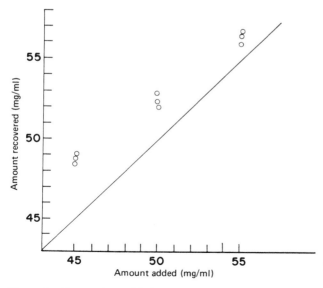

Figure 5   Prospective validation—a plot of amount added versus amount recovered based on triplicate assays by a single analyst. ○Analyst one—first try.

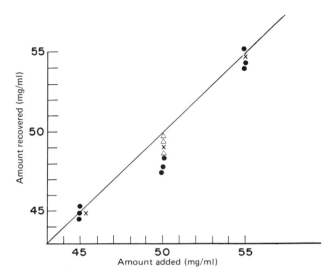

Figure 6 Prospective validation—a plot of amount added versus amount recovered based on replicate assays conducted by three different analyst using proper drying technique. ○Analyst one—first try; □Analyst one—second try; •Analyst two—one result; ×Analyst three—one result; △Analyst three—two results.

Pharmaceutical Technology detailing the Pharmaceutical Manufacturers Association companies' view of what constitutes adequate validation.

Computer validation proceeds in four sequential phases: prequalification (specification and design), qualification (installation and operational checkout), validation (testing), and ongoing evaluation (change control, security, maintenance, and backup and recovery). In the prequalification stage the system is described in noncomputer language, hardware specification and system schematics are prepared, and the design phase is completed. The design phase consists of preparation of functional requirements and a detailed design. The qualification stage consists of:

1. Software preparation
2. Hardware installation
3. Installation qualification

During this phase, each piece of equipment must be installed and identified correctly, and then it must be verified that it performs as intended. The validation phase starts with the preparation of a document, the protocol, which describes the functions to be tested, the number of trials for each test, the acceptance criteria for each function, and operational limits within which the system is expected to operate and against which validation testing should be performed. The data from the validation tests are analyzed and evaluated, a report is written, and the validation process is approved by appropriate authorities. The final phase is the ongoing evaluation of the system to ensure its continued successful operation. The most obvious element of the ongoing operation is change control, which is thoroughly discussed by Agalloco [21]. Security measures, preventive maintenance programs, and backup and recovery procedures all should be documented and followed to provide for a reliable system.

Documentation is the heart of computer validation. To start with, all the expectations for the system should be put in writing and approved by appropriate authorities. A complete description of the hardware to be used in the system and the details of how it is to be connected is another important step. Next comes the documentation of the software with a description of software functions and organization. A system logic diagram is required showing how each module/program functions. Detailed software testing is a component of software documentation. A description of the file for data base structure is needed. Software documentation should include a historical log of the software programs/modules used. Documentation of the operation phase should include a user's manual and instruction for routine recordkeeping operation. Documentation of the validation (testing) process is the next logical step. Installation qualification consists of providing evidence that the environment and hardware are installed as specified in the design.

Operational qualification consists of providing evidence that the computer system performs as specified in the design. The validation protocol is a written plan describing the tests to be run to demonstrate that the previously qualified system will perform as specified in the design. Rice and Stoll [22] discuss a strategy taken to validate a computerized data acquisition system for chromatographic analysis. The results of the validation should be recorded, analyzed, approved, and maintained for future reference. A computer system in operation also requires documentation of the various activities required to keep it viable. These include change control, preventative maintenance, security, and backup and recovery.

REFERENCES

1. *Federal Register*, Vol. 43, No. 190-Friday, September 29, 1978.
2. USP XXII, *The United States Pharmacopeia*, Mack Printing Company, Easton, PA (1989).
3. Federal Register, Vol. 36 No. 10-Friday, January 25, 1971.

4. Wernimont, G., *Anal. Chem. 18*:587–592 (1946).
5. Wernimont, G., *ASTM STP No. 103* (1949) and *ASTM Bulletin No. 166* (1950), American Society for Testing and Materials, Philadelphia.
6. Youden, W. J., and Steiner, E. H., *Statistical Manual of the Association of Official Analytical Chemists*, AOAC, Washington, DC (1975).
7. Kavanagh, F., *Analytical Microbiology*, Academic Press, New York (1963).
8. Kavanagh, F., *Analytical Microbiology II*, Academic Press, New York (1972).
9. *The Greenbrier Procedure*, Pharmaceutical Manufacturers Association/QC Section, Washington, DC (1977).
10. Wernimont, G., *ASTM Standardization News 5*, 3 (1977).
11. Mandel, J., *Interlaboratory Testing Techniques*, Chemical Division Technical Supplement, ASQC, Milwaukee (1978).
12. DeVoe, J., *Validation of the Measurement Process*, ACS Symposium Series, American Chemical Society, Washington, DC (1977).
13. McGonigle, E. J., and Kaminski, E. E., *Analytical Method Validation*, Chemical Institute of Canada (April 29, 1980).
14. Youden, W. J., and Steiner, E. H., *Statistical Manual of the Association of Official Analytical Chemists*, AOAC, Washington, DC, p. 5 (1975).
15. FDA, *Guideline for Submitting Samples and Analytical Data for Methods Validation*, Food and Drug Administration, Washington, DC (February 1987).
16. Ott, E. R., *Process Control*, McGraw-Hill, New York (1975).
17. International Standard 5725-1981 E, *Precision of Test Methods—Determination of Repeatability and Reproducibility Interlaboratory Tests*, International Organization for Standardization, Switzerland (1981).
18. FDA, *Guide to the Inspection of Computerized Systems in Drug Processing*, U.S. Department of Health and Human Services, Washington, DC (February 1983).
19. Kuzel, N. R., *Pharmaceut. Technol. 9*:60–76 (September 1985).
20. PMA's Computer Systems Validation Committee, *Pharmaceut. Technol. 10*:24–34 (May 1986).
21. Agalloco, J. P., *Pharmaceut. Technol. 14*:20–40 (January 1990).
22. Rice, J. X., and Stoll, F. P., *Pharmaceut. Eng. 9*:15–19 (November/December 1989).

14

Computer Systems Validation

James E. Krueger *Krueger Associates, New City, New York*

Jonathan Krueger *Ingres, an ASK company, Alameda, California*

I. INTRODUCTION

You are going to install a computer in your production or your quality control function.

Why do you want to install a computer system anyway?

- to reduce your chance of FDA problems?
- to prevent the mix-ups that invite 483's and worse?
- to improve your compliance posture?

Well, maybe. What about improving your response time to schedule changes? Reducing costs? Coming to terms with the poor quality of today's high school graduates? What did you tell the CEO, the board of directors, or whomever when you made your pitch for the funds to bring computers into your operations?

No one denies the advantages of staying on good terms with the FDA, but was that all you thought about? The agency does not get involved with your efforts to improve efficiency, costs or profits, except when you seem to be getting into trouble with the GMPs, your NDAs, or the FD and C Act, itself.

Therefore, although the validation of a computer system certainly must meet FDA's guidelines, it should also lead to a system that meets your business needs, reliably and repeatedly.

II. DEFINING YOUR COMPUTER SYSTEM NEEDS

Validation of any system operation starts with a statement of what you need to accomplish, expressed in your own terms.

For example, a large pharmaceutical manufacturing firm needs to maintain an online warehouse inventory. If the inventory is inaccurate and out of date, or the information faulty, there are some regulatory risks such that accountability errors may result in FDA actions. But there are also some business risks too. Raw materials may not be ordered on time, accounting will not reflect actual usage, and materials may sit unfound and unused. Buying materials you already have in stock is poor management. For example, unreleased materials may end up in finished products and result in a product liability risk.

How could these things happen with the computer system? Sources of error include keying errors when updating the database, software errors in the database application, and poor specification of the procedures for maintaining the database. An example of a keying error would be accidentally entering an extra digit for purity of a raw material. This is also an applications error for failing to reject a purity of more than 100%. An example of an applications software error might be a screen that confuses lot number with product code. An example of a procedural error would be unclear instructions on how to generate a batch record, resulting in the carefully correct formulation of the incorrect finished product.

All of these are avoidable errors. But you have little hope of avoiding them without a clear statement of what you need to accomplish, expressed in your own terms. It may already be seen that in our example, "an online warehouse inventory, kept accurate, up-to-date, and correct" failed to mention some important things that companies need to accomplish. One could add, for example, "system will provide range checking; applications software will interact with users in a way that provides reliable, repeatable entry of data into correct fields; SOPs will identify product on every page of every batch record." But the specification needs to be made stronger, more specific, more testable, more precise, at many other points in the system. It needs to be made comprehensive too: it needs to include all functions the system will perform and all sources of error at each point.

Once you have a clear statement of what you need to accomplish expressed in your own terms, your MIS function (or consultants) can reduce this to a black-box, don't-understand-how-it-works description of the inputs to the system and outputs it provides. This includes operator procedures for interacting with the system. To some it may seem strange to design screens before the software has been created. This is wrong. Screen design is a powerful way for you to confirm that your MIS people have described the same system you want. Screen design specifies input and outputs. You will need to compare this with the running software to validate the system at a later date.

III. MANAGEMENT INFORMATION SYSTEM (MIS) RESPONSIBILITIES

Screen design is not enough. Your MIS function must specify the following:

- Access to the system will be restricted to authorized persons.
- Operator keying will be checked for erroneous inputs.
- Review and approval by another person will be required before the computer can go ahead and act on critical input.
- Computer will alert responsible people when it receives questionable inputs.
- Complete audit trail of all transactions and changes will be kept and made available to authorized users for review.

None of these is a screen design problem. All are part of the system specification your MIS function must provide. None however, is more than a black box specification. No specifics with respect to implementation are necessary or desirable at this time.

Before specifying anything at a lower level, your MIS function must specify the software that will be used to implement this specification. It is wise to buy instead of build most relevant software, in particular the building blocks of your computer system. For instance, your system should almost certainly have a strong database component. Homegrown database software is unlikely to provide as high reliability as applications built on existing general purpose database systems. Your MIS function must decide what parts to buy and what to build in house. In practice this is an enormously difficult task. Fortunately, it isn't critical to reliability because you have stated what the system must do, in your own terms, before this takes place. (If you have *not* done so, this may be the weak point where all is lost and may never be made reliable again.)

IV. SOFTWARE ENGINEERING

It is true that whatever you have heard about software engineering is actually worse. Some substantive and prescriptive facts, however, about software engineering have been learned in the last 40 years. One of them is that early mistakes, so called design and specification mistakes, take more time and money to fix than later mistakes—such as implementation, coding, and documentation mistakes. In fact the development of nontrivial systems usually has several choice points. At each step the prudent manager verifies that the work is correct up to that point. The early points are the most critical. Errors made and not caught then are usually so expensive to fix later that it is cheaper to start over. Errors made at later points can be fixed at some reasonable cost. (Reference: The Mythical Man-Month, Fred Brooks).

During this stage, it is possible to specify the hardware. For starters, it must run the software you have just specified. Traditionally, this is where systems people also worry about whether it will be fast enough. The good news is that today, you usually don't need to worry. You do need to perform some back-of-the-envelope calculations to make sure it is in the right ballpark. But this concern should no longer get your immediate attention. A valid concern is that it should be able to be scaled up. Today, most vendors can do this for the client.

V. HARDWARE DEVELOPMENT

Your back-of-the-envelope calculation should take the number of online users you need to support, the subset of them who will be active at peak times, a short textual description of the work performed by an active user, and a time latency for each user to proceed from task completion to the next task. There are other metrics in use. These are the ones that usually determine what size hardware you need to buy. Above a certain price range, you will find that the hardware manufacturer will be happy to assist you in specifying which hardware in their line will meet your needs.

Scaling usually should be expressed in these same terms: how many online users and how many of them will you expect to scale to? The company might decide it needs to supply 10 online users with 3 active during peak periods, bringing up each new task screen within 5 seconds of the previous screen. It might decide it needs the ability to scale up to 100 online users with 30 active during peak periods. Order-of-magnitude growth of their operation represents a reasonable ceiling on growth. So, they need the 10 user system now, and any vendor who can demonstrate an upgrade path to 100 should provide enough scalability for your future operations.

What your hardware vendor may not understand is what goes on in the factory. The company will have to evaluate hardware in terms of a host of environmental issues.

VI. ENVIRONMENTAL CONCERNS

Pharmaceutical manufacturing environments are known to be dusty, full of vibration, and supplied with unreliable electrical power. (Even if your local power is dependable, turning on 8 horsepower blenders can cause a transient voltage drop while they come up to speed.) Keyboards, disk drives, printers, power suppliers, and fans, all may need to be stabilized against changes in voltage during the work day.

Possible interference with the signals as they are carried on cables from terminals to the computer, then to its memory units and printers, will also require stabilization.

Your hardware vendor usually understands shutdown issues. You will have to tell them what kinds of shut-downs you can tolerate, with what notice, and with what guarantees about data integrity. In turn they will have to tell you whether and how the operating system accomplishes this. You may also need to get the same information from software suppliers of your major system components. Again, it may seem strange to be working through all these issues before a single line of applications software has been written. It is a hard fact that no applications software will save you if you have to go down and your hardware and major software components cannot perform fast and graceful shutdowns.

It is not your hardware or software vendor's responsibility, however, to specify what will happen to you if a fire destroys the computer. In practice, computer fires are rare particularly in pharmaceutical manufacturing. Damage from supplied power or water is more common but just as final. Plugging the machine into 220V is also exciting. Your hardware supplier, or the representative associated with this line, must provide adequate backup solutions. Today, it is seldom the case that any hardware is lacking some provision for backing up data. The issue is which option to choose. The backup solution must also be able to scale up if the main hardware does. You have not specified the hardware completely until you have specified the backup.

VII. PROGRAMMING REQUIREMENTS

Now, you have a description of the complete system, and the tasks it is to perform, expressed in "black box" terms. Next, the systems analyst must create a technical description of what the programmers have to accomplish and how they should go about doing it. This is a crucial step, because typically an individual programmer is not going to know enough about the overall system to avoid conflict, contradiction, or contention for computer resources in every situation. There is nothing wrong with this approach. Division of labor and expertise in building nontrivial systems proceed best along lines of responsibility. Systems analysts are responsible for specifying how the chosen hardware and software will be used to implement the specified tasks. Programmers are responsible for coding, testing, and putting the pieces of the system together.

As much as possible, programmers should use tools and techniques that eliminate or minimize programming errors. These powerful techniques make it possible to increase the productivity of a programmer and at the same time dramatically improve the quality of the output. Your systems analysts should specify which tools each programmer will use to build his or her piece of the system. Your MIS function computer systems will need to know enough about the state of the art to understand how the implementation will meet systems specification.

VIII. PROGRAMMING TOOLS

The major software components you choose to buy are often sold as software productivity tools. More important is their use as reliability tools. Examples include compilers, which flag dead code; screen interfaces with the ability to do range checks on fields; libraries of well-tested arithmetic functions; query languages that replace low-level disk accesses, source control systems. It may be seen that some of these are programmer tools, some are application designer tools, and some are system specification or component isolation tools.

Some operating systems provide better support for software tools than others. A notable example is UNIX, developed at Bell Labs for testing the viability of software tooling ideas. Today, it continues to offer a rich set of programming tools. However, many of these tools are available today on other operating systems as well.

Major software components bought from third parties are reasonably expected to provide a software tool set relevant to their area of use. For example, the database system that does not provide tools to reliably build applications, interface with users, and work with standard programming languages, is not a very useful item. For instance, if it is difficult to work with standard programming languages, programmers will make mistakes. The vendor-provided tools should make it easy to use and straightforward, not just possibly useful.

Of course the programming team will test their creations. First they will test each module separately. Then they will test the assembled modules.

When the programming activity is drawing to a close, you should receive a final draft of the program. The validation process begins at this stage.

IX.   INITIATION OF COMPUTER SYSTEMS VALIDATION

Let us start by admitting that no computer can ever be 100% reliable. In that they share the common frailty of all manmade inventions, and we can progress only by admitting this fact. Then our task must be to improve on the reliability of other, presumably manual methods and of course to save money and time.

The first step is to create a task force, work group, or committee that will design tests of the tasks the computer system is going to perform, using simulated inputs and looking at the outputs. To do this, the group usually will create an imaginary task (or tasks) similar to that which the system will have to handle but also including all the exceptional situations that can be thought of. Such tasks should be preserved for future use or for whenever the system has to be changed— and it will be changed.

In planning these test cases all the common errors of input should be deliberately included to demonstrate that the system can handle them, if it can.

X.   COMPUTER SYSTEMS VALIDATION PROTOCOL

An experimental plan describing the tests and the expected outputs, usually called a protocol, must be written before the tests are carried out. The protocol should be reviewed by all interested company functions: users, managers, quality assurance, MIS, hardware function, and signed off by all of them as adequate from their viewpoint.

A typical validation protocol contains the following elements [4]:

- the number of runs required to demonstrate that the system reproducibly performs each function as expected
- acceptance criteria for each function
- definition of operational limits within which the system is expected to operate and against which validation testing should be performed
- description and documentation of how changes to the system and/or modules that occur during validation studies will be evaluated, including an evaluation of the effect of each change
- description of measures to be used for promulgating approved supplements and/or changes to the protocol, if required.

In the execution of the validation protocol, each step is followed according to predetermined methods and the data are gathered as prescribed. Data are then analyzed, and the results are evaluated, documented, and summarized. Either the full report or a summary of its conclusions is presented for formal approval by designated authorities representing appropriate disciplines within the organization. All pertinent data produced during the execution of the validation protocol are filed for historical reference.

XI. CHANGE CONTROL

Someone must write procedures to provide for the security of the system, and in particular to prevent any unauthorized changes to hardware or software, an area often called change control or configuration management. These too must be reviewed, and as soon as the validation testing is complete, these procedures must be enforced. From then on, even the programmers cannot change the final version without written, carefully authorized permission. For research purposes, an experimental version of the program can be created and made available to the programmers, of course, but this version must be carefully kept separate from the "production" version of the program.

Changes will be needed or at least desired for a variety of reasons: new or improved functions, errors not detected earlier, alterations to accept new equipment in the system, etc. Some of the original programmers will have moved on. Can the newly hired maintenance programmers figure out what the original programmers did? Unless you have taken suitable precautions at the outset, the answer will be no.

To avoid this predicament, it is necessary to provide suitable instructions to the original programmers, covering such things as the data dictionary; the tools provided by the operating system, database, and programming language; a library of terms and symbols; another library of subroutines to accomplish standard tasks; common entry points into every module in the program; explanatory comments in the code; etc. It is useful to audit the programming function periodically. It is also prudent to hire competent maintenance programmers.

XII. REVALIDATION

Many errors are introduced into large, complex programs as they are modified. The result after about five years is accumulated errors that have nullified the value of the program, and it must therefore be rewritten from scratch at considerable cost. There is a monetary incentive to get clear, maintainable code and to control and validate all changes to it at the outset.

Validation of changes follows the same pattern as the initial validation. You may be able to avoid revalidating the whole body of code with each change if the original code is structured to show all the modules affected by a change to any given module, and if each proposed change is evaluated to determine all its effects before it is incorporated into the program. In this situation you can make good use of an experimental version of the program, where you can try out the change before incorporating it into the production version. If you have kept the original set of validation tests, annotated to show what each one does, you will find good use for them at this time.

Operating systems and utility programs change every few years. Your application program relies on this lower-level software, and some of the results of such changes cannot be foreseen. Therefore, new versions of this software must be installed in such a way that only the experimental version of your program is exposed to them, and the effect must be evaluated by suitable testing and validation before you go online. You can refuse to install the new versions, but then you risk being unable to use other new software written to be compatible with the revised system of software.

XIII. SUMMARY OF KEY ISSUES IN PUBLICATIONS ON COMPUTERIZED SYSTEMS

Inspection*

This document points out what aspects of computerized systems to address during inspections and offers suggestions on how to accomplish the task.

Overview. Begin by determining exactly what processes and functions, and what aspects, are under computer control or monitoring. For each, determine the system loop (sensors, processor, and activator). Identify which of these are most critical to drug product quality.

Hardware. Obtain a simple block diagram of the hardware showing the major components and how they are linked. Identify the makers and suppliers, including model designations, all major components, including terminals. Determine where they are located. Look for evidence of the following potential problems:

---

*Guide to inspection of computerized systems in drug processing. Feb. 1983. Division of Drug Quality Compliance (HFN-320) and Division of Field Investigations (HFO-500) [1].

1. Hostile environments, including extremes of temperature, humidity, dust, static electricity, power fluctuations, and electromagnetic interference.
2. Signal-carrying lines which are too long for the kind of line shielding (if any), and the electrical interference present.
3. Convenience of the location of input devices to the operators who must use them.
4. Accuracy and performance of input/output (I/O) devices, the non-digital equipment which links the computer system to a controlled process.
5. How errors and command overrides in one of several linked computers affect the other computers and the devices they control.
6. What arrangements have been made for maintenance (written procedures, diagnostic software, availability of qualified servicepersons and spare parts).

Validation of Hardware. The suitability of the hardware for the functions it is to perform must be demonstrated by appropriate tests, which together provide support for a high degree of confidence that the system will consistently do what it is purported to do. The following questions should be addressed:

1. Does the capacity of the hardware match its function?
2. Have the operational limits of the hardware been identified and taken into consideration in setting up the production procedures?
3. Do the tests include the worst conditions which will be encountered?
4. Will the tests be repeated enough times to demonstrate that the results are reproducible? At least three test runs should be made.
5. Will the documentation include a validation protocol and test results which are specific and meaningful?
6. Is there a system to assure revalidation when significant changes have occurred?

Much of the hardware validation may be carried out by the manufacturer, but the pharmaceutical manufacturer is responsible for assuring that the equipment is suitable. When validation data are produced by an outside firm, the drug establishment must keep information (protocols and results) which are sufficient to show that the validation was adequate.

Software. Determine who developed the software. If it was produced by an outside firm and contains proprietary code, determine what the firm has done to demonstrate that this code does not compromise the performance of the software. If it was developed in-house, review the SOP for documenting the approval process.

Determine each program's language, name, function, inputs, outputs, and process setpoints (fixed and variable). Learn how it can alter inputs and outputs, and whether it can be used to falsify information. Determine how it processes, manipulates, or performs calculations on input data, and make or obtain a flow chart showing the steps. Determine what overrides of the program by the operator are allowed.

Determine how the firm prevents unauthorized changes to the code and how it prevents data from loss, alteration, or erasure. Determine whether this control extends to storage media such as disks and tapes which can be removed from the computer. Find out who is authorized and/or able to write, change, or access programs. Look at the SOP for security.

Software Validation. Consider the following points:

1. Does the software accept all the variations that could appear in the operation it controls?
2. Have the validation tests been performed under the most challenging conditions of process speed, data volume, and data frequency?
3. Have the tests been repeated at least three times?
4. Has the validation been documented, including a protocol and the test data? Are the people who reviewed and approved the validation effort named in the report? Is the testing aimed specifically at the attribute being tested, and does it produce detailed data?
5. Is there a system to trigger revalidation when programs, process parameters, or data handling are changed?

Computerized Operations. If the computer is on a network, find out what the rest of the network does or can do with the GMP-controlled parts, how it is monitored, and what security measures are used to prevent unauthorized changes from elsewhere on the network.

If there is a manual backup process control system, determine its scope and capabilities, especially what process controls it can affect. Find out what it can do to override the computerized system. Find out how manual intervention is documented. See that an SOP describes what manual overrides are allowed, who may use them, and under what conditions.

Determine whether personnel monitor the computerized operations periodically and which functions they watch. Spot-check operations by comparing with correct information:

1. calculations against manual results
2. input records against sensor indicators
3. Component quarantine against warehouse location and status of required tests
4. Timekeeping against a separate clock
5. Automated cleaning-in-place against SOP, residue tests, and the firm's method of assuring adequacy.
6. Tailings accountability against the firm's controls

Determine what functions are linked to alarms, the alarm thresholds or conditions and whether operators can change them, types of alarm signals, how the firm responds, how often and how they are tested, how alarm activation is recorded, and whether all alarm conditions can be displayed or heard simultaneously.

Determine the shutdown recovery procedure. How does it bring the process into a condition which protects the product? Where is the point of restart? Is process data preserved before shutdown is obtained? How long does recovery take, and where does it exceed established limits or compromise product quality?

CGMP Guidance. Hardware must be suitably located to facilitate operations and be covered by maintenance and calibration programs (CFR 211.63, 67, 68). Software is regarded either as records or SOPs and the following regulations apply:

1. Inputs and outputs must be checked for accuracy in a way that provides strong assurance of their accuracy (211.68). Determine the degree and nature of the firm's input-output checks, how inputs are edited to prevent error, and what other audits are built in. Determine the error handling procedures, including records, error verification, correction verification, and allowed over-rides of errors (including required over-ride records).

2. There must be accurate and secure backup files of input data (211.68). Find out what backup system is used and how it is protected.

3. The computerized system must generate records which contain all the information they are required to contain (211.180-198).

4. The accuracy of computer inputs, outputs, and data must be ensured (211.68).

5. Records required by the regulations must be accessible at the firm as part of an authorized inspection and are subject to copying under reasonable conditions (211.180).

6. Records may be originals or true copies; this applies also to magnetic and electronic media (211.180).

7. Record retention requirements are the same regardless of medium (211.180).

8. Computer programs should be accessible as part of an inspection where this is reasonable (FD&C Act, Section 704 (a)). Factors which bear on reasonableness are include whether access would disrupt operations, would disclose information FDA is not entitled to review, or would involve disclosure of programs which are copyrighted and licensed by a vendor.

9. Periodic record review may involve computerized collection and trend analysis of the data to be reviewed (211.180).

10. Batch record review prior to release for distribution may be done by means of a computerized exception report if it has been demonstrated to be at least as comprehensive and accurate as manual review. The batch record must still be retained. Portions of the record which are still manual must still be manually reviewed (211.192).

11. The required double check of components added to a batch may be replaced by an automated single check if it demonstrably provides at least as much assurance of correctness. This includes such visual checks as the appearance of a component (211.101).

12.   Batch records must document that each step was performed by identifying each person who conducts, checks, or supervises each step. If a series of steps is carried out automatically, it is enough to record only the first and last steps, if the program has been validated (211.188).

13.   A batch record must contain an accurate reproduction of the master record. There must be evidence that a computerized batch record is accurate. Determine whether the original approved, endorsed master record and the batch record are identical.

14.   Since a supplement must be submitted for changes in manufacturing and control processes, a change to a computerized system requires a supplement.

Documentation Requirements*

In Part I, the author discusses some unsettled issues. Records required by Part 211 must be available for authorized inspection. If information and data are collected and maintained in electronic form, there must still be a way for FDA investigators to see the records during an inspection and to obtain copies. The author routinely obtains electronic copies during inspections. The information must be in a format that can be subjected to audit. If not, the inspector will cite this as an objectionable condition on form FD-483. The author also suggests that if an inspector cannot perform ad hoc queries on data, the data may be considered unavailable. Possible ways to provide FDA access to original records include:

read-only access at a terminal
electronic copies in formats accessible to FDA auditors
customized software to retrieve requested information

Other issues mentioned are the use of electronic signatures, the meaning of "original records," and cautions pharmaceutical firms not to consider moving to a paperless system until they have a satisfactory validation in place.

Part II shows a nonspecific chart used by the author during FDA inspections as a guide for systematic reviews of GMP documentation. It includes the validation process. He defines a validation plan as one which need not include specifics, but which does spell out management's philosophies and expectations and establishes responsibilities. The author states that if the firm does not have a formal written validation plan, the system cannot be in a state of validation. As in any scientific endeavor, the objectives and approaches used in validation must be defined. If vendors perform some validation activities, they too must have formal validation plans.

Protocols are written descriptions of objectives, methods, and acceptance

---

*GMP Documentation Requirements for Automated Systems: Parts I and II. *Pharmaceutical Technology*, March, April 1992 [8].

criteria for tests. They must be prepared in advance of testing, and should specify responsibilities, test methods, how data are to be collected and reported, and the review and evaluation procedures to be used to determine if the acceptance criteria were met. Three stages are often distinguished: installation qualification, operational qualification, and performance qualification. Protocol changes should be controlled by written SOPs which define responsibilities, the testing required, and the format and mechanism for making changes.

Test results must be recorded. Validation reports should contain written conclusions based on comparison of the test data (input-output checks) against specifications (acceptance criteria). Approval statements should include the basis for acceptance. There must be SOPs which provide complete instruction on how to operate the automated system.

There must be complete, clear, written specifications for the system which permit measurement or quantification of all important operating parameters, and these documented are subject to the usual complete review/approval process. The author uses incomplete specifications as a symptom of trouble elsewhere. Because of the many interactions, an automated system may require hundreds of specifications, and a formal system to track them is necessary to avoid errors and omissions.

There should be a record of all events, both normal and unexpected. Some events are recorded automatically; others must be recorded manually. Events that bear on the system controls should be recorded on forms that are clear, easy to read, and easy to understand. Significant input-output checks should be verified by a second person. Records should be reviewed and approved by a responsible person.

Validation generates much data, which is frequently increased when the first tests show the need for changes to the system. Both the data and the activity which produced it must be recorded. This requires SOPs for the documentation process.

All reviews of validation records must state clearly and completely the basis for decisions made. Final validation reports should be verified for accuracy and should show that the data are completely reported and free of typographical errors, and should show which criteria and data were used in making decisions. If the approvals are based on reviews of summary reports, this should be stated.

FDA expects a firm's documentation for automated systems to be complete, accurate, and sufficient to prove proper performance. Unless they have documented evidence of the proper performance of a vendor's software, FDA cannot consider the systems to be validated. When this happens, the consequences may include legal sanctions or disapproval of NDAs.

Some examples of the validation documentation problems in the paper are:

excessive limits
failure to perform input-output checks at proper places or times

failure to cite protocols or required tests

failure to define record format, content, and retention

failure to clearly state objectives or test methods

criteria or specifications that lack measurable parameters

failure to require double-checking of key data and reports for accuracy

failure to require approval signatures by two or more responsible persons

lack of defined responsibilities and mechanisms for approval, including independent approval by the QC unit.

failure to define what each approving signature means

failure to identify each record which must be prepared and/or approved

failure to provide for exception reporting

failure to provide for conditional approvals and actions to be taken if some tests do
not meet acceptance criteria.

APPENDIX: LEXICON OF COMPUTER SYSTEMS VALIDATION TERMS AND DEFINITIONS*

Application software: a program adapted or tailored to the specific requirements
of the user for the purpose of data manipulation, data archiving, or process
control.

Change control: a formal monitoring system by which qualified representatives
of appropriate disciplines review proposed or actual changes that might affect
a validated status to determine the need for corrective action that would ensure
that the system retains its validated state.

Computer program: a collection of logically interrelated statements or instructions that when executed by a computer makes possible the performance of a
predefined task.

Computer system: a group of hardware components assembled to perform in
conjunction with a set of software programs, which are collectively designed
to perform a specific function or group of functions.

Documentation: manuals, written procedures or policies, records, or reports that
provide information concerning uses, maintenance, or validation of a process
or system involving either hardware or software. This material may be
presented from electronic media.

Environmental factors: those outside influences on the computer system that may
affect its operation, including temperature, moisture, electrical interference,
electromagnetic flux, power supply, and so on.

Flow chart: a graphical representation of the logical steps involved in a procedure
or program.

---

*The PMA's Computer Systems Validation Committee and presented in *Pharm. Tech.*, May 1986 [4].

Functional testing: a process for verifying that the software performs the intended functions.

Hardware: physical apparatus that makes up a computer. This term is also used to describe the various pieces of equipment in the computer system, including the central processing unit, the printer, the modem, the cathode ray tube (CRT), and so on.

HIPO chart: a software charting technique used to define and document programming systems in a manner that facilitates communication between the programmer and the user. HIPO is an acronym for *hierarchy plus input-process-output*.

Installation qualification(IQ): documented verification that all key aspects of hardware installation adhere to appropriate codes and approved design intentions and that the recommendations of the manufacturer have been suitably considered.

Life cycle: an approach to computer system development that begins with identification of the user's requirements, continues through design, integration, qualification, validation, control, and maintenance, and ends only when commercial use of the system is discontinued.

Module: a unit task or subdivision.

Ongoing evaluation: a term used to describe the dynamic process employed after a system's initial validation to maintain the validated state of a computer system.

Operating system: a set of programs provided with a computer that function as the interface between the hardware and the applications program.

Operational qualification (OQ): documented verification that the system or subsystem performs as intended throughout representative or anticipated operating ranges. The term *performance qualification* is sometimes used in the same context.

Peripheral: a device attached to a computer, such as a terminal, a printer, a disk drive, a magnetic tape unit, a plotter, and so on.

Process: the controlled system.

Pseudocode: common language (such as English) in an arbitrary code-like format used to describe meanings of routines and subroutines written in a programming language. In other words, an English translation of a computer program.

Retrospective validation: establishing documented evidence that a system does what it purports to do based on an analysis of historical information.

Revalidation: repetition of the validation process or a specific portion of it.

Software: a collection of programs, routines, and subroutines that controls the operation of a computer or a computerized system.

Software development standards: written policies or procedures that describe practices a programmer or software developer should follow in creating, debugging, and verifying software.

Software diagnostic procedures: tests for predicting errors of malfunctions in programs.

Source code: an *original* computer program expressed in human-readable form (programming language), which must be translated into machine-readable form before it can be executed by the computer.

Utility programs: special programs frequently supplied by the producer of the operation system. They perform general functions such as making backup copies of programs and copying files from tape to disk.

Validation: establishing documented evidence that a process does what it purports to do.

Validation plan: the collection of activities that include and are specifically related to computer system validation itself.

Validation protocol: a prospective experimental plan that when executed is intended to produce documented evidence that the system has been validated.

REFERENCES

1. FDA References Materials and Training Aids for Investigators: Guide to inspection of computerized systems in drug processing. Feb. 1983 and Software development activities. July 1987.
2. FDA Compliance Policy Guides for Computerized Drug Processing: Input/output checking. 7132a.07. Oct. 1982. Identification of persons on batch production/control records. 7132a.08. Dec. 1982. CGMP applicability to hardware and software. 7132a.11 Dec. 1984. Vendor responsibility. 7132a.12 Jan. 1985 Source code for process control applications. 7132a.15 Apr. 1987.
3. ANSI/IEEE Standards: Glossary of software engineering terminology. 729-1983. Software configuration management plans. 828-1983. Software test documentation. 829-1983. Software quality assurance plans. 730-1984. Software requirements specifications. 830-1984.
4. PMA Computer Systems Validation Committee: Validation concepts for computer systems used in the manufacture of drug products. *Pharm. Tech.*, May 1986. Computer system validation—staying current: introduction. *Pharm. Tech.*, May 1989. Change Control. *Pharm. Tech.*, May 1990. Validation of computer-related systems. *Pharm. Tech.*, Nov. 1991.
5. A. S. Clark. Computer systems validation: an investigator's view. *Pharm. Tech.*, Jan. 1988.
6. K. Diggins. Development standards for software used in drug production. *Pharm. Tech.*, Sept. 1987.
7. G. C. Myers. The art of software testing. Wiley Interscience, New York: 1979.
8. R. F. Tetzlaff. GMP documentation requirements for automated systems: Part I. *Pharm. Tech.*, March 1992. Part II, April 1992. Part III, May 1992.

15

Validation of Lyophilized Products

Edward H. Trappler   *Lyophilization Technology, Langhorne, Pennsylvania*

I. INTRODUCTION

A. Process Description

Freeze drying, or lyophilization, is a drying process used for the preservation of a substance for long-term storage. The material is dried to prevent decomposition via chemical or biological reactions that occur in the presence of water. This process is applied to the manufacture of a number of health care products; freeze drying is used to produce a stable product and provide extended stability for increased shelf life. A product that is not stable as a solution or that contains significant amounts of water is freeze dried to remove any water that may be chemically active and lead to degradation of the product.

Lyophilization has been defined as the process of making a product lyo-philic, i.e., water loving. Material that has been lyophilized has been described as "bone dry." A simple definition of lyophilize is to dry a product while it is in the frozen state. The process of freeze drying encompasses preparing a material for and subsequently removing water by a combination of sublimation and desorption. The objective is to obtain a finished product that is stable, easily reconstituted, and provides acceptable activity (chemical or biological) for its intended use.

Since the 1940s, freeze drying has been used in the production of health care products. Penicillin and human serums were the first commercial applications of the technology for human use [1]. The ability to preserve a pharmaceutical product has made many products conveniently available to clinicians. Lyophilization has been applied to a wide range of pharmaceuticals, biologics, diagnostic reagents, and fine chemicals. These products are sometimes frozen and freeze dried in bulk but most often are processed in their final package. Of most recent interest and study is the freeze drying of biopharmaceuticals, specifically protein materials [2,3].

Lyophilization consists of three separate, unique, but interdependent processes: freezing, sublimation, and desorption (Fig. 1). Freezing of the solution is required for preparation of the product for subsequent freeze drying. This part of the process is often most critical and has an effect on the process to follow as well as on the finished-product characteristics. Most of the water crystallized as

THE PROCESS OF LYOPHILIZATION

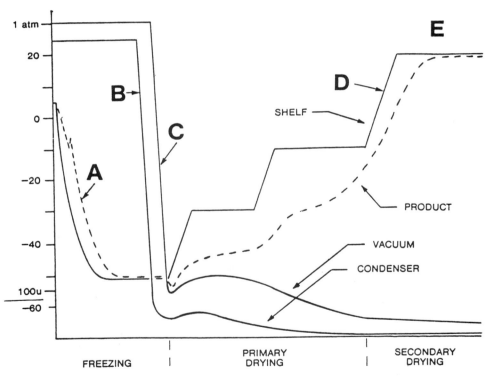

Figure 1 (A) Freezing to below the phase transition temperature to solidify the product. (B) Chilling the condenser to collect the water from sublimation. (C) Evacuating system to permit sublimation of ice. (D) Elevating shelf temperature to supply heat for continued sublimation. (E) Maintaining warm temperature for desorption to low residual levels of water.

pure ice during the freezing is removed by direct sublimation. The low residual water content necessary to assure acceptable product stability is achieved by subsequent desorption during the final drying steps of the process.

The freezing process must be completed in such a manner in order to maintain the original activity. The method of freezing can have an adverse effect on the product as in the physical and/or chemical denaturation of biological material. An example of this is when the growth of ice crystals physically ruptures a biological cell or deforms a protein's structure. In addition, in solutions that are formulated to be isotonic and with a specific pH range, shifts in concentrations of components of the formulation may occur as the water freezes out of solution [3].

Freezing of dilute aqueous solutions occurs in a series of steps. As an example, in a binary system of the salt in water, the freezing point of a sodium chloride solution is depressed due to the presence of NaCl as a solute in water. Upon cooling, when the material reaches a temperature below the depressed freezing point, pure water begins to crystallize out as ice. The remaining solute in solution therefore increases in concentration because there is less water in the liquid state. This process continues as additional water crystallizes until the solution has reached a saturated condition. At this concentration and at a sufficiently low temperature, the remaining solution will undergo a phase transition from liquid to solid and crystallize as immiscible components: NaCl will crystallize as a salt and the remaining water will crystallize as ice. As shown on a solid-liquid phase diagram for eutectic materials, this phase transition occurs at a specific concentration and temperature and is referred to as the eutectic point.

The process described above parallels that which occurs with many organic materials with one important exception: the material may not exhibit eutectic behavior when undergoing a phase transition upon cooling. Rather, the material increases in viscosity as ice is formed until the solution can no longer increase in concentration. With the increase in viscosity and the lowering of the temperature, a phase transition occurs in which the material solidifies in the amorphous form. Many of the pharmaceutical products and excipients used in formulations exhibit this type of behavior. Examples of these are the polymer povidone (PVP) and the antibiotic doxycycline hyclate.

Consideration should also be given to how the material is frozen for its effect on the removal of water during the sublimation and desorption processes that are to follow. For example, slow freezing leads to the formation of larger ice crystals. This aids sublimation by the creation of relatively large voids where the water vapor may pass as the sublimation front proceeds through the material. Along with aiding the water vapor to escape during sublimation, these large voids also provide ducts for the water to permeate the dried cake upon reconstitution. However, freezing that is too slow results in undesirable conditions such as increasing the potential for concentration shifts of components such as buffers, as described above. Also, slow freezing may increase the thickness of a skin that forms along the top of the product. The rate of freezing also affects the physical appearance of the plug: voids left from the large ice crystals that have sublimed lack a desirable level of "pharmaceutical elegance."

In the "primary drying" step of the process, the water that is first crystallized out as ice is removed via sublimation. Sublimation is the vaporization of water directly from solid ice to gaseous vapor without the water entering the liquid state. In the lyophilization of dilute aqueous solutions, most of the water is removed by sublimation. The sublimation of the water that was first crystallized during freezing must be completed while maintaining the material in the frozen state below its phase transition temperature. In the case of NaCl, this is below the melting point of the eutectic solution, −21°C [4]. A PVP solution must be maintained below the temperature at which the material may soften and become viscous, leading to what is referred to as "collapse" [5].

Sublimation requires drying at reduced product temperatures and environmental pressures. During the sublimation, heat is provided to the product to replace that heat lost as a result of water vaporizing. The amount of heat provided dictates the rate at which sublimation progresses. Supplying heat in excess of that which is removed by the ice subliming increases the temperature of the product [6]. If the temperature of the frozen product increases above the phase transition temperature, the product may melt or collapse.

Completing this process in a controlled environment requires that the sublimed water condense at a significantly lower temperature at which the ice has a lower vapor pressure. Condensation must occur at a rate greater than that of sublimation so that a sufficiently low pressure is maintained within the environment.

As the sublimation front or ice-vapor interface progresses through the material, it leaves behind a matrix composed of the solutes that were in solution. The apparently "dried" material still contains water that may be chemically active and degrade the product upon storage. This chemisorbed water is removed by desorption. Desorption is accomplished during freeze drying by providing sufficient heat to release the "bound" water to achieve a low residual level of moisture. This removes any trace water that may become chemically active during storage. This water is also collected by condensation at low temperatures so that the vapor pressure of the condensed ice is below the pressure in the environment.

B. Equipment Overview

Freeze drying is a special application of vacuum technology. This low-temperature vacuum drying utilizes common types of equipment combined in a unique configuration. A freeze drying system may be described as six integrated subsystems (Fig. 2). Each subsystem must be configured and operate in a precise way to carry out successfully the process of freezing and freeze drying. Following is a brief description of the basic components of a typical freeze drying plant.

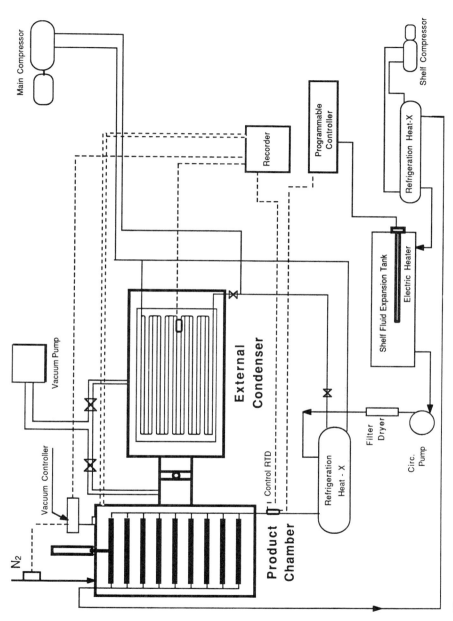

Figure 2 Mechanical equipment and subsystems.

Because freeze drying must be completed in a controlled environment, a vacuum chamber is used to house the product during the process. The vessel must be able to withstand a pressure differential that occurs when the inside of the chamber is under vacuum of approximately 15 pounds per square inch. Since the process is conducted under subatmospheric pressures, it must also be vacuum tight, precluding any uncontrolled air entering the chamber and spoiling the vacuum.

Within the chamber are shelves on which the product is placed. The shelves function to hold the product, either in bulk containers such as trays or in finished product vials. The shelves are also used to fully seat the stoppers at the completion of the lyophilization cycle for products processed in vials where the stoppers are partially inserted for drying. The shelves also form the heat sink during freezing as well as a heat source during drying. Here, the shelves function as heat exchangers. Heat transfer fluid is circulated through the hollow shelves. The fluid is either cooled during freezing or warmed for drying.

The heat transfer fluid system, including the shelves, is the most complicated mechanical subsystem of the entire plant. Shelf temperature control is provided by cooling the fluid using mechanical refrigeration through heat exchangers or by warming with immersion-type electrical heaters. The fluid must pass through the shelves in a manner which ensures that each and every shelf as well as the inlet and outlet of each shelf is within acceptable temperature limits, even under heavy heat loads, as is the case when freezing a large batch of product. Since the fluid's quality affects the efficiency of the heat transfer and therefore control of the process, the fluid must be kept clean and free of extraneous agents. This is particularly true for water that might freeze out at low temperatures and cause a blockage in the system. A filter/drier is often included in the circuit to keep the fluid clean and dry. Consider also entrapped air in the circuit. Air pockets within the heat exchangers limit the efficiency of heat transfer. A chemical pump circulates the fluid through the system at a constant rate to ensure efficient heat transfer through the refrigeration exchangers and the heating elements, as well as through the shelves.

To collect the water evolved during sublimation and desorption, a refrigerated condenser is used. Condensers may be located within the product chamber (internal condensers) or in an attached but separate vacuum vessel (external condensers). Condensers are most commonly chilled by direct expansion of a refrigerant. The condensing surface may be in a number of configurations, according to a manufacturer's preferred design.

A mechanical refrigeration system is used to provide chilling of the shelves for freezing of the product and for chilling the condenser to collect the sublimed water vapor. Systems commonly used include internally compounded two-stage compressors, using principally R-502 but sometimes R-13B1. Cascade systems, where a high stage cools another low stage refrigeration unit, may use combinations of R-12 and R-13B1, respectively. The refrigeration compressor(s) can be engaged to chill the shelves through the shelf heat transfer fluid heat exchangers for freezing the product at the beginning of the cycle. During the drying phase of the process, the compressors can be diverted to allow direct expansion of the refrigerant to the condensers. The most common systems can provide temperatures to below −50°C on the shelves for freezing and to −65°C on the condenser for collecting water vapor. There is often a second refrigeration system dedicated to maintaining shelf temperatures during drying. These units may be either single state or two stage. Single-stage units commonly provide shelf temperature control down to −30°C during drying.

The vacuum pumping system evacuates the air and maintains the low pressures required for freeze drying. Vacuum pumping systems consists of either single-stage, two-stage, or sometimes three-stage vacuum configurations. The pumps used in single-stage and two-stage systems may be oil-sealed rotary piston or rotary vane type. Three-stage pumping systems use a combination of two-stage pumps in conjunction with a mechanical blower. Pumping systems are rated by volume displacement (cubic feet per minute or liters per minute) and ultimate achievable vacuum, or blank-off pressure (microns or millibars). The pumping systems are sized according to the volume of the lyophilization plant and conditions of operation. Purely aqueous product processing commonly utilizes the oil-sealed units. Systems handling considerable amounts of noncondensable gases and/or organic solvents incorporate mechanical blowers in combination with oil-sealed units [7].

Control and monitoring of the process may be divided into four functional groups: shelf temperature, pressure (vacuum), recording, and sequencing. Shelf temperature control is initiated by a controlling instrument monitoring the shelf fluid and engaging either the heater or refrigeration units. Vacuum can be both monitored and controlled when a vacuum probe located on the chamber (and condenser) senses the pressure in the chamber. Control is commonly accomplished by bleeding a small amount of an inert gas into the chamber. Permanent records of the process are generated by a recording instrument with input from product probes, from sensors within the system such as for the shelf-temperature, and from the vacuum instrument. Automatic sequencing can be achieved to advance the equipment functions through the steps of freezing, chilling the condenser, evacuating the system, and shelf temperature profiles for drying [8,9].

C. Design Considerations

Beyond the basic lyophilization plant as described previously, there are design considerations for the application. Those presented here are focused on applications for the production of pharmaceutical and diagnostic products. They are based on practical concepts, requirements to meet current good manufacturing practices and industry standards, with attention given to compliance issues.

Vessels, shelves, and hardware are available in stainless steel and constructed to withstand both vacuum and the temperatures and pressures for sterilization with pressurized steam. The materials of construction may be of the 300 series of stainless steel such as type 304L or 316L. It is important that L grade stainless be used for corrosion resistance to the aggressive clean steam used in sterilization. It is imperative that the stainless steel be properly passivated after all welding, finishing, and polishing operations are completed. After any rework that is done, as may be necessary for changes or modifications after passivation has been completed, the stainless must again be passivated. Failure to passivate properly surfaces that will come in direct contact with clean steam will lead to corrosion of the stainless steel after repeated sterilization.

Product chambers must be constructed to allow ease of cleaning and adequate distribution of steam during sterilization. Access to ports for cleaning and the sloping of penetrations for drainage, particularly of steam condensate, are important details in the construction of the vessel [9]. Penetrations should follow the "6 to 1 rule"; that is, a port 1 inch in diameter should protrude no more than 6 inches from the vessel proper. This ensures adequate steam penetration during sterilization. It is also important to allow ease of cleaning. These ports should end in a sanitary- type connection. Access to the bottom of the chamber by raising the lower shelves allows ease of cleaning and removal of any material that may have fallen from the shelves during loading and unloading. The bottom of the vessel should be adequately sloped for proper drainage of cleaning solutions and steam condensate. A screen installed at the drain port prevents items from clogging the drain or becoming lodged in the drain valve, potentially creating a vacuum leak.

Access to the chamber for product loading and unloading can be achieved in a multitude of ways. Conventional designs offer a full chamber door opening to the product processing area. Pass-through configurations, with access achieved from two separate areas, have been utilized since the 1970s. Such an application is in bulk processing of hygroscopic material, where the liquid product is loaded in a "wet" processing area. After lyophilization, the material is unloaded and bulk packed in a separate humidity-controlled room through the opposite door. Costly floor space can be conserved by utilizing a pass-through configuration with a subdoor for loading in an aseptic processing area. Use of a subdoor eliminates the area required for the swing of the full chamber door. A full door on the opposite side provides access for unloading and cleaning operations. Subdoor access has also been used for integrating automated loading operations in combination with mechanical transferring devices and automated guided vehicles (AGVs).

Product shelves within the chamber are multifunction heat platens. The shelf construction is hollow, allowing circulation of heat transfer fluid through a serpentine pattern. Multiple shelves must be connected in parallel to supply and return manifolds to ensure even flow of the transfer fluid. This is necessary for even distribution of temperatures across all shelves during freezing and freeze drying. Restrictions within the shelves must be limited to achieve sufficient flow for even temperatures across each shelf, ensuring batch uniformity. The shelves may also function as stoppering devices. Flatness is important for achieving even forces to all the vials during stoppering.

The heat transfer system supplying heating and cooling to the shelves must have the range and capacity to achieve sufficient rates and temperatures for the parameters of the process. Any changes in the flow rate due to clogged filter/driers, restrictive piping, or poor performance of the pump will result in temperature gradients across the shelves during freezing and drying. As well, air pockets in heat exchangers or the shelves will limit the heat transfer capability. The presence of water in the fluid will result in temperature deviations during chilling of the fluid. For these reasons, proper protection and care of the circulation system are essential. A closed system, blanketed with a constant head pressure on the expansion/storage tank such as a regulated nitrogen supply, helps in maintaining a clean system. The pressure differential across the filter/drier should be monitored as a routine maintenance check. Excessive differential pressures indicate a clogged unit. As a result, fluid flow would be affected, leading to potential temperature variations across the shelves.

Many heat transfer fluids have been used in freeze drying systems. Requirements of the fluid are:

Good viscosity profile
High specific heat
Low freezing point
High boiling point
Thermal stability
Good wetting properties
Low toxicity

These requirements for the heat transfer fluids limit the acceptable fluids that are available for this special application. 1,1,2-Trichloroethylene (TCE) has been widely used but has been replaced because of toxicity and environmental impact issues. Lexsol (Santa Barbara Chemical Company), a composite fluid, has been used as a replacement. This material consists of 63% naphthenes, 31% paraffins, 5% alcohols, and 1% xylene and aromatics. Low-viscosity silicone fluids (methylpolysiloxane) are also used. In small research units, use of Freon 12 is common.

Collection of water during the freeze drying process is accomplished by use of a refrigerated trap, referred to as the condenser. The condenser may be configured internally within the product chamber or externally in a separate vessel. Internal condensers have been commonly used for development and pilot plant units. They are also commonly used in diagnostic manufacturing operations. External condenser systems have been used more in pharmaceutical manufacturing units, although this trend appears to be changing. The condenser must be of adequate capacity for the total amount of water evolved during drying. It also must have sufficient surface area to accommodate rates at which water vapor is being sublimed [11]. The rates of sublimation are greatest at the beginning of the drying cycle, when the sublimation front (or ice-gas interface) is close to the top of the product plug. With the ice-gas interface near the surface, the water has the least resistance in leaving the plug and the rate of sublimation is at a maximum [12]. Therefore, the largest surface area is required at the beginning of the cycle. The condenser design must also be optically dense. This creates a tortuous path for the water vapor, assuring that all the vapor is condensed before it can pass to the vacuum pump [13]. A well-designed condenser also provides sufficient dwell time for the water vapor traveling at high velocity to be in the area of the cold surface and condense.

The optical density of the condenser also aids in limiting the opportunity for oil vapors to migrate into the chamber from the vacuum pump. In secondary drying, where pressures are well below 100 microns, oil vapors from the vacuum pump may diffuse into the product chamber. Unless there is a cold trap positioned such that any vapors may be condensed, the oil may enter the chamber and contaminate the product [14].

If it is suspected that product formulations contain components that may be volatile or that the process presents opportunities for oil migration, then the condenser design must easily accommodate cleaning between batches. The condenser should be constructed to provide ease of access for cleaning. It has also become common practice to steam sterilize the condenser. The design criterion is therefore the same as that of the chamber, as previously described.

The refrigeration systems used to support the process are often separated into two functions. Main refrigeration units can be selectively diverted to the heat exchangers or to the condenser. The main units are required for both functions because the large heat loads occur during both freezing of the product and condensing of the sublimed water vapor. During freezing, the refrigeration unit must remove heat from the heat transfer fluid through the heat exchanger. Part of the heat is due to cooling of the liquid and containers, removing the sensible heat. Also, the heat of fusion is removed as the solution undergoes the exothermic event of the phase change in freezing. During drying, the refrigeration is diverted to the condenser. Here the heat of vaporization in addition to the heat of fusion must be removed. This is due to the water undergoing two phase changes: from vapor directly to ice (Fig. 3).

Often a dedicated refrigeration unit is part of the heat transfer circuit design. The function of this unit is to aid in both freezing the product and providing cooling on an as-needed basis for maintaining desired shelf temperatures. Compressors for this function are often smaller than the main units and may be single-stage or two-stage units. Single-stage units with R-502 operate to suction temperatures to $-40°C$, providing shelf temperatures to $-30°C$. Two-stage units operate

PHASE CHANGES FOR WATER DURING LYOPHILIZATION

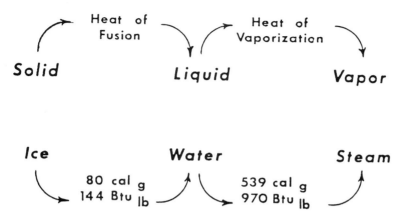

Figure 3 Lyophilization involves numerous phase changes for water. First is the freezing of a liquid to a solid with the heat of fusion being removed. Second is the sublimation of ice where the phase change includes heat of fusion and of vaporization. Third is the condensation of sublimed water vapor to ice on the condenser.

to temperatures below $-62°C$, allowing them to be used continually during freezing and to provide lower temperatures during drying.

Oil-sealed vacuum pumping systems, either single-stage or two-stage, are most commonly used. Mechanical booster pumps are often used when mixed solvent formulations are processed. As discussed earlier, the refrigerated condenser must be adequate to remove all the water vapor. The vacuum lines from the condenser to the pump must be placed so that the water cannot bypass the condenser surface. The pumps must be protected from water vapor contaminating the vacuum pump oil in order to maintain their pumping capacity and the ultimate vacuum that can be achieved. Failing to do so will cause spoiling of the vacuum and a process that is out of control.

Preservation of health care products by lyophilization is a complicated process that integrates various technologies [15,16]. The technologies applied to lyophilization encompass not only the process but also the equipment. The product quality is affected by the product characteristics and the environmental conditions for the process. The environment is created by the equipment. Therefore, aspects of both the product characteristics and the operating principles of the equipment are important in developing and implementing a validation study.

II. VALIDATION OF LYOPHILIZATION

A. Introduction

The comprehensive validation program includes equipment qualification, product and formulation aspects, and detailed studies for process validation. The actual validation protocol includes equipment, installation, and operational qualifications followed by process validation. Approaches to the validation studies parallel those of many other pharmaceutical operations, but with some unique aspects because of the technology. These become clear and obvious with an understanding of the process and will be presented in this text. Some of the considerations that are of greatest concern as compliance issues have been described in the literature [17–19]. Implementation of the protocol is often completed in the order presented above. The validity of the conclusions drawn from the validation studies is maintained with a thorough and comprehensive change control program. A detailed discussion of each part of the validation study is presented after a brief introduction.

The equipment qualification section encompasses specifications for the equipment, including the hardware and control system, along with the operational performance of the system. Also included may be the equipment acceptance documentation covering equipment verification and performance tests completed at the manufacturer's facility prior to shipment.

The installation qualification encompasses a general description of the application, process, equipment, and control system. Along with the general description are specific listings of the system hardware that include details such as the manufacturer and model number of the component. Services and utilities are included in this section of the protocol, along with an installation checklist and initial calibration records.

In the operational qualification of the validation study, equipment performance tests are conducted to demonstrate that the installed system performance is adequate to support the processing of product. Examples of studies conducted are shelf temperature control and uniformity, processing rates, and sterilization capabilities.

Aseptic processing and filling validation also should be considered when validating a lyophilization unit operation for sterile pharmaceutical products. The procedures should encompass all the container sizes and fill volumes anticipated for processing, emulating actual manufacturing procedures. The media fills are an integral part of the validation study to demonstrate a high level of sterility assurance.

Lyophilization process validation measures actual processing conditions and includes independent variables such as shelf temperature and the dependent variables such as resulting product temperatures. It is important to consider in the approaches to validation of lyophilization that the specific contents of the protocol such as the acceptance criteria are based on the products to be processed, the equipment used, and the procedures followed in the manufacturing steps. The foundation of all of these is based on the characteristics and requirements of the products to be processed. A product with a formulation consisting of mixed solvent systems such as alcohol and water would utilize equipment having a unique design and require different operating procedures than a product with a single solvent formulation.

The protocols should be comprehensive and of sufficient detail. For example, the shelf temperature and resulting product temperatures monitored within the process validation study should span from the loading operation to terminal secondary drying steps. One should also include the rates of change from one shelf temperature to another during the process.

As in all validation efforts, the objective is to demonstrate adequately the operation's ability to support the process and develop documentation to show that the unit operation can be maintained within a state of control. Therefore, any and all conditions that may affect the product quality, from adequacy of water cooling to the refrigeration units for optimal performance to the method and criteria for evaluating finished product, should be included within the validation studies. Further details of each of these portions of the protocol are presented in their respective section of this chapter.

B. Preparation for the Validation Study

Preparation of a protocol for validation of a lyophilization unit operation first requires the collection and development of critical data. Information on product characteristics, such as the phase transition temperature, and processing requirements, such as temperature to which the shelves must be chilled to complete the phase transition to a frozen product, should be collected from the formulation and process development data within the drug master file submitted in the IND, NDA, or ANDA. Processing details, including such parameters as total solution quantities to be frozen and water quantities to be sublimed and condensed, are data on which test challenges can be derived. Such challenges to the equipment can be extracted from the processing requirements in master batch records and standard operating procedures.

Designing the protocol to validate the process is based on the collective data for the product (if the equipment is dedicated to one specific product) or range of different products that are to be processed. The parameters to which the validation study is conducted stem from the requirements of the process that is based on the product characteristics. The data on the product characteristics are therefore the foundation of developing the validation protocol. For example, the product's phase transition temperature determines to what temperature the product needs to be chilled to ensure that it is completely solidified. This temperature therefore determines the shelf temperature that must be achieved in order to freeze the product. During the actual process validation, this ability is demonstrated to be both achievable and reproducible. Preceding the process validation studies, a shelf temperature control test is completed at some temperature at or below the temperature used within the process. Such performance capabilities of the equipment ought to be demonstrated first to show that this temperature can be achieved. This may be accomplished during the initial performance testing and again within the operational qualification portion of the validation study. In this example, the product characteristic of phase transition is the critical data for establishing acceptance criteria for operational qualification and process validation sections of the validation protocol.

The data required on the product characteristics should be established as part of product and process development for the particular product. The development data are a primary source for judiciously establishing acceptance criteria for the protocol. The manufacturing parameters such as batch size, coupled with processing parameters required for the product, lead to developing the equipment and process challenges for the validation study.

Definition of the operational capabilities of the equipment is an important factor. This is established within the installation and operational qualification efforts of implementing the protocol. Both the installation and operational qualities of the unit operation are important because they have a direct impact on the performance of the process. This is crucial in lyophilization, where the process is completed in a balanced environment of controlled pressures and temperatures. Since the control of the environment is established and maintained by the equipment, the operational quality of the equipment is paramount [20].

C. Installation Qualification

The installation qualification of the protocol must be implemented before the operational qualification, process validation, and institution of any Change Control Program. Documentation should include a general description and specifications for the equipment, the support utility services of the facility, description of the equipment subsystems, and installation checklist for the freeze drying system. This portion of the protocol parallels the approach used for any unit operation to be validated.

1. General Description

A general description simply tells what the system is, what it will be used for, and how it is to be used. The description should be written so that a novice may gain an understanding of the process to be implemented, the equipment itself, and general operating procedures.

An explanation of the process may be a brief summary as presented in the beginning of this chapter. A definition of basic terms and principles may be helpful for someone reviewing the validation protocol. A description of the product(s) along with the processing requirements should be given. The range of process variables and how they are to be controlled should be explained. A general description of the equipment used to process the products completes a comprehensive introduction.

The types of products to be processed by the equipment may be cited as examples in the general description. A brief description should highlight such important facts as type of product (cephalosporin antibiotic, adrenocortical steroid, etc.), formulations (excipients and concentrations), special sensitivities in solution (e.g., ultraviolet light), and phase transition temperature. The descriptions should be general and cover what may be a range of products unless there are specific requirements that should be noted. For example, a product that contains an organic solvent or has a very low phase transition temperature requires special equipment that may be unique to the drier being described.

Additional support processes that the equipment may perform should also be noted in the general description. Sterilization, automated vacuum integrity testing, and clean-in-place are examples.

A description of the equipment would include the subsystems of the freeze drying plant:

Chamber
Condenser
Heat transfer system
Refrigeration units
Vacuum pumps
Instrumentation

It is important to include detailed specifications for the equipment as part of an installation qualification. As a description of the equipment, the specifications are more detailed than the general description presented in the introduction. This section may include such documentation as the specifications used as part of the purchase order for the equipment. Engineering drawings should also be referenced in the protocol. The design and performance criteria developed by the user-vendor project team may also be included. In addition, documentation from the final acceptance of the system should be included.

2. Services and Utilities

Since the performance of the system is strongly dependent on the utility services available, it is important to determine that sufficient quantities of the required utilities are available. Common utilities are:

Electricity
Cooling medium
Compressed air

Nitrogen
Cleaning medium
Sterilizing medium

It is important to verify that adequate quantities of utilities are available in order to ensure proper performance of the equipment. Utility supplies less than those necessary on a continual basis or less than that required on an intermittent basis will affect the performance of the system. Such conditions lead to a process that may be out of a state of control. For example, if the temperature of the cooling water for the refrigeration compressor rises above the maximum design temperature of the unit, the performance of the compressor is hampered. The result might be a rise in the condenser temperature. This would affect the system pressure (vacuum). Because the condensing rate is lowered, the system pressure increases. A decrease in the rate of condensation to less than the rate of sublimation causes a decrease in the vacuum. This increase in the system pressure then increases the rate of heat transfer and therefore increases the rate of sublimation, causing an increase in the product temperature. If the product temperature increases above the collapse or phase transition temperature, melting or collapse of the product will occur. These conditions also apply for systems that are air cooled. Different performances may be observed with changes in room temperature such as those that may occur during winter and summer months.

Quantifying the utility supplies to ensure that there are sufficient amounts is fundamental to the performance of the lyophilization equipment. It is important that the utility supplies be checked with maximum plant consumption. The utility supplies that may support a number of unit operations should be adequate for all operations running concurrently. This can be verified as part of a review of the facility validation.

3. System Hardware

The hardware and components portion of the installation qualification is a listing of the major components of the system. This listing documents the components that are installed on the equipment and make up the freeze drying system. It is also important for implementing a change control program for the freeze drying plant. This listing should include the manufacturer of the component, the model number and serial number, and any information that would describe its performance characteristics. When a change in hardware is planned, the change should be documented in a supplement to the hardware description as part of the change control procedure. This permits the change to be reviewed for any impact on the process and product.

4. Installation

Documentation of the installation and start-up should be included in the installation qualification portion of the protocol. Verification of the installation procedures should be documented, whether the installation is completed by in-house personnel or by an outside contractor. Installation documentation provided by the system manufacturer should be used as the guideline for the installation and be included within the validation protocol.

Documentation of the installation follows the order of activities completed; as a task is finished, it is signed for as being complete by the person doing the work. Each activity may be countersigned or the work spot checked by a person on the validation team. An example is the electrical wiring; all wires in the electrical and control circuits must be numbered, with the wires and numbers indicated in the electrical schematic. The wires that need to be reconnected during the installation could be checked to show that they are reconnected properly and according to the wiring diagram of the electrical schematic. This same approach can be used for the piping and hardware that would be reconnected during installation. Also, the connections to the utilities should be verified using the same approach.

5. Calibration

An initial calibration must be completed to ensure that the instrumentation is in workable condition after shipment and that any data collected during start-up of the system is accurate. Calibration procedures and results should also be documented. These data must be referenced in the protocol and maintained as part of the calibration records.

Since one of the process parameters is temperature, the instruments used for control and monitoring require routine calibration. Temperature sensors (thermocouples, RTDs, or thermistors) and the instruments used to display their values should be calibrated over the entire temperature range of the process. If normal processing includes steam sterilization, the calibration should include a temperature slightly above 121°C. A well-behaved eutectic solution may be used as a reference at subambient temperatures. An ice-point bath is also used as a reference to show accuracy across the entire operating range.

Pressure measurement devices (electronic transducers or thermocouple gauges) also require calibration. For thermocouple vacuum gauges, no calibration can be done on the sensor; calibration consists of generating a voltage input and reading a corresponding value on the panel meter. Electronic transducers can be effectively calibrated (zero and span) by first pumping the transducer below its greatest resolution (often 1 micron) and then adjusting the zero setting for the transducer. A decade box can be used as an input to the panel meter for calibration of the instrument's circuitry. The instrument (transducer and panel meter) can be referenced to an NIST referenced transducer for checking against higher pressures of up to 10,000 microns. Specific reference should be made to the calibration procedures recommended by the manufacturer. It is important to document the procedures used with a calibration standard operating procedure

(SOP) for future reference. These procedures should be referenced within the validation protocol in the procedure section.

D. Operational Qualification

Quantifying the operational qualities of the lyophilization process encompasses measuring the performance of the equipment. This demonstrates its ability to support the processing parameters necessary to produce the product. The performance of the system may be measured against either the original equipment manufacturer's specifications or the process parameter requirements. The protocol would include a series of tests to support the conclusion that the equipment can perform to a level necessary to carry out the process. The design of the validation studies would be based on the required functions of the equipment used in processing product. This series of tests is described in the following paragraphs.

1. Shelf Temperature Control

Both freezing and drying of the product are directly dependent on the shelf acting as a heat exchanger. Therefore this function must be accurately controlled within an acceptable range and the control must be achieved reproducibly. The goal of a shelf temperature study is twofold: to show that the shelf temperature can be controlled for both dynamic and static conditions over the entire temperature range required for the process and that the shelf temperature is uniform at all points across all of the shelves. This is accomplished by mapping the shelf surfaces and implementing control over a range of temperatures. Thermocouples are placed at various locations on the shelves, including their inlets and outlets. It is important that good thermal contact be achieved during the test in order to be sure that the true shelf temperature is monitored. The shelves are then controlled at various temperatures that span the operational range of the equipment. For example, shelf temperature variation may be checked where the shelves are chilled and controlled at $-50°C$, warmed and controlled to 0 degrees, and then warmed and controlled at $+50°C$. With a sufficient dwell time at the control temperatures, the variation should fall within an acceptable range where each of the points is compared to the average of the temperatures. The results should show that the shelf temperature is uniform across the shelf bundle and that the heating and cooling functions for control at a setpoint can be effectively implemented by the instrumentation and reproducibly controlled by the system.

2. Condenser Cooldown

The ability of the equipment to achieve an acceptable cooling rate and ultimate condenser temperatures is demonstrated in this section of the validation study. Here, the condenser surface temperature is monitored while the refrigeration is engaged in chilling the condenser. Although the rate of cooling would not directly affect the process, it is a good indication of the operating performance of the refrigeration system. It is the temperature that can be maintained during drying that directly affects the process. The condenser maintains the ice at a temperature at which the vapor pressure of the ice must be below the pressure within the system during processing. Therefore, the condenser performance affects the ultimate pressure achievable during both the primary and secondary drying portions of the process. For example, if the chamber is controlled at 100 microns, then the refrigeration system must operate at a temperature at which the condensing surface is below −40°C. During secondary drying, when full vacuum may be desired (e.g., 10 microns or less), the condensing surface must be at −60°C or below.

3. Vacuum Pumping Rates

The vacuum pumping rate and the ultimate pressure that can be achieved parallel the effect on the process, as do the condenser functions described above: the rate of evacuation indicates the performance of the equipment and the ultimate pressure achieved affects the process. The vacuum pump-down time is generally timed as the number of minutes to achieve a specific pressure level such as 100 microns. The vacuum pumping system is then allowed to continue to evacuate the system to achieve the ultimate pressure. The performance of the vacuum pump and its ability to achieve an ultimate low pressure will affect the pressure that can be achieved during both primary and secondary drying.

4. Vacuum Integrity Tests

Vacuum integrity tests show the "tightness" of the freeze drying system. This is important for both achieving adequate control of the process and maintaining a confident level of sterility assurance. If, for example, there is a large leak in the system, the vacuum pump will not be able to achieve the ultimate pressure required for the process. For sterile products, if the leak is large enough and occurs from a source that would allow contaminants from nonsterile air to enter the chamber, the sterility of the product may be compromised. In implementing a vacuum integrity test, one needs to distinguish between the effects of outgassing of volatilite materials in the chamber and an actual leak of air into the chamber. This can be accomplished by first removing the volatile components by pumping on the system at low pressures for a period of time (often 12 to 18 hours) to remove any volatile materials. Then, with the vacuum pump isolated from the chamber, a rate of rise can be measured. If the volatile materials have been removed, any increase in pressure would indicate leakage of air into the chamber.

5. Vacuum Level Control

Control of the system pressure at one or a series of pressures is sometimes used during the process of freeze drying. The ability of the control instrument and the equipment to achieve a specific pressure is to be verified. Low, high, and midpoint pressures should be selected to demonstrate that the equipment can achieve control over the entire range of pressures to be used. Pressures selected may be 100, 500, and 1000 microns as low, midpoint, and high pressures, respectively.

6. Sublimation and Condensation Rates

The ability of the equipment to adequately sublime and condense the water to be removed from the product during actual processing is demonstrated in this study. Both the rate of sublimation and the capacity of the condenser are challenged. Water is placed on the shelf and optimal conditions for achieving a maximum sublimation rate are implemented. These optimal conditions may be selected on the basis of the most aggressive process parameters used for producing actual product. If the warmest shelf temperature used during primary drying for any product is +30°C, then the test may be run using this shelf temperature. The pressure may be selected in the same manner. Another approach is to select conditions that would exceed routine conditions. For example, sublimation rates are high with conditions of +26°C for the shelf temperature and controlled pressures of 300 to 400 microns [21]. A third approach is to duplicate the parameters used during the performance testing completed at the equipment manufacturer's facility.

A quantity of water matching the condenser capacity may be sublimed over a set period of time. It is most convenient to place the water for the test in bulk pans, being sure to cover the entire shelf area. With the water measured during dispensing and then the remaining water left after the test is run for a specified time, the volume sublimed may be determined. It is important that all the shelf area be covered with material, that the pans provide intimate contact with the shelf, and that sufficient water be placed in each container so that there are no bare spots (spots not covered with ice that can sublime) during the test. Results can be expressed as volume per unit of shelf surface area per unit time. The acceptance criteria can be established based on design capacity for the equipment or the largest batch size of product to be processed in the unit.

7. Sterilant Penetration Tests

For the preparation of parenterals or other sterile products, the equipment must be sterilized to adequately support aseptic processing. Part of the validation of sterilization is a sterilant penetration test. If steam is used to sterilize the system, the test would parallel that which may be used to qualify a steam autoclave. If ethylene oxide is used, the validation would be conducted as if the system were an ETO chamber: distribution of the gas, humidity, and temperature control. The validation of these processes parallels that described in their respective sections presented in this book.

Completion of the tests conducted as part of implementing the validation protocol assures that the system will adequately perform to levels required to support the process. The tests must be in compliance with the procedures described in the protocol and standard operating procedures and satisfy the selected acceptance criteria. Testing of these parameters is also an opportunity to gain experience with the operation of the system. It is advantageous to engage operations personnel in these tasks. It also provides an opportunity to gain operational time on the system for developing and evaluating any new and additional standard operating procedures, as well as the training of operators.

E. Filling Validation

Lyophilized products as a dry solid dosage form are unique pharmaceutical injectable preparations: the level of the drug to be administered is directly dependent on the amount of the drug in the vial. The quantity of drug within the vial (and therefore the amount administered to a patient) is directly dependent on the amount of drug initially dispensed in the vial as a solution during filling. Hence, care and attention must be given to the accuracy and precision of the fill quantity. As compared to the assay of a liquid product that is a quantitative measure of concentration of the solution (e.g., milligrams per milliliter), assay of a lyophilized product is based on the amount of drug within the container. If the dried product is reconstituted with the labeled amount of diluent, the delivery of a given volume of the solution will yield a specific amount of drug. Comparing liquid formulations, filling limits and the precision of fill volumes are not as critical: the amount of solution withdrawn and administered yields the drug quantity. Therefore, the filling limits during manufacturing may be a range above a minimum volume necessary for complete withdraw of the amount claimed on the label. In contrast, with a lyophilized product a wide range of filling limits above a certain minimum would yield a superpotent dosage when reconstituted with the indicated volume of diluent.

Because the quantity of drug delivered is dependent on the initial fill volume of the solution before freeze drying, validation of the filling operation is critical. Accurate quantities filled with precision for each vial in a lot along with precision between a number of batches must be demonstrated. Testing for fill accuracy and precision is accomplished with both filling volume and finished-product assay. The primary test is the fill quantity test during the filling operation. Increased accuracy may be obtained with fill checks done using weight rather than volume. Here, the frequency of fill volume checks is often higher than with liquid products and should be scheduled on the basis of a number of units rather than on time. Doing so accommodates both low- and high-speed filling operations. The selection of frequency should be based on achieving a statistical confidence interval of greater than 95%.

Along with weight checks during the actual filling operation, finished-product assays for dose uniformity should be done. The sampling size for the uniformity study during the process validation may be greater than that routinely used during the normal production operations. Again, the number of samples should be sufficient to provide a high level of confidence that the dosage of a vial is within the compendial limits for the product.

The second part of the filling validation is that of stopper placement. A given stopper, when inserted to the designed location, provides a vapor port for the sublimed vapor to leave the vial and proceed to the condenser. If this port is restricted because the stopper is set too low in the vial, the rate at which the water vapor leaves the vial is decreased. If this decrease is significant, or if the ports are completely closed off, the product may undergo collapse or melt completely. In addition, stoppers placed in varying positions generate a questionable level of uniformity with a batch. Stopper placement may be monitored by simple observation for a statistically significant number of vials during the same filling validation studies completed for fill volume.

F. Aseptic Processing Validation

As with liquid filled sterile products, aseptic processing must be part of the overall processing validation. Approaches to this validation have been presented in another chapter of this book. However, there are some unique aspects and special requirements of aseptic processing validation for lyophilized products [22].

Lyophilized products undergo typical filling procedures, as do liquid filled products. The significant difference is that the lyophilization process occurs between the steps where the vials are partially stoppered and finally sealed with an aluminum overseal (Fig. 4). Between these steps, the vials are placed in freeze drying trays, offloaded from the filling line, and then placed in the lyophilizer to be dried. In addition to media fills for the filling operation itself, the aseptic transfer of the sterile product must be validated. This is often accomplished by segregating a number of vials of a typical media fill and performing the transfer into the lyophilization chamber. The vials then undergo the stopper seating operation in the freeze drying chest and are removed and incubated. A number of variations have been used: the media fill may be simply transferred and stoppered in the freeze drier, the chamber may be evacuated to a slight vacuum and backfilled before stoppering, or dilute media may be filled and an abbreviated freeze drying cycle used to return the solution to the proper concentration. A standard technique has not yet been established in the industry; however, the procedure most commonly used is to transfer the vials to the lyophilizer, pull a slight vacuum (a few inches of mercury), backfill to atmosphere (using filtered air), and stopper the product [23].

G. Lyophilization Process Validation

Because of the nature of the process, validation of lyophilization is done concurrently and retrospectively. Concurrent validation is utilized where the process

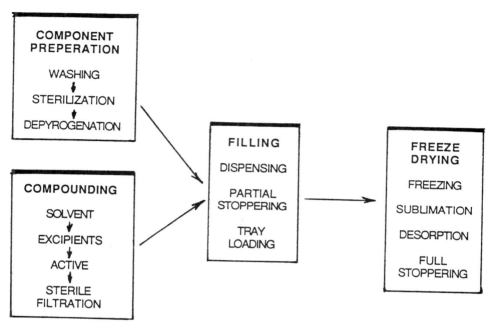

Figure 4 Lyophilization of parenterals and other sterile products requires aseptic processing techniques be utilized just as in other sterile product manufacturing. This includes the transferring of product and loading into the lyophilizer chamber.

data are collected and analyzed for product being produced to be marketed. The validation is done retrospectively through analysis of historical batch data: selected data are gathered from records, evaluated, and analyzed. The concurrent and retrospective approach to validation is particularly applicable to validation of lyophilization (see also Lee, Chapter 19 for further discussions). With a working knowledge of the technology and following the discussion below, one would understand the aspects that make this approach to the validation justified.

Completing validation for a new product and/or process first requires definition of the product characteristics and processing parameters. This should be accomplished during the development studies as part of the research and scale-up efforts. Beyond the clinical material manufacturing and stability studies that are completed during development, the first three batches of commercial product may be used for validation of the process in a production environment. Here, extensive data can be collected and analyzed. The depth, scope, and quantity of data as well as the amount of analysis may be much more extensive than would be routinely done on a normal production batch. Samples from these batches may also be placed on an accelerated stability study as well as a routine commercial stability program for periodic evaluation.

Concurrent validation is justified on the basis of the complexities and practical realities of applying lyophilization technology to producing pharmaceutical products. Because the process parameters and product characteristics are interdependent, a perspective approach to validation with such practices as using placebo to emulate actual product runs cannot be effectively utilized. The exception, of course, is to dedicate the entire batch to the validation study. This may be possible if the batch size is small, but becomes unreasonable with larger batch sizes. The concurrent approach is easily justified with lyophilization because the product characteristics dictate the dependent variables of the product response to the process parameters. For example, the influence of excipients on both the freezing point depression and the final phase transition of the product is significant [24]. Because the presence (or absence) of components has such an influence, even at relatively small concentrations, the temperature at which the onset of crystallization of ice occurs may differ. In addition, a change in the final phase transition may be observed.

During the freezing of the material, the crystallization of ice involves the greatest evolution of heat. Also, the heat capacity removal of the refrigeration system varies with temperature. If a solution missing one component from the formulation freezes at a higher temperature than the same formulation with the active ingredient, the refrigeration capacity (because of the higher temperature) is greater: the refrigeration capacity available increases with increasing temperature and the rate of heat removal is greater at warmer temperatures. This may yield different-sized ice crystals, promoting different physical attributes in the product plug. One of these attributes would be the resistance to mass transfer. Generally, larger ice crystals result in less mass flow resistance of water vapor out of the dried portion of the plug, promoting lower product temperatures and accelerated drying. This should be compared to product that may have a freezing point depressed to a lower temperature, resulting in different freezing rates and different ice crystal sizes, yielding varied water vapor mass transfer rates with correlating product temperatures. Such influences of product on the occurrence of thermal events during the process and the effect of those events on subsequent steps illustrate the need and justify the use of actual product batches for validation. Based on satisfactory process data and finished product testing, the material may be released as actual commercial product for human use.

Finished-product qualities such as assays for batch uniformity of dose and moisture, dried product stability, and reconstituted solution stability should be included in the process validation study. The above explanation, along with the differences observed with different batch loads in the lyophilizer, dictates the need to run actual product with a full load complement for the process validation studies.

The validation protocol would include both process data and product characteristics data. Process data include the controlled independent variables of time, temperature, and pressure. Along with these controlled variables, the dependent variables of product temperature and the final dried product characteristics are monitored. The resulting product data, such as moisture and reconstitution time, become an integral part of the process evaluation and therefore are included in the acceptance criteria. The product data for the initial three batches would include not only finished product but also extensive in-process data.

An understanding of the process and its effect on the product qualities dictates the significant process parameters that need to be quantified. Following are examples of data that may be defined within the protocol and measured during the studies.

1. Shelf Loading Temperature

Upon completion of the filling operation, the product is placed on the shelves in the lyophilizer. This may be where the product is loaded onto shelves that are controlled at room temperature, slightly cooled, or prefrozen to some low temperature. Since the temperature at which the product is maintained during loading may affect the freezing of the product, the loading temperature should be controlled. It must be demonstrated that the product is maintained at an acceptable temperature and the stability is not affected when stored for a period of time under these conditions. The time for which the product may be held at a loading temperature should encompass the longest filling operation that may occur in production. This should include a maximum time to accommodate an extended period if there is a delay in the filling operation. Samples for bulk assay are therefore taken at the beginning and end of the longest filling period. These samples may be analyzed for active and degradation products, pH, and, if necessary, any change in the phase transition temperature.

2. Shelf Freezing Rate

The rate at which product is frozen many have a significant effect on the quality of the resulting product. The freezing step may induce changes in concentrations of materials, create pH shifts, or affect the size of ice crystals. Since these may have an impact on the drying rates and finished product characteristics, the rate at which the product is frozen should be controlled and, hence, part of the process definition. Therefore, the rate of chilling of the shelves needs to be included as part of the validation studies.

Process points to be monitored would include the independent variable of the shelf inlet temperature that is being used for control. Dependent variables to be monitored would be product temperatures. Here, a number of temperature probes would be placed in product vials located throughout the batch. Special temperature probes may be placed at multiple positions in a select number of vials. The locations of the probes may be at the top of the fill volume in addition to the bottom of the vial. Having probes at these positions would yield results indicating that the entire volume of product was at the same temperature.

3. Product Freezing Rate

With the shelf cooling rate defined for freezing the product, a resulting product cooling rate within a range of temperatures should be observed. It is important to consider that a variation in supercooling often occurs at temperatures below 0°C during product cooling. This variation must be accommodated within the acceptance criteria. Also, different product cooling rates often occur when the product is a solution as compared to when ice is present. A significant variation may be observed when scaling up from development- to production-size batches and sometimes may occur between production units of different sizes. Here, then, the acceptance criteria may simply be similar profiles with broad limits.

4. Frozen Product Dwell Temperature and Time

The temperature below the final phase transition to which the product is chilled and the length of time it is held at that temperature should be established during the development activities. This should be carried through to production as a minimum time. In scaling up to production lot sizes, one should consider the additional time to ensure that all the solution within the vial and all the vials within the batch are completely frozen. For this reason, there is often an extended time at low temperatures after the product has reached the freezing temperature to ensure that all the product is completely frozen, both the entire volume of the vial and each vial in the batch. The freezing parameters should therefore be included in the validation protocol. The acceptance criteria would be based on defined limits for the product samples as monitored by the temperature probes.

5. Shelf Temperature Ramp and Soak Functions

The steps of shelf cooling, product cooling, and complete freezing are followed by initiation of the drying portion of the process. With heat being supplied to control the rate of sublimation of the ice in the product, ramp and soak temperatures and times are dictated. The shelf temperature profile as monitored at the control point should be reproducible to within a range of limits from batch to batch. The range may be based on the cumulative acceptable accuracies and precision of the measuring devices and instruments. For example, if the acceptable range for the control RTD within the shelf fluid entering the shelves is 0.5°, the controlling instrument range is 1°, the monitoring instrument is 1°, and the range of control capability is 1°, then the range may be 3.5°, or ±1.75°.

6. Product Temperature

Product temperature is normally monitored by placing a temperature sensor in a number of selected vials within a batch. The temperature is monitored using an RTD, thermistor, or more commonly a thermocouple. It is important to acknowledge the differences one may observe using the different types of sensors. RTDs and thermistors are often housed within a small stainless steel or platinum sheath. Because the sheath is often large (from 1 to 3 cm), the temperature measured is often a physical average of the product temperature over the length of the sensor housing. Thermocouples are generally preferred because they indicate the temperature at the point at which the wires are in contact with each other and therefore a more exact location within the vial.

The product temperature that results from the shelf temperature profile should also be reproducible within a range. This range may be significant and is dependent on the placement of the sensor within the product. Therefore, care must be taken to ensure that the sensor is placed at the proper location and that the placement is consistent. Commonly, a thermocouple is located at the bottom of the vial, slightly above the glass surface. This location indicates the onset of freezing at the bottom of the vial and the time at which the sublimation front passes by the thermocouple during drying, indicating that primary drying is approaching completion.

Monitoring of the product temperature provides an idea of how the cycle is progressing. When the onset of freezing occurs, one may observe a shift in temperature, particularly if the solution has undergone supercooling. Since supercooling is a random event based on the probability of nucleation of ice, there may be ranges of time and temperature for the samples within the batch. During drying, the temperature of the product will rise and approach the shelf temperature, indicating that sublimation is diminishing and the ice has all been removed from the product. Again, it is important to understand that the temperature is in and around the area where the sensor is located. Even if the sensor is carefully placed just off the bottom of the vial, there still may be ice that has yet to be sublimed. For this reason, there is often a wide range of product temperatures and the lag time within the cycle to assure that all the material within a vial and each and every vial within the batch has been sufficiently dried.

7. Condenser Temperature

The condenser temperature during the drying portion of the cycle results from the rate at which water vapor is being condensed. The condensation rate is dependent on the rate at which water is being sublimed from the product. It should be expected that the equipment is operating at a minimal performance level and the sublimation rate resulting from the heat being supplied to the product from the shelves is reproducible. Therefore, the condenser temperature should be within a range of temperatures for the same size batch.

The acceptance criteria for the reproducibility of the condenser temperature may be stated as a minimum temperature or as a fairly wide range below a minimum temperature. Looking at the values for the vapor pressure of ice at varying temperatures, it becomes evident that there is a maximum temperature for safe conditions of the process. This maximum temperature, corresponding to a vapor pressure of ice, must be below the operating pressure for the process. For example, if the chamber pressure is controlled at 100 microns, then the condenser temperature must be maintained to less than $-40°C$ since the vapor pressure of ice is 96.6 microns at that temperature. If the parameters of the process were consistently observed to be $-50°C$ or less, than there would be little significance whether the temperature was -52 or $-56°C$, since the vapor pressures are 23 and 14 microns, respectively. The process would not be appreciably affected by the difference of $4°$ (9 microns) at the condenser temperature.

8. Vacuum Level

The pressure (vacuum) level is a primary parameter that should be monitored and demonstrated to be reproducible. Any change in the pressure is due to water vapor generated from sublimation in transit from the product to the condenser, where it is removed by condensation back to ice. When the pressure is not controlled during the drying portion of the cycle, the vacuum indicates the amount of water vapor that is in transit. If the batch size, sublimation rate, and condensation rate are all the same, then the vacuum level should fall within a range and be reproducible from batch to batch. Since a relatively small change in the sublimation and/or condensation rate may impart a significant change in the pressure, the limits selected for the acceptance criteria should reflect such variation. However, if vacuum level control is implemented to maintain the pressure at a specific level, then the pressure range should be reproducible and within the range demonstrated during the pressure control study completed as part of the operational qualification. In this case, either the gas composition or partial pressures making up the total pressure may be studied. This can be accomplished by use of an instrument that can distinguish the presence of water vapor as part of the gas composition. Examples include a residual gas analyzer, electronic moisture sensor, or differences in readings of a thermocouple gauge to an electronic manometer [25,26].

The process parameters described above would be actively monitored as on-line data at greater frequencies than are routinely used on a normal basis for a production batch. This would allow a greater, more detailed data base to be developed and archived for later analysis. Here, supplementary instrumentation may be required over and above that which may already exist on the equipment. One example of this may be monitoring the partial pressures during the drying operation as described above. Such a monitoring program would be defined in the procedure section of the protocol.

In addition to extensive process monitoring, in-process and expanded stability testing of the final product would be in order. One such program might be increased sampling at locations throughout the freeze drying chamber to demonstrate uniformity of the entire batch. These samples may undergo complete analysis, including moisture, reconstitution, and a stability-indicating assay. In addition, samples from selected locations may be placed on stability, both at label indicated storage and accelerated conditions such as 37° and 45°C (assuming first-order rates for Arrhenius extrapolation). The testing program may parallel those at initial sampling, including a stability-indicating assay.

H.   Product Evaluation

The process parameters identified above document that the process was completed within a set of predefined conditions. One would expect that with the product preparation and lyophilization cycle controlled within acceptable and reproducible limits, a predictable product quality would result. This conclusion would be supported when product characteristics are tested and product quality verified. The measurable characteristics that demonstrate product quality may be unique to each product. These may include aspects described in the following paragraphs.

1.   Phase Transition Temperatures

Phase transitions for the product may be monitored during the validation studies in addition to the development and scale-up activities. As a minimum, the phase transition should be determined for the bulk material, at the end of any holding period, after filtration, and at a time that would reflect the end of the longest filling operation. This would verify that changes did not occur during routine processing steps. One could easily justify completing these tests when considering that shifts in pH, dissolved gases, and the presence of slight amounts of degradation products (of either the excipients or the active materials) may change the temperature where the product is solidified to a composition sufficient for successful freeze drying. These tests may be worthwhile even though they may have been completed during the development of the formulation or processing procedures, particularly if batching procedures and sizes have changed [27].

2.   Product Physical Form

The product's physical form is induced during the freezing of the product solution. Freezing of the material in solution would result in either an amorphous or crystalline form of the active material. Either form may have an effect on the ease of processing, reconstitution, and/or solubility of the drug product upon adding the diluent. In addition, there may be an impact on long-term product stability; one should be sure that no solid-state reactions are occurring in the dried product [28]. Although generally it does not change during the freeze drying of the material, it would be a worthwhile test to perform on the dried product after processing. As well, one may consider repeating the test as part of the stability testing program for both elevated and recommended storage temperatures.

3.   Dry Cake Physical Appearance

Promoting desired pharmaceutical elegance during product development efforts generally includes establishing the range of acceptable product appearance standards. These standards are to be used during inspection by the production and quality control departments. The same standards should also be implemented with the inspection of the validation batches. Doing so not only provides a measure of expected quality but also verifies that such results can be achieved in a production setting. For example, limits that may be judged as less desirable during development or clinical manufacturing and are observed at a low incidence may have a significantly higher occurrence in a large production batch. Since full production batches are used for both scale-up and concurrent validation studies, adjustments may be necessary for acceptable physical appearance. Since a range for physical appearance may be considered a minor quality characteristic, adjustments may be made without a major impact on overall product quality standards.

4. Moisture Content

Stability studies completed during development should establish the maximum acceptable moisture content for adequate stability over the shelf life of the product. A predictable moisture content should be achieved by processing the product within the established process parameters. Therefore, moisture content would become an acceptance criterion for the cycle validation studies. An extensive and well-defined sampling plan should be used to show batch uniformity. Here, trays of the product should be labeled to enable the freeze drier load to be mapped. Samples taken from various parts of the batch should include the beginning, middle, and end of the filling run. The sampling plan should also encompass various physical locations within the drying chamber.

The method of moisture analysis should be the same as that used during the initial development and stability activities. Differences in the methodology of moisture analysis have been well documented [29]. The most common is the Karl-Fisher method, detecting all the moisture available in the product, including "bound" moisture. Comparing this with loss on drying, either by drying over phosphorus pentoxide or by thermogravimetric methods, the Karl-Fisher method extracts all water present. Therefore, one should reference acceptable methods as suggested in the CFR, USP, or documentation submitted for regulatory product approval.

5. Reconstitution Rate

Reconstitution rates should be completed for finished product and as part of the testing protocol for stability studies. The reconstitution is often considered as the time from complete addition of the solvent to the time the material is completely in solution as indicated by a clear solution. The reconstitution rate is a product characteristic dependent on the formulation and is therefore established during formulation development. This product characteristic should be monitored for production material as a finished-product release but may be optional as an in-process test.

6. Product Assay

Paralleling determination of phase transition, product assay studies may be pursued for the various stages in the manufacturing process. Here, groups of samples from the beginning and end of the filling and loading operation may be included in the protocol. As well, assays should be completed on accelerated and long-term stability samples from the batches used in the validation studies. For biological products and biopharmaceuticals, justification may support analysis of some product characteristic measured by abbreviated analytical testing (e.g., high-performance liquid chromatography or electrophoresis) rather than a comprehensive analysis scheme that would be used for finished product. Note that there may be product degradation due to solid-state chemical reactions; one should be sure to accommodate monitoring the degradation products that result from those reactions. Any such reactions must be identified during the development process. In addition, analysis should be completed on reconstituted material stored according to the label directions.

7. pH

Tests for pH should be routine and accompany the product analysis within the testing plan. The pH should also be monitored during the storage and filling according to a defined sampling plan used for monitoring the assay. One need also consider the procedure for adjusting the pH of the bulk material. For example, if the compounding log allows for pH adjustment, the results of any adjustments indicated should be studied and understood, since such adjustments may affect the final phase transition of the formulation [30].

I. Retrospective Validation

Retrospective validation encompasses review and analysis of historical data from product analysis and process monitoring. Here, data from commercial lots are used as the data base. Results should show performance to within defined limits to meet the acceptance criteria. This approach demonstrates that the unit operation can be maintained within a state of control and that acceptable product characteristics are maintained. This includes finished product from manufacturing as well as product held for periods up to the expiration date. The approach therefore involves the batch process data, quality control lot release data, and results from the commercial stability program. Analysis here is similar to product evaluation paralleling the concurrent validation study. The value of retrospective validation is that the data base would be larger than just the three batches used in the concurrent validation. Implementation may also be on an ongoing basis and is useful in tracking process and product performance, demonstrating that the process is maintained within a state of control.

III. SUMMARY

Lyophilization is a complicated and sophisticated process. It is an integrated process for preservation of a drug product where the quality of the process directly affects the quality of the product. The process is heavily dependent on the characteristics of the product and the finished quality aspects desired. Development of the protocol requires an understanding of the procedures and results established in the development activities. Implementation of the installation and operational qualification follows common concepts for validation of many pharmaceutical unit operations. The importance of the detail and thoroughness of the IQ/OQ lies in the impact of the system's performance on the critical processing parameters.

Approaches to process validation should consider that the qualities of the product and formulation affect the process and the process affects the final product quality. This, along with the associated costs and/or limited supply of the materials, is justification for a concurrent validation approach. Retrospective validation is useful in demonstrating that the operation is within a state of control and allows a data base to be developed for determining trends of critical parameters and for subsequent statistical analysis.

REFERENCES

1. Flosdorf, E. W., Hull, L., and Mudd, S., Procedure and apparatus for preservation in "lyophile" form of serum and other biological substances, *J. Immunol.* 29:389 (1938).
2. Pikal, M. J., Freeze drying of proteins. Part I. Process design. *Biopharmacology* 3:18–27 (1990).
3. Pikal, M. J., Freeze drying of proteins Part II. Formulation selection. *Biopharmacology* 3:26–30 (1990).
4. DeLuca, P., and Lachman, L., Lyophilization of pharmaceuticals. IV. Determination of eutectic temperatures of inorganic salts. *J Pharm. Sci.* 54:1411–1415 (1965).
5. MacKenzie, A. P., Collapse during freeze drying—qualitative and quantative aspects. In *Freeze Drying and Advanced Food Technology*, Goldblith, S. A., Rey, L., and Rothmayer, W. W., (eds.), Academic Press, New York, p. 278.
6. Pikal, M. J., Shah, S., Senior, D., and Lang, J. E., Physical chemistry of freeze drying: Measurement of sublimation rates for frozen aqueous solutions by a microbalance technique. *J Pharm. Sci.* 72:635–650 (1983).
7. Roper, D. L., and Ryans, J. L., *Process Vacuum Systems Design and Operation*, McGraw-Hill, New York, p. 300 (1986).
8. Nail, S. L., and Gatlin, L. A., Advances in control of production freeze driers. *J Parenter. Sci. Technol.* 39:16–27 (1984).
9. Hlinak, A., and Ingold, E. A., A computer control system for freeze drying. *Pharm. Eng.* 4:23–26 (1984).
10. Avellone, H., Regulatory issues of parenteral equipment and systems. *J. Parenter. Sci. Technol.* 42:93 (1988).
11. Beisswenger, H. L., Product improvement through advanced freeze drying techniques. *Bull PDA* 23:95–96 (1969).
12. Pikal, M. J., Roy, M. L., and Saroj, Mass and heat transfer in vial freeze drying of pharmaceuticals: Role of the vial. *J. Pharm. Sci.* 73:1224–1237 (1984).
13. Dushman, S., and Lafferty, J. M., *Scientific Foundations of Vacuum Technique*, 2nd ed. Wiley, New York, pp. 200–204 (1969).

14. Lopez, F. V., Solis, I. P., and Castro, F. A., Oil foreign particles in freeze-dried injectable powder, *J. Parenter. Sci. Technol. 36*:259–266 (1982).
15. Williams, N. A., and Polli, G. P., The lyophilization of pharmaceuticals: A literature review. *J Parenter. Sci. Technol. 38*:48–59 (1984).
16. Moore, D. W., The state of the science of pharmaceutical freeze-drying, *Pharmaceut. Technol. 7*:84–88 (1983).
17. Lee, J. Y., GMP compliance for lyophilization of parenterals: Part I. *Pharmaceut. Technol. 12*:50–60 (1988).
18. Lee, J. Y., GMP compliance for lyophilization of parenterals: Part II. *Pharmaceut. Technol. 12*:38–42 (1988).
19. Avalone, H. A., Current regulatory issues regarding sterile products. *J. Parenter. Sci. Technol. 44*:228–230 (1990).
20. Food and Drug Administration, Small volume parenterals, Compliance program CP7356.002A. U.S. Department of Health and Human Services, Washington, DC (1985).
21. Nail, S. L., The effect of chamber pressure on heat transfer in the freeze drying of parenteral solutions. *J. Parenter. Drug Assoc. 34*:358–368 (1980).
22. Avalone, H. A., GMP inspections of biopharmaceutical manufacturing facilities. *Pharm. Eng. 9*:40–48 (1989).
23. Agalloco, J. P., and Gordon, M., Current aspects in the use of media fills for the validation of aseptic processing. *J. Parenter. Sci. Technol. 41*:137–139 (1987).
24. Patel, R. M., and Hurwitz, A., Eutectic temperature determination of preformulation systems and evaluation by controlled freeze drying. *J. Pharm. Sci. 61*:1806–1810 (1972).
25. Jennings, T. A. Residual gas analysis and vacuum freeze drying. *J. Parenter. Drug Assoc. 34*:62–69 (1980).
26. Pikal, M. J., and Roy, M. L., Process control in freeze drying: Determination of the end point of sublimation drying by an electronic moisture sensor. *J Parenter. Sci. Technol. 43*:60–66 (1989).
27. Avalone, H. A., Current regulatory issues regarding sterile products. *J. Parenter. Sci. Technol. 44*:228–230 (1990).
28. Byron, P. R., DeLuca, P. P., and Townsend, M. W., The effects of formulation additives on the degradation of freeze dried ribonuclease A. *Pharm. Res. 7*:1086–1091 (1990).
29. Grim, E., May, J. C., West, J., and Wheeler, R. M., Determination of residual moisture in freeze-dried viral vaccines: Karl Fisher, gravimetric, thermogravimetric methodologies, *J. Int. Biol. Std. 10*:249–259 (1982).
30. Trappler, E. H., Effect of pH on phase transition temperatures of lyophilization formulations (poster presentation, 1991 annual meeting of the Parenteral Drug Association, Philadelphia).

16

Validation of Inhalation Aerosols

Scott Bozzone   *Parke-Davis Pharmaceutical Research Division, Warner-Lambert Company, Morris Plains, New Jersey*

I. INTRODUCTION

Inhalation aerosols are intended for delivery to the lungs by inspiration through the mouth or nose. The most common dosage form for inhalation is the metered-dose inhaler (MDI), where the drug is delivered from a pressurized container of liquefied gas or propellant. With each spray, the drug dose is emitted through a metered valve of precise volume.

The metered-dose aerosol may be considered as a unique pharmaceutical dosage form since the drug is delivered directly to the lung [1,2]. It should not be classified as either an oral dosage form, delivered through the gastrointestinal tract, or a parenteral dosage form administered directly into body fluids or tissues. MDIs are classified as nonsterile products but should exhibit lower bioburdens than oral or topical dosage forms since they are nonaqueous systems. The metered-dose aerosol is also unique in the use of chlorofluorocarbons (CFCs), which create a self-propelling dosage form with the contents under pressure. As a result, different manufacturing and testing requirements are involved during the validation phase of new product introduction.

A. Types of Metered-Dose Aerosols

Nearly all MDI products are intended for delivery through the oral cavity [3]. However, there are few products that are intended for administration via the nasal cavity. Moreover, one metered-dose aerosol is administered sublingually. The site of administration will determine the type of actuator or adapter accompanied with the aerosol canister.

The medical use of metered-dose aerosols is usually for bronchial asthma or chronic obstructive pulmonary disease (COPD). The drugs used represent different classes. Beta-adrenergic agents and the more selective beta$_2$-adrenergic agents are the common bronchodilators, usually sympathomimetic amines. Corticosteroids help reduce edema and inflammation. Anticholinergic compounds and a mast cell inhibitor are also found. Other therapeutic uses include systemic application, such as vasodilation (nitroglycerin) and antimigraine (ergotamine).

There are two general types of formulations. First, the micronized active ingredient may be suspended in liquefied propellants of chlorofluorocarbons. This is the most common type. Second, the drug may be dissolved in a mixture of CFCs and ethanol, forming a solution. Less than 25% of MDI products are formulated as solutions, and most of these products have been marketed for over 20 years.

In metered-dose inhalation products less than 12 different excipients have been formulated into metered aerosols. The use of established ingredients limits the formulator to a select few components. Table 1 lists excipients that are currently used in metered-dose inhalers and approximate amounts of some of these excipients. MDIs always contain Propellant 12 because this component is required for proper propellancy.

1. Solutions

Older drugs such as isoproterenol or epinephrine were formulated as aerosol solutions, with the drug solubilized in a chlorofluorocarbon-ethanol system. Approximately 6 of 28 marketed products are solution MDIs. These aerosol solutions contain 30–38% (w/w) ethanol as a cosolvent and other additives to

Table 1 MDI Inactive Ingredients

Type	Ingredient	Amount[a] (%)
Propellants	11, 12, 114 (always 12)	60–99
Dispersing agents	Sorbitan trioleate	0.01–0.8
	Oleic acid	0.01–0.8
	Soya lecithin	0.01–0.1
Cosolvent	Ethyl alcohol	2–38
Antioxidants and flavors	Ascorbic acid	0.1
	Saccharin	N/A
	Menthol	N/A
Antimicrobial	Cetylpyridinium chloride	N/A

[a]Approximate amounts derived from package inserts and literature.
N/A, Not Available.

mask the poor aftertaste of the ethanol. Menthol, saccharin, and flavors are all currently used in some of these marketed products. Antioxidants such as ascorbic acid are also used to enhance the drug's stability in solution form. It is rare that the drug is solubilized in the propellant system without ethanol. A past product contained no cosolvent (octyl nitrate) [4], but there are no marketed MDIs in the United States today utilizing a solution composed of only propellants [3].

2. Suspensions

The active ingredients in MDIs are usually water soluble and chlorofluorocarbon insoluble. Since the vehicle in MDIs must be propellant based, a product with the drug suspended in the propellant may be the most stable dosage form.

Nearly all suspension products contain a dispersing or suspending agent to facilitate wetting of the drug during manufacture of the suspension. All MDI suspensions with two exceptions contain sorbitan trioleate, oleic acid, or soya lecithin, all of which have surface-active properties. Two triamcinolone acetonide products do not contain a typical dispersing agent but do contain a small amount of ethanol. Most suspensions contain sorbitan trioleate. These ingredients also have a lubricating action on valve components, although experimental studies have shown that they are unnecessary for their proper functioning [5].

Suspensions contain micronized drug for proper delivery and absorption in the respiratory system. Typical particle sizes of the micronized drug are 1 to 5 microns [6]. Aerodynamic mean particle sizes as measured by cascade impactor or by direct method of microscopic analysis are usually 0.5–4 microns [7,8].

In North America, the amount of drug in marketed products varies from 10 micrograms (Pro-Air® in Canada) to 800 micrograms (Intal®) per actuation, as delivered from the actuator or mouthpiece. The amount of drug administered to the patient is small relative to that in other dosage forms. Potent drugs are thus utilized and should have special care during raw material handling and manufacturing.

In a filled aerosol canister or pack, most of the contents represent amounts that are capable of sprayable use for the patient. However, it is important to recognize that nonsprayable contents exist in each filled unit. Each filled canister will deliver at least a labeled number of actuations, and the actual can contains an overage to ensure delivery of the labeled number of actuations. As an example, Fig. 1 shows the approximate disposition of a 20-gram filled unit.

In this example, if the lot average of the metered spray weighs 70 mg, then an average of 250 metered actuations per canister will be obtained (sprayable 17.5 g). The nonsprayable contents, 2.5 g, are derived from (1) CFC vapors in the can when empty of the liquefied portion, (2) allowance for filling variation leading to slight underfilling of contents during manufacture, (3) leakage of CFC during the life of the unit, and (4) partial sprays (tail-off) due to incomplete filling of the valve chamber when the can is nearly empty. Any residual drug remaining in the unit is a

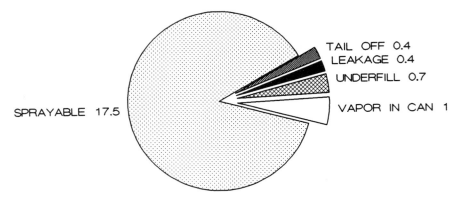

Figure 1   Approximate disposition of a 20-gram filled unit.

negligible amount on a weight basis, less than 0.01 g, compared to the other items. The losses indicate why larger overages are used for this type of dosage form compared to an injectable drug.

B. Manufacturing

In the United States in 1991, there were five manufacturers of metered-dose inhalers producing marketed products: Armstrong Labs (subsidiary of Armstrong Pharmaceuticals), Glaxo, Riker Laboratories (subsidiary of 3M), Schering, and Sterling-Winthrop [9]. Boehringer-Ingelheim is expected to be a new manufacturer in the near future.

Two general types of aerosol MDI manufacturing are used today, cold filling and pressure filling [10]. These methods describe the manner in which the propellant, usually Propellant 12 (CFC 12), is added to the can or bottle. Solution or suspension formulations may be filled by either method.

In cold filling, ingredients including drug, suspending agents, excipients, and all CFCs are mixed and chilled prior to addition to the empty container. Filling occurs at temperatures well below the mixture's boiling point and before the valve is inserted onto the canister. CFC 114 may be added in the cold-filled concentrate to alter the boiling point and vapor pressure.

In pressure filling, only concentrate containing drug, Propellant 11 (CFC 11), and other excipients are filled before valve crimping. The propellant (CFC 12) is filled after crimping by high-pressure injection through the valve. The propellant is usually at room temperature. CFC 114 may also be used in propellant-filled products but is more likely used in cold-filled products.

Of the five U.S. manufacturers of MDIs, two utilize primarily cold filling and three are principally pressure fillers. Figure 2 depicts the process flow indicating both types of filling.

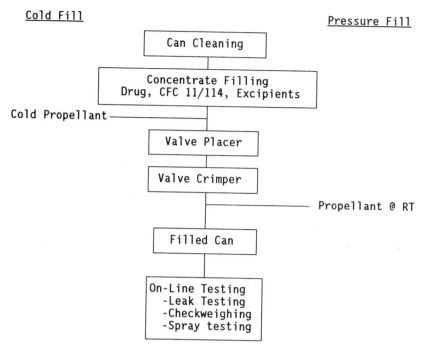

Figure 2 Types of aerosol filling.

Since metered-dose aerosols are not claimed to be sterile products, filling of the product does not require rated clean room standards as described in Federal Standard 209C. Frequently, however, the use of high-efficiency particulate air, class 100, is employed above any open tanks and filling lines. This is good practice to reduce the likelihood of particulate and microbial contamination in the product.

C. Marketed Products

In the United States, there were approximately 28 brands of metered-dose aerosols on the market in 1991. Table 2 depicts most of these products along with certain product characteristics. The largest sales volume product is albuterol (internationally, Salbutamol), which is comarketed by two companies.

The total sales of MDIs in 1990 were estimated to be about 75 million units [11]. There are 10–15 million asthma sufferers in the United States [12] and at least 24 million Americans use MDIs [11].

In the United States, these 28 products utilize metered values from three suppliers: Riker (24), Bespak (2), and Valois (2). Can suppliers are usually either

Table 2 Marketed MDI Products[a]

Brand product	Company	Solution or suspension	Surfactant	Propellants
AeroBid	Forest	Suspension	Sorb. trio.	11/12/114
Alupent	Boeh. Ing	Suspension	Sorb. trio.	12/114
Atrovent	Boeh. Ing	Suspension	Soya lecithin	11/12/114
Azmacort	Rorer	Suspension	None (dehydrated OH)	12
Beclovent	Allen & Hanburys	Suspension	Oleic acid	11/12
Beconase	Allen & Hanburys	Suspension	Oleic Acid	11/12
Brethaire	Geigy	Suspension	Sorb. trio.	11/12/114
Bronkometer	Winthrop	Solution	Alcohol (30%) Other ingred.	12/114
Decadron Respihaler	MSD	Suspension	Alcohol (2%)	12/114
Decadron Turbinaire	MSD	Suspension	Alcohol (2%)	12/114
Duo-Medihaler	3 M	Suspension	Sorb. trio, other	11/12/114
Intal	Fisons	Suspension	Sorb. Trio.	12/114
Isuprel	Winthrop	Solution	Alcohol (33%) others	12/114
MaxAir	3 M	Suspension	Sorb. trio.	11/12
Medihaler-Epi	3 M	Suspension	Sorb. trio. Cetylpyrid.	11/12/114
Medihaler-Ergotamine	3 M	Suspension	Sorb. trio.	11/12/114
Medihaler-Iso	3 M	Suspension	Sorb. Trio.	11/12/114

Drug	Type	Label drug delivered (μg)	Amount	# Inhal.	Manufacturer
Flunisolide	Steroid	250	7 g	100	Riker
Metaproterenol sulfate	Beta$_2$-adrenergic	650	21 g	300	Riker
Ipratropium bromide	Anticholinergic	18	14 g	200	Riker
Triamcinolone acetamide	Corticosteroid	100	20 g	240	Armst.
Beclomethasone dipropionate	Corticosteroid	42	16.8 g 6.7 g	200 sample	Glaxo
Beclomethasone dipropionate	Corticosteroid	42	16.8 g	200	Glaxo
Terbutaline sulfate	Beta$_2$-adrenergic	200	10.5 g	300	Riker
Isoetharine mesylate	Beta$_2$-adrenergic	340	10 mL 15 mL	200 300	Sterl.
Dexamethasone sodium phosphate	Corticosteroid	84	—	170	Armst.
Dexamethasone sodium phosphate	Corticosteroid	84	12.6 g	170	Armst.
Isoproterenol HCl	Beta adrenergic	160	15 mL	300	Riker
Phenylephrine Bi	Alpha stimulator	240	22.5 mL	450	
Cromolyn sodium	Antiallergy	800	8.1 g 14.2 g	112 200	Riker UK
Isoproterenol hydrochloride	Beta adrenergic	131	11.2 g (10 mL) 16.8 g (15 mL)	200 300	Sterl.
Pirbuterol acetate	Beta$_2$-adrenergic	200	25.6 g	300	Riker
Epinephrine bitartrate	Beta adrenergic	300	15 mL	—	Riker
Ergotamine tartrate	Antimigraine	360	2.5 mL	—	Riker
Isoproterenol sulfate	Beta-adrenergic	80	15 mL (21 g) 22.5 mL (31.5 g)	300 450	Riker

Table 2 Marketed MDI Products[a]

Brand product	Company	Solution or suspension	Surfactant	Propellants
Metaprel	Sandoz	Suspension	Sorb. trio.	11/12/114
Nasacort	Rorer	Suspension	Alcohol	12
Nitrolingual	Rorer	Solution	Inactives	12/114
Norisodrine Aerotrol	Abbott	Solution	Alcohol (33%)	12/114
Primatene Mist	Whitehall	Solution	Alcohol (34%)	12/114
Primatene Mist	Whitehall	Suspension	Sorb. trio.	(b)
Proventil	Schering	Suspension	Oleic acid	11/12
Tornalate	Winthrop	Solution	Alcohol (38%)	12/114
Vancenase	Schering	Suspension	Sorb. trio.	11/12
Vanceril	Schering	Suspension	Sorb. trio.	11/12
Ventolin	Allen & Hanburys	Suspension	Oleic acid	11/12

[a]Abbreviations: Boeh. Ing, Boehringer Ingelheim; Sorb. trio., Sorbitan trioleate; Cetylpyrid., cetyl-pyridinium.
[b]Contains water along with propellants as indicated on label.

Riker, Presspart, or Cebal. Mouthpieces or actuators are usually injected molded for precision and are obtained from various suppliers.

Mouthpieces or oral adapters vary considerably from small elbow types (e.g., metaproterenol) to full sheaths (albuterol, beclomethasone) to those with a tube spacer (e.g., oral triamcinolone acetamide). They may be small, one-piece units (e.g., ergotamine) or two-piece units (e.g., ipatropium bromide). More elaborate designs with hinge-type swivels (Max-air®, Tornalate®) are also marketed. Also, a nasal preparation differs from other inhalers by containing a full sheath mouth-piece accompanied with a carrying case to protect the unit. Mouthpieces are critical in that they affect spray or plume patterns, particle size, and amount of drug delivered and retained on the mouthpiece. The orifice size of the mouthpiece and angle of the mouth extension piece are two critical design parameters [13,14].

1. Additional Characteristics

Nearly all products are unique in at least one package or formulation character-istic. Table 3 shows additional features of marketed products.

Drug	Type	Label drug delivered (μg)	Amount	# Inhal.	Manufac- turer
Metaproterenol sulfate	Beta$_2$-adrenergic	650	21 g	300	Riker
Triamcinolone ac.	Corticosteroid	55	10 g	100	Armst.
Nitroglycerin	Vasodilator	400	13.8 g	200	Pohl-Bosh.
Isoproterenol HCl	Beta-adrenergic	120	15 mL	—	—
Epinephrine	Beta-adrenergic	220	15 mL	—	—
Epinephrine bitartrate (salt)	Beta-adrenergic	300	15 mL 22.6 mL	—	—
Albuterol	Beta$_2$-adrenergic	90	17 g	200	Schering
Bitolterol mesylate	Beta-adrenergic agonist	370	15 mL (16.4 g)	300	Sterl.
Beclomethasone dipropionate	Corticosteroid	42 μg	16.8 g	200	Schering
Beclomethasone dipropionate	Corticosteroid	42	16.8 g	200	Schering
Albuterol	Beta$_2$-adrenergic	90	17 g	200	Glaxo

D. Compendial (USP) Products

Eight metered-dose inhalation products are specified in the United States Pharma-copeia XXII, shown in Table 4. The tests and specifications are also listed and include assays of the aerosol can contents, unit spray content or amount delivered from the mouthpiece, particle size, leak testing, alcohol content, and pressure testing. The actual number of actuations per test as specified in the product monograph is also shown. The unit spray content has wider limits due to the nature of the test. It is performed by spraying from the product's mouthpiece into an USP apparatus ⟨601⟩ and will include loss of drug onto the mouthpiece. The number of actuations is contingent on the amount of drug per actuation and the sensitivity of the assay methods. Ideally, repeated assay of the least number of actuations for quantification gives the best indication of the content uniformity of the product.

A new revision of the USP chapter ⟨601⟩ includes tests for the "respirable fraction" of the dosage form and specifies the apparatuses to be used to evaluate it [15]. The mass median aerodynamic (MMAD), geometric standard deviation

Table 3 Additional Features of Marketed Products

Brand	Product and package comments
AeroBid	One of smallest fills. Same drug as Nasalide (nasal solution).
Alupent	One of two products containing metaproterenol sulfate. Avoid excessive humidity (label). Differs chemically from isoproterenol in position of hydroxyl group on benzene ring.
Atrovent	Smallest amount of drug delivered, 18 μg; only marketed MDI in United States with lecithin. Two-piece actuator. Chemically related to atropine.
Azmacort	Printed can; MDI with Propellant 12 only. Only suspension without typical dispersing agent (alcohol used); large tube spacer. Similar in structure to Flunisolide except fluorine substitution.
Beclovent	Pressure filled; 65-μL valve. Chemically related to prednisolone and dexamethasone.
Beclonase	Nasal inhaler; same product as Beclovent but includes a nasal adapter.
Brethaire	25-μL valve. One extra methyl group compared to metaproterenol.
Bronkometer	Contains alcohol (30% w/w), ascorbic acid (0.1%), menthol, and saccharine.
Decadron Respihaler	High crown valve, related to beclomethasone.
Decadron Turbinaire	Nasal inhaler with nasal mouthpiece.
Duo-Medihaler	Largest package (450 actuations).
Intal	Largest amount of drug delivered, 0.800 mg per actuation; manufactured in United Kingdom.
Isuprel	One of oldest products, PVC-coated glass container contains alcohol (33% w/w) and ascorbic acid.
MaxAir	One of newest MDIs on market, either cold fill or pressure fill.
Medihaler-Epi	Contains cetylpyridinium chloride (antimicrobial)
Medihaler-Ergotamine	Smallest fill (label 2.5 mL)
Nasacort	Newest inhaler. Carrying cap over mouthpiece. See Azmacort
Nitrolingual	Sublingual, manufactured in Germany; Somova (Italy) valve with diptube. Contains caprylic/capric/diglyceryl succinate, ether, flavors.
Noridodrine	Contains alcohol (33% w/w), ascorbic acid (0.1%), natural and artificial flavors.
Primatene Mist	OTC, contains 34% alcohol and water. Packaged with can and mouthpiece separated. Prepared with aid of mineral acid.
Primatene Mist Susp.	OTC
Proventil	Patented, unique valve. Highest sales volume. Bespak valve, 65 μl; same formula as Ventolin.
Tornalate	Newest solution aerosol. Contains alcohol (38%), ascorbic acid, saccharin, and menthol.
Vancenase	Nasal inhaler, with nasal actuator.
Ventolin	One of highest sales volume.

Reference 3 and package inserts.

Table 4 MDIs in the USP XXII

USP drug	Assay			Unit spray content[b]		Particle size[c]	Other[d]
	Limits (%)	Method[a]	Actuations	Limits (%)	Actuations		
Dexamethasone sodium phosphate							
Inhalation aerosol USP	90–110	(1)	10	N/A		N/A	L, P, AC (1.7–2.3%)
Epinephrine							
Inhalation aerosol USP	90–115	(2)	Can	75–125	4	N/A	L
Epinephrine bitartrate							
Inhalation aerosol USP	90–110	(3)	3	75–125	6	LT 5 μ NMT 10/10μ	L
Ergotamine tartrate							
Inhalation aerosol USP	90–110	(3)	2	75–125	4	LT 5 μ NMT 10/10μ	L
Isoetharine mesylate							
Inhalation aerosol USP	90–110	(3)	90	75–125	15	N/A	L, AC (25.9–35.0%)
Isoproterenol HCl							
Inhalation aerosol USP	90–115	(3)	3–4	75–125	7–8	N/A	L, AC (28.5–38.5%)
Isoproterenol HCl and phenylephrine bitartrate							
Inhalation aerosol USP	90–110 (each)	(3)	6	75–125	12	LT 5 μ NMT 10/10μ	L
Isoproterenol sulfate							
Inhalation aerosol USP	90–110	(3)	5	75–125	10	LT 5 μ NMT 10/10μ	L

[a](1) Using needle, actuate into solvent; (2) chill can, open, dilute, and assay contents; (3) actuate from stem below surface of solvent (e.g. $CHCl_3$, PI1, HCl) and assay solvent.

[b]USP apparatus ⟨601⟩ is used for unit spray content determinations.

[c]N/A, not applicable.

[d]L, USP, leak testing; P, pressure test; AC, alcohol (ethanol) content.

(GSD), and material balance (90–110%) measurements are described. A metering performance test which is a spray weight test conducted over the dosage administration interval, uniformity of spray content, and content uniformity are also explained.

II. RAW MATERIALS

A. Ingredients

In aerosol dosage forms, the micronized active ingredient, suspending agent, and chlorofluorocarbon propellants are usually the most critical raw materials. Other additives such as antioxidants or flavors may also be crucial.

1. Active Ingredient

Important characteristics of the active ingredient are impurities, degradation products, water content (if hygroscopic), particle size, static charge, crystallinity, and microbial content. With micronized active ingredients, the milling or micronization process parameters should be recorded to verify the conditions that were used.

The finished product characteristics of the MDI may be related to the bulk drug substance, such as particle size. A reproducible drug particle size distribution along with a validated manufacturing process ensures lot-to-lot consistency of the final product. In addition, an acceptable water content of the drug substance prevents changes in agglomeration, crystallinity, or stability. Any additional tests performed on the active ingredient that are nonroutine release tests, such as X-ray, DSC, DTA, or particle size, may be done for information.

Any specific test method used that was not part of the bulk drug testing specifications needs to be documented. For example, particle size or moisture content determined by a second method should be added to the validation report, along with the specific methods used. Reference samples of bulk drug should also be established. This may be a benefit in evaluating any future test methods.

2. Propellants

The propellants used in MDIs are trichloromonofluoromethane NF (CFC 11), dichlorodifluoromethane NF (CFC 12), and dichlorotetrafluoroethane NF (CFC 114). As a minimum, they should meet compendial grade specifications. A single supplier should be preferred and used in the validation lots. Handling and storage techniques such as temperatures, tank type, size, and head space should be noted for the propellants. Any mixtures of CFCs used as a raw material for MDI manufacturing, whether purchased or prepared in house, must meet assay specifications of each CFC. Specifications of a mixture such as water content or other compendial tests may also apply [15]. For foreign use additional testing such as distillation range and free acidity tests may pertain. Assays and tests similar to the compendial ones are needed until a satisfactory history of that supplier can be obtained. Table 5 lists key physical properties [16] of the three MDI propellants.

The propellants used in MDIs are usually shipped in steel cylinders or drums and are under pressure. They may be stored outdoors before or during aerosol manufacture provided temperature effects are known.

It is industry practice to filter propellants before compounding or filling to ensure against particulates. The 0.22- or 0.45-micron (nominal) "solvent-grade" Teflon®, Nylon®, mixed cellulose acetate, or polyvinylidene difluoride (PVDF) filters are reported to be compatible with CFCs. These sizes are used to remove particulates of micron or submicron sizes similar to the drug. Pharmaceutical sanitary housings and setups are preferred, and all contact parts such as O-rings must be nonreactive to fluorocarbons. Cartridge-type filters are more common due to ease and output attainable.

Fractionation of propellant mixtures inside a storage tank or cylinder must be monitored [17]. This occurs when the propellant with the higher vapor pressure fractionates into the vapor head space in a container, leaving a lower proportion in the liquid phase. When the liquid is pumped for filling it would then have an undesirable composition. Different pressures would result, and thus measuring can pressure may be a way to monitor fractionation within propellant tanks.

Sampling techniques for propellant mixtures should be performed quickly and in a manner to prevent evaporation of any of the propellants. Some techniques are the use of prechilled cans, dipping with ladles, and crimping on the spot. Condensation of moisture onto the container and into the propellant must also be watched.

In the last few years, industry-wide concern over the phase-out of CFCs has arisen [18]. A Montreal Protocol consisting of 38 nations that agree to restrictions of CFCs has been signed. Amounts will be frozen at 1986 levels by the year 2000. A political group, Pharmaceutical CFC Coalition, was formed in 1989 to address this issue. The objective of this group is to increase the government agencies' awareness of the medical importance of CFCs. Alternatives are being investigated and tested for toxicity [19].

Table 5 Key Physical Properties of Propellants

Propellant or CFC	Boiling pt. (°F)	Vapor pressure at 77°F (psig)	Density, liquid at 77°F (g/mL)	Solubility of water in CFC at 77°F (wt %)
11	74.9	<1	1.48	0.011
114	38.8	16	1.46	0.009
12	−21.6	78	1.31	0.009

From ref. 16.

3. Suspending Agents

Suspending agents may have special requirements, such as specific storage and stability requirements. An example is soya lecithin, which is sensitive to light and air and might degrade into an odorous, discolored substance. Other natural products similarly need careful evaluation. Short-term expiry dates of 6 months may be best for unstable suspending agents. Special sampling programs for these raw materials might be extended to test for drum-to-drum variability within a lot of these types of raw materials.

Sorbitan trioleate ("SPAN-85")* is noncompendial and does not seem to be as critical as other natural products. Oleic acid NF and lecithin NF must meet their compendial requirements. Soya lecithin was recently replaced in Alupent® for the suspending agent sorbitan trioleate with discontenting consequences [20].

4. Cosolvents

The grade of alcohol should meet the tests for alcohol USP. The amount of water may be critical, sincé MDIs are nonaqueous systems.

5. Miscellaneous

Other inactive ingredients used in the product should meet compendial requirements as a minimum. These include ascorbic acid USP, ether USP, menthol USP, saccarhin NF or USP salts of saccarhin, cetylpyridinium chloride USP, and flavors.

B. Package Components

The packaging components of the multiple-dose MDIs are an integral part of the dosage form. Consistent delivery depends on the proper functioning of the valve throughout the use of the unit. The fit of the valve and actuator can also influence the drug delivery. If possible, obtaining the valve and actuator from the same vendor permits the vendor to test the combination in addition to the individual components, minimizing the chance for improper function of the combination.

1. Metered Valves

As with other packaging components, the incoming tests and specifications of metered valves, inspection attributes, and AQLs (Acceptable Quality Levels) will need to be coordinated with the supplier. The valve should be considered as a critical package component and have incoming performance tests, such as spray weights and weight loss [10,21]. The performance test could be conducted on a sample of the valve lots from either scale-up or pilot trials before the validation lots are prepared. This information may also be available for each lot from the supplier. It is recommended that each test shown in Table 6 be conducted on at least three valve lots as part of the validation program.

---

*A suitable grade is available from ICI Americas Inc., Wilmington, DE 19897.

Table 6 Important Valve Tests per Lot

Test	Number of valves	Characteristics
Inspection for attributes	MIL-105E	Appearance, identity, proper assembly
Dimensional check	40	Proper components, identity
Valve delivery (spray weights), mean, RSD	40	Meter chamber size, in-use test, meter chamber variability
Valve delivery at labeled number of actuations[a]	6	Ruggedness of multiple sprays
Weight loss[a] (leakage)	12	Sealing capability, proper rubber sealability
Loss of prime[a]	12	Meter chamber sealability
Particulates[a]	12	Valve cleanliness
Extractables[a]	12	Rubber contaminants

[a]Tested for information; not part of routine testing of all valve lots.

The metered valves should be well characterized before beginning the process validation lots. The typical performance attributes such as spray weight variations within and between valves of a single valve lot, spray weight variation between valve lots, leakage, crimp dimensions, and incoming inspection criteria should be well known. In addition, the loss of prime [22] and single-shot assay data [23,24] should be generated beforehand during development. Additional characterization of the valve done during development involves rubber extractables, compatibility with valve componentry [25,26], and particulate cleanliness.

The crimped metered valve on an aluminum can or plastic-coated glass bottle creates uniqueness of the MDI dosage form. Thus the dimensions of the valve parts related to the crimp, such as ferrule and gasket thickness, may be critical in the finished package. Other critical dimensions are related to the metering chamber size for dosage reproducibility, stem dimensions for mouthpiece fitting, orifice sizes for meter chamber refilling and pressure filling rates, and stem stroke length or travel for spring resilience.

All valves contain rubber components (gaskets, tank seals, seats, or sleeves) and at least one stainless steel part (spring). Both are vital to valve functionality. Some types of valve contain more plastic or stainless steel components than others. Drawings of individual pieces of the valve should be on hand for inspection to the incoming components. Periodic checking of the rubber or other components may be needed to ensure that the supplier has not changed any compositions or processing procedures.

The normal rejection rate during a 100% spray testing step such as percentage of no-sprays and continuous sprays would be helpful before validation. Should any deviations occur during the process validation lots, it is imperative to determine the cause of the deviation. If it involves leakage, spray weight, crimp appearance, or other attributes related to the valve, then the incoming-component testing of the valve will be helpful. The component release test results should be gathered and compared to the finished-product testing. As stated, the incoming tests may be evaluated on pilot equipment or from scale-up lots using actual drug formulation. Alternatively, if it has been demonstrated that the drug has an insignificant effect (such as less than 0.2% drug of a suspension formulation) on the valve performance for release testing, a placebo may be used to test incoming valves. Only after significant historical validation should the testing scheme in Table 6 be reduced.

It is imperative to consult the vendor also to determine an adequate number of valves for spray weight testing. If the metered chamber is plastic, valves totaling at least twice the number of the vendor's mold impressions should be tested to guarantee complete evaluation of the lot of valves.

Figure 3 depicts the results of two spray weigh methods conducted on the same lot of valves at different sites. Method 1 employed an automatic firing apparatus, whereas method 2 utilized a manual spray firing technique. Ruggedness is essential in evaluation of the valve performance.

Valves should be well characterized for leakage during development. Figure 4

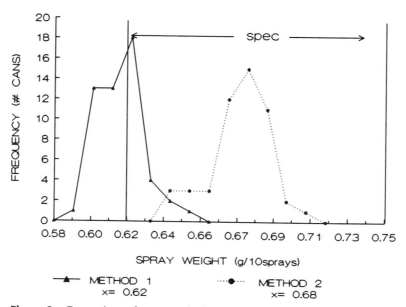

Figure 3 Comparison of spray methods.

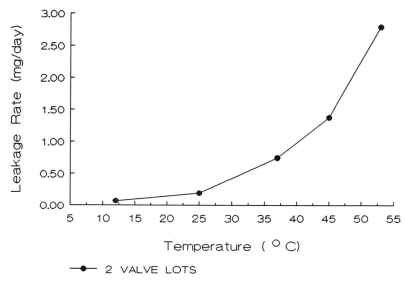

Figure 4 Effect of temperature on leakage rates.

shows leakage rates or weight loss at storage temperatures from 12 to 45°C, where an exponential relationship was observed.

Valves may have special shipping or storage requirements. For example, some valves are shipped in hermetically sealed bags to prevent moisture adsorption to plastic or rubber parts. Others are shipped in plastic pails. Any expiration period of the valve must be known. Expiration periods result from aging of rubber componentry, which causes the rubber parts to lose their sealing or resilience, affecting spray weights and leakage.

2. Aluminum Can or Plastic-Coated Bottle

The drawing of the can or bottle should be on hand at the manufacturing site as part of the validation package. The drawings should specifically state the following:

1. Drawing number and date
2. Supplier code number or part number
3. Type of materials used (e.g., aluminum 5502, glass type)
4. Chemical treatments or coatings (e.g., glass treatment, aluminum anodizing, epoxy lining)
5. Container dimensions
   a. Heights and widths, inside and out
   b. Wall thickness

    c.   Neck and bottom curvatures and radials
6.   Empty can or bottle weight
7.   Special imprints or lettering (label copy, if preprinted can)
8.   Any revisions to the drawings

The can may have had special cleaning procedures at the supplier's location prior to receiving. Testing of cans on incoming inspection usually involves identity, attributes, and dimensional checks. During development, any special coatings may require a chemical test such as pH or acid resistance. Key dimensions are usually related to the neck configuration, since slight changes may affect the crimping and leakage.

3. Mouthpieces

Oral adapters, mouthpieces, or actuators are made of plastic polyethylene or polypropylene. As with the can requirements, drawings should be part of the validation package. Frequently, this component is omitted from validation protocols of filled, crimped aerosol cans. However, this piece is critical to the functionality of the unit.

The finished assembled package unit should have a packaging validation program. All MDIs in the United States are packaged with the can and mouthpiece in one box, and all are preassembled with the unit inside the mouthpiece ready for use. A dust cap is provided to cover the end of the mouthpiece that is in contact with the lips.

An incoming inspection and performance testing program should be in place for the mouthpiece. Some of the critical dimensions of the mouthpiece are the design configuration, valve stem and mouthpiece coupling, spray orifice size, and spray angle. The performance of a mouthpiece may be evaluated by measuring the spray pattern emitted from adapter. This is usually performed by thin-layer chromatography [27] or video imagery [28,29]. The durability of the mouthpiece should also be checked as a kind of in-use test. One recall was due to faulty mouthpieces that were improperly manufactured and tested [30].

Instructions to patients usually include washing the mouthpiece daily with water. This is to prevent buildup of residue near the orifice, which prevents adequate delivery or clogging. The type of buildup may be a unique characteristic of that product. The mating of the mouthpiece and valve stem is also important to the integrity of the package.

4. Auxiliary Device

Auxiliary devices such as a tube spacer are available for the patient. Some examples are Inspirease® and Inhalaid® devices [31]. Since they are provided separately from the MDI to the patient, they should not be considered as part of process validation.

III. MANUFACTURING

A. Concentrate Preparation

1. Suspensions

During a cold-filling operation, the suspending agent, micronized drug, and CFC 11 and/or 114 are mixed, forming a concentrated drug suspension. Mixing may be done by impeller, turbine, or homogenizer. Thus the mixing conditions utilized throughout all the process validation lots should be well documented. These include mixer details, position in the tank, speeds, direction, and recirculation conditions (if used). The mixers used should have qualification reports describing the design and performance details.

For compounding, jacketed stainless steel tanks capable of airtight sealing are frequently used. The temperature of the drug preparation should be monitored and sufficient to prevent evaporation of the CFCs. Temperatures too low may lead to condensation of atmospheric moisture on recirculation lines, on filling equipment, or possibly within the tank. Thus N_2 gas is usually used to blanket the head space before and during concentrate preparation. Gas flow rates, nozzle positions, and other conditions used in the tank should be recorded. Temperatures above 55–60°F may be too high if drug concentrate preparation requires more than 1 hour. In these cases temperature fluctuations could lead to evaporation of the Propellant 11, which boils at 75°F, and thus change the concentration of drug.

Tanks are preferably set on load cells or scales to ensure accurate weighing of the volatile CFCs and drug concentrates. Any evaporation or loss of CFCs can thus be monitored. Without a means of obtaining tank concentrate weights, accurate in-process assays will be required to verify the lack of loss of CFCs.

In suspensions, some drugs are easily dispersed, whereas others require extensive mixing. If a homogenizer or colloid mill is used, these conditions will also require documentation.

The drug concentrate may be filtered before further processing as assurance of aggregate-free suspensions [11]. This may not be needed if validation testing shows it to be unnecessary.

2. Solutions

Since solution aerosols use ethanol as a cosolvent to render the drug soluble, the ethanol and CFC 114 and/or 12 are mixed and drug is added. The solution may include these two CFCs but not CFC 11, which is incompatible with ethanol [32]. Temperatures must be low enough to assure minimal evaporation rates during filling but also enable suitable dissolution of ingredients. Temperatures from −50 to +5°C have been used [11,32]. The CFC mixture must provide sufficient vapor pressure to propel the contents for inhalation, usually 35–60 psig (at 21°C). Higher pressures are also used (CFC 12 alone, 68 psig at 20°C). The presence of

CFC 114 in the formula is a good indication that the product is cold filled because Propellant 114 lowers the vapor pressure of Propellant 12 for filling but provides a high enough vapor pressure for propellance.

3. Types of Filling Equipment

In filling concentrate in MDIs, amounts from 1 to 15 mL are typical. Common methods involve either gravity filling with timed microswitches or use of positive piston fillers. Pistons fillers are used on units such as Pamasol filling equipment. Amounts by gravity filling may be controlled by nozzle size and time. Gravity filling is usually best for volumes of 2 mL or greater. Piston filling is controlled by piston size, bore size, and length. This method is usually very accurate and precise.

It may be necessary to shroud the filling area with nitrogen to prevent moisture condensation on the filling equipment and nozzles. Equipment may be fabricated to prevent outside atmospheric moisture from entering. Nitrogen flow rates should be monitored as part of the process validation protocol.

B. Propellant Filling

1. Cold Fill Method

The propellant in cold-fill products almost always is a mixture of CFC 114 and CFC 12. CFC 114 reduces the vapor pressure of 12, enabling it to be cold filled at higher temperatures without evaporative loss. Mixtures of CFCs 114 and 12 may be added to the drug concentrate containing CFC 11 and then filled into the can or bottle or may be cold filled separately after the drug concentrate.

2. Pressure Fill

During pressure filling, the CFC 12 may be pressure filled alone or with a mixture of CFC 114. Pressure filling requires two filling steps, drug concentrate and propellant filling. Figure 5 shows a schematic sequence of MDI manufacture [10]. Figures 6 and 7 illustrate an aerosol filling line with two tracks.

Tolerances must be established for each filling stage, control limits for adjustment and tolerance limits for acceptance or rejection. In-process check weights are usually performed at specified time intervals during validation to verify the accuracy of filling. Control charts are then assembled for each filling operation of each validation batch. Upper and lower limits are usually clearly marked for simplicity.

For a two-step filling operation with drug concentrate followed by propellant filling, the acceptable drug concentration in the can may be used to calculate acceptable filling amounts. For example, a lower limit of drug concentrate fill and upper limit of propellant fill will provide the lowest possible final drug concentration. For the suspension of the filled can to be within 90 to 110% of the label claim, the specifications can be determined as shown in Table 7. In this example, a

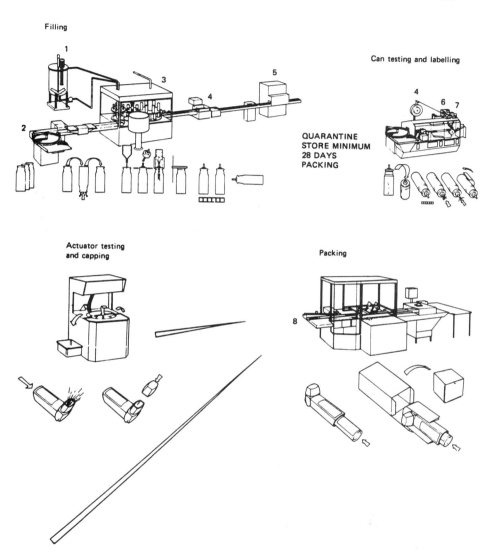

Figure 5   Schematic production sequence for the manufacture of metered-dose inhalers by pressure filling. (1) Suspension mixing vessel; (2) can cleaner; (3) can crimper and filler; (4) check weigher; (5) can coder and heat tester; (6) priming and spray testing; (7) labeler; (8) feeds for tested cans and actuators. (Courtesy of Ellis Horwood Publishers, Reference 10.)

Figure 6 The filling bowls and nozzles are just behind the worker here inserting valves into the container. Valves are crimped to the containers at the next station and then pressurized with propellant. (Courtesy of Armstrong Pharmaceutical Co., West Roxbury, MA.)

Figure 7 Amount of drug concentrate varies with the product. Here a small stainless steel jacketed and agitation vessel is used to maintain a homogenous drug composition in solution at a controlled temperature. Drug is recirculated between this vessel and the filling nozzles. (Courtesy of Armstrong Pharmaceutical Co., West Roxbury, MA.)

Table 7 Example of Fill Weight Ranges for Suspension

	Lower Limits	Target	Upper Limit
Concentrate	4.60 g (92.0%)	5.00 g	5.40 g (108.0%)
Propellant	14.15 g (94.3%)	15.00 g	15.85 g (105.7%)
Total	18.75 g (93.8%)	20.00 g	21.25 g (106.3%)
	Low-potency fill (g) mg/g fill	Target fill (g) mg/g fill	High-potency fill (g) mg/g fill
Concentrate	46/4.60	50/5.00	54/5.40 (high)
Propellant	0/15.85	0/15.00	0/14.15 (low)
Total	46/20.45	50/20.00	54/19.56
mg/g	2.25	2.50	2.76
% theory	90	100	110
Specifications			
Concentrate	4.60–5.40 g		5.00 ± 8.0%
Propellant	14.15–15.85 g		15.00 ± 5.7%
Total	18.75–21.25 g		20.00 ± 6.2%

concentrate fill of 1% drug (50 mg/5.00 g) provides a final can potency of 2.50 mg/g. It is important that the specifications, equipment, and fill quantities be coordinated so that limits are attainable. The original fill amounts and ratios of propellants should be formulated in such a way that ranges of acceptable concentrate and propellant are adequate.

Since more than 99.99% of filled cans would be within 4 standard deviation units of a normal distribution, 4 standard deviation units appears to be an acceptable target for fill weight variations. In the example shown in Table 7, the concentrate filler should exhibit a relative standard deviation of less than 2.0%, one fourth of the 8.0% upper and lower limits of the concentrate fill. Figure 8 depicts an example of a concentrate fill target of 3.89 g and specification of ± 0.23 g (5.9%).

In the example shown in Table 7, the propellant fill should have a relative standard deviation (RSD) less than 1.5%, one fourth of the 5.9% limit. Tightening of either propellant or concentrate filler will allow loosening of the second fill limits, while maintaining the same specifications of the final product. Figure 9 shows a control chart for a propellant fill target of 12.13 ± 0.30 g (2.5%).

C. Crimping

The crimping station on an aerosol line occurs after the valve has been placed on the canister. The valve may have been placed either manually or with automatic equipment. Crimping should occur as soon as practical after filling and valve

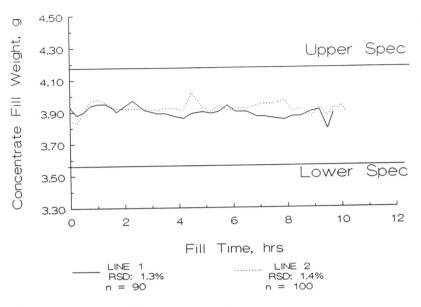

Figure 8   Concentrate fill weight control chart.

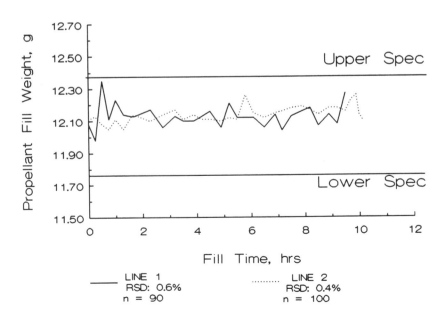

Figure 9   Propellant fill weight control chart.

insertion to minimize air entrapment and CFC evaporation. During crimping, the ferrule of the valve is compressed by closing the jaws on the collet, crimping the valve under the neck of the can or bottle. Crimping parameters and measurements are recorded during process validation to verify the suitability of the crimping process [33]. An adequate crimp is needed for acceptable leakage, appearance, valve function, and propellant filling. Crimping parameters are usually:

1. Head pressure, downward pressure exerted on the top of the valve
2. Collet pressure of closing collet
3. Pad pressure (if this type of equipment is used)

If the crimp settings are stressed to extremes during development, corresponding acceptable limits may be established. For example, the collet pressure would be increased in stages to a point of unacceptable appearance or leakage. The height or diameter of the crimp would also be determined for the different settings. Before limits are finalized, several lots of valves and cans will have to be measured, since these components have an effect on the final crimp measurement. Critical crimp measurements [34] taken on the crimped valve are:

1. Height or depth of crimp
2. Diameter or radius of crimp
3. Roll-off
4. Gasket compression
5. Can deflection
6. Appearance

1. Height

The height of a crimp is measured from the top of the crimp jaw marks to the top of the ferrule. The height of the crimp should be correlatable to the leakage. When the height is too large, the valve has been improperly seated and leakage may be excessive. If the height is too small, excessive pressure may have been applied during crimping, affecting the valve function or appearance. Usual values are 6.5–7.5 mm (0.26–0.30 in.). The tool for measurement is calipers or another specialized device such as a Socoge* gauge for measuring the depth of a crimped valve at a constant 19-mm radius. Figure 10 depicts a control chart showing crimp depth using both devices. Figure 11 illustrates the differences between the two devices where calipers measure the crimp height at a radius of 17.9 mm and Socoge gauge (H) at a radius of 19 mm.

2. Diameter

This measurement is taken from one point on the crimp circumference to the other point at 360°. The diameter is correlated to the pressure applied on the jaws during

---

*Available from Sopim s.a., Caville Pineuilh, 33220 STE-FOY-LA Gde, France.

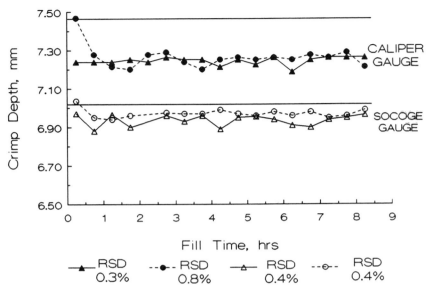

Figure 10 Crimp depth control chart.

closing of the collet. Usual values are 17.5–18.5 mm for a valve and can with 20-mm uncrimped diameters.

3. Roll off

Measurements taken at four locations, 90° apart, of the top of the ferrule to the bottom of the can indicate the uniformity of pressure applied to the valve during crimping. The difference between the highest and lowest of the four values is called roll-off (or run-out). The results should be small and typically less than 0.1 mm.

4. Gasket Compression

This indicates the percentage of compression of a sealing gasket on the crimped unit. The rubber gasket is compressed a certain percentage, enabling a seal to occur between the ferrule of the valve and the can. It is determined by subtracting an uncrimped gasket thickness from the crimped unit thickness. The crimped unit gasket thickness is measured by subtraction of parts from the crimp height after disassembly of the filled unit:

$$j' = H - (2 \times e) - h' \tag{1}$$

where H, h', and e are measured dimensions of the valve as defined in Fig. 11. For example, a crimped unit of height (H) 7.00 mm, ferrule thickness (e) 0.36 mm,

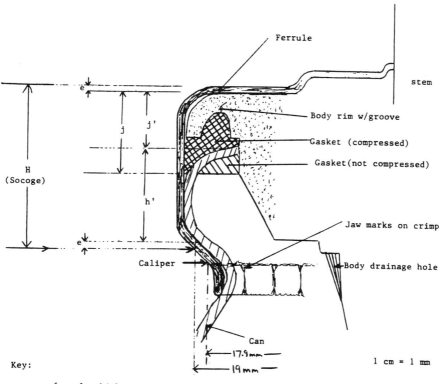

Key:

e - ferrule thickness

j - compression seal (no load), includes gasket and body rim

j' - compression seal after crimping (gasket compressed)

h (not on drawing) - can neck height (no load), measured with Socoge gauge

h' - can neck height after crimping, measured with Socoge gauge

H - crimp control measurement of crimped unit, measured with Socoge.

     H = 2 x e + j' + h'

Caliper measurement is greater than Socoge since location is at the crimping jaw marks.

Figure 11 Gasket compression and crimp depth measurements (Socoge gauge).

and can neck height (h') 3.85 mm yields a crimped gasket and rim thickness (j') of 2.43 mm. If the before-crimp gasket and rim thickness (j) is 3.04 mm and only the gasket of thickness 1.26 mm has compression, then the percentage compression is 48%. In other words, the gasket has compressed 0.61 mm (3.04–2.43 mm) of 1.26 mm.

For valves with O-rings the gasket compression is more difficult to measure. Gasket compression has also been correlated to leakage, where a decrease in leak rate occurs with increase in gasket compression. Figure 8 shows a schematic of a valve crimped onto a can and the measurement of the compressed gasket.

5. Can Deflection

The aluminum cans are deflected a small distance from their original height during crimping when a high pressure is exerted downward. Deflection is measured by carefully removing the valve of a crimped unit with pliers and measuring the height of the deflected can compared to an uncrimped can. Also a Socoge gauge may be used to measure deflections at a constant 19-mm diameter (h' in Fig. 11).

6. Appearance

The crimp should be aesthetic and free from exposed or sharp edges at the end of the valve. It should tightly fit the contours of the can.

D. Leak Testing

All filled aerosol cans are leak tested before distribution to prevent an empty or near-empty product from reaching the patient.

Four methods are currently used for leak testing:

1. Hot water bath for visual examination and/or check weighing afterwards.
2. Induction oven where cans are quickly heated [35], and check weighed at a later date.
3. Storage for a predetermined time period before checkweighing [10].
4. Pressure reading [36].

Hot water baths are maintained at temperatures above the boiling point of the product, such as 100°F. More common temperatures are 120–130°F, since the time to raise the can contents would be shorter. At least 1.5 to 3 minutes is usually required to bring the can contents to a temperature that would emit propellant vapor in a leaky unit. Cans are examined visually by inspectors who look for the presence of faulty crimps, valves, etc. Emergence of bubbles signifies a probable reject. Protection from possible dangerous discharges should be taken. Filtered tap water has been used to test for leakage because it does not come into contact with drug product. Types of defects usually arise from poorly crimped valves (process defect), where bubbles appear from the side of a valve skirt or ferrule. Other rejects may be due to poorly assembled valves (valve defect), where leakage from the side of stem may occur.

Induction heaters [35] heat the units instantaneously on the aerosol line after filling and crimping. Any faulty units or poor crimps would burst upon testing and be removed from the line. Subsequent checkweighing is usually performed to remove any intact units that are leakers. Induction heaters were introduced as an improvement over the visual inspection method.

Storage of the filled units for a set period of time is becoming more common as a method for leak testing. Units are held for a sufficient period of time that leakers will fail a subsequent checkweighing step. Twenty-eight days have been used to ferret out faulty units [10]. Inventory considerations have to be taken into account with this process requirement. Also, the probability that slow or latent leakers will pass undetected must be regarded.

Pressure readings are designed to check the integrity of componentry before filling. This was designed to check the tightness of the crimp, which could be used later for performance evaluation [36].

E. Checkweighing

This step is commonly carried out to ensure that all cans reaching the consumer contain an adequate supply of medication [37]. This may be conducted on units after filling or leak testing but must be done before secondary packaging and distribution. In setting the limits of the checkweigher, the allowable fill weight variation and component weights must be factored. The checkweigher must have low tolerances (usually less than 100 mg), well within the ranges of the filled aerosol unit. Units filled with steel beads may be used to set the upper and lower limits. The rate of the checkweighing step, set limits, along with the number of high and low rejects should be tallied during validation. Units that fail may also be individually weighed to verify the accuracy of the checkweigher.

For characterizing the expected leakage during development, histograms over periods of months may be generated, as shown in Fig. 12. These are then compared to histograms of the same cans that were generated immediately after manufacture.

F. Spray Testing

This step is performed on all filled units to remove any defectively spraying MDIs such as no-sprays or continuous spray units [38]. Two general methods are used today, an automatic and a manual method. The automatic unit may employ different techniques such as light or sound.* For example, the sounds of acceptable and unacceptable actuations are programmed and used for testing. Continuous or no-spray valves will sound different from a single-fire acceptable valve.

---

*Available from Charles Wyle Engineering Corp., Torrance, CA 90505 or William Sessions Limited, York YO3 9HS, England.

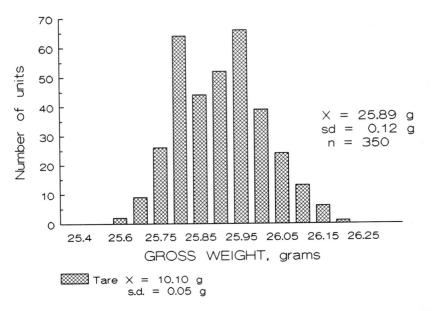

Figure 12 Histogram of gross weight after storage (8 months at room temperature).

The presence of a powder, aerosolized mist may be used so that testing will be done by an electronic eye.

Manual methods include listening devices for sound inspection or spray booths for visual inspection of sprays. Hoods or spray booths are used on line where inspectors manually actuate units and observe for defective sprays. Manual actuation for sound may be performed into vacuum setups with microphones that amplify the valve actuation noise for listening.

The usual number of actuations for testing is between three and five. At least two are considered as priming shots, followed by a test fire. Rejection rates vary from lot to lot and suppliers but are usually less than 0.1%. The rejection rate, classified by defect, and testing method should be documented for the validation lots. Rejected units should be closely examined for any false results and may be used to improve the valve manufacturer's quality control.

IV. VALIDATION PROTOCOL

A. Development Report

A development report should be written prior to the process validation protocol by research and development and serve as the basis for items in the validation protocol. Parameters such as process limits, formulation compatibility with process equipment, time limitations of production, and any problems encountered and their resolution should be addressed. Aerosol product characteristics such as microbial challenge data, through-life testing of units [39], resuspendability [40,41], first-shot assays, and typical loss of prime should also be well known. The effect of spray assay methodology [42] on the product results is beneficial information. The product also should be fingerprinted for three-dimensional plume patterns and particle size distribution by two or more methods. One of the methods should evaluate the aerodynamic particle size. A development history that describes chronological events during formulation is also beneficial and frequently will help the specialist preparing the protocol. Reference to the development report(s) may be included in the protocol.

B. Preparation and Execution

The process validation protocol of a new aerosol product should be written by a qualified manufacturing or validation specialist familiar with aerosols. Others experienced in oral dosage forms such as suspensions or solutions would also be helpful. These technical specialists may be within the research, validation, or technical support departments, since this work will be done prior to approval of a new product. Approval of the protocol should be given by quality assurance, quality control, production management, and research.

In aerosols, other experts will be involved. A packaging specialist will also play a critical role, since the functionality of the dosage form depends on the package performance (i.e., valve and mouthpiece). Secondary packaging, where the filled unit may be checkweighed, spray tested, and assembled with the mouthpiece into a boxed unit, also will need qualification and validation. In the case of third-party or contract manufacturing, production and quality control management at the manufacturing site should be reviewers or approvers of the validation protocol and report. In some instances, the third party may prepare a protocol; however, the final responsibility for validation approval lies with the new drug application (NDA) holder and marketer of the aerosol.

The validation protocol should be prepared after the master batch record is approved and signed by responsible parties, i.e., the manufacturer and NDA holder. The batch directions should be detailed and easily understood. For example, mixing speeds and times, mixer positions, and method of adding ingredients should be explained clearly. The protocol must agree in process descriptions and flowcharts and be specific enough to remove any ambiguities on process conditions, decisions, or product specifications. For these reasons, it is usually beneficial to prepare a production-sized, prevalidation batch with the proposed final batch record. This batch should also be completely tested and meet finished-product specifications.

The manufacturing or validation specialist should execute the protocol. That is, that person should carry out and coordinate any process monitoring, aerosol line conditions, sample collection, and physical testing. The quality control unit that will routinely analyze the product after routine production starts should test the validation batches. This unit would also be responsible for stability tests conducted on the validation batches.

C. Final Process and Product

The process must be validated at the manufacturing site(s) specified in the regulatory filing [NDA or abbreviated NDA (ANDA)]. The aerosol product must be prepared with the manufacturing equipment and process intended for routine production. It is enticing to make batch record changes during or after validation batches have begun as a means of improvement. Changes in any manner such as order of addition of raw materials, method of weighing, screening of any raw materials, aerosol line functional changes, mixing conditions, or mixing equipment should be considered as major changes and be documented accordingly. Revalidation would be required for any changes made.

The batch record must be diligently followed during validation. Process or formulation variations, quantitative or qualitative, are not permitted. A change in any process step(s) will require restarting or amending the validation program. Examples would be adding a dilution step for dissolving or dispersing ingredients or changing homogenization times of wetting a suspension.

It is also alluring to begin validation before the final setup is in place due to time-related goals. An example might be to use a temporary filter setup, tank cover, agitator propeller, or other piece of equipment. A short-term delay in the start of validation batches would be preferred until the equipment and laboratory readiness is complete. Testing must include validated analytical procedures using the mouthpiece intended for marketed package.

D. Worst-Case Conditions

Meaningful process limits on conditions will need to be established if not done previously during development. Operating outside the set limits may or may not lead to failure of the process or product specifications [43]. Limits may also be used to demonstrate that process conditions are under consistent control. Examples may be the fill room humidity range (e.g., 30–45%), mixer speed ranges (45–55 rpm), mixer position (angle or distances), nitrogen flow to a tank (2–4 scfh), or suspension temperature range (20–30°F).

Evaluating worst-case conditions will justify many of these process limits. A "subprotocol" for testing the worst-case scenario should be clearly specified in the validation protocol. An alternative and preferable procedure would be to test these conditions during development. For example, drug uniformity might be verified by using the lowest mixer speed (45 rpm), lowest temperature (20°F), and highest nitrogen flow rate (4 scfh). Lack of volatility may be confirmed by testing with a high mixer speed (55 rpm), the highest temperature (30°F), and the highest nitrogen flow (4 scfh). Rates of addition of raw materials (1–5 minutes) may also need evaluation. These tests may be conducted during the prevalidation batch in order not to interfere with a supposedly production (validation) batch.

E. Timing

The protocol must be approved and signed before the first production batches are started. Since aerosol manufacturing involves more package components (valves, cans, mouthpieces) than other dosage forms, receipt and release testing of these components must be incorporated in the planning schedule. Also, since aerosol products involve more lengthy finished-product tests than other dosage forms, release testing usually requires more analytical laboratory time.

F. Testing and Specifications

Due to extensive testing for aerosol products, the sampling and testing scheme must be carefully reviewed before starting validation. Most MDI aerosols are suspensions involving volatile propellants that are mixed and filled over long periods (greater than 6 hours). Thus many drug uniformity samples may be required to demonstrate reproducibility and show that volatility or loss of propellants and drug is under control.

Some aerosol tests that frequently need to be monitored are filled unit yields [44], leakage rates, valve-spray reject rates, moisture values, assays, and valve rubber leachables.

Alert limits for critical tests are suggested to avoid uncertainty over pass/fail situations and act as guide when there is a cause of concern. Tentative limits could be used until a history of production batches is obtained. Examples may be a content uniformity RSD of 5.0% versus specification of 6.0%. Developmental data on the pilot-scale batches will assist in setting initial alert limits. These alert limits do not substitute for the actual limits but merely serve as a guide for investigation.

G. Stability

Stability testing of the validation batches should be conducted at the official NDA site quality control laboratory. It should be conducted at labeled storage conditions as a minimum. Accelerated conditions are not usually required because this is supplemental stability, not primary.

H. Protocol Format

Examples of the format and sections of a validation protocol are described below.

1. Objective

The objective briefly describes the purpose of the validation program. Common objectives are to demonstrate that the manufacturing process as described in the master batch record consistently produces product that meets in-process and finished-product requirements. An additional objective is to provide supplemental manufacturing information beyond that recorded in the batch documents.

2. Scope

The scope section describes what the process validation protocol covers, the number of batches, and what it does not cover. In this part, usually packaging validation or mouthpiece testing is included or excluded. Any worst-case tests may be briefly described. Stability commitments and stability protocols should be mentioned.

3. Formulation and Components

The specific quantitative formulation and components should be listed along with the identification or company code numbers. The amounts per can, per batch, and percentages should be listed here. Additional formulation information also may be enumerated:

Amounts per actuation
  Drug formulated (μg drug and mg total)
  Drug delivered from mouthpiece
  Drug retained on mouthpiece
Amounts per can
  Sprayable contents (number of labeled sprays $\times$ mg/spray)
  Nonsprayable contents (tail-off sprays, vapor retained, drug retained)
  Leakage over expiration period
  Spray-testing loss
  Fill weight allowance (underfill tolerance)
  Material balance

4. Process Flowcharts

A flow diagram should indicate the process steps and addition of raw materials. If possible, major equipment and special environmental conditions may be included in the flowchart. In-process tests may be also be included. A second flowchart for site activities, raw materials' suppliers, shipments, and testing would also assist in the overall picture of the aerosol manufacturing scheme, especially for multiple-site or third-party activities. An example of a process flowchart for a fictitious suspension product (2160.4 kg batch size for 100,000 units) is shown in Fig. 13.

CONCENTRATE PREPARATION:

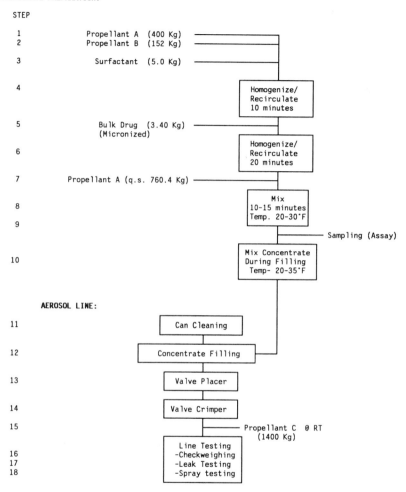

Figure 13 Process flowchart.

5. Document Checklist

All documents that should be examined and in proper order prior to the initiation of the validation batches are listed. They are checked for availability and accuracy. Preparation of batches should not commence unless these documents are finalized and signed. An example is shown below.

A. New drug application (applicable sections)
B. Calibrations
   1. Scales and balances
   2. Temperature measuring devices
   3. Tachometers
   4. Environmental conditions measurements
      a. Room temperature, humidity, pressure
      b. HEPA filter certification
   5. Pressure gauge
C. Standard operating procedures
   1. Physical tests
      a. Pressure testing
      b. Spray-dosage
      c. Number of sprays
      d. Moisture in unit
      e. Weight loss
      f. Testing of valves, cans, actuators, overcaps
   2. Chemical tests
      a. In-process assay
      b. Identification test
      c. Drug assay (mg per can)
      d. Drug valve testing
D. Product specification sheet
    Line check form, bill of materials
E. Training documentation
F. Cleaning procedures
   1. Cleaning procedures
   2. Cleaning validation report
G. Certificates of analysis of components (for each validation batch)
   1. Each raw material (active, flavors, cosolvents, surfactants, antioxidants, antimicrobials)
   2. Propellants (CFCs)
   3. Nitrogen or other inert gases
   4. Metered valves
   5. Canisters
   6. Overcaps
   7. Mouthpieces
H. Master batch record documents
   1. Batch card
   2. Chemical weighing records
   3. Yield reconciliations sheets
   4. In-process data sheets
   5. Production area readiness checklist

    6.   Computer system documentation

    7.   Mechanical line setup sheets

I.   Qualification reports and equipment manuals

    1.   Tank or vessels

    2.   Mixers

        a.   Homogenizer (colloid mills)

        b.   Tank agitator

        c.   Mixers

    3.   Concentrate filler

    4.   Recirculation pumps

    5.   Crimper

    6.   Pressure filler

    7.   Checkweigher

    8.   Spray-testing unit

    9.   Environmental control areas (temperature and humidity)

J.   Development report (research report #)

K.   Safety documents (material safety data sheets)

L.   Validation protocol (current document)

6. Process Monitoring

This section depicts the intended process conditions and parameters that will be measured. Items not recorded in the batch record but which may be critical should be tabulated here, along with target or expected values. The frequency of the measurement (e.g., once), method (e.g., timer), and where it will be recorded (e.g., form A) should be tabulated. Many of these items will depend on past experience during development. An example may be the rate of addition and location of the micronized active ingredient or observations of the aerosol solution or suspension appearance. In short, if a quantitative measure of a given step is obtainable, this number should be recorded. A thorough and detailed master batch record will minimize the additional monitoring required for validation.

Filling line items on a line setup sheet will also need monitoring. Items not recorded in batch documentation should be tabulated or listed in the protocol as intended for monitoring during validation. Examples might be crimping collet numbers, line speeds, or propellant injection pressures during the filling process.

7. Sampling and Testing

This section provides specifics on the sampling, testing, and acceptance criteria intended during the validation batches. Methods of sampling concentrate or removing filled cans from the line should be clearly described. Lists of in-process tests, where sampled, number of cans, and responsibility should be tabulated. A separate table may be needed to describe the test, method, frequency, specification, and comments.

All in-process samples must pass specifications in order to claim a validated process. Statistical testing at the beginning, middle, and end of the process usually can demonstrate the consistency of manufacturing. Similarly, tables of finished product tests showing expanded testing regimens (e.g., beginning, middle, end, and composite), methods, and specifications will be needed.

8. Responsibility and Timing

This section will provide a guide for specific goals of each group. The target timing requirements (e.g., 6 weeks to place on stability) will show the responsibility of each person(s) from protocol writing to report approval.

9. Appendix

Forms with blanks may be provided in the protocol to be filled out during each validation batch. These forms are for process monitoring of compounding, line functions, in-process sampling, etc. They should include specifics such as types of measuring devices (serial numbers) and include sign-offs for done by and checked by. A clearer indication of the process requirements results from preparing and reviewing these forms.

V. ADDITIONAL VALIDATION PROTOCOL ITEMS

Additional items may be monitored during validation that were not detailed in the aforementioned protocol description.

A. Materials Monitoring

Metered valves are extremely critical to the functionality of this dosage form, and a thorough understanding of this component is essential. Table 6 shows some common tests conducted on metered valves. Footnoted items are special tests performed for valve characterization, not necessarily for individual lot release.

Storage and handling of the propellants (chlorofluorocarbons), types of filters, transfer piping, and storage tanks should be standardized. Any observations of the appearance of the CFCs should be recorded. The supplier's specifications should be reviewed.

Other ingredients and packaging components might require special environmental storage conditions. Room temperatures and humidities should be documented during facilities qualification prior to process validation. This includes bulk drug, surfactants, cosolvents, flavors, and other miscellaneous ingredients.

Containers for storing the raw materials should be specified in the material specifications sheets or packaging bill of materials. Although outside the scope of validation, the manufacturing specialist should be aware of such issues.

Weighing of ingredients by the weighing or chemical dispensing department should include the gross, tare, and net of each ingredient. Future abnormalities of yielding or potency may be found by having unusual tares or discrepancies arising from the weighing of components. Unusual tares such as for tanks should include specifics (coolant, lid, etc.) and the method of taring.

B. Process Monitoring

1. Preparation of Suspension or Solution

Validation should confirm the order of addition of raw materials, rate of addition, method of addition, and mixing conditions during compounding of the aerosol suspension or solution. The specific type of mixer(s), blade(s), speed(s) and position (pitch) or placement in the vessel should be specified in the batch directions. The batch temperature and room conditions (temperature, humidity) should be fully documented if not recorded in the batch directions.

a. *Air cleanliness.* Air cleanliness may be an important factor, especially if the compounding is done in open vessels exposed to the ambient air. Air cleanliness (type of air) by recording high-efficiency particulate air (HEPA) filter types, airborne particulate counts, and any microbial monitoring such as sampling and incubating with media may be part of the environmental testing plan. Air pressures and cleanliness testing, although good measures of conditions, are not required for other oral products. A qualification or facilities testing program is usually beyond the scope of the specific process validation program.

b. *Purging.* Prior to compounding of batch ingredients, preparatory steps should be monitored. Any purging of tanks, lines, etc. with dry gas should be recorded for any filtration, flow rates, and position of gas lines. For many products it is desirable to purge the drug concentrate tank prior to and during batch preparation with an inert gas such as N_2. This serves to remove undesirable moisture and oxygen in the tank head space. The type of gas and any treatment such as drying agents or filtration should be verified during validation. Frequently, stainless steel piping or tees into tank covers are employed to introduce dry nitrogen NF into the tank. The source and grade (e.g., high-purity nitrogen) should be documented, along with details of the method and position of purging the tanks.

c. *Recirculation.* Recirculation of drug concentrate may be used during the filling operation to maintain a sufficient source to the filling device. Concentrate may be pumped between the drug suspension or solution tank to the filling system, and then the excess is returned to the tank. The type, model, and serial number of pumping equipment and flow rates must be monitored. The time recirculation is started and stopped should be known. If alternative mechanisms are used, such as a level controller (float valves), settings should also be documented. In some instances a filter may be used for solution or suspensions. Similar to filtration of CFCs, a challenge test of the filter with small particles may be conducted to demonstrate adequate retention. This would be described in a separate testing protocol, preferably during development.

d. *Residual losses and yields*. The yield of the concentrate, filling, and any residual tank or pumping loss is an important measure of how the process behaved. Accounting for drug suspension and solution should be complete and rigorously done. An investigation of losses should be made when these losses exceed unusual amounts (about 5 to 7%) of the drug suspension or solution. Tentative specifications of the yield should be considered after the validation batches and reviewed after several more production batches are made.

2. *Aerosol Line Functions*

The amount and type of purge at the can vacuum station (can cleaning) should be known. The pressure and amount of vacuum applied to the empty can should also be measured. A challenge test may be done in which particulates are intentionally placed in empty cans to observe visually the removal of the foreign contaminants. As for a filtration challenge, a brief protocol should be written if this is elected.

During filling the cans with appropriate drug solution or suspension, any items not written in the batch directions, line setup, or other batch records should be reported during validation. For example, any special N_2 shroud assembling for environmental control or other devices for filling accuracy should be known.

In addition, during validation an entire group of cans may be isolated for each filling nozzle in between checkweighing intervals. For example if every 500th can is manually checkweighed, then a group of 500 cans should be separated and passed individually through the checkweigher to verify the in-between values. Also, the filling variation, such as standard deviation, should be calculated for each filling nozzle or piston. Relative standard deviations of less than 3% are considered acceptable, although values less than 1.5% should be a goal.

The type and amount of gas purged into the canister will be verified during validation. The location where this is done on the line is recorded, and the time before and after purging is known. The flow rate of the gas into the can as well as position inside the can is also known.

The method of valve placement after filling and equipment specifics must be documented.

a. *Crimping*. Since crimping is delicate and complicated, this step will require more attention than others [33]. The specific equipment, such as collet numbers, settings of pads, or downward head pressures, must be known. The details should be clearly spelled out in product setup documents, especially if different personnel are used among the validation batches. Several measurements are used to evaluate the valve crimp. Specifications for these measurements should be set along with acceptable leakage or weight loss data justifying these crimps and their measurements. Valve delivery such as that measured by spray weights should also be recorded to verify that the operation of the valve is not affected by the crimping step.

During validation batches, crimp measurements should be taken at specified intervals to ensure an acceptable and reproducible process step. Statistical sampling would be best, such as samples taken hourly during the duration of the batch. Alternatively, groups of 12 cans at the beginning, middle, and end of the batch may be done. This will ensure statistical equivalence throughout the batch. Pressure settings on the crimping equipment are to remain unchanged. Any change in settings will necessitate resampling and retesting to verify the new settings.

b. *Propellant filling.* Propellant filling must likewise specify the setup and any important quantitative values of this process step. Pressure testing verifies that the proper propellant is utilized. The type of equipment, such as cylinder and piston type, and size, injection head nozzle, O-ring specifics, and special features should be well known as for concentrate filling. Settings of downward pressure and injection pressure must conform. The propellant filling step should be individually validated as done for the concentrate filling. Control charts for propellant fill weights should be included in the validation batches. These will verify that specifications are met and adequate control limits have been determined. The process capability may also be determined from the individual weights.

c. *Checkweighing.* Checkweighing of all cans after the unit is crimped and filled must not be neglected. Type and orientation of cans, ranges set, speed of checkweighing, and an appropriate challenge of the accuracy of the checkweigher must be monitored. The type and line position of the checkweigher need to be verified. The weight ranges, zones, and can feed rate should be written. The number of rejects (high and low) should be part of the batch reconciliation documentation. After validation, a good grasp of the usual allowable rejects will be available. Any inconsistencies should be traced to the specific filler. The weight rejects may also be individually weighed on a sensitive balance to confirm the accuracy of the checkweigher. Cans for setting the checkweigher with heavy and light filled units are frequently used, as well as empty units for taring.

d. *Leak testing.* Leak testing, like checkweighing, will have its specified conditions that do not affect the product but similarly allow for inspection of faulty units. The temperature for the can and the duration must be described in the batch directions and confirmed during validation. Sometimes one may wish to know the temperature the product reaches. Thermocouples or temperature indicators may be used to assess this. All cans are leak tested to cull out any faulty units that may leak in the field. For example, submersion at 120°F for 3 minutes may be adopted, since the contents may approach that temperature after that time. The labeling and regulatory requirements (Department of Transportation) may best be applied here. A desired temperature should have a temperature range and time range. It must also be verified that this step does not alter the quality and stability of the dosage form.

Immediately after the test, the units may remain warm for a given period of time. The cans should not be further processed (spray testing) but should be allowed to cool to room temperature. Frequently, for small MDI units, 1/2 to 1 hour is usually sufficient.

3. Other Line Functions

Storage of the aerosol product after filling must be described in the batch records. Sometimes the cans are stored valve down (for seating the valve gaskets) or valve up to minimize exposure to leachables in the rubber componentry. The shipper description should be in the bill of materials packet.

Spray testing is a critical step to prevent continuous or no-fire units from reaching the customer. All units are tested during the filling operation or during the packaging operation. Process monitoring may encompass verifying the proper number of valve depressions for testing, challenging the method with intentionally faulty units, and establishing the normal expected reject rate for a given valve in the validated process. The number of depressions of the valve is more descriptive than the number of sprays. The first valve depression of a new unit is frequently a prime, nonspraying shot. The actuator used should be specified in the batch records. If a manual inspection system is utilized, proper training of operators must be conducted. Actuators should be used only for a given period of time before being replaced with new ones. A history of the particular valve's defects and frequency should be known before validation production-size batches begin.

Other functions such as can coding (lot numbers, line designation) must be considered a process step. Can coding is a means of identifying an unlabeled unit by lot number or code. It is usually done with an ink-jet labeler or similar device. Another coding system may differentiate between filling tracks (front, back) within one lot. For example, the back track may be marked with a small black mark to differentiate it, if needed, from the front track. These code marks are covered with the can label during that operation.

4. Cleaning Validation

Cleaning validation for the aerosol products should be similar to other cleaning protocols. In these products, however, swabs and rinses with CFCs are frequent after removing drug residues with the proper solvents. Solubility of the drug determines the type of solvent used to rinse the equipment. Detectable limits such as scans of rinse solvents need to be established in the cleaning program.

5. Microbiological and Personnel Requirements

Microbiological monitoring, as with RODAC or slit/agar plates of the filling or compounding areas, is conducted by some manufacturers, but this is not expected to be a crucial requirement if proper cleaning procedures are followed. CFCs products are well known to be free of microorganisms [45–48], despite the recent report of mold contamination [49]. Gowning requirements are usually normal garments for oral suspensions as a minimum. Clean room garb may not be required but may still be used because the practice minimizes particulates in the production area.

C. Storage of Drug Product

The manner in which cans are removed from the aerosol line and packaged into shipper boxes should be recorded. The orientation for storage before labeling (e.g., inverted or upright) should be specified.

A packaging bill of materials will describe all cartons, shippers, inserts, etc. Shipping tests in the final packages are usually a worthwhile evaluation. Sample packages (e.g., shippers) are shipped from location to location, simulating a shipment. Samples are tested and evaluated according to a shipping test protocol.

VI. TESTING PROTOCOL FOR MDIs

A. In-Process

Many tests may be done as in-process tests to monitor the process during filling. Some of these tests (e.g., pressure, spray weights) may also be done as finished-product tests in another laboratory. In-process tests can be presented to show consistency throughout the process. Examples are concentrate and propellant fill weight checks, crimp measurements (height, depth, radial), spray weights, pressure, environmental monitoring, 100% checkweighing, and 100% spray testing. Control charts may be established and used to present extensive in-process testing results. Figure 14 illustrates one example of concentrate assays analyzed during the filling operation.

B. Finished Product

An example of one finished-product testing protocol is shown in Table 8, and a short description of the test is given in the following list. The testing scheme depends on the specific product [50], the NDA tests, and historical development, clinical, and scale-up lots.

1. *Appearance.* Two types of examination are conducted for appearance: (1) proper valve, canister, actuator, and their assembly, and (2) residual contents of the unit after opening. This is usually accomplished by bringing the MDI canister to a low temperature for safe opening. Visual examination of the residual contents is conducted after the CFCs have evaporated.
2. *Identification.* The identity of the drug substance should be verified in the MDI. Two methods, such as high-performance liquid chromatography, thin-layer chromatography, infrared, or ultraviolet, are preferred, as for other new dosage forms. Extraction from the surfactant or other excipients may be required.
3. *Drug content (assay).* A whole-can assay that is determined analytically. Figure 15 shows a plot of finished-product assays on samples removed during manufacturing.
4. *Degradation products/impurities.* This test is typical for all dosage forms.

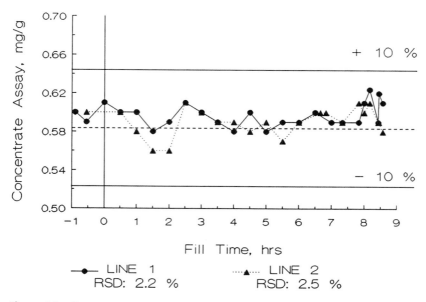

Figure 14 Concentrate drug assays during filling.

5. *Drug content uniformity*. This is usually a can-to-can uniformity test, typically done on at least 10 cans. It demonstrates consistent amounts of drug among all cans within a lot. The USP ⟨905⟩ is usually used unless there are individual NDA or USP monograph requirements.
6. *Unit spray content* (medication delivery). This is another content uniformity test performed on amounts (sprayed) delivered to the patient. This encompasses the uniformity within a can because partial amounts (a limited number of sprays) are utilized. Ideally, the number of actuations per assay should be approximately the same as the labeled dose.
7. *Extractables/leachables*. This test depends on the nature of the valve componentry and is primarily independent of process validation. It is conducted as a routine finished-product test.
8. *Water content*. This is usually a critical test. The amount of water has been known to influence drug crystallinity and stability. In most cases, the amount of water must be controlled by manufacturing conditions and sometimes raw material control. CFCs have saturable limits of water (for example 110 ppm, 0.011%, for Propellant 11) [16] from which phase separation is observed.
9. *Particle size distribution*. The active ingredient particle size must be controlled and monitored. Validation might show that control of the raw material

Table 8 Example of Finished Product Testing Protocol

Test	Beginning	Middle	End	Composite
1. Appearance				X
2. Identification				X
3. Drug content (assay)	X	X	X	X
4. Degradation/impurities				X
5. Drug content uniformity	X	X	X	X
6. Unit spray content (medication delivery)				X
7. Extractables/leachables				X
8. Water content	X	X	X	X
9. Particle size distribution	X	X	X	
10. Net fill weight	X	X	X	
11. Valve spray weights	X	X	X	
12. Leak testing	X	X	X	
13. Pressure testing	X	X	X	
14. Number of actuations			X	X
15. Spray pattern (plume)				X
16. Microbial limits			X	X
17. Other (alcohol content)				X

is sufficient, but careful evaluations of stressed manufacturing conditions must substantiate the effect on particle size. A number of methods (microscopy, cascade impactor, Malvern light scattering) are used for this test [51].

10. *Net fill weight.* Conducted to verify that the proper amount has been filled. This may be accomplished by either opening cans or, alternatively, using established tare values. The gross weight is determined for at least 30 cans, a representative population sampling.

11. *Valve spray weights.* This is determined to verify the proper valve, metering chamber, and functionality of the units. At least 30 cans should be sprayed. This test may be used in conjunction with a raw material (valve) release test.

12. *Leak testing.* This test is performed to determine the lot average weight loss or leakage as measured over time. Loss is due to leakage of CFCs through the valve seals. USP requirements are usually adopted. One product recall has occurred due to excessive leakage rates [52].

13. *Pressure testing.* This is carried out to verify the proper propellancy of the units and, if a mixture of CFCs was used, serves as a confirmatory measure of the proper ratio.

14. *Number of actuations.* This test is conducted to verify the proper functionality of the valve and that the crimping and aerosol line functions did not

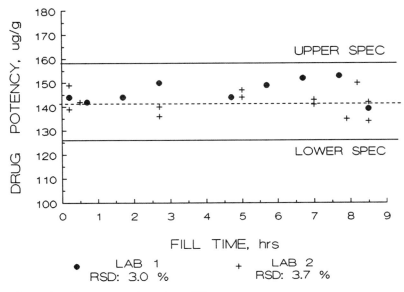

Figure 15 Drug assays throughout filling.

adversely effect the valve. The labeled number of actuations must be met both initially and from stability samples at expiration.

15. *Spray pattern* (plume). This test verifies the proper joining of the valve and mouthpiece and that assembling did not adversely affect the final performance of the unit. This test is more realistically a packaging-type test of the mouthpiece and valve.

16. *Microbial Limits*. This test is conducted as for most oral liquid preparations. Due to the nonaqueous nature of most formulations, this is rarely a problem.

17. *Other (alcohol content)*. Depending on the specific product, specific tests may be recommended. Examples are tests for alcohol, flavors, antioxidants, clathrates, and crystallinity.

VII. VALIDATION REPORT

A. Content

The validation report should contain the approved validation protocol, tabulated or graphical results, process monitoring (forms), and all analytical results of the validation batches. A copy of the batch records and raw material releases may be in the appendix, although this usually adds considerably to the size of the report.

The presentation of data should be spread out over many pages and easily understood and neat. Small tables of process conditions or data should be in one style that appears concise and is easily read. Stability data can be amended at a later date if desired. Special investigations or additional tests or retests may have to be explained in the report if deviations of any kind occurred.

The validation report should have a conclusion that explains the manufacturing specialist's (preparer's) statement and opinion. Appendices may be used to explain detailed equations (e.g., control chart statistics) or specific methods (e.g., spray delivery methods). Information that is included in the batch records may not have to be repeated but in some instances (e.g., crimp measurements) may be beneficial for presentation. The use of figures or graphs is strongly suggested because these plots may show some trends and insights from a large data base. Recommendations may also be made in the report, such as preparing more batches, amending certain tests, expanding batch directions, or creating alert limits.

The validation report should be approved prior to product distribution and kept permanently on file in quality assurance. Furthermore, production should not commence until the validation report is approved. The data in the report should serve as a foundation for future troubleshooting; i.e., they should be specific enough, along with the batch directions, for the process to be easily duplicated.

Any equipment qualification reports, such as filling equipment, crimper, checkweigher, homogenizer, or propellant gasser, should likewise be readily available if this is warranted.

B. Validation Costs

The cost of drug and preparing the validation batches could be a factor in the planning. For example, orphan drug status may allow a provision from the usual three-batch requirement. Nevertheless, the proper production batch size needs to be finalized with a market forecast. Once this is accomplished, validation should be done on a minimum of three production batch sizes or until manufacturing reproducibility is demonstrated.

C. Stability

Stability testing on all validation batches must be performed according to the protocol, according to the NDA stability plan.

VIII. POSTVALIDATION

The better and more comprehensive the validation program, the less likely that there will be a need to revalidate or that problems will surface. Invariably they do, however, and in these cases the more thorough the development history and validation testing/report, the easier will be a scientific investigation into the problem. With the MDI dosage form, it is best to revisit the validation testing from time to time, especially if production is infrequent or any changes whatsoever occur in the process.

An annual audit of the MDI process is beneficial. This would include a review of the batch record revisions and change procedures. Process changes should not be allowed without an assessment of the change and study of data as a result of the change.

REFERENCES

1. Kanig, J. L., Pharmaceutical aerosols, *J. Pharm. Sci.* 52:513–553 (1963).
2. Sciarra, J. J., Pharmaceutical and cosmetic aerosols, *J. Pharm. Sci.* 63:1815–1837 (1974).
3. *Physician's Desk Reference*, 45th ed., Medical Economics Co., Oradell, NJ (1991).
4. Porush, I., Pharmaceutical products. In *Aerosols: Science and Technology*. Shepherd, H. R. (ed.), Interscience, New York, pp. 387–408 (1961).
5. Pengilly, R. W., and Keiner, J. A., The influence of some formulation variables and valve actuator designs on the particle size distributions of aerosol sprays, *J. Soc. Cosmet. Chem.* 28:641–650 (1977).
6. Dobkin, A. B., *Ventilators and Inhalation Therapy*, 2nd ed., Little, Brown, Boston, p. 103 (1972).
7. Mitchell, R. I., Retention of aerosol particles in the respiratory tract, *Am. Rev. Respir. Dis.* 82:627–630 (1960).
8. Gonda, I., A semiempirical model of aerosol deposition in the human respiratory tract for mouth inhalation, *J. Pharm. Pharmacol.* 33:692–696 (1981).
9. Package inserts of marketed metered-dose inhalers.
10. Hallworth, G. W., The formulation and evaluation of pressurized metered-dose inhalers. In *Drug Delivery to the Respiratory Tract*, Gandeston, I., and Jones, I. (eds.), Ellis Horwood, Chichester, U.K., pp. 87–118 (1987).
11. Pharmaceutical Aerosol CFC Coalition, Technical Assessment, Terrance Coyne at International Conference on CFC, Washington, DC (October 11, 1989).
12. Starr, C., Incidence of asthma on new growth swing among Americans, *Drug Topics* 133(18):37 (1989).
13. Polli, G. P., Grim, W. M., Bacher, F. A., and Yunker, M. H., Influence of formulation on aerosol particle size, *J. Pharm. Sci.* 58:484–486 (1969).
14. Hallworth, G. W., and Padfield, J. M., Comparison of the regional deposition in a model nose of a drug discharged from metered-aerosol and metered-dose nasal delivery systems, *J. Allergy Clin. Immunol.* 77(2):348–353 (1986).
15. Physical Tests and Determinations, ⟨601⟩ Aerosols, In-Process Revision, *Pharm. Forum* 18(2):3158–3174 (1992).
16. Freon® Fluorocarbons, Properties and Application, Brochure G-1, Wilmington, DE 19898.
17. Gorman, W. G., Popp, K. F., Hunke, W. A., and Miriani, E. P., Process validation of aerosol products, *Aerosol Age* 32(3):24–28 (1987).

18. Sullivan, D. A., International gathering plans ways to safeguard atmospheric ozone, *Chem. Eng. News 67*(26):33–35 (1989).

19. Dalby, R. N., Byron, P. R., Shepherd, H. R., and Papadopoulos, E., CFC propellant substitution: P134a as a potential replacement for P12 in MDIs, *Pharmaceut. Technol. 14*(3):26,28,30,32–33 (1990).

20. *The Pink Sheet 52*(25):9–10 (June 18, 1990). Brandname and generic bronchodilators: Composition changes should be tested for unexpected adverse events, FDA's Pulmonary-Allergy Panel Recommends. F-D-C Reports, Chevy Chase, MD.

21. Cutie, A., Burger, J., Clawans, C., Dolinsky, D., Feinstein, W., Gupta, B., Grueneberg, A., and Sciarra, J., Test for reproducibility of metered-dose aerosol values for pharmaceutical solutions, *J. Pharm. Sci. 70*:1085–1087 (1981).

22. Fiese, E. F., Gorman, W. G., Dolinsky, D., Harwood, R. J., Hunke, W. A., Miller, N. C., Mintzer, H., and Harper, N. J., Test method for evaluation of loss of prime in metered-dose aerosols, *J. Pharm. Sci. 72*:90–93 (1988).

23. Cyr, T. D., and Graham, S. J., Low first-spray drug content in albuterol metered-dose inhalers, *Pharm. Res. 8*:658–660 (1991).

24. Haywood, P. A., Martin-Smith, M., Padfield, J. M., Smith, L. J., and Woodhouse, R. N., Establishing more meaningful specifications and tests for metered-dose pressurized inhalers formulated as suspensions, *Pharm. Forum 15*(3):5193–5202 (May-June 1989).

25. Hopkins, J. L., Cohen, K. A., Hatch, F. W., Pitner, K. P., Stevenson, J. M., and Hess, F. K., Pharmaceuticals, *Anal. Chem. 59*:785–790 (1987).

26. Beard, W. C., Valves. In *Aerosols: Science and Technology*, Shepherd, H. R. (ed.), Interscience, New York, pp. 119–211 (1961).

27. Benjamin, E. J., Kroeten, J. J., and Shek, E., Characterization of spray patterns of inhalation aerosols using thin-layer chromatography, *J. Pharm. Sci. 72*:380–385 (1983).

28. Miszuk, S., Gupta, B. M., Chen, F. C., Clawans, C., and Knapp, J. Z., Video characterization of flume patterns of inhalation aerosols, *J. Pharm. Sci. 69*:713–717 (1980).

29. Dhand, R., Malik, S. K., Balakrishnan, M., and Verma, S. R., High speed photographic analysis of aerosols produced by metered dose inhalers, *J. Pharm. Pharmacol. 40*:429–430 (1988).

30. *The Pink Sheet 49*(44):T&G 11 (November 2, 1987). Recall actions. F-D-C Reports, Chevy Chase, MD.

31. Cutie, A., Ertefaie, S., and Sciarra, J. J., Aerosolized drug delivery accessories, *Aerosol Age 29*(3):24–25,47 (March 1984).

32. Sanders, P. A., *Handbook of Aerosol Technology*, 2nd ed., Van Nostrand Reinhold, New York, pp. 25–29, 116–125 (1979).

33. Haase, F. D., Techniques of crimping and clinching, an overview, *Aerosol Age 32*(1):21–24 (1987).

34. Grieves, I. J., and Starkey, A. J., Report on the results of a joint crimp depth study, *Aerosol Age 27*(4):21–30 (1982).

35. Induction heating tests aerosols in pharmaceutical operation, *Aerosol Age 27*(1):14–17 (1982).

36. Has Pamasol dumped the water bath? *Aerosol Age* 27(6):22–25 (1982).

37. Mintzer, H., Scale-up and production considerations for therapeutic aerosols, *Aerosol Age* 30(3):22–24 (1985).

38. Pharmaceutical Manufacturer's Association. The production and quality control of metered-dose inhalers (MDIs), *Pharm. Forum* 11(6):934–940 (November-December 1985).

39. Miller, N. C., Schultz, R. K., and Schachtner, W. J., Through-life dose uniformity in pressurized metered dose inhalers, *Pharm. Res.* 7(9, Suppl):S-88 (1990).

40. Ranucci, J. A., Dixit, S., Bray, R. N., and Goldman, Controlled flocculation in metered-dose aerosol suspensions, *Pharmaceut. Technol.* 14(4):68,70–72,74 (1990).

41. Schultz, R. K., Miller, N. K., and Christensen, J. D., Method for evaluation of suspension characteristics relevant to metered dose inhaler formulations, *Pharm. Res.* 7(9, Suppl):S-88 (1990).

42. Graham, S. J., Ormsby, E. D., Cyr, T. D., and Lovering, E. G., "Comparison of two apparatuses for collecting single sprays from metered-dose inhalers (MDIs)," Pharmaceutical Sciences Group 3rd Annual Technical Conference, Alliston, Ontario (October 1991).

43. Guideline on General Principles of Process Validation. Center for Drugs and Biologics and Center for Devices and Radiological Health, Food and Drug Administration, p. 4 (May 1987).

44. Miller, N. C., Scale-up of manufacturing process for metered-dose inhalers. In *Proceedings of Second Annual Respiratory Drug Delivery Symposium*, Dalby, R. W., and Evans, R. (eds.), Vol. 2, Armstrong Pharmaceuticals, New Canaan, CT, University of Kentucky Lexington, KY (March 28, 1990).

45. Brinkley, M. A., Johnson, K., and Roberts, W. L., Determination of the survivability of microorganisms in a pharmaceutical aerosol formulation as a function of water concentration, *Pharm. Res.* 7(suppl):S-6 (1990).

46. Van Auken, O. W., Healy, J., and Kaufmann, A. J., Comparison of the effects of three fluorocarbons on certain bacteria, *Can. J. Microbiol.* 21:221–226 (1975).

47. Prior, B. A., Fennema, O., and Pate, J., Effect of dichlorodifluoromethane on the appearance, viability, and integrity of *Escherichia coli*, *Appl. Microbiol.* 29(5):685–691 (1975).

48. Stretton, R. J., Gretton, W. R., and Watson-Walker, J., The effect of halocarbon aerosol propellants on bacteria, *J. Appl. Bacteriol.* 34(4):773–777 (1971).

49. Schering-Plough Research's response to FDA-483 observations, letter dated June 21, 1990, p. 13. Obtained through the Freedom of Information Act.

50. Chowhan, Z. T., Casey, D. L., Byron, P. R., Kelly, E. L., Chandry, I., Lovering, E. G., Vadas, E., Thiel, C. G., Barnstein, C. H., and Srinivasas, V., Report and recommendations of the USP advisory panel on aerosols on the USP General Chapter ⟨601⟩ on aerosols, *Pharm. Forum* 17(2):1703–1713 (March-April 1991).

51. Atkins, P. J. (ed.), Particle size of metered dose inhalers, current methodologies. In *Proceedings of Second Annual Respiratory Drug Delivery Symposium*, Dalby, R. W., and Evans, R. (eds.), Vol. 2, Armstrong Pharmaceuticals, New Canaan, CT, University of Kentucky, Lexington, KY (March 28, 1990).

52. *The Pink Sheet* 51(45):T&G 17 (November 6, 1989). Recall Actions. F-D-C Reports, Chevy Chase, MD.

17

Analysis of Retrospective Production Data Using Quality Control Charts

Peter H. Cheng *New York State Research Foundation for Mental Hygiene, New York, New York*

John E. Dutt *EM Industries, Inc., Hawthorne, New York*

I. INTRODUCTION

In industry, because of in-house demands and GMP requirements, the acquisition and subsequent retention of in-process and final-product data are necessary. For example, before releasing a product, many pertinent tests are performed on product batches to ensure that active ingredients and essential product attributes meet desired specifications. Data from such pertinent tests, accumulated over time, are often called historical, or retrospective, data.

In this chapter, several types of control charts for the analysis of historical data are discussed. Explanations of the use of $\bar{x}$ and $\bar{R}$ charts, for both two or more measurements per batch and only one measurement per batch, are give, along with explanations of modified control charts and cusum charts. Starting with a brief exposition on the calculation of simple statistics, the construction and graphic analysis of $\bar{x}$ and $\bar{R}$ charts are demonstrated. The concepts of "under control" and "out of control," as well as their relationship to test specifications, are included. The chapter concludes with consideration of the question of robustness of $\bar{x}$ and $\bar{R}$ charts.

Much of the discussion here stems from experience with quality control charts in the pharmaceutical industry. For the use of quality control charts in other industries, the following requirement established by the Nuclear Regulatory Commission [1] may be useful.

The licensee shall establish and maintain a statistical control system including control charts and formal statistical procedures, designed to monitor the quality of each type of program measurement. Control chart limits shall be established to be equivalent to levels of (statistical) significance of 0.05 and 0.001. Whenever control data exceed the 0.05 control limits, the licensee shall investigate the condition and take corrective action in a timely manner. The results of these investigations and actions shall be recorded. Whenever the control data exceed the 0.001 control limits, the measurement system which generated the data shall not be used for control purposes until the deficiency has been brought into control at the 0.05 level.

II. SIMPLE STATISTICS

Consider the following example in which a batch of drug D has been assayed four times, with the following potencies reported: 46.2, 44.4, 44.9, and 43.8. An *estimate of the overall potency* is obtained by calculating the *mean*, or *average*, of these four values. Using the notation $\bar{x}$ for the mean, $\bar{x} = 44.825$. The value $\bar{x}$ is an estimate of the batch's true potency, which is symbolized by μ.

The *range* and *standard deviation* are two simple statistics for expressing the amount of variability or "scatter" of the four potencies. The range is easier to compute because it is the difference between the maximum and minimum values. Using $\bar{R}$ for the range, $\bar{R} = 46.2 - 43.8 = 2.4$. The standard deviation, symbolized by s, is not as easy to compute, and its formula is presented later. For the four potency values, $s = 1.021$. The value s is an *estimate of variability*, of the assay-measuring process. The *true standard deviation* is noted by σ.

These computations give an estimate of the batch's potency and indicate the variability of data within a batch. A complete analysis consists of computing the estimated potencies of all batches, as well as the variability of the batches' data values.

Because there are not always four measurements per batch, the following notation is presented to facilitate the generalization to any number of assays per batch:

n = total number of data (assay) values per batch

x_i = ith data value, where i ranges from 1 to n

$\sum x_i = (x + \cdots + x_n)$ = sum of all data values

x_{max} = largest data value

x_{min} = smallest data value

With this notation, the simple statistics take the form

$$\text{Mean } \bar{x} = \frac{\sum x_i}{n}$$

$$\text{Range } R = x_{max} - x_{min}$$

$$\text{Standard deviation } s = \sqrt{\frac{\Sigma (x_i - \bar{x})^2}{(n-1)}}$$

$$= \sqrt{\frac{\{(\Sigma x_i^2) - n(\bar{x})^2\}}{(n-1)}}$$

The second expression for the standard deviation is usually computationally easier. The term Σx_i^2 is calculated by squaring each data value and then summing all the values up to n.

Initially it will be assumed that the *variation of the measurement* around the true batch potency follows a normal distribution. This assumption means that if the same batch were repeatedly assayed, the data values would be distributed in a symmetric bell-shaped curve as in Fig. 1. Most values would be clustered near the center (true potency), with some extreme values lying farther away. In theory, 68.2% of the data values would be found between $\mu - \sigma$ and $\mu + \sigma$, 95.4% of the values would be between $\mu - 2\sigma$ and $\mu + 2\sigma$, and 99.7% of the values would be within the range $\mu - 3\sigma$ to $\mu + 3\sigma$.

For example, suppose a batch was known to have a true potency $\mu = 101$ and that the assay has a variability expressed as $\sigma = 2$. Then 68.2% of the future assay values would be expected between $101 - 2 = 99$ and $101 + 2 = 103$, 95.4% of

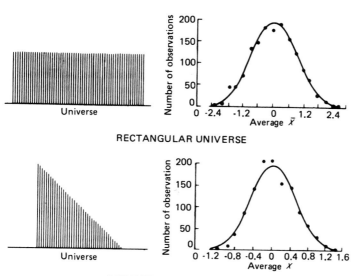

Figure 1   Even from rectangular and triangular universes, the distribution of $\bar{x}$ values from samples of four is approximately normal.

the values would be between 97 and 105, and 99.7% of the values would be between 95 and 107.

III. QUALITY CONTROL (QC) CHARTS

I. $\bar{x}$ and R charts (for at least two measurements per batch).
  A.   Construction (for at least two measurements per batch) [2–4]. It is reasonable to assume that at least 20 batches are available in a retrospective study. Suppose at least two measurements were obtained from each batch. In terms of the previous notation, assume n is greater than or equal to 2.
    1.   For each batch, calculate the mean $\bar{x}$ and range $\bar{R}$. Sometimes for historical data, only the mean, high, and low values are recorded.
    2.   Construct two graphs. In the first graph, plot the batch means versus batch number or any other similar ordering variable denoting time, such as week or month. In the second graph, plot the batch ranges versus the same batch number of other similar variable used for the first graph.
    3.   Calculate $\bar{\bar{x}}$, which is the average of all the batch means, and $\bar{R}$, which is the average of all the ranges. Draw a solid horizontal line for $\bar{\bar{x}}$ on the $\bar{x}$ graph, and do the same for $\bar{R}$ on the R graph.
    4.   Calculate the control limits as follows:

	$\bar{x}$ chart	R chart
UCL (upper control limit)	$\bar{\bar{x}} + A_2\bar{R}$	$D_4\bar{R}$
LCL (lower control limit)	$\bar{\bar{x}} - A_2\bar{R}$	$D_3\bar{R}$

Values of A_2, D_3, and D_4 for different values of n, the number of measurements per batch, are given below:

n	A_2	D_3	D_4	n	A_2	D_3	D_4
2	1.880	0	3.267	7	0.419	0.076	1.924
3	1.023	0	2.575	8	0.373	0.136	1.864
4	0.729	0	2.282	9	0.337	0.184	1.816
5	0.577	0	2.115	10	0.308	0.228	1.777
6	0.483	0	2.004				

For $n > 10$, A_2, D_3, and D_4 can be found in standard texts, for example, Ref. [2].

5. Draw dotted horizontal lines for the UCL and LCL on $\bar{x}$ and R charts, respectively.

Example: Suppose there are 50 batches of retrospective data, with two potency values recorded for each batch. How would the $\bar{x}$ and R charts be constructed?

First, calculate mean $\bar{x}$ and range R for each batch. Because there are two values per batch, the range is the difference between each pair of values, with a positive sign in front of each difference.

These calculations give 50 $\bar{x}$ values and 50 R values. The averages of each set of these values form $\bar{\bar{x}}$ and $\bar{R}$, respectively. Suppose $\bar{\bar{x}} = 105$ and $\bar{R} = 2$. Plot the 50 calculated $\bar{x}$'s and R's on two different graphs, and draw the horizontal lines for $\bar{\bar{x}} = 105$ and $\bar{R} = 2$. With $n = 2$, $A_2 = 1.88$, $D_3 = 0$, and $D_4 = 3.267$, the control limits for the $\bar{x}$ chart are:

$$\text{UCL} = 105 + (1.880)2 = 108.76$$
$$\text{LCL} = 105 - (1.880)2 = 101.24$$

Similarly, limits for the R chart are:

$$\text{UCL} - (3.267)2 = 6.334$$
$$\text{LCL} = (0)2 = 0$$

These control limits are particularly useful to identify any points that exceed the limits.

B. Discussion. When control charts are employed for process control, two sets of control limits are frequently used: $\bar{\bar{x}} \pm A_2\bar{R}$ (action limits) and $\bar{\bar{x}}T \pm 2/3\, A_2\bar{R}$ (warning limits). When the process exceeds the action limits, corrective steps are necessary. When the process exceeds only the warning limits, the user is alerted that the process may be malfunctioning.

The results of the construction of the $\bar{x}$ and R charts may resemble the top two graphs in Figs. 2–6. The points in Fig. 2 show little evidence of trends (i.e., a rising, falling, and rising distribution of points). In such a situation, the process is said to be *in control*.

Some indicators that a process has not been in control in the past are:

1. Two or more consecutive points on the $\bar{x}$ or R charts fall outside control limits.

2. Eight or more consecutive points on the $\bar{x}$ or R charts fall on the same side of the central line, even if none of the points exceed the control limits.

3. When the batch mean exceeds its control limits, but its corresponding range does not exceed its limits, this suggests the process may

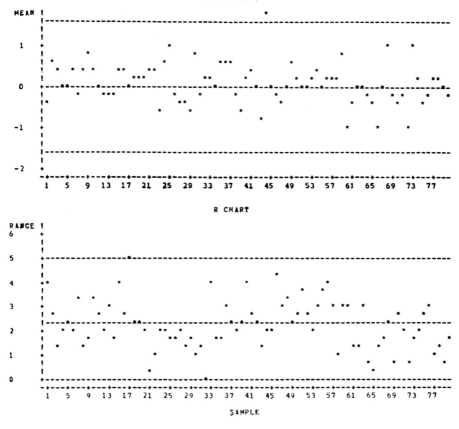

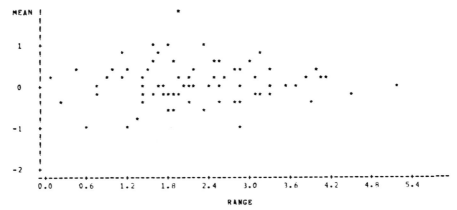

Figure 2 Normal distribution.

534

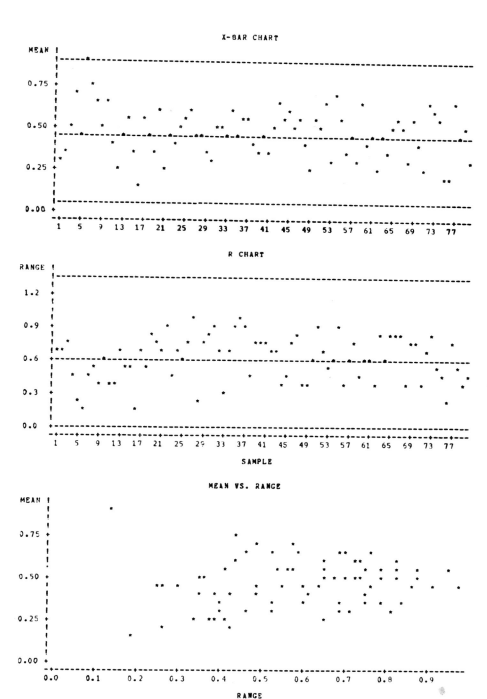

Figure 3 Uniform distribution.

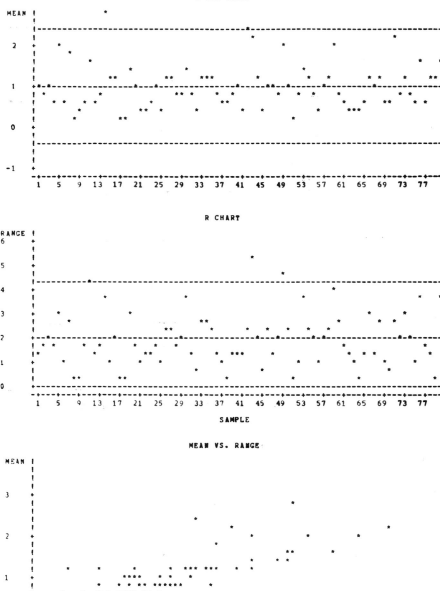

Figure 4 Exponential distribution.

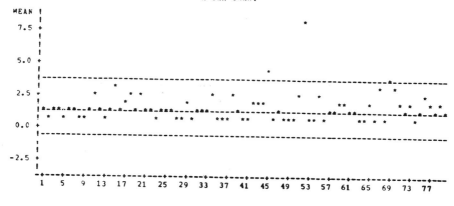

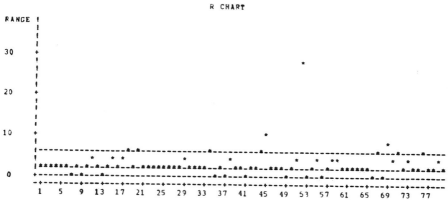

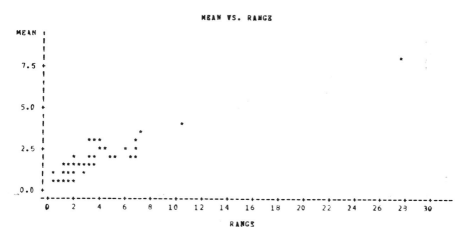

Figure 5 Lognormal distribution.

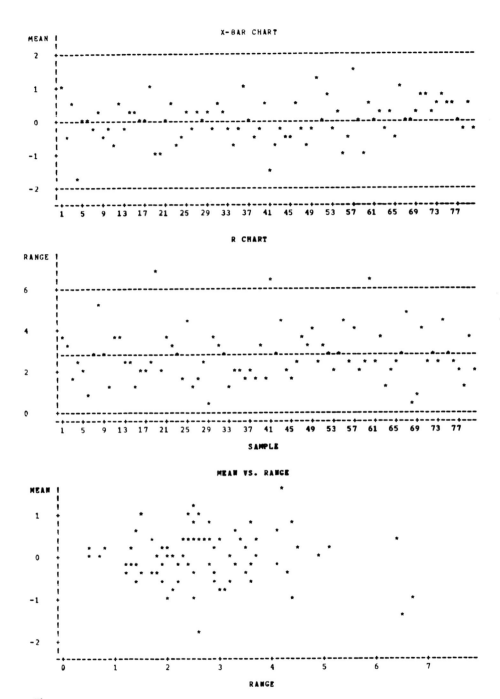

Figure 6 Double exponential distribution.

be operating on a new mean level or the level of the process has shifted.

In contrast, when the batch mean is within its control limits, sometimes operator carelessness or local disturbances not related to the machine setting or process may be the cause. A cluster of $\bar{x}$ or R values outside the control limits has real significance, because it indicates a pervasive influence.

It is not uncommon for a product batch to be assayed at several stages in processing (e.g., as raw material after mixing, after drying, and as finished product). If the retrospective data exist, then control charts should be set up for each stage, using batch number as the horizontal variable on the $\bar{x}$ and R charts. Matching the different stage charts with the common batch numbers affords the opportunity to examine how well the process is in control at each stage. If each stage is judged to be in control, it is reasonable to conclude that the entire process is in control. If, however, some stages are not in control while others are, questions about the validity of the process are raised.

When specifications are set for individual testing results, it is misleading and meaningless to plot them on $\bar{x}$ charts. However, when specifications are set for the sample average $\bar{x}$, or when individual specifications and control charts for one measurement per batch are used, it is advantageous to include them on the $\bar{x}$ chart. In fact, whether under control or not, a process can either meet the specifications or not. Below are the four possible actions to be taken in each of the four situations.

a. Process in control and specifications met.
   i. No change is required.
   ii. Skip-lot (batch) test can be instituted.
b. Process in control but specifications failed.
   i. 100% inspection.
   ii. Fundamental change in the production process.
   iii. Change specifications.
c. Process out of control but specifications met. Investigate the process to identify and remove assignable causes for out-of-control occasions.
d. Process out of control and specifications failed. Similar to item c, but prompt investigation is mandatory.

In the analysis of retrospective data, the use of $\bar{x}$ and R charts has advantages and disadvantages. If no data points exceed the $\bar{x}$ or R control limits, then it is reasonable to say the process has been in control and that the standard operating procedures are fulfilling their functions. While not explicitly discussed here, data obtained from new batches can be plotted on new $\bar{x}$ and R charts using the same control limits. This new plotted data can help to warn the operator when the process is close to being or is out of control.

      If control limits were exceeded in the past, however, corrective action now can hardly be taken. If control limits were frequently exceeded, it may be worthwhile to institute a search for an assignable cause, or causes. The necessary data may not exist, or no reasonable cause may be found. In such cases, maintaining control charts for new batches will probably be more effective in identifying perturbing influences on the process.

II. $\bar{x}$ and R charts (for one measurement per batch).

   A.   Frequently only one record per batch is available. While a range for any batch cannot be computed, the control limits for the $\bar{x}$ chart depend on finding $\bar{R}$. The procedure for constructing $\bar{x}$ and R charts needs to be modified and is described below in stepwise fashion, using an example.

      1.   Suppose 30 batch values are recorded, one potency result per batch. Let these values be written as $x_1, x_2, \ldots, x_{30}$. The mean for each batch is simply $\bar{\bar{x}} = (\Sigma\, x_i)/30$.

      2.   Form the values $x_2 = x_1$, $x_3 - x_2, \ldots, x_{30} - x_{29}$, and take the absolute value of each difference.

      3.   Calculate the mean of these 29 values and call the result $\overline{MR}$ (for moving range).

      4.   Calculate the control limits as follows:

	$\bar{x}$ chart	R chart
UCL	$\bar{\bar{x}} + 1.88\overline{MR}$	$3.267\overline{MR}$
LCL	$\bar{\bar{x}} + 1.88\overline{MR}$	0

Using $n = 2$, the values of $A_2 = 1.88$, $D_3 = 0$, and $D_4 = 3.267$, are taken from the table under item d in Section I.

III.   Modified Charts.

   Here is discussed the situation in which the R chart shows that the within-batch variation is under control, but the $\bar{x}$ chart suggests the between-batch variation is out of control. When the specifications are wise, a modified control chart can be employed. Example: In the following, each batch has two determinations. The upper specification for an individual determination is 15 mg/g. (Lower specification can be considered similarly.)

Batch	Determinations		Mean	Range
	1	2		
1	7.3	7.3	7.2	0.2
2	9.7	9.5	9.6	0.2
3	3.2	3.0	3.1	0.2
4	10.2	10.4	10.3	0.2
5	5.3	5.1	5.2	0.2
Average			7.08	0.2

The upper control limits would be $7.08 \pm A_2(0.2) = 7.08 + (1.88)(0.2) = 7.46$. Concerns over batches 2 and 4 arise naturally. The modified control chart calls for the use of $15 - (\sqrt{2} - 1)(1.88)(0.2) = 14.2$ as the UCL and thus eliminates the questions over batches 2 and 4. In the application of process validations, these situations are frequently encountered, and modified control charts enable us to claim the validation of the process.

IV. Cusum charts.

A cumulative sum (or cusum) chart is a type of control chart that can detect changes in process average more powerfully than an $\bar{x}$ chart. A reference value K is chosen. K can be the process target value, historical average, or any convenient value. As new values $x_1, \ldots, x_n$ are observed, the cumulative sums

$$S_\tau = \sum_{i=1}^{\tau} (x_i - K)$$

are calculated and plotted sequentially. Note $S_1 = x_1 - K, S_2 = x_1 + x_2 - 2K$, $S_3 = x_1 + x_2 + x_3 - 3K$, etc. The important characteristic of cusum charts is the slope of the cumulative sums S_τ. If the process is at some level μ which is larger than K, each new cumulative sum will be $\mu - K$ units larger than the previous sum (except for random variation). The cusum chart will show a steadily increasing sequence of sums.

If the process shifts to a new mean μ^* which is less than μ, and sums will tend to decrease promptly. The slope will change, and this change in slope informs the user that the process level has changed.

Example: Table 1 gives an example of using a cusum chart for manufacturing data. The slope of cumulative sums changes for the sums formed from batch 103, suggesting that the process operated at a lower mean level.

Table 1 Product X Data (Target $K = 11.971$)

PRODUCT X DATA -- TARGET K = 11.971

BATCH	PART	SAMPLE	MEAN	MEAN_K	CUSUM
100	A	1	11.9915	0.02050	0.02050
		2	12.1317	0.16075	0.18125
		3	11.9759	0.00487	0.18612
		4	12.0368	0.06580	0.25192
		5	12.1227	0.15175	0.40367
	B	1	12.1320	0.16100	0.56467
		2	12.1742	0.20325	0.76792
		3	12.1537	0.18270	0.95062
		4	12.1114	0.14037	1.09100
		6	12.0647	0.09375	1.18475
		7	12.1345	0.16350	1.34825
101	A	1	12.1029	0.13187	1.48012
		2	12.0712	0.10025	1.58037
		3	12.0901	0.11912	1.69950
		4	12.1441	0.17312	1.87262
		5	12.1087	0.13775	2.01037
	B	1	12.0970	0.12600	2.13637
		2	12.0891	0.11812	2.25450
		3	12.0694	0.09837	2.35287
		4	11.9731	0.00212	2.35500
		5	12.1049	0.13387	2.48887
102	A	1	12.0490	0.07800	2.56687
		2	12.1279	0.15687	2.72375
		3	12.0687	0.09770	2.82145
		4	12.1406	0.16962	2.99107
		5	12.1351	0.16412	3.15520
	B	1	11.9925	0.02150	3.17670
		2	12.0614	0.09037	3.26707
		3	11.9881	0.01712	3.28420
		4	12.0017	0.03075	3.31495
		5	12.0285	0.05750	3.37245
		6	12.0214	0.05037	3.42282
		7	12.0025	0.03150	3.45432
103	A	1	11.6545	-0.31650	3.13782
		2	11.9680	-0.00300	3.13482
		3	11.7564	-0.21463	2.92020
		4	11.9781	0.00712	2.92732
		5	11.9026	-0.06838	2.85895
		6	11.9307	-0.04025	2.81870
	B	1	11.9219	-0.04913	2.76957
		2	11.9481	-0.02288	2.74670
		3	11.9085	-0.06250	2.68420
		4	11.9047	-0.06625	2.61795
104	A	1	12.0265	0.05550	2.67345
		2	12.0207	0.04975	2.72320
		3	12.0357	0.06475	2.78795
		4	12.0337	0.06275	2.85070
		5	12.0397	0.06875	2.91945
		7	12.0146	0.04362	2.96307
		8	12.0762	0.10525	3.06832
	B	1	12.0726	0.10162	3.16995
		2	12.0781	0.10712	3.27707
		3	12.2047	0.23375	3.51082
		4	12.0022	0.03125	3.54207

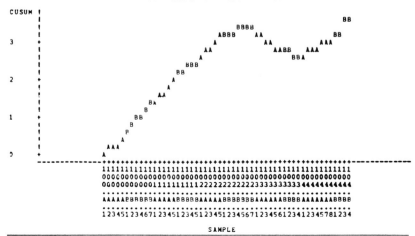

CUSUM CHART FOR PRODUCT X DATA

IV. ROBUSTNESS OF $\bar{x}$ AND R CHARTS

The factors A_2, D_3, and D_4 used in the construction of $\bar{x}$ and R charts were derived from the assumption that all the retrospective data follow a normal distribution. However, random variation occurs in other nonsymmetrical forms. The term *robustness* refers to the extent to which the charts are still useful when the random variation of retrospective data is not normal.

For comparison, five types of random variations, following distribution forms of normal, uniform, exponential, log-normal, and double exponential, are presented in Figs. 7A–E, respectively. It is not as important to know the algebraic forms of these curves as it is to appreciate the distinct differences among them in appearance.

So, what happens if the random variation of the retrospective data is not normal, but has some other distributional form? Are $\bar{x}$ and R charts useful in such a situation? The $\bar{x}$ chart is probably useful, but the R chart is not.

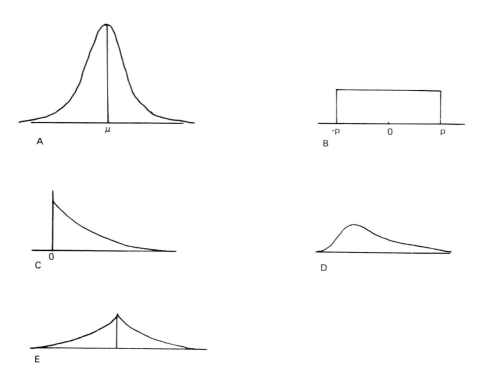

Figure 7 (A) Normal distribution (mean $= \mu$, std. dev. $= \sigma$). (B) Uniform distribution (mean $= 0$, std. dev. $= p^2/3$). (C) Exponential distribution. (D) Lognormal distribution. (E) Double exponential distribution.

1. $\bar{x}$ *charts*. Even if the number of measurements per batch is as small as four and the random variation is not normally distributed, the distribution of the mean of the four will be reasonably normal, so $\bar{x}$ charts would still be meaningful. Shewhart demonstrated this with distribution of means of 1000 simulated "batches" of four observations each. The true random densities were uniform (rectangular) and triangular (see Fig. 1), but the distribution of the average of four nearly follow the normal curve.

2. *R charts*. Many published studies [5–7] show that for small sample sizes per batch the factors D_3 and D_4 used in setting control limits are not much changed for nonnormal random variation. For large sample sizes, the calculated control limits are no longer reliable for nonnormal random variation, therefore, one should be cautious about R charts based on large sample sizes, unless it is known that the random variation is normally distributed. Unfortunately, one seldom knows that the true distribution is normal.

As an example, 80 "batches" with four observations per "batch" were each simulated for the following random variation forms: normal, uniform, exponential, lognormal, and double exponential (see Fig. 7A–E). $\bar{x}$ and R charts were constructed for each set as if the true random variation were normal. The charts appear in Figs. 2–6. The results appear in Table 2. This table shows that roughly the same number of points falls outside the $\bar{x}$ control limits, regardless of the form of the random variation. However, the lognormal distribution has many more R values outside the control limits than the other four distributions. The operator of the process would mistakenly think this process was frequently out of control. The R chart shows greater susceptibility to nonnormality in the random error structure.

Figures 2–6 also illustrate a method for checking the assumption of random errors forming a normal distribution. $\bar{x}$ is plotted versus R at the bottom of each figure. These graphs show different forms for the different distributions. Most of the points from the normal, uniform, and double exponential distributions form an essentially horizontal elliptical shape. For the exponential and lognormal distributions, the points form tilted elongated ellipses because of the heavy "tails" in these distributions. If a plot of $\bar{x}$ versus R shows a tilted elliptical shape, then the assumption of normality is not reasonable. Horizontal elliptical shapes do not prove normality, but they do suggest the random errors are equally likely to be

Table 2 Number of Points Outside Control Limits

	Normal	Uniform	Exponential	Lognormal	Double exponential
$\bar{x}$ chart	1	1	2	3	0
R chart	1	0	3	10	3

positive or negative. In such cases, probably little harm will be done in using the assumption of normality. More details are in Appendix I. These figures need a large number of historical batch records but can be very useful when the records contain mean, high, or low only.

APPENDIX I.   DISCUSSIONS RELATED TO TABLE 1 AND THE $\bar{x}$ VS. R PLOT IN FIGS. 2–6

1.   Normal distribution, $N(0, 1)$, with density function $\phi(x) = \exp(-x^2/2)/\sqrt{2\pi}$.
   a.   Sample mean $\bar{x}$ and range R are independently distributed, statistically (see Fig. 3).
   b. $E(R) = d_2 = 2.059$ as in [6].
2.   Uniform distribution, $U(0, 1)$, with density function $f(x) = 1$ for $0 \leqslant x \leqslant 1$.
   a.   Variance $= 1/12 = (0.2887)^2$.
   b. $ER = (n - 1)/(n + 1)$
   c. $d_2 = \sqrt{12} \, (1 - 2/(n + 1)) \uparrow \sqrt{12} = 3.46$ as $n \to \infty$.
   d. x and R are not independently distributed but $E(\bar{x}R) = E\bar{x}ER$.
   e.   The mode of the joint distribution $(\bar{x}, R)$ is $(n/2, n/2(n - 1))$, which is $(1/2, 2/3)$ for $n = 4$, in agreement with Fig. 4.
3.   Exponential distribution with density e^{-x} for $x \geqslant 0$.
   a. $ER = \sum\limits_{k=1}^{n-1} 1/k$.

   b.   The simple inequality $\bar{x} \geqslant R/n$ gives the lower boundary in Fig. 4.
4.   Lognormal distribution with density $\phi(\log t)/t$ for $t > 0$ with $\phi(t)$ as defined in item 1.
   a.   Variance $= e^2 - e = 4.671 = (2.161)^2$.
   b.   The same boundary as in item 3b holds.
   c. $ER = n \int_0^\infty \phi(t)(e^t - e^{-t})(\phi^m(t) - \phi^m(-t)) \, dt$, where $m = n - 1$ and $\phi(x) = \int_{-\infty}^X \Phi(t) \, dt$. for $n = 4$ utilizing subroutine for $\Phi(x)$ in IMSL (International Mathematical and Statistical Library), 16-point Gaussian quadrature gives $ER = 3.189977$ and 20-point gives 3.189989.
5.   Double exponential with density $\int (x) = \tfrac{1}{2}e^{-|x|}$ for $-\infty \leqslant x \leqslant \infty$.
   a.   Variance $= 2$.

   b. $Er = 2\left[\sum\limits_{k=1}^{n}(1 - 2^{-k})/k\right] - \dfrac{1}{n2^{n-1}}$. For $n = 4$, $ER = 133/48$ and $d_2 = ER/\sqrt{2} = 1.959275$.

   In Appendix II, another frequently mentioned quantity, $d_2 = ER/\sigma$, is presented for $n = 2(2)20$ for all five distributions. d_2 and A_2 are related by the formula $A_2 d_2 = 3/\sqrt{n}$. Table 3 gives only the case for sample size $n = 4$.

APPENDIX II. $d_2 = ER/\sigma$ VALUES FOR FIVE DISTRIBUTIONS

Sample size n	Normal	Uniform		Exponential		Lognormal		Double exponential	
	(1) $d_2 = ER/\sigma$	(2) ER/σ	(2)/(1)	(3) ER/σ	(3)/(1)	(4)[a] ER/σ	(4)/(1)	(5)[a] ER/σ	(5)/(1)
2,	1.238380	1.154701	1.023326	1.000000	0.8862263	0.7941517	0.7037981	1.060660	0.9399849
4,	2.058750	2.078461	1.009574	1.833333	0.8905050	1.476028	0.7169537	1.959275	0.9516819
6,	2.534410	2.474358	0.9763054	2.283333	0.9009329	1.898555	0.7491112	2.483713	0.9799964
8,	2.847200	2.694301	0.9462986	2.593857	0.9106691	2.220070	0.7797381	2.863243	1.005635
10,	3.077510	2.834265	0.9209604	2.828968	0.9192393	2.484310	0.8072466	3.161907	1.027424
12,	3.258460	2.931163	0.8995546	3.019877	0.9267805	2.710700	0.8318961	3.409341	1.045997
14,	3.406760	3.002221	0.8812542	3.180134	0.9334775	2.910134	0.8542233	3.618145	1.062049
16,	3.531980	3.056560	0.8653857	3.318229	0.9394812	3.089469	0.8747131	3.800814	1.076114
18,	3.640060	3.099459	0.8514858	3.439552	0.9449164	3.253217	0.8937263	3.962571	1.088600
20,	3.734950	3.134187	0.8391510	3.547740	0.9498761	3.404396	0.9114970	4.107714	1.099804

[a]Columns (4) and (5) are based on 20-point Gaussian quadrature.

Table 3 $d_2 = ER/\sigma$ Values for Sample Size $n = 4$

	Normal	Uniform	Exponential	Lognormal	Double exponential
σ	1	.2887	1	2.161	1.414
ER	2.059	.6	1.883	3.190	2.771
d_2	2.059	2.078	1.833	1.477	1.959

Appendix II suggests d_2 are quite robust except for a small-sized sample taken from the lognormal distribution.

When examining $\bar{x}$ and R charts to see if the process is under control, the normality of the underlying distribution should be considered, at least, for example, in the following two situations:

1. A sample mean is within the $\bar{x}$ chart control limits, but not the corresponding sample range in the R chart.
2. $\bar{x}$ and R charts have points outside the control limits sporadically but not in clusters.

REFERENCES

1. *Federal Register 33653*:40–155 (1975).
2. Grant, E. L. and Leavenworth, R. S., *Statistical Quality Control*, 6th ed., McGraw-Hill, New York (1980).
3. Ott, E. R., *Process Quality Control*, McGraw-Hill, New York (1975).
4. Schrock, *Quality Control and Statistical Methods*, Reinhold, New York (1957).
5. Cox, D. R., *Biometrika 41*:469 (1954).
6. Tippe-t, L. H. C., *Biometrika 17*:364 (1925).
7. David, H. A., *Biometrika 41*:463 (1954).
8. Duncan, A. J. In *Quality Control and Industrial Statistics*, Richard D. Irwin, p. 451 (1974).
9. Keen, J. and Page, D. J., *Appl. Statistics 2*:13 (1953).
10. Woodward, R. H. and Goldsmith, P. L., *Cumulative Sum Techniques*, Oliver & Boyd (1964).

18

Multivariate Graphical Analysis in the Validation of Pharmaceutical Products

Stephen T. Horhota   *Boehringer Ingelheim Pharmaceuticals, Inc., Ridgefield, Connecticut*

I. PROCESS VALIDATION AND OPTIMIZATION

A. General Comparisons

Process validation has evolved into a discipline concerned with the rigorous demonstration of process performance. Although the regulatory aspects make it somewhat unique to the pharmaceutical industry, its technical aspects are less so. It is, in fact, possible to classify process validation as a subset of general optimization problems. This can be done because validation shares four common attributes that factor into the definition of and techniques for solution of optimization problems:

1. It is assumed that there are relationships between independent (input) and dependent (output) variables.
2. It is assumed that there is quantifiable and predictable behavior between input and output variables.
3. It is recognized that constraints on independent and dependent variables can exist.
4. It is desirable to define conditions and a required level of control which ensure attainment of demanded results.

B. Classification of Optimization Problems

Solution techniques for optimization problems are variable directed; that is, they are driven by consideration of the nature of the independent and dependent

549

variables in the problem set. In a generalized scheme, optimization problems can be classified into four specific case types according to the number of variables involved:

	Number of independent variables	Number of dependent variables
Case 1	Single	Single
Case 2	Single	Multiple
Case 3	Multiple	Single
Case 4	Multiple	Multiple

Case 1 problems, dealing with only one independent and one dependent variable, are the easiest to handle but are rarely encountered in real-life situations. Most products involve multiple formulation components and multiple processing steps and typically are required to meet a number of criteria (specifications) simultaneously. Most real-life optimization and product validation issues are Case 4 problems.

1. Categorization of Independent Variables

The multiplicity of independent variables involved in pharmaceutical products can be simplified somewhat by categorizing the variables into five general groups:

1. Physical and chemical properties of formulation materials chosen (e.g., bulk density, particle size, moisture content, solubility, morphology, acid-base behavior)
2. Amounts of each component used (the specific formulation)
3. Type of equipment used in processing (e.g., high-shear vs. low-shear mixer, fluidized bed vs. tray drying)
4. Specific equipment parameters (e.g., temperature, air flow, force, speed)
5. Order of component addition and order of processing steps (e.g., addition of lubricant before or after dry milling, intra- or extragranular incorporation of disintegrant)

Despite this simplification, the list is rather imposing in its magnitude.

2. Dealing with Dependent Variables

Case 4 problems must also contend with multiplicity in dependent variables:

1. Products must meet multiple dependent variable constraints (specifications) simultaneously.
2. A single independent variable may affect many dependent variables.

3. A single independent variable may affect two dependent variables in opposite ways (e.g., compression force effect on hardness and dissolution).

Process validation is mandated under good manufacturing practices (GMPs) where the intent is to prevent changes in the safety and efficacy attributes of a drug product that are affected by manufacturing variables. A classical scientific approach to validation would propose that each variable in each category be independently and exhaustively studied. The costs in time and money make such an enterprise forbidding, nor would the experimental capacity in the relevant production environment be available. In addition, important information about product manufacture would be lost because formulation and process variables would be considered in isolation. Hard-won experience confirms that these must be evaluated in parallel because:

1. Processes are implemented to alter the properties of materials to a more desirable state. Looking at a formulation isolated from its processing route is not logical.
2. Interactions are possible and likely considering the large number of variables involved. Interacting independent variables, by definition, are mutually linked and yield a greater (or less) than expected response for a given change in either or both variables. They must be considered simultaneously.

II. PRODUCT VALIDATION AND THE NEED FOR MULTIVARIATE DATA ANALYSIS

Because of this high level of dimensionality and interrelationships between independent and dependent variables, a truly modern and compliant process validation program must concern itself with the broader issues of *product* validation. To be effective, such a program must address and provide scientifically legitimate data on:

1. Which dependent variables are important and how they are related to product safety and efficacy.
2. How responses can be predicted and controlled.
3. Whether all independent variables are important.
4. Whether it is necessary to measure all responses. When responses are highly correlated, full testing on all parameters is redundant and expensive.
5. Whether there are similar behavior patterns across formulations and processes.
6. How these similar behavior patterns or clusters can be identified.
7. Whether they can be exploited to support validation decisions on new products or when product changes are implemented without fully repeating expensive and resource-intensive validation protocols.

A. Statistical Methods Applied to Pharmaceutical Dosage Forms

1. Multiple Regression

A number of multiple variable (i.e., multivariate) statistical techniques can answer some of these key validation questions. Most familiar is the multiple regression approach, which identifies relationships between independent variables and a single response variable (case 3 problems). A classical example of the use of this method was given by Schwartz et al. [1] in their report on tablet formulation optimization. Five independent variables representing both formulation and processing factors were examined for their influence on each of 10 dependent variables. In the case of key responses of hardness, disintegration, and dissolution, the complex regression equations (with 20 terms each) were excellent predictors for combinations of bulk excipient, starch, compression force, granulating gelatin, and magnesium stearate. Examination of the regression equations can give useful validation information. Important independent variables can be identified as well as the occurrence of possible variable interactions. The degree of process control and allowable ranges for independent variables needed to meet product specifications can be obtained quite easily. However, regression analysis is limited by the fact that it best handles only one dependent variable at a time and again, most validation issues must consider multiple responses.

2. Principle Components Analysis (PCA)

This deficiency was somewhat overcome in a later publication by Schwartz and co-workers [2], where a second technique known as principal components analysis was applied to the same experimental data. PCA seeks to take a large multivariate data set and reduce the apparent dimensionality or complexity by identifying the more important variables. Fewer variables just become easier to deal with. The analysis in this example was directed at the dependent variables and attempted to determine how sensitive the responses were to changes in the independent variables and whether it was possible to classify the original set of 10 responses as important or unimportant. Dissolution, disintegration, and hardness were shown to dominate the response variables from the statistical standpoint, quite conveniently matching practical concerns. The remaining seven responses were less significant in this system. The value of PCA in product validation comes from its ability to identify truly critical variables upon which risk decisions for experimentation can be made. It also highlights which variables should be the focus of effort if revalidation is needed. In addition, it points out the response variables that should be tracked as part of a statistical process control program.

A very relevant example of the use of PCA in solid dosage form evaluation was presented by Benkerrour et al. [3], who measured a total of 12 different granule and tablet properties in a series of 18 experiments with varying excipient compositions, binder types and binder concentrations. The $3 \times 3 \times 2$ factorial experiment used in this study is presented in Table 1 along with the response variables. Principal components analysis was able to show that there were two main groups of dependent variables or principal factors that afforded a discriminating view of the data. An axis system was constructed from the two principal components and the position of each formulation plotted. With such a projection (Fig. 1), it can easily be noticed that there are three main clusters of points on the plot. The composition of the filler is largely responsible for the clustering behavior. Differences in binder type and concentration have very little influence. The first principal component (horizontal axis) is correlated with information related to the tablet porous volume, massic area, micropore volume, tablet hardness, and ratio of axial to radial forces. These parameters are most sensitive to changes in the composition of the matrix. The second principal component (vertical axis) is related to the bulk volume before tapping and tablet friability, and changes in these parameters are sensitive to changes in independent variables but to a lesser degree.

Of course, other statistical techniques can be applied to the analysis of validation data, but the ones discussed above have found application in pharmaceutical dosage forms. They are statistically intense, and consequently the power of their practical conclusions can easily be lost in reams of printout.

B. Graphical Analysis

Often overlooked in the documentation aspects of process validation as currently practiced is the value of multivariate graphical approaches to data analysis. A number of techniques are available that take advantage of the fact that a substantial part of the human cerebral cortex is devoted to the processing of visual information. Imaging, clustering, and pattern recognition of exceedingly complex information sets are routine for us, although we may not appreciate it. Color, shading, texture, and intensity differences are easily discriminated by the human eye and can be related to quantitative information arising from validation exercises.

1. Limitations of Classical Cartesian Projections

Usually, when a graph of scientific data is constructed, it projects information in a two-dimensional Cartesian coordinate space commonly denoted by X and Y. Plots of this type are easily reproduced in print, which is important in the transmission and application of the information they contain. The informational content of X-Y plots has been expanded by overlaying multiple sets of data that project as a family of curves. More recently, there has been a tremendous expansion in the use of three-dimensional views of data either as classical response surface contours or three-dimensional plots. Overlays with these type of plots are also possible, further expanding dimensional capabilities.

Product validation makes some special demands on graphical techniques because of the number of variables that have to be dealt with and the complexity of

Table 1 Data Set Formulation Identification and Response Variable Data

Formulation designation	Excipient composition	Gum type	Gum concentration (%)	Fines (%)	Bulk volume before tapping (cm³)	Settling rate (%)	Flow rate (g/s)
A	Tricalcium phosphate	A	0.5	16.0	184	12.0	9.5
B	Tricalcium phosphate	A	1.0	14.9	186	11.8	9.8
C	Tricalcium phosphate	A	1.5	18.6	188	11.7	9.4
D	Tricalcium phosphate	B	0.5	17.4	184	12.0	9.5
E	Tricalcium phosphate	B	1.0	16.4	182	11.0	9.9
F	Tricalcium phosphate	B	1.5	15.4	186	11.8	9.6
G	50:50 mixture	A	0.5	20.6	182	13.2	9.1
H	50:50 mixture	A	1.0	21.9	176	13.6	9.3
I	50:50 mixture	A	1.5	18.6	181	13.8	9.0
J	50:50 mixture	B	0.5	19.9	172	13.4	9.4
K	50:50 mixture	B	1.0	19.3	174	13.8	9.7
L	50:50 mixture	B	1.5	16.0	178	13.5	9.2
M	Lactose	A	0.5	29.8	217	14.1	8.7
N	Lactose	A	1.0	22.7	200	15.0	8.6
O	Lactose	A	1.5	24.0	202	14.9	8.2
P	Lactose	B	0.5	26.8	212	13.2	7.7
Q	Lactose	B	1.0	22.7	200	14.5	8.5
R	Lactose	B	1.5	25.7	203	14.1	8.4
Mean				20.4	189	13.2	9.1
RSD				21.0	7.0	9.1	6.8

Adapted from Ref. 3.

the production environment in which these variables are operating. Furthermore, individual data and means must often be assessed simultaneously to determine whether a process is under control and performing at the expected level.

Consider a case constructed from the data presented by Schwartz et al. [1]. Using the regression coefficients from response surface modeling (Table 2) [4], it is possible to reconstruct the data set for the 28 experimental trials that were performed (27 as part of a statistical design and 1 for confirmation of the predicted optimum formulation). Because of the factorial design chosen by the original

Granule strength (%)	Micropore volume (mm³/g)	Total pore volume (mm³/g)	Ratio of axial to applied pressure (%)	Tablet hardness (N)	Fria- bility (%)	Tablet porous volume (mm³/g)	Massic area (m²/g)
79.0	476	554	87	8.0	2.2	289	38
84.0	485	539	88	8.0	1.8	284	37
85.5	481	538	88	8.0	1.6	286	36
82.0	478	533	86	9.0	2.4	289	39
87.0	474	529	87	8.0	2.0	292	37
86.5	475	546	88	8.0	1.7	285	36
77.0	292	373	81	6.0	1.7	221	19
91.5	259	327	82	6.0	1.6	208	16
91.0	268	336	83	6.0	1.5	228	18
88.0	258	313	81	6.0	1.9	221	19
86.5	258	325	82	5.5	1.8	245	20
87.0	255	330	81	6.0	1.6	211	16
85.0	148	268	76	3.5	4.0	145	8
92.0	141	272	75	4.0	3.2	154	8
92.0	156	279	78	5.0	2.6	151	9
86.0	139	320	79	4.0	3.3	151	8
91.0	143	278	79	4.5	3.2	147	8
91.0	132	295	79	5.0	2.8	150	9
86.8	295	386	82	6.1	2.3	220	21
5.0	48.3	29.7	5.2	27.2	32.8	26.6	58.5

authors and the use of factor levels to denote the value of the five independent variables, the absolute magnitude of the regression coefficients is directly related to the relative importance of the associated variable or interaction. In this case, the amount of magnesium stearate in the formulation plays a large role in determining tablet disintegration time. A plot of individual data for disintegration time vs. amount of magnesium stearate for each of the experiments (Fig. 2) confirms typical behavior, increasing disintegration time with increasing magnesium stearate. This trend can be further discerned by addition of a linear regression profile

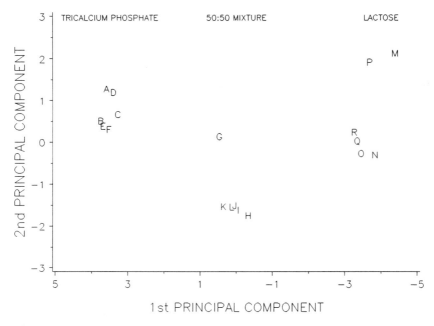

Figure 1 Projection of data from 18 experimental formulations into the axis system defined by the first two principal components, showing clustering patterns. (Adapted from Ref. 3.)

to the plot. From further examination of regression coefficients, it will be noticed that the percent dissolved in 50 minutes is also strongly influenced by magnesium stearate. Overlaying dissolution data vs. amount of lubricant on Fig. 2 generates Fig. 3. Practically the only discernible information on this graph comes from the regression line projections which tell us about average tendencies. Individual data point examination, despite the use of different symbols, is difficult at best. The use of color to differentiate the two dependent variables does improve discrimination but is easily lost with standard photocopying or offset reproduction, as is the case here.

2. Bubble Plots

a. *Three-dimensional with dependent and independent variables.* Consider now the projection of the same data from Fig. 3 as a bubble plot (Fig. 4). In a simple bubble plot, a standard X-Y format plot is generated, but instead of using a simple symbol to denote the position of a data point, a circle or dot is used with the size of the dot varying according to the magnitude of a third variable. Figure 4 shows disintegration time vs. amount of magnesium stearate as the Cartesian variables

Table 2 Regression Coefficients for Second-Order Polynomial Equation
for Three Tablet Parameters Used in the Generation of Data for Figs. 2–7

Term	Disintegration time (min)	Tablet hardness (kg)	% dissolved in 50 min
	Factorial coefficient		
Intercept	18.78408	5.40570	31.83333
Excipient ratio	−.09869	−.02163	−4.18818
Compression force	4.95884	.81953	−7.93586
Starch disintegrant	2.27261	.26516	5.84675
Gelatin binder	3.48627	.26625	−1.85159
Lubricant	3.26791	−1.18309	−21.46401
Excipient ratio^2	.73112	.30197	−2.11218
Compression force^2	−1.14051	−.22034	7.48791
Starch disintegrant^2	−.24389	.14005	−.60270
Gelatin binder^2	−2.15901	.09826	7.33121
Lubricant^2	−1.27109	.34375	7.48791
Excipient × force	−.66406	−.22969	1.31875
Excipient × starch	−.18489	−.28594	1.29375
Excipient × gelatin	−1.46616	−.38594	2.15937
Excipient × lubricant	1.44009	.10781	−5.69688
Force × starch	−.28906	.28906	1.33438
Force × gelatin	−.20572	.32656	−7.43125
Force × lubricant	−.00782	−.57344	5.15625
Starch × gelatin	−.10156	.17656	2.96250
Starch × lubricant	−1.07031	−.21094	5.59375
Gelatin × lubricant	−.05989	.02469	4.01563

Coefficients are coded for use with the experimental design given in Table I of Ref. 1.

and dissolution percentage is proportional to the area of the plotting symbol.
Circle radius could also be used in generating the bubbles (Fig. 5) but sometimes
leads to problems in the range of bubble sizes that appear on a plot. Open or filled
circles can be used, although open circles will better show points that are close to
each other or even superimposed (examine data points on Fig. 4 with 1 mg of
magnesium stearate). Because of the clarity of this type of presentation, data
interpretation is substantially improved. The relationship between disintegration
time and lubricant amount is identical to that given by Fig. 2, and the increase is
disintegration caused by addition of magnesium stearate is still readily apparent.

Bubble size increases as the amount of lubricant declines, highlighting the
inverse relationship between these two parameters. Also easily seen is the inverse
relationship between disintegration time and percent dissolved.

b. *Three-dimensional with dependent variable comparisons.* A particularly

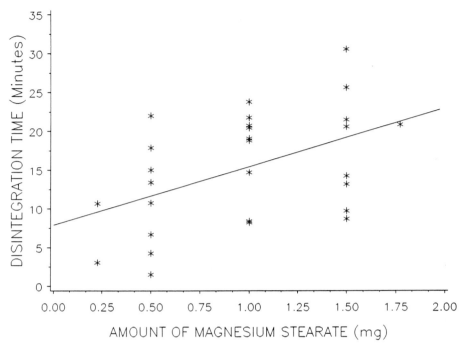

Figure 2 Plot of disintegration time vs. magnesium stearate content and regression line for 28 tablet formulation experiments described in Ref. 1.

valuable view of the data set can be obtained by using only dependent variables in the plot. Figure 6 shows disintegration time vs. tablet hardness on the Cartesian axes with bubble area proportional to percent dissolved at 50 minutes. Evident is a modest yet interesting negative correlation between disintegration and hardness; as tablet hardness increases, disintegration time is reduced! The expected increase in dissolution rate is similarly apparent. In this instance the bubble plot expands our ability to examine multiple dependent variables simultaneously.

c. *Four-dimensional cases.* As a final expansion on the bubble plot, it is possible to shade, color or otherwise identify the bubbles in relation to yet a fourth variable to further visualize a data set. In Fig. 7 the information from Figs. 4 and 6 is combined with bubble size proportional to percent dissolved in 50 minutes and bubble identification related to the amount of magnesium stearate in the particular formulation. The interpretations made with Figs. 4 and 6 apply here, with the advantage that all information is concisely displayed on a single plot.

Bubble plots have not been widely applied in the analysis of scientific or validation data despite the fact that they offer a number of distinct advantages in

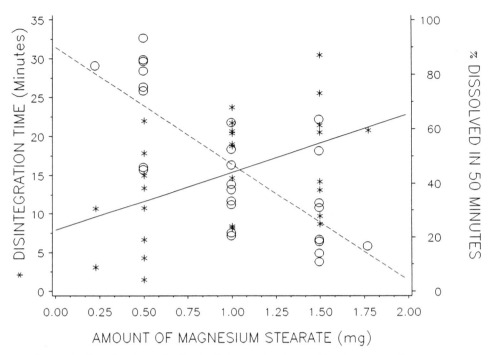

Figure 3   Double axis projection for disintegration time and % dissolved in 50 minutes vs. magnesium stearate with regression lines for 28 tablet formulation experiments. ∗ = disintegration time; ○ = % dissolved.

multivariate data projection. They are clear, concise, and put a considerable amount of information in front of the viewer. They can make large data sets coherent and, most important, they invite data analysis and comparison. Different interpretations of data can be brought forth and conclusions that would not be obvious with other projection techniques now become apparent. Bubble plots can be used prior to in-depth statistical analyses as a way to focus hypothesis testing. More practically, they can present detailed statistical analyses in a way that makes the results meaningful to those who are not trained as statisticians yet must make important validation decisions based on statistical conclusions.

3.   Andrews' Plots

There are, of course, limits to the number of variables or dimensions which can be effectively presented with bubble plots. In product validation it is likely that many more variables, in particular dependent variables, have to be dealt with. Andrews [5] proposed an alternative technique that extends the limits of multidimensional data projection into the classic X-Y coordinate space.

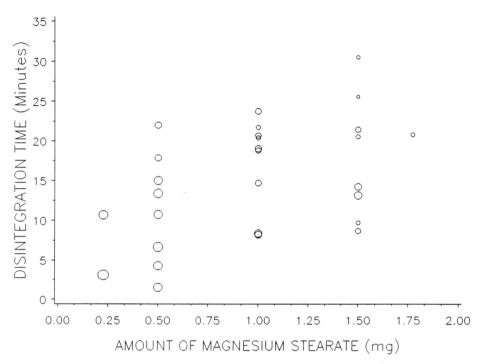

Figure 4 Bubble plot for disintegration time and % dissolved in 50 minutes vs. magnesium stearate for 28 tablet formulations. Bubble area is proportional to % dissolved in 50 minutes.

a.   *Background and construction.* For a p-variate point Y' representing the vector of measurements for a particular experiment $(y_1, y_2, y_3, \ldots, y_p)$ we can define

$$f(t) = y_1 t_1(\theta) + \cdots + y_p t_p(\theta)$$
$$= Y't \quad \text{for } c \leqslant \theta \leqslant d$$

where $t = t(\theta) = \{t_1(\theta), \ldots, t_p(\theta)\}$ is a set of orthogonal functions over the interval $[c,d]$. Orthogonal simply refers to the fact that the elements of the function are at apparent right angles to each other much in the same way that Cartesian X-Y coordinates are at right angles to each other.

The choice of $t = \{1/\sqrt{2}, \sin\theta, \cos\theta, \sin 2\theta, \cos 2\theta, \ldots\}$ conveniently satisfies the conditions of orthogonality for $-\pi \leqslant \theta \leqslant \pi$. This is so because sine and cosine functions are 90° out of phase with each other.

With the vector t defined in this fashion, an Andrews function plot can be presented as an X-Y graph of $f(t)$ over the range of $-\pi$, π and will appear as a

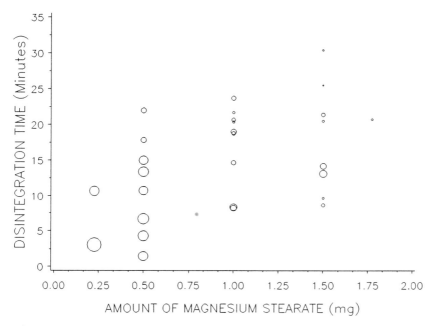

Figure 5 Bubble plot for disintegration time and % dissolved in 50 minutes vs. magnesium stearate for 28 tablet formulations. Bubble radius is proportional to % dissolved in 50 minutes.

mixture of sine and cosine waves. The wave pattern will depend on the observed values of the p variables. Andrews showed that the "distance" between two functions is defined as

$$\int_{-\pi}^{\pi} [f_i(t) - f_j(t)]^2 \, dt$$

which is proportional to the squared Euclidean distance between Y_i and Y_j. This means that experiments or observations that are "close together" in p-dimensional space give wave patterns that are somewhat similar. Conversely, well-separated curves suggest distant observations in the same p-dimensional space. Thus, it is possible to visualize the presence of multivariate clusters from the function plot.

The method also has potential for studying interrelationships within variables. If a group of functions are close together for some values of θ, then the corresponding observations are close in the directions defined by the allied vector t. For values of θ at which curves are well separated, the magnitude of the

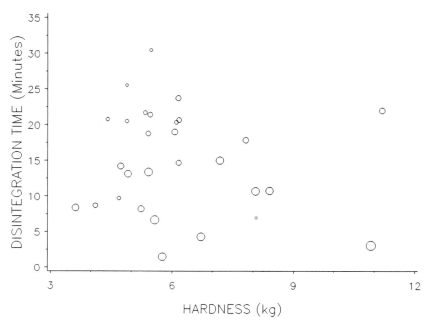

Figure 6 Bubble plot for disintegration time and % dissolved in 50 minutes vs. tablet hardness for 28 tablet formulations. Bubble area is proportional to % dissolved in 50 minutes.

individual component terms of the Andrews function can be examined to identify which variables are contributing most to the separation. In this fashion the Andrews function can be considered as a pseudodiscriminant function.

b. *Analysis and Interpretation.* To illustrate the use of the Andrews function, return to the tablet and granule data set from Benkerrour et al. Data are transformed into the Andrews frequency domain according to the trigonometric series expansion in the following manner:

$$F(t) = \frac{y_1}{1.414} + y_2 \sin t + y_3 \cos t + y_4 \sin 2t$$
$$+ y_5 \cos 2t + y_6 \sin 3t + y_7 \cos 3t + \ldots + y_{12} \sin 6t$$

where y_n are values of the respective dependent variables measurements for an experiment or formulation trial.

$t = [-\pi, \pi]$ radians

Thus, for trial A, starting at $-\pi$ radians, the equation appears as

$$F(t) = F(-3.14)$$

$$= \frac{16.0}{1.414} + (184)\sin(-3.14) + (12.0)\cos(-3.14) + (9.5)\sin 2(-3.14)$$

$$+ (79.0)\cos 2(-3.14) + (476)\sin 3(-3.14) + (554)\cos 3(-3.14)$$

$$+ (87)\sin 4(-3.14) + (8.0)\cos 4(-3.14) + (2.2)\sin 5(-3.14)$$

$$+ (289)\cos 5(-3.14) + (38)\sin 6(-3.14)$$

$$= -767.3$$

This calculation is then repeated at various incremental values of t up to $t = 3.14$ and plots of $F(t)$ vs. t are constructed. From experience, 100 points along the t axis (increment t by 0.0628) will generate reasonably smooth curves when plotted. Many computer plotting programs offer smoothing functions such as spline interpolations that can further enhance the appearance of the graph. For the

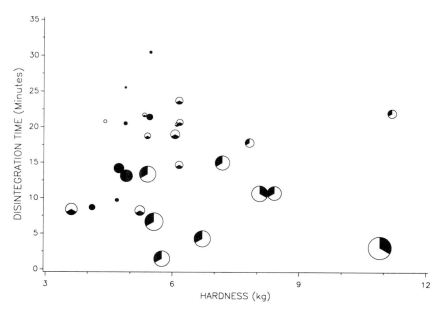

Figure 7 Four-dimensional bubble plot for the variables disintegration time, % dissolved in 50 minutes, tablet hardness, and amount of magnesium stearate for 28 tablet formulations. Bubble area is proportional to % dissolved in 50 minutes. Bubble pattern represents amount of magnesium stearate—◐ 0.23 mg; ◑ 0.50 mg; ◒ 1.00 mg; ● 1.50 mg; ○ 1.77 mg.

examples presented here, calculations and plotting were performed using the Statistical Analysis System (SAS, Version 5.08) on an IBM 370 computer.

Andrews' function plots for the 18 formulation trials of Benkerrour are shown in Fig. 8. It is immediately obvious that there are three main groupings of curves. Preliminary analysis on graphs generated with different combinations of colors and line types (dashed, dotted, etc.) identified the individual curves. Alternatively, the functions can be plotted using letter or number designation as the plotting symbol. Either method will show that the separation, or clustering, is associated with changes in the composition of the bulk excipient. Within each cluster, the curves are very closely grouped, nearly superimposed in the case of the tricalcium phosphate trials. This indicates that changes in gum type and concentration have negligible effect on granule or tablet characteristics. Curves for 50:50 mixtures of lactose and tricalcium phosphate fall intermediate to those of the pure component formulations, suggesting a proportional relationship between response variables and admixtures of these excipients.

As a pattern recognition tool, Andrews' plots are of greatest value when

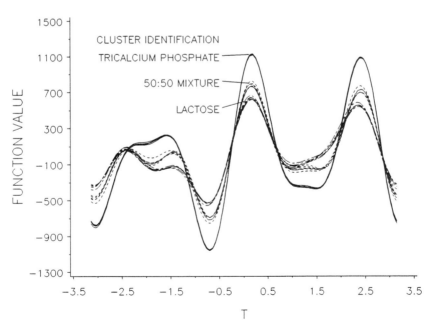

Figure 8 Andrews plot of combined granule and tablet data for the 18 experimental trials described in Ref. 3. The order of variable entry into the Andrews transform was as published originally.

variable ordering is chosen to maximize fluctuations in amplitude as this will lead to greater differentiation. Consequently, it is recommended [6] that the order of entry of variables into the trigonometric transform be according to their relative importance in the data set. This can be done by the researcher but is not recommended because of the potential for observer bias. A number of techniques are available for the determination of variable importance, and most commonly they involve analyses of the variance or covariance structure. The simplest form of such an analysis of variance structure is the ranking of variables based on their relative standard deviation (RSD). If it can be assumed or directly shown that experimental or measurement error is small in relation to the overall effects due to independent variable changes, dependent variables with high RSD can be viewed as more sensitive or more important in gauging the overall behavior of the system. In other words, high-RSD variables are discriminators for the system. Andrews' plots for the same data set with variable ordering determined by ranking according to RSD are shown in Fig. 9. The consequences of changing order are easily seen. While clusters are readily apparent in either plot, greater amplitude differences are

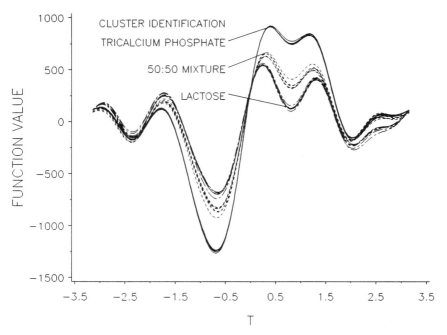

Figure 9 Andrews plot of combined granule and tablet data for the 18 experimental trials described in Ref. 3. The order of variable entry was determined by ranking according to decreasing relative standard deviation for the dependent variables.

observed when ordering is performed according to diminishing relative standard deviation. In all cases, the waveforms are remarkably similar, with maxima, minima, and inflection points all occurring at the same values of t. This implies that the formulations have related mechanistic or physical behavior patterns. Differences in waveforms for the various formulations are not due to different mechanisms of behavior but are reflective only of differences in magnitude of effects contributed by the various formulation variables.

The Andrews' function can be further manipulated to gain information concerning the nature of the data set, particularly which parameters are responsible for the differentiation observed. To do this, a point is chosen on the t axis at which there is a maximal separation between two curves. In. Fig. 9, $t = 0.75$ meets this criterion. Using trials A (tricalcium phosphate) and M (lactose) as representative of the two clusters, the terms of the function are calculated.

$$F(t) = F(0.75)$$

$$= \frac{38}{1.414} + (476)\sin(0.75) + (2.2)\cos(0.75) + (554)\sin 2(0.75)$$
$$+ (8.0)\cos 2(0.75) + (289)\sin 3(0.75) + (16.0)\cos 3(0.75)$$
$$+ (12.0)\sin 4(0.75) + (184)\cos 4(0.75) + (9.5)\sin 5(0.75)$$
$$+ (87)\cos 5(0.75) + (79.5)\sin 6(0.75)$$

$$= 26.87 + 324.46 + 1.61 + 552.61 + 0.57 + 224.86 + (-10.05)$$
$$+ 1.69 + (-182.16) + (-5.43) + (-71.39) + (-77.71)$$
$$= 785.93 \quad \text{for trial A and}$$

$$F(t) = F(0.75)$$

$$= \frac{8}{1.414} + (148)\sin(0.75) + (4.0)\cos(0.75) + (268)\sin 2(0.75)$$
$$+ (3.5)\cos 2(0.75) + (145)\sin 3(0.75) + (29.8)\cos 3(0.75)$$
$$+ (14.1)\sin 4(0.75) + (217)\cos 4(0.75) + (8.7)\sin 5(0.75)$$
$$+ (7.6)\cos 5(0.75) + (85.0)\sin 6(0.75)$$

$$= 5.66 + 100.88 + 2.93 + 267.33 + 0.25 + 112.82 + (-18.72)$$
$$+ 1.99 + (-214.83) + (-4.97) + (-6.24) + (-83.09)$$
$$= 164.01 \quad \text{for Trial M}$$

The largest differences in terms are associated with the variables granule micropore volume, tablet porous volume, and granule total pore volume. Values for these are greater for tricalcium phosphate than for lactose.

The Andrews technique is somewhat limited by the number of variables that can be incorporated in an analysis. It may be necessary to eliminate certain variables as insignificant prior to constructing Andrews' plots. Principal components analysis can be useful in performing the necessary variable identification. For the data under analysis here, the greatest clarity in differentiation is present in Fig. 10, which displays the eight variables most highly correlated with the first three principal components axes and which in fact are responsible for 94.6% of the variance in the data structure. In all cases, formulation G, which appears as a possible outlier in PCA projections, is well within its cluster. The original paper cited experimental error as leading to a particularly low value for granule strength for this formula, which affected the overall variance structure and hence the PCA results. The Andrews transformation, while it preserves variance structure, may be less prone to the effects of single-point data "abnormalities" due to experimental error.

In all cases of variable ordering, three clusters are evident corresponding identically to that proposed by Benkerrour et al. Function curves within each cluster are nearly superimposible, suggestive of minimal within-cluster dispersion. Clustering occurs on the basis of excipient, and the curves for 50:50 mix-

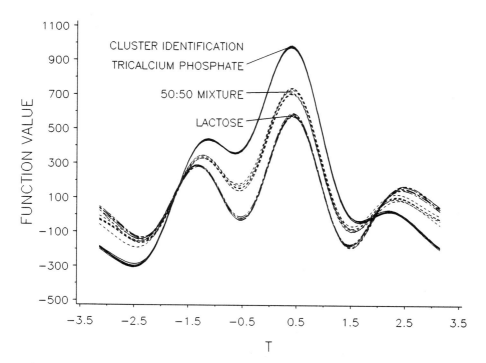

Figure 10 Andrews plot of the seven parameters most highly associated with the two major principal components axes for the data set. The order of variable entry was determined by the loading of the dependent variables on the principal components axes.

tures of tricalcium phosphate and lactose fall intermediate to those of either diluent used alone. The conclusion from PCA that binder type and concentration are not major factors is fully supported with the Andrews method.

Examination of plots for only granulation or tablet characteristics, Figs. 11 and 12, is particularly revealing. Ranking on the basis of relative standard deviation was adequate in this instance because of the small number of dependent variables in each subset. Again, three clusters are clearly evident and associated with excipient composition. The curves within a cluster are closely aligned, suggestive of little effect of binder type or binder solution concentration compared to that of diluent. In Fig. 12, which depicts the curves for the tablet parameters, a point of maximum separation occurs near $t = 0.6$. The function vector shows (Table 3) that tablet porous volume and massic area are the primary discriminants between tablets produced with the two excipients. Also at this point function mean values of 333.7 and 178.9 for tricalcium phosphate and lactose clusters, respectively, are calculated. The mean function value for the 50:50 diluent mixture cluster at the

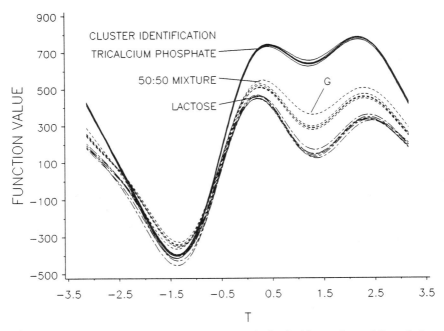

Figure 11 Andrews plot of granule parameters only for the 18 experimental formulations. The order of variable entry was determined by ranking according to decreasing relative standard deviation. In contrast to PCA results, formulation G is closely identified with its cluster.

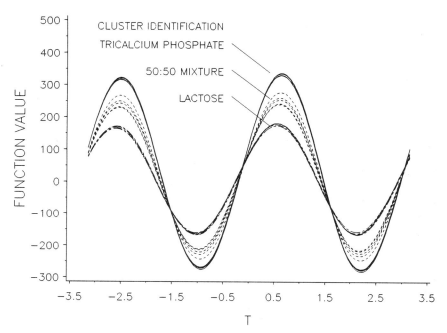

Figure 12   Andrews plot of tablet parameters only for the 18 experimental formulations. The order of variable entry was determined by ranking according to decreasing relative standard deviation.

same value of t is 255.4. This corresponds nearly identically to a calculated value of 254.3 for the midpoint between the single-component curves. Because proportionality in Euclidean distance is preserved by the Andrews plot, the data may be interpreted as showing that tablet properties depend only on the mass composition of the diluent. Thus, it may be inferred that while wet granulation of the diluent materials effects changes in bulk powder properties, these changes have little to do with the characteristics of the final tablet matrices. It is important to note that weight uniformity was not one of the tablet parameters reported. Different conclusions could have come about if this measurement were a part of the data structure, since granulometric properties could play a role in mass flow of material into the die cavity. Clearly, however, at the final compression stage, only the matrix composition influences behavior of this system.

Interpretation of Fig. 11, granulation parameters only, is not as straightforward. Two distinct patterns are seen across the range of t. For values of t less than -0.5 the curves are nearly the same, showing that there is little difference in formulation characteristics. This changes for values greater than -0.5, where

Table 3 Vector Components for Andrews Functions at
Discriminant Values of t

Variable	Trigonometric modifier	Formulation	
		A	M
Figure 11 $t = 1.25$			
Micropore volume	$1/\sqrt{2}$	336.6	93.4
Total pore volume	$\sin t$	527.7	280.0
Percentage of fines	$\cos t$	5.0	8.1
Settling rate	$\sin 2t$	7.2	8.4
Bulk volume before settling	$\cos 2t$	−147.4	−162.6
Flow rate	$\sin 3t$	−5.4	−4.8
Granule strength	$\cos 3t$	−64.8	−74.7
Function value		658.9	147.8
Figure 11 $t = 1.40$			
Micropore volume	$1/\sqrt{2}$	336.6	93.4
Total pore volume	$\sin t$	−545.9	−290.7
Percentage of fines	$\cos t$	2.7	4.4
Settling rate	$\sin 2t$	−4.0	−4.7
Bulk volume before settling	$\cos 2t$	−173.4	−191.3
Flow rate	$\sin 3t$	8.3	7.3
Granule strength	$\cos 3t$	−38.7	−44.6
Function value		−414.4	−426.3
Figure 12 $t = 0.60$			
Massic area	$1/\sqrt{2}$	26.9	6.4
Friability	$\sin t$	1.2	1.6
Tablet hardness	$\cos t$	6.6	4.1
Tablet porous volume	$\sin 2t$	269.4	139.8
Axial:applied pressure	$\cos 2t$	31.5	28.6
Function value		335.6	180.5

clustering patterns begin to emerge. An analysis of the vector (Table 3) defining $f(t)$ at $t = 1.25$ for trials A and M shows that micropore volume and total pore volume are the parameters most responsible for the differences between the two diluents. Unlike the tablet parameters, however, it can be seen that the curves for the 50:50 compositions are not positioned at the midpoint between the two single-composition matrices. The curves are uniformly biased toward the lactose cluster, indicating some nonlinearity or constant proportionality as a function of composition that leads to effects on micropore volume and total pore volume. For the vector at $t = -1.40$, the terms for micropore volume and total pore volume sum to approximately the same value for the formulations. In effect, then, a comparison between formulations neglecting these two parameters is being made and shows that the remaining variables are largely unaffected by excipient alterations.

Isolation of particular patterns of behavior for granulation parameters in the formulations opens opportunities for speculation regarding mechanisms. Certainly the difference in solubility between the two diluents can be viewed as a major factor, with the aqueous solubility of lactose dominating in the 50:50 mixtures despite an adjustment of granulating solution volume reported by the authors intended to compensate for this. Particle or surface properties could also be invoked as possible factors. For the formulations studied, differences in particle size distribution were reported [7] (1–15 micron range for tricalcium phosphate and 1–150 micron range for lactose) and represent a possible confounding factor in surface area, wetting characteristics, or packing arrangement that could have affected the results.

The Andrews approach to pattern recognition has been used successfully in molecular modeling [8], in the analysis of sexual dimorphisms in primates [9], and for statistical quality control of multivariate processes [10]. The case is now established for application in the analysis of pharmaceutical formulation problems. It is a companion technique to PCA and other multivariate procedures. The Andrews plot is unable to provide a mechanistic explanation for the behavior of the formulations. Its prime value is in identifying groups that behave in a similar fashion, and it serves as a stepping point for a second level of data analysis or experimentation on targeted variables that are known to be key factors in the system. As a tool in validation, Andrews' plots can be used to compare product attributes in the course of scale-up and production transfer to make sure that fundamental dosage form research is preserved during development phases. They can be used to assess quantitatively whether a pilot-scale process is in fact a true replica of a commercial environment. They can be used to show that different products manufactured using the same process technology are mechanistically related (belong to a cluster) to justify a general product validation rationale instead of an individual product-by-product approach. This would allow a legitimate extension of validation information across different products, enhancing overall compliance while pointing out opportunities for cost optimization. In a production setting they can be used as a statistical process control tool to track product performance and ensure that proven acceptable limits are being maintained. The greatest value of Andrews' plots probably lies in their potential to view multiple *in vitro* and *in vivo* responses simultaneously in the same dimensional space.

III. CONCLUSIONS

Multivariate graphical techniques have tremendous power for conveying complex information. They can be used independently or as adjuncts to statistical analyses for reducing a vast array of numerical output to a comprehensible domain. For maximal results, Tufte [11] advises that good graphical displays should:

Show as much individual data as possible
Induce the viewer to think about the substance of the data and not methodology, design, or graphics technology
Avoid distorting the data
Present many numbers in a small space
Make large data sets coherent
Encourage comparison

These points serve as reminders to avoid overzealous use of the many graphics packages now available and accessible. Many were not designed with scientific data presentation in mind. A graphics package for use in the presentation of validation data should be chosen carefully and verified for accuracy in output.

REFERENCES

1. Schwartz, J. B., Flamholz, J. R., and Press, R. H., Computer optimization of pharmaceutical formulations. I. General procedure, *J. Pharm. Sci.* 62:1165–1170 (1973).
2. Bohidar, N. R., Restaino, F. A., and Schwartz, J. B., Selecting key parameters in pharmaceutical formulations by principal component analysis, *J. Pharm. Sci.* 64:966–969 (1975).
3. Benkerrour, L., Dunchene, D., Puisieux, F., and Maccario, J., Granule and tablet formulae study by principal components analysis. *Int. J. Pharmaceut.* 19:27–34 (1984).
4. Schwartz, J. B., personal communication.
5. Andrews, D., Plots of high dimensional data. *Biometrics* 28:125–136 (1972).
6. Chatfield, C., and Collins, A., *Introduction to Multivariate Statistics*. Chapman & Hall, London, pp. 49, 57–87 (1980).
7. Benkerrour, L., Puisieux, F., and Duchene, D., Influence de la nature du diluant, de la viscosité et de la concentration en liant du liquide de mouillage, sur les charactéristiques des grains et des comprimes. *Pharm. Acta Helv.* 57:301–308 (1982).
8. Henry, D., and Block, J., Pattern recognition of steroids using fragment molecular connectivity. *J. Pharm. Sci.* 69:1030–1034 (1980).
9. Oxnard, C., Sexual dimorphisms in the overall proportions of primates, *Am. J. Primatol.* 4:1–22 (1983).
10. Kulkarni, S. R., and Paranjape, S. R., Use of Andrews function plot technique to construct control curves for multivariate processes. *Commun. Stat. Theory Methods* 13:2511–2533 (1984).
11. Tufte, E. R., *The Visual Display of Quantitative Information*, Graphics Press, Chesire, CT (1983).

19

Recent Trends in Process Validation

John Y. Lee *Pharmaceutical Compliance Associates, North Massapequa, New York*

I. INTRODUCTION

Validation to show that a process can consistently produce what it purports to do was in practice by the pharmaceutical industry well before the word validation first appeared in proposed Food and Drug Administration (FDA) regulations. The validation concepts, however, remain nebulous at times despite FDA and industry definitions, discussions, debates, and educational programs on the subject. This lack of clarity, along with insufficient directions on the practical application of the validation concepts, has often resulted in FDA observations of validation deficiencies. One of the major reasons for this continuing difficulty in the application of, and compliance with, the validation concepts has been the rapid technological advancement of the pharmaceutical industry within the past 10 years. The concept of validation had to be redefined and reevaluated to accommodate these technological changes. For example, the increase in the automation of pharmaceutical processes in the 1980s sparked many debates and redefinitions of the validation concept and procedures for application to automated systems. Traditional validation concepts and procedures that were acceptable years ago may no longer be applicable to today's operations and equipment. One example is the long-accepted practice of simulating the production process when performing media fills, which may not be acceptable for lyophilized products. There are industry and FDA concerns that simulating the entire lyophilization process (e.g., freezing and vacuum) for the media fill could mask contamination introduced into the media during the filling process [1].

573

This chapter reviews the FDA's and the pharmaceutical industry's perspectives and philosophy for process validation and the compliance impact of the FDA's perspectives on industry practice. The interpretation of the FDA's validation perspectives and philosophy is based on FDA regulations, guidelines, compliance policy guides, inspection guides, compliance programs, and speeches. Recommendations for the organization of a validation project and the preparation of a validation protocol are also included.

II. REASONS FOR VALIDATION

The three basic and most important reasons for validation are quality assurance, economics and compliance.

A. Quality Assurance

Product quality cannot be assured for a process by routine quality control testing because of the limitation of statistical sampling and the limited sensitivity of finished-product testing. Quality variations among units within a batch, or among different batches, are seldom detected by testing of finished-product samples. Sterility testing is frequently referenced to show the limitation of end-product testing. According to *Remington's Pharmaceutical Science*, for example, a product batch with a true 1.0% contamination would be released eight times out of ten based on the United States Pharmacopeia (USP) sterility sample size of 20 units [2].

Validation challenges the adequacy and reliability of a system or process to meet predetermined criteria. A successful validation, therefore, provides a high degree of confidence that the same level of quality is consistently built into each unit of the finished product, from batch to batch. The product quality assurance concept of validation has been recognized by the Pharmaceutical Manufacturers Association (PMA) and the FDA [3,4].

B. Economics

The direct economic benefit of validation is a reduction in the cost associated with process monitoring, sampling, and testing. A validated water for injection system, for example, would eliminate the requirements to batch water and to sample and test each batch prior to use. Analysis of multiple samples would not be required in order to show homogeneity for a validated blending process. Intensive monitoring of each sterilization cycle with temperature sensors and biological indicators could be replaced by the validation of the sterilization process itself. In addition, validated sterilization processes may qualify for parametric release, which eliminates the necessity for finished-product sterility testing and results in additional cost savings. Parametric release has been employed by medical device manufacturers for many years. The FDA has recently offered parametric release for parenterals sterilized by a validated terminal sterilization process [5].

The consistency and reliability of a validated process to produce a quality product provide indirect cost savings resulting from a decrease or elimination of product rejections, reworks, and retesting. Final release of the product batch would be expedited and freed of delays and complications caused by lengthy investigations of process- or analytical-related variances. In addition, product quality complaints and potential product recalls would be minimized.

C. Compliance

Specific current good manufacturing practice (CGMP) references to validation are found in the following sections of 21CFR211 [6]:

211.68—Validation of computerization or other automated processes.

211.84(d)(2)—Validation of supplier's test results for components when these tests results are accepted in lieu of in-house testing after receipt.

211.84(d)(3)—Validation of supplier's test results for containers and closures when these test results are accepted in lieu of in-house testing after receipt.

211.110(a)—Validation of manufacturing processes to ensure batch uniformity and integrity of drug products.

211.113(b)—Validation of sterilization processes.

211.165(e)—Validation of analytical methodologies.

Although the word validation was not specifically mentioned, the requirement for validation is implied in 211.100(a). This section of the GMP requires that written procedures and process controls be established to assure that the drug products have the "identity, strength, quality and purity they purport or are represented to possess." It is interesting to note that this section of the GMP, which does not mention the word validation, is actually the "catch-all" for validation requirements that were not specifically included in the GMPs: cleaning validation, reprocessing validation, packaging validation, etc.

The implication of validation requirements as in 21CRF211.100(a) has been replaced with more specific definitions of the requirement in recent FDA publications. The FDA's draft Mid Atlantic Pharmaceutical Inspection Guidance Program for Prescription Drug Plants, issued in January 1990, emphasizes the importance of validating the manufacturing process. In addition to validation of processes and controls, this inspection guide instructs the FDA investigator to review validation programs for clinical manufacturing, scale-up, filed new drug application (NDA) or abbreviated NDA (ANDA) manufacturing procedures, reprocessing and process modifications, laboratory equipment, and cleaning procedures [7]. Another example is the FDA's recent revision of the compliance program, CP7356.002A, for Sterile Drug Process Inspections (issued in March 1990). This revised program contains over a dozen references to validation requirements for various sterilization systems and controls [8].

III. VALIDATION TERMINOLOGY AND CONCEPTS

There are many definitions of validation, and choosing the best or most appropriate definition is not important. Emphasis, instead, should be placed on the understanding and practical application of the validation concepts. This includes knowing when and how to employ prospective, retrospective, and concurrent validation; understanding the significance, impact, and interpretation of validation results; and evaluating the significance of variations from validated parameters.

A. Prospective Validation

This concept is usually employed when historical data are not available or sufficient, and in-process and finished-product testings are not adequate, to ensure reproducibility or a high degree of confidence for product quality attributes. In some cases, a prospective validation of the system or process is required prior to the production or release of the product batch. For example, a sterile solution filled on a new piece of equipment should not be released without a prospective media fill validation. In this instance, the lack of historical data and the limitation of the sterility test could not guarantee the sterility of the batch. Prospective validation is usually the only alternative when new equipment or components are used. Examples include condenser capacity and leak testing for lyophilizers, switching to a new filter medium, and HVAC systems.

According to the PMA, prospective validation must be performed for the validation of sterile processes [3]. This is a very conservative view considering that there might be situations in which an instant sterilization run can be validated concurrently. An example of such a situation is running an ethylene oxide sterilization load through a half cycle followed by a full cycle. The data from the biological indicators and monitoring sensors, from both the half and full cycles, could then be used to demonstrate the achievement of a sterility assurance level of 10^{-6} for that particular cycle run (presuming that the additional exposure to ethylene oxide has no adverse effects on product quality and stability).

The FDA considers prospective validation as a preproduction quality activity [9]. They favor prospective validation for the obvious reason of minimal risk; i.e., the process is proved to be effective and under control prior to the manufacture or release of any products. The FDA recommends the prospective validation concept over the others when there are new products, or modifications in the manufacturing process, that might affect product quality attributes [10]. In most cases, prospective validation does offer a higher degree of confidence; however, this is usually accompanied by a much higher cost. The decision for selecting the validation mode, when the alternatives are available, should include a cost-to-benefit evaluation as well as the consideration of the FDA's preference.

B. Retrospective Validation

When historical data are sufficient and readily available, retrospective validation is the method of choice because of its cost-effectiveness. One preference for the use of retrospective validation is that the large data base of historical data might provide a better picture, and a higher confidence level, than prospective validation data generated from a few (usually no more than three) trial runs or batches.

The retrospective validation is acceptable to the FDA under certain conditions. One condition is the availability of specific test results, generated by reliable analytical methods, to allow for statistical analysis. For example, a pass/fail test result would be unacceptable to be used as part of a retrospective validation review. Documentation must be available to show the conditions under which the batch was processed. For example, it would be difficult to claim retrospective validation, based on satisfactory test results, if operating parameters such as mixing time and machine speed settings were not recorded in the batch records [4]. Another FDA viewpoint is that process variables must have been under a state of control and standardized before the data and test results from that process could be used to support a retrospective validation. These process variables include, for example, raw material characteristics, environmental controls, microbial controls, manufacturing procedures, and analytical methodologies and specifications. Discrepancies or failures in the historical data may be excluded from the retrospective validation provided that there is sufficient documentation to show that the failures or discrepancies were caused by isolated occurrences (e.g., employee error) and were not the result of process variations [11].

Documents and records required for a retrospective validation of a solid dosage, according to the FDA, should include a diagram or flowchart of the process, general historical data for the product and process, raw material sources and characteristics, in-process test results, content uniformity, product formulation, and complaints. It was also pointed out that if this information and data have been included and evaluated as part of the product annual review program (21CFR211.180e), that program could be used as supporting documentation for the retrospective validation [12].

Although the FDA included the provision for retrospective validation in the 1987 validation guideline, some FDA investigators have recently expressed reluctance in accepting this method for process validation.

C. Concurrent Validation

This method may be used when extensive testing and monitoring are performed as part of the instant run or process. The testing and monitoring must ensure, with a high confidence level, that the desired quality attributes have been attained.

Another condition is that the methods for testing and monitoring have the appropriate degree of specificity and sensitivity to measure the product quality attributes. For example, it may be acceptable to validate concurrently the secondary drying time for a lyophilization cycle if a sufficient number of thermocouples were placed in the product throughout the load and representative samples of the product were collected from the chamber, at various intervals, for moisture analysis (presuming shelf temperature mapping had been prospectively performed).

The PMA supports the use of concurrent validation when quality attributes can be determined with a sound sampling program and definitive and validated test methods [13,14].

The FDA had argued against the concurrent validation terminology. It should be noted that this terminology did not appear, nor was it discussed, in any of the FDA's draft guidelines for process validation. In the FDA's final validation guideline issued in May 1987, a short paragraph on "Acceptability of Product Testing" was included at the end of the document. The contents of this section paralleled the concept of concurrent validation, but the term "concurrent" was not mentioned. The FDA's concerns with the concept of concurrent validation are reproducibility and consistency. They feel that concurrent validation "verifies" the quality characteristics of a particular batch. The results from that instant run, however, do not provide a high degree of assurance that the same quality characteristics would be attained again when subsequent batches are processed under the same conditions and parameters [15].

The FDA recognizes that prospective and retrospective validations may have limited applicability under certain situations. In those instances, product testing during the run, in conjunction with data obtained during the manufacturing process, may be used to "demonstrate that the instant run yields a finished product meeting all of its specifications and quality characteristics." The condition for accepting the manufacturing data and test results is a "much more extensive" than usual evaluation of the data and test results [4].

Despite the FDA's criticism of the concurrent validation terminology, the concept has been accepted based on the incorporation of the Acceptability of Product Testing provision in the validation guideline. Concurrent validation, although not used as frequently as prospective and retrospective validations, remains as a critical concept and is incorporated in many validation projects.

D. Worst Case and Limits

The FDA has defined worst case as "a set of conditions including those within standard operating procedures, which pose a greater chance for process or product failure than ideal conditions" [4]. The FDA does not expect all process specifications to be challenged, but only those critical specifications or process variables that affect the fitness of the product [15]. For example, a terminal sterilization cycle should be validated at both the upper and lower temperature limits—the former to ensure that the higher temperature has no adverse effects on product quality and stability and the latter to demonstrate achievement of the appropriate sterility assurance level. Unfortunately, process variables are not always easy or possible to manipulate. It would be very time consuming and difficult to alter the air balancing for a sterile area to simulate varying air velocities and differential pressures. It would be impractical to create high particle or microbial counts during media fill validations. Also, the presence of many critical process variables might result in numerous validation runs just to accommodate the many permutations of potential situations that might exist during normal production. Consider the many validation runs that might be required to challenge a computer system if all operating variables such as temperature, humidity, voltage, vibration, and load level had to be included. Although it is unlikely that all these operating variables would be at their extremes at any one time, it is difficult to anticipate what a typical "stressed" situation might entail. The FDA does not expect all variables to be challenged at their extremes, but rather at a stressed condition "somewhere in between." This might be difficult to determine, especially with a new system.

The negative aspect of not performing the validation under stressed or extreme conditions is potential questions of product quality when actual processing parameters fall outside validated parameters. Consider the situation in which particulate counts during an actual filling operation exceeded the counts recorded during the media fill runs, or there was a momentary drop in temperature during a production sterilization cycle that was not anticipated when the validation was performed. These runs are clearly outside validated limits, but are the variations significant enough to warrant rejection of the batches due to inadequate validation support? The underlying question here is whether validation runs are actually establishing operating parameters and rejection limits. One FDA representative commented that he typically uses the firm's contact plate (e.g., RODAC) counts from media fill runs as the baseline limit for evaluating contact plate counts from production runs. This investigator's philosophy is that if the firm could attain a certain microbial cleanliness level during the validation runs, then the same level of microbial cleanliness should be attainable for production runs. In this case, the validation run is establishing limits for production.

The practical actions for batches produced outside validated limits should include additional testing, investigation, and evaluation to determine the significance of the deviation and to show whether validated quality attributes had been compromised. In the situation with the momentary drop in temperature during the sterilization cycle, the cycle lethality, F_0, could be calculated to determine whether it is sufficient to provide for a 12 log reduction of the biological indicator used for the validation (presuming that the overkill approach had been employed). The high counts encountered during the filling operation should be followed up with additional sterility testing of samples collected during the affected time period and an evaluation of the significance of the adverse condition by correlating the high counts with microbial monitoring results, if available [16].

In some cases, validation results that consistently fall near established limits might be subject to criticism concerning the quality of the "validated" process. One FDA representative commented that if the media fill runs consistently exhibit a 0.1% contamination rate, the manufacturer cannot demonstrate a true contamination rate not greater than 10^{-3}, even though the 0.1% contamination rate is an industry standard that has been accepted by the FDA [17].

IV. VALIDATION AND OPTIMIZATION

It is important to remember that process validation is not an opportunity to optimize or modify a process. Validation and optimization are two distinct programs that must not be performed at the same time for a particular process. The validation goal is to demonstrate the reliability and reproducibility of a process, not to modify or improve the process.

There are compliance and regulatory concerns associated with attempts to optimize a process during validation. In the case of a new product, the NDA/ANDA was approved by the FDA based on processing procedures and data generated from biostudy, clinical, stability, and scale-up batches. If the FDA-approved manufacturing process was modified during the validation stage to optimize the process, the modified process would be in violation of the NDA/ANDA commitments. This is true even if the optimization resulted in a superior product. The modified or optimized process, in essence, is not supported with the necessary biostudy, clinical, and stability data, and the product from the optimized process could be considered as a new drug.

Obviously, if the validation uncovers significant flaws in the process that could adversely affect product quality or integrity, the process requires appropriate modification.

V. ORGANIZATION FOR VALIDATION

Organizing for the validation project includes the collection of appropriate information to prepare specifications and procedures, assigning responsibilities to ensure that the required tasks are performed, and preparing the final validation protocol.

A. Collecting the Information

Specifications and operating instructions for equipment and accessories, which need to be included as part of the validation, should be obtained from engineering, purchasing (e.g., purchase order), or the equipment manufacturer. Processing procedures, specifications, and test methods should be determined for a process validation. These are usually available from the following sources:

1. Review existing production procedures for a similar product (if available); otherwise, review the procedures, manufacturing specifications, and parameters employed during the development and scale-up for the product. It is important that the procedure selected for validation comply with NDA/ANDA commitments.
2. Consult the product development department for a translation of the product's physical and chemical characteristics into specifications and acceptance range/limits in readily measurable terms. This information should be in the development report for the product.
3. Review the USP for any specific monograph for the product, or general requirements for that class of product (e.g., metal particles test for ophthalmic products).
4. Consult with the quality control department for sampling, in-process monitoring, and test procedures that are performed for the product or the process.
5. Consult with regulatory affairs for compliance with NDA/ANDA product specification commitments.
6. Review industry and regulatory standards for process or manufacturing limits, current practices, and recommendations—for example, media fill quantity and contamination rate, environmental monitoring methods and limits, and sterility assurance levels for sterilization processes.

B. Preparing a Validation Protocol

There are some basic rules for preparing a validation protocol. The protocol should include only the necessary details and information for the performance of the specific tests. The tests procedures, operating parameters, specifications, and limits must be practical and attainable. Finally, the protocol should be kept short and concise to facilitate its review and approval. Recommendations for organizing and preparing a validation protocol are presented as follows:

1. Identify what the system is supposed to do, describe the specific product/process that is the subject of the validation, and list the goals of the validation.
2. Break the process or system into modules (e.g., media fills, sterilization, condenser capacity study), and qualify and/or validate each module individually. This is important in that it facilitates the validation, review, and approval. For example, disagreements concerning a specific module would not delay the validation of other modules. This would not be the case if all the modules were part of one validation project covered by one protocol. Another advantage of this approach is that there is a sense of accomplishment as each module is completed, in contrast to a massive validation that seems to never end. In addition, any changes in personnel during the validation project would affect only the modules which are in progress.
3. Include a flowchart of the process to be validated.

4. Where possible, include simple line drawings or a blueprint of the equipment, along with the manufacturer's specifications. The reason for including these as part of the protocol is to have these documents readily available for reference during the equipment qualification and validation process. Also, these references tend to be most difficult to locate when you need them.

5. Include a description of the components of the system. For a lyophilization system, describe the vacuum chamber, condenser, heating/cooling systems, vacuum system, instruments, and controls.

6. Identify the critical process parameters and limits for the process and the quality attributes for the product. For a lyophilized product, these would include temperature, vacuum, fill volume, potency, and moisture.

7. Specify the procedures and tests to be conducted, the responsibilities for sampling and testing, the data to be collected, the method for reporting test data (e.g., individual results, averaged results, graphs, charts), the method for analyzing test data (e.g., statistical treatment), and the criteria for acceptance.

8. Define the upper and lower processing limits. As discussed earlier, these could be based on manufacturing procedures, standard operating procedures (SOPs), and actual limits encountered in product development and scale-up batches.

9. Specify a sufficient number of replicate process runs to demonstrate reproducibility, and include provisions for measuring the variability among successive runs. This could include control charting, trending, or statistical analysis of process data and critical finished-product test data.

10. Include provisions for the inclusion of in-process and finished-product data, generated from validated test methods, that are specific indications of product quality attributes—for example, moisture, potency, and content uniformity.

11. Include procedures for monitoring and evaluating the stability data generated from the validation batches—for example, test intervals, tests to be performed, and method for analyzing the data.

12. Include a protocol change control provision to describe how modifications and deviations from the approved protocol should be handled. Deviations from the protocol should be documented and explained. These deviations should be approved in advance by the responsible individuals who approved the original validation protocol.

C.   Responsibilities

Validation is a team effort. The PMA concept paper for the Validation of Non-Sterile Dosage Forms states that "The validation effort will generally require the involvement and close interaction of the R&D, Quality Control, Engineering and

Production functions in consultation with other appropriate support groups, such as Regulatory Affairs." A typical validation team should include representation from various departments to provide the necessary expertise and guidance as follows:

Process validation. This department coordinates the entire validation process by scheduling meetings and discussions for the validation team, preparing the validation protocol, monitoring the validation process, compiling and analyzing validation data and test results, and preparing the final report.

Research and development. For a new product or process, R&D has to define the process to be validated and provide technical assistance for the validation process by defining specifications, limits, and analytical methods.

Quality control. The laboratories should be prepared to provide the necessary supports for sampling, testing, and reporting of test results. Support groups in quality control should also perform the necessary monitoring (e.g., environmental monitoring) during the validation process.

Engineering. The project engineer should define the necessary equipment specifications, limitations, capacity, and maintenance requirements and provide training on the proper operation and maintenance of the equipment. The department should be responsible for providing the necessary utilities and equipment accessories. In most cases, engineering is needed to assist in the equipment installation and operation qualifications and provide technical support to ensure proper and efficient equipment function during the validation process.

Production. Production personnel should perform the validation steps whenever possible for training and personnel qualification. The department should prepare the necessary SOPs for the new process or equipment and assist in the collection of validation data.

Regulatory affairs. NDA commitments for processing procedures, parameters, specifications, limits, equipment, and components should be defined for the validation team. Regulatory affairs should also keep the validation team abreast of any new or revised regulatory requirements for the validation process.

Quality assurance. All documentation associated with the validation should be reviewed by quality assurance for completeness and compliance with CGMP requirements.

VI. COMPLIANCE ASPECT OF VALIDATION

Of the three basic reasons for validation discussed earlier, compliance has the most significant impact on a company's business and operations because of the potential administrative and legal actions resulting from noncompliance. The compliance aspect of validation, therefore, deserves additional discussion of the FDA's inspection of validation studies.

The ultimate goal of the validation effort is compliance with FDA requirements and satisfactory review by FDA investigators. The validation process should be performed, and the report prepared, in a manner to achieve these goals. It is, therefore, desirable to know what FDA investigators might look for in a validation study and documentation. Unfortunately, the areas and levels of FDA inspectional coverage and review vary among investigators, depending on each investigator's area of expertise. An investigator with a higher level of technical expertise may concentrate on the scientific aspects of the validation. Another investigator with less experience may concentrate primarily on the documentation and recordkeeping aspects.

Although it may seem that a technical audit would be more stringent and critical, this is usually not the case because many of the deficiencies found associated with a validation study are related to recordkeeping and documentation. The most common deficiencies are usually failure of the firm to adhere to its own approved validation protocol, failure to perform the procedures and tests specified in the protocol, failure to report test results, and lack of documentation to explain and justify unsatisfactory results and deviations from the protocol.

These frequent findings of recordkeeping and documentation deficiencies stress the importance of a detailed review and audit of the validation results and report. The following recommendations should be considered as part of the validation documentation review, approval, and audit processes:

1. Compare the validation procedures and steps in the protocol against the actual work performed. A validation report should be reviewed alongside the approved validation protocol. Without the protocol, the reviewer would not be able to detect any deviations from the protocol or nonperformance of a validation step.
2. Ensure that the performance of each significant step has been properly documented.
3. Ensure that test results meet specifications and limits. Test failures should be properly reported, investigated, and explained.
4. Ensure that deviations from protocol requirements are properly reported, explained, and approved by the responsible department management.

Organization of the protocol, test results and data, and final report is very important. Documentation that is difficult to locate, contains many errors and/or pen and ink changes, is poorly organized, and lacks documentation of review and approval by the responsible individuals gives the FDA investigator a poor first impression of the validation study. The investigator will tend to review such documentation in more detail, based on his or her experience that organization effort is usually reflective of the validation effort. A well-organized report, on the other hand, will signal to the investigator that the same degree of care and time had been devoted to the performance of the validation. In this case, the investigator may perform only a cursory review of the validation documentation.

VII. SUMMARY

It may be important to some individuals to argue terminologies and seek the best definitions for validation. Such academic exercises are of little practical use to the professionals responsible for designing and performing the validation. A practical understanding of the validation concepts and when and how to apply them is of greater importance to ensure a meaningful, efficient, effective, and economical validation program. Because practicality and compliance are both important aspects of validation, the validation professional must be familiar with the current FDA and industry perspectives, requirements, and practices for validation. To ensure a successful validation, the validation effort must be well organized and include the necessary input and cooperation from many departments within the company. Finally, as with any project, the validation is not complete without the necessary documentation. The recordkeeping and documentation should be prepared with the FDA in mind. Special attention should be afforded to the physical appearance of the report, as well as its technical contents.

REFERENCES

1. Lee, John Y., GMP compliance for the lyophilization of parenterals: Part I, *Pharmaceut. Technol. 12*(10):54–60 (1988).
2. Phillips, G. Briggs, Sterilization. In *Remington's Pharmaceutical Science*, Gennaro, Alfonso R. (ed.), Pennsylvania, Mack Publishing Company, pp. 1452–1453 (1982).
3. "Process Validation Concepts for Drug Products," Pharmaceutical Manufacturers Association, Washington, DC (April 22, 1985).
4. "Guideline on General Principles of Process Validation," Food and Drug Administration, Rockville, MD (May 1987).
5. "Parametric Release—Terminally Heat Sterilized Drug Products," Compliance Policy guide 7132a.13, Food and Drug Administration, Rockville, MD (October 21, 1987).
6. "Current Good Manufacturing Practice for Finished Pharmaceuticals," Code of Federal Regulations, Part 211, Office of Federal Register National Archives and Records Administration, Washington, DC (1989).
7. "Inspection Guidance for Prescription Drug Plants," Mid Atlantic Region Pharmaceutical Inspection Program (Draft), Food and Drug Administration, Philadelphia (January 1990).
8. "Sterile Drug Process Inspection," Compliance Program CP7356.002A, Food and Drug Administration, Rockville, MD (March 5, 1990).
9. Health Industry Manufacturer's Association, letter to the Legal and Regulatory Section on the New FDA Draft Guideline for Process Validation (October 8, 1985).

10. "Retrospective Validation," presented by Henry L. Avallone (FDA), at the NAPM meeting in Rye, NY (September 14, 1983).
11. "Process Validation," presented by Henry L. Avallone (FDA), at the Eleventh Annual Quality Control Seminar for the Food, Drug and Cosmetic Industry, Clifton, NJ (March 20, 1980).
12. "Validation of Solid Oral Dosage Forms," presented by Henry L. Avallone (FDA), at the FDA Process Validation Workshop, New Brunswick, NJ (June 28, 1984).
13. Pharmaceutical Manufacturers Association, letter dated May 31, 1983, on FDA's "General Principles of Process Validation; Current Good Manufacturing Practices Draft Guideline," 48 Federal Register 13096 (March 29, 1983).
14. Pharmaceutical Manufacturers Association, Validation Advisory Committee, presentation before the Food and Drug Administration, Medical Device Good Manufacturing Practices Advisory Committee, on "Guideline on General Principles of Process Validation" (March 29, 1984).
15. "The Gold Sheet," *Quality Control Report 20*(3), Chevy Chase, MD (March 1986).
16. Lee, John Y., Environmental requirements for clean rooms, *Bio-Pharm 2*(2):42–45 (1989).
17. Fry, Edmund M., FDA update on aseptic processing guidelines, *J. Parenteral Sci. Technol. 41*(2):56–60 (1987).

20

Validation Terminology

Kenneth G. Chapman   *Pfizer, Inc., Groton, Connecticut*

I. INTRODUCTION

Since 1976, FDA's emphasis on the term validation has had a significant impact on drug and device manufacturers. Historically, FDA's early emphasis focused on validation of sterilization processes. By the early 1980s, considerable regulatory attention was also being directed toward validation of nonsterilization processes.

Communications surrounding sterilization validation generally appeared clear to audiences in academia, industry, and in regulatory circles. Unfortunately, substantial confusion developed as the use of the term expanded into nonsterile operations.

The purpose of this chapter is to offer some specific meanings for several contemporary validation practices and to develop them in a logical and understandable way.

The term validation, that is, establishing documented evidence that a system does what it purports to do, attained its popularity after 1976 as a direct result of new Current Good Manufacturing Practice (CGMP) regulations. Since these regulations emphasize need for documentation [1], it is not surprising that documentation became integrally associated with all forms of validation. Systems to be validated often involve various combinations of the following:

Equipment	Software	Personnel
Environment	Controls	Facilities
Materials	Processes	Operating procedures
Methods		

The terms quality assurance and validation are often used interchangeably, for good reason. Quality assurance is validation of the quality function. These three terms can be defined as follows [2]: Quality Function is the entire collection of activities from which we achieve fitness-for-use, no matter where these activities are performed. Quality Control is the regulatory process through which we measure actual quality performance, compare it with standards, and act on the difference. Quality Assurance is the activity of providing, to all concerned, the evidence needed to establish confidence that the quality function is being performed adequately.

A quality assurance system usually involves a matrix of written procedures. Thus, CGMPs are frequently equated with quality assurance systems. By similar lines of reasoning, validation, quality assurance, and CGMPs are often associated with each other and even, on some occasions, treated synonymously.

Process Validation means "establishing documented evidence that a process does what it purports to do." Validation of a sterilization process differs from validation of a nonsterilization process in several significant ways. Sterilization Process is a treatment process from which probability of any microorganism survival is less than 10^{-6}, or one in a million. Nonsterilization Process is any treatment process which purports to do something other than to sterilize. It may be a method associated with, or even integral to, one which sterilizes.

Validations of sterilization processes are usually performed prospectively and are relatively independent of in-process or end-product testing. Validations of nonsterilization processes can be performed prospectively, concurrently, and/or retrospectively and usually depend on in-process testing. Concurrent and retrospective process validation are based on batchwise control of the process. Batchwise Control is the use of validated in-process sampling and testing methods in such a way that results prove the process has done what it purports to do for the specific batch concerned, assuming control parameters have been appropriately respected. Control Parameters are those operating variables which can be assigned values that are used as control levels. Operating Variables are all factors, including control parameters, which may potentially affect process state-of-control and/or fitness-for-use of the end product. State-of-Control is a condition in which all operating variables that can affect performance remain within such ranges that the system or process performs consistently and as intended.

Sterilization validation involves proving that a system sterilizes, whether or not testing is performed on the end product. Need for such proof stems from the fact that sterility is not an absolute product attribute that can be determined by end-product testing alone.

Validation of a nonsterilization system has been often referred to as process validation or solid dosage validation. While both terms are descriptive, neither is comprehensive. Validation of a new nonsterilization process is synonymous with but not identical to the term process development. The key difference is that process development includes optimization of control parameters while validation does not.

Process Development is establishing evidence that all process control parameters and all control parameter ranges are validated and optimized. Control Parameter Range is a range of values for a given control parameter that lies between its two outer limits, or control levels.

While there is nothing new about the need for process development to prove meaningfulness of its control parameter ranges, it is probably true that regulatory emphasis on validation brought with it an increased tendency by industry to document such proof.

Several terms used today are occasionally misunderstood in connection with development of control parameter ranges. One is called edge-of-failure [3]. Edge-of-failure is a control parameter value which, if exceeded, means adverse effect on state of control and/or fitness for use of the product. This can be useful, but it is not necessary to identify edge-of-failure when validating a process.

Another common term is worst case, or the highest or lowest value of a given control parameter actually evaluated in a validation exercise. A proven acceptable range (PAR) is all values of a given control parameter that fall between proven high and low worst case conditions.

It is often convenient practice to set a control parameter range somewhat inside a proven acceptable range, as illustrated by the pyramid in Figure 1. Then, if equipment or human failure causes the process to drift slightly outside the control parameter range, the resulting quality assurance investigation may find that actual conditions still fall within the PAR and conclude that fitness for use has not been impaired.

Sterilization validation received its first major attention in 1976, with publication of three sets of proposed new CGMP regulations: Drugs [4], devices [5], and large volume parenterals [6]. Since 1976, intensive, cooperative effort by industry, academic, and FDA has yielded considerable insight to the subject and has produced many well-established technological approaches for validating essentially all kinds of sterilization processes.

II. PROSPECTIVE VALIDATION

Sterilization validation usually requires a prospective approach. The most common steps in prospective validation (Figure 2) are:

1. Qualification of systems and subsystems
   a. Installation qualification
   b. Operational qualification
   c. Calibrations
2. Approval of validation protocol

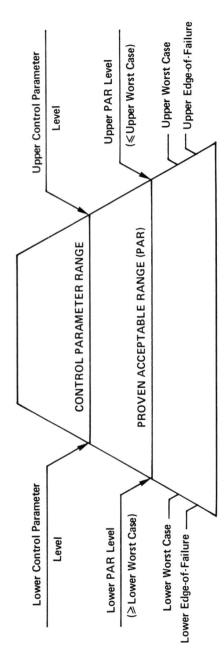

Figure 1 Pyramiding the operating variables.

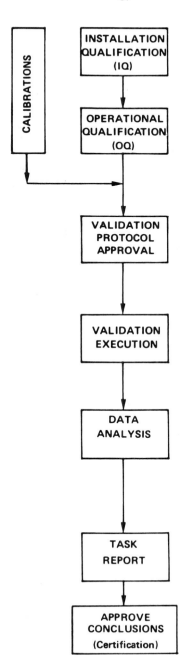

Figure 2 Prospective process validation.

3. Protocol execution
4. Analysis of results in a task report
5. Approval of task report conclusions

Many firms today start by qualifying each subsystem. To qualify, of course, means to prove that a system does what it purports to do, which is synonymous with validation; however, more explicit terms like installation qualification and operational qualification have been adopted in useful (although unfortunately varied) ways. Installation qualification (IQ) may be defined as documented verification that all key aspects of the installation adhere to manufacturer's recommendations, appropriate codes, and approved design intentions. Operational qualification (OQ) is documented verification that the system or subsystem performs as intended throughout all specified operating ranges. Some firms also use the term performance qualification, often as a synonym for OQ. It is worth noting that in the case of nonsterilization subsystems (e.g., equipment), operational qualification and validation are actually synonymous.

The OQ term is particularly useful to sterilization validation; it establishes that a system or subsystem does everything it should except for sterilization itself. Validation covers that.

Calibration of measuring devices is important to all kinds of process validation. It is convenient to treat calibration as a form of qualification, separately from the IQ and OQ functions, since it usually straddles both. Calibration may be defined as demonstrating that a measuring device produces results within specified limits of those produced by a reference standard device over an appropriate range of measurements. This process results in corrections which may be applied if maximum accuracy is required.

Measuring devices used for validation are often calibrated both before and after experimental work is conducted. Both the instruments and their calibration methods are often more sophisticated than those needed for subsequent process control. The latter, of course, are also fully qualified before use and are provided with maintenance calibration systems (schedules and procedures) which assure their continuing state-of-control.

Once all qualifications, including calibrations, have been addressed, a validation protocol is usually drafted and approved. This is a prospective experimental plan which, when executed, is intended to produce documented evidence that the system has been validated. The validation protocol usually includes a definition of the system to be validated (often by referring to its written operating procedures) and identifies operating variables and probable control parameters. It also indicates the degree of replication considered appropriate to provide statistical significance.

Qualification protocols (IQ and OQ) are also used formally by many firms as part of their overall validation programs.

In the course of executing any experimental plan, whether or not it is described by a protocol, results will sometimes differ from expectations. When this occurs in executing a validation or qualification protocol, it can be useful to prepare and approve a protocol supplement, rather than, for example, rewriting the protocol. Such practice provides a clear chronological history and avoids creating an impression that the experiment was designed after its execution. A protocol supplement is a document which explains a change to the original protocol, including reasons for its need.

Once validation execution is complete, the data are analyzed and a task report is written. Worst case conditions actually validated may have different values from those predicted. Such observations do not mean the work must be repeated, but simply that the proven acceptable ranges should be appropriately adjusted.

Many firms find a task report conclusion form useful for formal approval. This obviates need for formally approving the entire task report. A validation task report is a scientific report of the results derived from executing a validation protocol. Validation task report conclusions are a brief summary of conclusions from a specific task report, usually indicating validation success and designating acceptable mean ranges that have resulted. The conclusions are formally approved. Qualification task reports and/or task report conclusion forms are sometimes used in a manner similar to those used for validation.

III. RETROSPECTIVE VALIDATION

Throughout most nonsterilization processes, there are stages at which representative samples can be taken by validated sampling methods and tested in a statistically significant manner to prove that the process has, up to that point, done what it purported to do, i.e., the batch itself is validated concurrent with its manufacture. When a series of such batches has been run by the same process, the data base generated lends itself to retrospective validation analysis (Figure 3).

There are two major areas in which concurrent and retrospective process validations are particularly useful, both involving nonsterilization processes: (1) established commercial processes for which original development data to support control parameter ranges are no longer available, and (2) new processes, usually in an R&D setting, for which limited history exists (here, prospective and retrospective approaches are used jointly).

In the first case, existing data, such as that from manufacturing batch records, in-process control testing, and stability-testing, are reviewed and analyzed to reconfirm formally that control parameter ranges are appropriate (i.e., validated). Review of process waivers (or process change notifications), quality assurance investigation results, and even product or in-process rejection data can also be helpful here in revealing worst case conditions and, sometimes, where edges-of-failure occur. Validation protocols are not generally needed for such retrospective

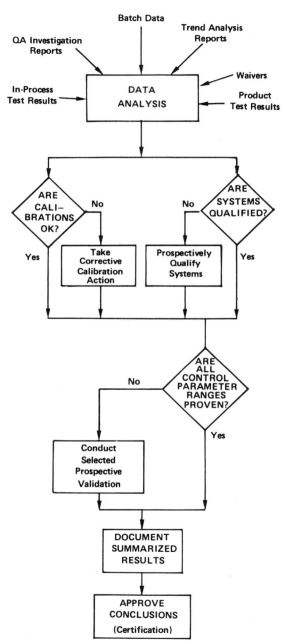

Figure 3 Retrospective process validation.

validation, but formal approval of final results is often deemed appropriate. The same data base mentioned above, as derived from numerous commercial batches run by a given process, can also be used to generate trend analysis profiles. Such analysis represents a long-standing quality assurance technique for predicting when processes, although still within their validated control ranges, may be heading toward trouble.

In the second case, development of processes for producing formulations of new drug entities, prospective, concurrent, and retrospective validation approaches are all useful. Initial lots, usually involving small quantities, are each tested in a far more extensive manner than would be appropriate for a commercial process. Each lot is proven to be exactly what was intended. It is not unusual, for example, for every capsule prepared in a small lot to be individually weighed, when the ensuing clinical experiment is of sufficient importance.

As the new product and its processes are developed, the history of such lots accumulates. Prior to preparing some lots, experimental protocols are designed to obtain certain development (or validation) data prospectively. History of all lots is reviewed retrospectively, however, to learn more about control parameters and where acceptable mean ranges lie. Thus, as the new process approaches commercial status, its validation also approaches completion from both prospective and retrospective efforts.

Prospective validation is establishing documented evidence that a system does what it purports to do based on a preplanned protocol.

Concurrent process validation is establishing documented evidence that a process does what it purports to do based on information generated during actual implementation of the process. Retrospective validation is establishing documented evidence that a system does what it purports to do based on review and analysis of historic information.

IV. REVALIDATION

Once a system has been validated, it is considered to be in a state of control. So long as all conditions and control parameters remain unchanged, the system continues in its validated state. Obviously, it is important for any significant change to be recognized before or at the time it occurs, so that appropriate action can be taken promptly to preserve validation status.

Many firms today use some sort of validation change control system, by which engineering work orders, revisions to standard operating procedures, proposed formulation order changes, and the like, are reviewed by a committee of the same disciplines responsible for validation approvals, to determine potential impact on validation status before formally approving the change. Often, through this mechanism, it is possible to take immediate action, prospectively, that makes it unnecessary to revalidate the entire system.

Validation change control is a formal monitoring system by which qualified representatives of appropriate disciplines review proposed or actual changes that might affect validated status and cause corrective action to be taken that will assure the system retains its validated state of control. Revalidation is the repetition of the validation process or a specific portion of it. In some cases, firms find it appropriate to revalidate certain systems on a periodic basis, even when no change is believed to have occurred.

Many long-established practices that deal with change control are already covered by quality assurance programs and by the CGMPs. For example, requirements for receiving, inspecting, sampling, testing, and storing raw materials; packaging materials and labeling; and for approving new suppliers of same all require formalized systems that include substantial documentation. Unless such systems fall below normally accepted standards, it should not be necessary to modify or repeat them in order to maintain a new validation program in a suitable state-of-control.

Finally, it should be recognized that different manufacturing and consulting firms use the term certification in many different ways. Task report conclusions forms represent a type of certification. Some find it useful to issue certifications for IQ, OQ, calibration results, and various stages of validation.

Certification of revalidation is often useful; however, the manner in which formal approvals are documented is best left up to each individual firm and use of formalized certifications should be considered entire optional. Certification is documented testimony by qualified authorities that a system qualification, calibration, validation, or revalidation has been performed appropriately and the results are acceptable.

V. SUMMARY

For human beings to communicate with each other effectively, especially regarding a subject as involved as validation has become, it helps if they can all communicate from the same set of definitions. This chapter is believed to reflect today's most common uses of fundamental validation terminology. Hopefully, it will prove useful to those readers who are trying to better understand the concepts.

REFERENCES

1. Chapman, K. G., Pfizer's DRUMBEAT Program. *Journal of the Parenteral Drug Association 34*:217–233 (1980).
2. Juran, J. M., *Quality Control Handbook*, 3rd ed. McGraw-Hill Book Company, New York (1974).
3. Anisfeld, M. H., *Validation Considerations in the Design of an Aseptic Processing*

Facility—An Overview, PMA Proceedings, 2d PMA Validation Seminar, Atlanta, Georgia, March 1–2, 1979.

4. FDA, *FDA's Proposed Revisions in Drug GMP's*, Federal Register *41*(31):6878–6894 (1976). Reprinted in "The Gold Sheet," 10(2) (1976) [FDA Reports, Inc.]

5. FDA, *Medical Devices: Good Manufacturing Practices for Manufacture, Storage, Packing, and Installation*, proposed, Federal Register, 42(40):11998–12008 (1977).

6. FDA, *Current GMP in the Manufacture, Processing, Packing, or Holding of Large Volume Parenterals* (proposed), Federal Register 41(106):22202–22219.

Index